AMONG THE CONTRIBUTORS:

Harold E. Anthony

William Beebe

Joseph M. Chamberlain

Arthur C. Clarke

Edwin H. Colbert

J. Frank Dobie

Willy Ley

Robert Cushman Murphy

Homer E. Newell

Donald Culross Peattie

Frederick H. Pough

Harry L. Shapiro

George Gaylord Simpson

Walter Sullivan

Edwin Way Teale

THE AMERICAN MUSEUM
OF NATURAL HISTORY
PRESENTS

THE ILLUSTRATED
LIBRARY
OF THE
NATURAL SCIENCES

EDITOR:
EDWARD M. WEYER, JR., Ph.D.

ART DIRECTOR:
FREDERICK L. HAHN

Volume IV

SIMON AND SCHUSTER
NEW YORK, 1958

Printed in the United States of America

Porcupine

The Porcupine is familiar to almost everyone who has passed any considerable time in the woods north of about 40° in North America. In the Rocky Mountains it is found almost as far south as Mexico. A large one may measure a yard or more in length, and the weight ranges from 15 pounds to a fat 35 or 40.

The porcupine has found such excellent protection in its sharp quills that it can afford to be sluggish and slow-witted. The quills have small backward-pointing barbs near the tip, which make them quite difficult to remove. The animal slaps its adversary with its tail, causing the spines to penetrate deeply. Dogs frequently get a face-full of quills, the removal of which may be a tedious and painful task even with pliers or tweezers.

Porcupines cause damage to trees by eating too much of the bark; and campers and cottagers are often annoyed to find that they have gnawed the handle of an ax or canoe paddle for the salt from perspiration left on it. Ice cream freezers are especially vulnerable.

On the other hand, the porcupine is the only animal of our woods that a man armed with no more than a heavy stick can kill for food in an emergency. It is to be found not only on the forest floor, where it feeds on bark, buds, and foliage, but also in trees. Occasionally one is ever seen swimming.

Fishes in Armor

They are protected from greedy sea marauders by a coat of sharp spines—and other devices

By Myron Gordon

Research Associate in Animal Behavior
The American Museum of Natural History

Not long ago an ingenious wolf hunter made the headlines by designing a hunting outfit that no beast would challenge. This hunter got a keg of nails and sewed the spikes into his hunting suit at close intervals. The iron spikes stood out on his homely coat of armor like the piercing quills on an alarmed razor-back hog. Someone called the inventor the porcupine man. The idea was good. No beast could touch the man-porcupine and go away unimpressed.

Long before man got the idea of a barbed-wire-like suit for defense, long before the porcupine itself developed its pelt of quills, the porcupine fish was swimming about in comparative safety, protected from its enemies by an elaborately constructed coat of sharp spines. The spines of a porcupine fish are reconstructed scales—scales that have grown to a point. The spines are "built in"; they are a part of the porcupine fish's external anatomy; they are warning signals to greedy sea marauders; they convey the idea of "*Verboten.*" They are effective.

When a porcupine fish is picked up, it swallows air and becomes balloon-like just the same. On the palm of your hand an inflated *Diodon* looks like an angry infant that lies helpless on its back in its crib and shows its impotent rage by pumping its lips and pounding the air with its feeble appendages. Its eyes gape wide for want of eyelids to close them. Its bloated, spherical body makes it look like a fish humpty-dumpty. Its small, soft and flabby fins fan the air feebly and ineffectually. Its two-toothed mouth is puckered up, and its lips and teeth move continuously as it tries to gulp more and more air to puff itself up more and more.

When returned to the water and released, the *Diodon* lies on the surface for a second, expels water and air explosively, deflating itself instantly, and swims away as fast as its ridiculously small fins and tail can take it.

Women in tropical lands have a method of inflating and drying the skins of porcupine fishes. When illuminated from within, these globular skins make grotesque lanterns. The spiny globes serve in times of festivity and in war. The South Sea island warriors cut holes in the bottoms of these inflated and dried fishy ornaments to suit the size of their individual heads. When going to battle, they use the spine-covered skins as protective helmets.

Porcupine fishes have scored successfully not only with their equipment of lances, but also with other means of defense. They have the ability to secrete a toxic substance from glands in their skin. One of the porcupine fish's closely associated family relatives, *Tetraodon,* the *muki-muki* of the Hawaiians, is re-

(Right)   A porcupine fish puffed up. The porcupine fishes occupy an enormous territory in the tropic seas of both the Atlantic and Pacific oceans, reaching Florida, Bermuda, and Southern California

(Left)   A porcupine fish at ease. This Diodon *was captured in a fine-meshed seine that was pulled along the shoals near a fine stand of live coral heads at Loggerhead Key, Florida*

garded by those natives as the most poisonous of all fishes. The South Sea islanders will not eat the flesh of this fish, but they do dip the tips of their arrows into the poison of its gall bladder.

All the porcupine fishes, *Diodon,* and most of their less spinous cousins, the puffers, *Tetraodon,* are marine, and are found in every tropic sea. A few, particularly the puffers of India, Ceylon, Malay, and Egypt, travel up the estuaries. Several species of *Tetraodon* actually pass beyond these tidal rivers and live in fresh-water streams. An Egyptian species, *Tetraodon fahaka,* lives in the fresh waters of the Nile. The *fahaka* is a famous fish and one that must have had some important symbolic virtue, for it appears commonly in the mural paintings of the ancient Egyptians. Unmistakable likenesses of it are found in the fishing scenes drawn on the walls of the pyramids of Giza and Saqqara. The eastern half of the south wall of Ptah Hotep's tomb at Saqqara is decorated with an elaborate battle scene being fought on water. The pictures represent a cross section of the battle. Above the water line the battle royal goes on furiously.

Below the water line, below the keels of the war vessels, as if in sharp contrast to the warlike scene above, the artists painted a lovely scene of peaceful aquatic life. A partly inflated *fahaka* may be recognized easily among the many aquatic creatures that seemingly live contentedly in this lower, but gentler, world.

The fresh-water puffers are popular in the home aquarium. They eat all kinds of fish food but prefer raw meat; they are inclined to be scrappy; they are too small to do much damage with their strong teeth when handled; they will go obligingly through the typical swelling antics of their tribe when lifted from the water and tickled under the chin.

The porcupine fishes (the *Diodons*) are entirely marine, and live among the living coral heads. They have rich pickings. With their strong, sharp teeth they break down the hard calcareous hiding places of worms, shrimps, and other tiny inhabitants of a heavily tenanted coral community. If pickings should become slim in one community, all they have to do is to inflate themselves with air and, with belly upward, float with the Gulf Stream until they come to new hunting grounds.

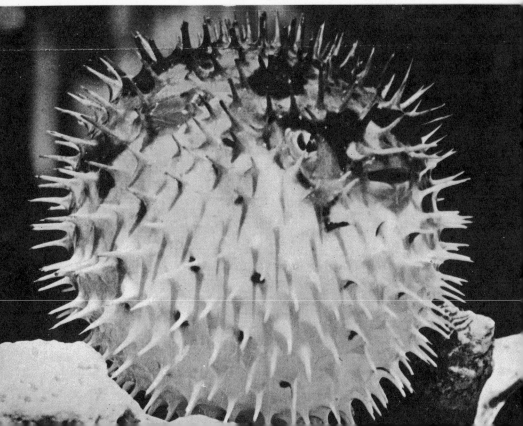

Marine Studios blazes the trail in the study of porpoise

psychology   and produces a star performer

Flippy—

the Educated Porpoise

By JOHN W. DILLIN

*Director, Public Relations,
Marine Studios*

Photographs by KURT SEVERIN
unless otherwise credited

DISCUSSING the accomplishments of Flippy, the trained porpoise under observation at Marine Studios, Marineland, Florida, someone commented:

"If Flippy gets any smarter, he'll be talking."

To which Adolf Frohn, Flippy's trainer, replied, "He does talk, but we aren't smart enough to understand him."

While Mr. Frohn meant this as a quip, it has foundation in fact. Porpoises are capable of making a wide variety of sounds including jaw clapping, whistling, chirping, squeaking, and the drawn-out grating noise of a rusty hinge. All are made underwater, and some are loud enough to the human ear to be heard at a distance.

Once when a mother and daughter porpoise were separated in the oceanarium of Marine Studios, there were definite signs of communication. They had been temporarily placed in separate tanks with a shallow connecting flume between them. Throughout the separation, the younger animal whistled persistently, and the mother, although she could not see her offspring, frequently answered while remaining close to the gate of the connecting flume.

This and other characteristics of the porpoise suggest the question: Just how much can these fishlike mammals be taught?

In 1947, the late Arthur F. McBride, Curator of Marine Studios, and D. O. Hebb of McGill University and the Yerkes Laboratories of Primate Biology, Orange Park, Florida, collaborated on a study of the behavior of captive porpoises. Among the problems they considered were ways of determining the relative intelligence of

➤ ONE OF FLIPPY'S most unusual feats is to leap through a hoop over which a paper is pasted. He breaks the paper with his snout and closes his eyes as he does it

these animals. It was known that the subjects of their investigation, the common bottle-nosed dolphin, or porpoise, *Tursiops truncatus,* has a brain larger than that of a man. It had also been reported that the convolutions of this brain are more marked than in man. But, of course, it cannot be assumed on the basis of these features alone that psychological development is at a corresponding level.

As McBride and Hebb pointed out, the word "intelligence" has never been defined to the satisfaction of everyone, and consequently there are no generally agreed-upon tests or criteria by which the mental capabilities of animals (including man) may be compared and rated. However, at the conclusion of their study they pointed out that the porpoise, so far as certain aspects of his behavior are concerned, appears to fall somewhere in the range of development between the dog and the chimpanzee—in other words, at a rather high level.

Within recent years, further evidence has been obtained to substantiate these findings as the result of a project undertaken at Marineland to determine the extent to which a porpoise can be trained to obey commands. In this respect, at least, Flippy, the animal selected for training, has exceeded all expectations.

Flippy is a member of one of the 22 species of small-toothed whales found along the Atlantic and Pacific coasts of North America. Although properly called dolphins, Flippy and his kind are commonly referred to as porpoises. Bottle-nosed porpoises have been

▲ ON COMMAND, Flippy will honk the horn—gently enough
not to puncture the rubber bulb with his teeth

⋏ GETTING FLIPPY into his first harness required much
time and patience. Now he willingly waits while it is
fastened

⋏ FLIPPY apparently ⁀njoys performing in harness. His
bland "smile," however, is simply the natural expression
his face assumes when he closes his mouth

successfully maintained at Marine Studios for a number of years and have even conceived and borne young in their giant oceanarium home. It was only natural that a member of this species should be selected for what were to prove some very popular experiments.

Flippy had been captured in an inlet by means of a net blocking his escape. Estimated to be about two years old, he weighed approxi-mately 150 pounds and measured close to 6 feet.

His name was suggested by Mrs. Cornelius Vanderbilt Whitney, wife of the Chairman of the Board of Directors of Marine Studios. To anyone who has ever seen a por-poise leaping clear of the water with only a few powerful flips of its tail, the name is quite appro-priate.

His first home was a 20-foot tank,

↟ FLIPPY became friendly with the fox terrier and seemed to enjoy having the dog lick his sunburned forehead

which received a constant flow of fresh sea water.

The man selected to conduct the training came from the fourth in that many generations of animal trainers. Adolf Frohn is a native of Germany, and in Europe he had been successful in working with white rats, pigeons, racoons, pigs, pelicans, seals, and sea lions. Prior to coming to Marineland, he had never seen a porpoise. Today he admits he lacked any confidence in teaching a "fish" to do "tricks."

The first step in training an animal is to teach it its source of food. Flippy, like all porpoises, is a fish-eater, and he soon learned that Mr. Frohn was the "fishman." First the fish were thrown into the water of the tank. In only one week, Flippy was taking fish from his trainer's hand. The porpoise ate well from the beginning, and achievement came fast as Mr. Frohn gained the mammal's confidence. In three weeks, the porpoise showed almost full trust and accepted food very gently from his trainer's hand.

From this point in the progressive training program, Mr. Frohn has jealously guarded his secrets of just how he has accomplished the final results. It is clear, however, that infinite patience was a prime requisite. His success was complete, as the porpoise itself will demonstrate with his performances.

Here are some of the accomplishments:

On a signal from hand or voice, Flippy has been taught to roll over and over in the water. He will continue to perform until Mr. Frohn ceases to command him.

◄ THE CLIMAX
of Flippy's performance

When the trainer throws a stick onto the surface of the water, the porpoise will swim to it, grasp it in his mouth, swim back to the thrower, and deposit it in his hand.

On instruction, Flippy will swim across the tank and raise his full length out of the water to grasp a rubber ball to which a bell is attached. In doing this, he causes the bell to ring. He then releases it, lowers himself back into the water, and returns to be rewarded. In other words, he rings his own dinner bell.

Mr. Frohn holds in his hand a small horn that is honked by a rubber bulb. Flippy will bite it hard enough to depress the bulb but not hard enough to puncture it. He will repeat the performance as long as his trainer tells him to do so.

The dolphin will swim through a hand-held underwater hoop, turn around and swim through it again and again, as he is instructed.

One of his more interesting accomplishments is to sit halfway out of the water and, on each flick of his trainer's wrist, swim a stroke backward with the upper part of his body well above the surface. Upon reaching a halfway point in the tank, he will stop to await a ball thrown to him. Flippy will catch it in midair and then return it to Mr. Frohn's hand.

Teaching the animal to jump out of the water and hurdle an object required more lengthy schooling. Now he will not only jump through a three-foot hoop suspended three feet above the water, but he will leap through it even with a piece of paper pasted over the hoop.

▲ FLIPPY patiently receiving his daily eyewash

▼ RECEIVING HIS REWARD after pulling the surfboard around the lagoon

Evidence of his enjoyment in performing is demonstrated when the animal swims into his own harness. Getting the mammal into his first harness required much time and patience and was one of the most difficult tasks undertaken in the program. Once the porpoise learned, however, he voluntarily

Photo by
Marineland, Florida

remained quiet until it was fastened.

Transferred to a lagoon after several months of work, Flippy was introduced to two new partners. One was Mr. Frohn's household pet, his fox terrier. In time they were friends.

In the training program, Flippy had his head out of the water so much that he actually became sunburned. As a treatment, Mr. Frohn applied petroleum jelly. Observing the trainer smoothing the jelly over the porpoise's head, the fox terrier offered its own natural treatment. On several occasions, the dog was observed licking Flippy's sunburn, for which the porpoise held still as though enjoying it.

The dog fitted into the training by being towed on an aquaplane by Flippy.

The second partner was a girl. Once accustomed to each other, the girl would enter the water with the porpoise. From Flippy's harness was a rope which she would grasp, and the porpoise would tow her.

↑ THE DOG, in turn, would avail himself of a ride on the surfboard whenever given the opportunity

He later gave her a ride on a surfboard, and sometimes both the dog and the girl would ride behind the porpoise on the board.

In the November, 1949, issue of NATURAL HISTORY Magazine, Dr. J. Kenneth Doutt, of the Carnegie Museum of Pittsburgh, gave an account of how a woman was caught in an undertow while swimming. Suddenly she was given a tremendous shove and landed on the beach, face down and exhausted. No person in the water was in sight, but approximately eighteen feet from the shore was a porpoise.

A witness informed the woman that the porpoise had shoved her ashore and, what is more, it was the second time that he had seen a person saved in a like manner.

The editor of Natural History pointed out that it would be easy to assume that the air-breathing porpoise was intentionally helping a creature who would drown if deprived of air. But most students of animal behavior, he noted, will prefer to explain the rescue as a result of the animal's natural curiosity and playfulness.

Whatever the full interpretation, the porpoise's inclination to nose a floating object through the water is given some verification by Mr. Frohn's experience in training Flippy. He used a boat in the lagoon to get from position to position. As he endeavored to paddle, the porpoise would push on the boat and steer it, sometimes on but more often off course.

Incidentally, Mr. Frohn can't swim, yet he spent much of his time in the boat without apparent fear. It might be surmised that he looked upon Flippy as his lifeguard.

During the period of schooling in the lagoon, Mr. Frohn was handing Flippy a fish. Either the porpoise was too affectionate or too eager to receive his food. Nevertheless, Flippy suddenly leaped completely out of the water into the lap of Brother Frohn, who was sitting in the boat. Startled for a moment, the trainer lifted the 200 pounds of wiggling porpoise back into the water.

Just how much further Marine Studios can go to demonstrate Flippy's learning ability, or that of any other porpoise, depends entirely on the ingenuity of the trainer.

All who have seen Flippy per-

▲ Trainer Frohn motions Flippy to ring the dinner bell at upper left.

➤ Following the signal from Mr. Frohn's hand, the porpoise rises out of the water and "calls for his own lunch."

form concede that he is a genuinely smart animal. However, Mr. Frohn says with commendable scientific spirit, "Actually, he may be a dumb one!" As yet he has had no opportunity to compare this particular specimen with other porpoises, since it is the only one with which he has worked.

Another porpoise is on the future program of Marine Studios. It is

Photo by Marineland, Florida

planned to obtain a female long-snouted dolphin, or spotted porpoise, (*Stenella plagiodon*), which is an offshore variety.

In the meantime, Flippy's training continues. He is learning now to pull a lanyard that raises Marineland's porpoise pennant to the top of a mast.

This he might be doing as a symbol of raising the porpoise flag over the marine mammal world on behalf of the many porpoises that

➤ VERY GENTLY and without endangering trainer or boat, Flippy takes his reward. Once, however, the porpoise became either too affectionate or too eager to receive his food. Mr. Frohn found Flippy in his lap and had to lift the 200 pounds of slippery porpoise back into the water·

∨ THE EDUCATED POR-POISE likes to be petted by his trainer

have become the favorite pets of the seas and in acknowledgment of the great popular interest that has been accorded these animals at Marine Studios during the past fourteen years.

∧ SITTING PART WAY OUT OF WATER and swimming backward, Flippy waits for Mr. Frohn to throw the ball. Flippy will catch it in mid-air and return it

Photograph by W. F. Kubeckek

YOUNG AMERICAN COOT
This youngster, occupying a comfortable nest among the reeds, is evidently the first of the brood to break from his shell

Feathered Water Babies
of our Prairies

Birds of the shallow ponds of the Dakotas: grebes, gulls, pelicans, cormorants, and terns

By ALFRED M. BAILEY
Director of the Denver Museum of Natural History

THE rolling prairies of the Dakotas, with their vast expanses of grazing grounds, were once the homes of great herds of bison. Antelope occurred in large numbers, and deer were abundant along the wooded bad lands. Today there are few of these mammals, for with the march of civilization it was inevitable that they should disappear.

As with the mammals, so it has been with the bird life. Flocks of wild fowl which "obscured the sun" were not uncommon in the old days, but now only a remnant remains. And yet, even now a visitor to the out-of-the-way lakes cannot help but marvel at the number of birds on all sides.

When the glaciers came from the north, they gouged great basins, and today we find the treeless Dakota prairies studded with a myriad of ponds, sloughs, and lakes, along which our wild fowl build their nests. Many of the lakes are alkali, and but little vegetation grows, so they are of little use to the nesting birds; but others are fresh and support a luxuriant

growth of cat-tails, tules, and cane (*Phrag-mites*).   Such a place is Rush Lake in northeastern South Dakota.

Wild ducks of several species,—mallards, blue-winged teal, gadwall, ruddy, pintail, shovellers, and red-heads may be seen daily, and occasionally, when one walks along the grass-grown banks, he is startled by a female duck flushing from beneath his feet.   The nesting birds are shy, however, and if given an opportunity, will sneak quietly from their nests.

While securing life history "nature studies" on motion films for the Chicago Academy of Sciences, our party had ample opportunity to study many species of birds at close range.   We found nests and erected blinds, and then, when the

⋏ A RING-BILL EGG, with the young Ring-bill seeing the light of day for the first time

⋎ A MATURE RING-BILLED GULL, showing the black ring on its bill from which it gets its name.

Photos by Clifford Matteson

Photograph by A. M. Bailey

RUSH LAKE, SOUTH DAKOTA
This shallow pond is similar to many others that dot the prairies from the sandhills of central Nebraska to the Canadian border and beyond

Photograph by F. W. Kubeckek

RING-BILLED GULLS
Far into the interior of the continent the gulls have penetrated, sometimes inhabiting the shores of lakes and ponds far removed from other bodies of water

Photograph by A. M. Bailey

AN ADULT HOLBOELL GREBE
When the young grebes are hatched, they are carried for a time on their parents' backs before they themselves take to the water

Photograph by A. M. Bailey

DOUBLE-CRESTED CORMORANTS
The cormorant is related to the pelican. These birds are powerful swimmers and expert divers, and their hooked bills serve them well when they catch the fish on which they live

parents returned to their nests, they were photographed. It was interesting to note how the different species reacted to the blind, and the reaction of individuals of the same species. Some birds that are ordinarily extremely shy, returned with little fear, while others that are considered tame, would not return at all.

The blue-winged teal is typical of the average species, for after eying the blind from all angles for an hour or so, the little female crawled mouselike through the brown grass, and crept upon her eggs without so much as showing her back above the protecting vegetation. Teal are numerous in the Dakotas, and many thousands nest there annually.

These lakes are particularly favored by the diving birds, and we saw hundreds of nests of the western, Holbœll's eared, and pied-billed grebes. It is possible that the horned grebe nests there also. In our moving-picture work we concentrated on the western, or swan grebe, which is known as the most beautiful of the divers, and on the Holbœll's, which is considered one of the shyest of water fowl. The former nested in the cane and tules of reed-grown ponds, while the latter built bulky nests of moss near the shores of large open lakes.

With the glasses we often could see several birds perched upon their mound-like nests, but when we showed ourselves, the birds quickly covered their eggs with a few deft dabs of the bill, and slid into the water. The western grebes were nesting in such deep water that it was

▼ A COOT and his reflection

Photo by Hugo Schroder

necessary to build a platform to support the blind, and from our narrow perch we could see a dozen of the beautiful fellows cruising among the golden yellow canes, their reflection mirrored in the quiet depths.

An adult would swim behind heavy growths of vegetation to the edge of her

Photograph by Earl G. Wright

THE NEST OF AN AMERICAN COOT

The average number of eggs in such a nest is from eight to twelve. Sometimes the number drops to six or seven and sometimes it is as high as seventeen or eighteen. On at least one occasion twenty-two eggs were counted in one nest, but it is probable that they were the product of more than one bird

Photograph by Edwin Komarek

BABY PIED-BILLED GREBES

Each of these youngsters, fresh from the shell, still bears the strange little "egg tooth" on the end of his beak. The only purpose of this "tooth" is to make it possible for the little fellow to break the shell. Shortly after the bird is hatched, the "tooth" falls off

Photograph by A. M. Bailey

NEWLY HATCHED WHITE PELICANS

These awkward birds are unattractive at this stage because of their nakedness. But even when they have attained a covering of down a few days after emerging from the shell, they still lack beauty

Photograph by A. M. Bailey

A MOTHER WESTERN GREBE ON HER NEST

The western grebes, sometimes called swan grebes, are without doubt among the most aquatic of birds. A cousin of this bird—the grebe of Lake Titicaca, South America—has lost some of its power of flight and is helpless, as well, on land

Photograph by Earl G. Wright

A YOUNG WESTERN GREBE

Unlike his cousin, the pied-billed grebe, this little fellow, just emerged from the shell, is not striped. Note the toad in the nest. This is a common occurrence in the marshes

<< A YOUNG TERN in the nest with 'unhatched eggs.

Photos by Clifford Matteson

∨ AN ADULT TERN, landing on its nest.

Photograph by W. F. Kubeckek

DOUBLE - CRESTED CORMORANTS. These birds are quite similar and closely related to the cormorants tamed in China and Japan for use in catching fish.

nest, and then remain quietly hour after hour, just eying the blind. Many of these swan grebes had hatched their young, and the downy little fellows would perch upon their parents' backs as the old ones cruised to and fro. Although we saw the adults continually, they were extremely shy, and remained under cover of the swamp growth. The bird we were attempting to photograph would swim to the edge of her nest, where she would "chuck" to the young one in an attempt to coax it away. The youngster became entangled in the grass of the nest and could not reach the parent, so—after hours in the stifling blind, we were rewarded by having this grebe climb upon her home.

The western grebes apparently do not conceal their eggs when they leave the nest,—at least not to the extent that the Holboell's do. This latter species is not so large as the former, nor so strikingly marked, but it nests on open lakes where one can see it at a long distance. We were in our blind many hours before the parents ventured to return to their nest, and then one of them climbed upon the mound and removed the mossy covering, rolled the eggs over with her beak, and settled down upon them without paying the slightest attention to the whirring of the camera. When we clapped our hands, she quickly covered her eggs and slid into the water, and so furnished us with a fitting close to that bit of film.

The Bartramian sandpipers are still found in many of their old haunts, although their numbers have been woefully diminished. We found a nest with three eggs upon a bowlder-strewn bit of prairie, and erected our blind. It was a stormy, blustery day, so the blind thrashed madly in the wind, and the brown grass whipped back and forth. It did not seem possible that this "wader," which inhabits the dry uplands, would return to her eggs, but in fifteen minutes we saw her standing motionless fifty feet away. She disappeared after a few moments, and when we next saw her, she was twenty-five feet away. In less than half an hour she had settled upon her eggs!

Coots are very tame, ordinarily, and yet they seemed very shy about returning to their nests. It took hours in the blind before the *poule d'eau* behaved satisfactorily. Another tame species is the black-crowned night heron. Ordinarily, colony nesting birds are very easily photographed, but, although we left our blind for days, and spent two days in the blind, we did not get a foot of film. We could hear and see young birds being fed all about us, but the youngsters we had under observation were fed at night. A horned owl was living in comfort on that little bird island, for he lived upon the young herons.

In Waubay Lake, a few miles from Rush Lake, is a little rocky islet known to the people of the vicinity as Bird Island. It is appropriately named for there was a colony of five hundred double-crested cormorants, and about three hundred of the common terns, and an equal number of ring-billed gulls. These birds were typical of many of the island colony nesting species, for they readily returned to their nests, and were little alarmed when the camera was turned upon them. The cormorants were well advanced in their nesting, and the hundreds of bulky platforms contained from three to four downy black fellows with long necks and reptilelike heads. They keep their heads bobbing, and they make a strange noise, the combined noises sounding like the

Photograph by W. F. Kubeckek

THE COMMON TERN

These little birds are widely distributed in Europe, Asia, Africa, and America

faint roaring of the wind. The beautiful gulls and terns were very tame, the former quickly returning to the large downy young hidden in the grass, while the terns settled upon their three dark-colored eggs.

One could write of many species which occur commonly, the beautiful Wilson's phalarope, Hudsonian godwit, western willet, killdeer, spotted sandpiper, Franklin's gull, and the black tern. One can hear the booming of the prairie hen and the querulous cry of the Forster tern, while during migration time, great hordes of blue, snow, and Canada geese honk their way through to their northern nesting grounds.

The ponds and swamps of North Dakota support a bird life which is as interesting as those of South Dakota, and on one of them, Chase Lake, in the south central portion of the state, we visited a large colony of white pelicans. There were about eight hundred of them nesting upon a large island in the middle of this alkali lake, which has been made a Federal Bird Reservation, and as they have been carefully protected, they were extremely tame. Anyone but a bird photographer could wax poetic about these beautiful white birds with their black pinions, as they sail on motionless wing against a dark storm-whipped sky, or as they settle to their nests, where their ugly youngsters are waiting with wide open beaks, but I must fight sunlight and shadow and drizzling rain to see that exposures are uniform. Weeks later, when the film assembled, he begins to appreciate the beauties of stormy billowy, Dakota skies, and the marvels of the bird life that still abounds.

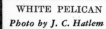

WHITE PELICAN
Photo by J. C. Hatlem

Mr

▲ THE FEMALE of the species. Her habit of devouring her mate gives a diabolical touch to the posture that has earned for her the name Praying Mantis.

ınd Mrs. Mantis

By ROBERT C. HERMES

Some remarkable poses and

practices in the life cycle

of one of our largest and

most interesting insects

⅄ "BOY MEETS GIRL." Here the
female has become aware of the
smaller insect who is her prospective mate. She turns her head
to watch him. The mantis is one
of the few insects able to turn its
head. (*Mantis religiosa*)

➤ As THE FEMALE approaches him, the male apparently tries to make himself as inconspicuous as possible. He crouches lower and lower until his head almost touches the surface, with his delicate antennae waving.

▼ WHEN the male gathers enough strength to approach his lady more closely, she immediately seizes him in her grasping forelegs and then holds him in a vise-like grip for about ten minutes. He frantically rubs his abdomen against his partly opened wings, creating a whirring sound. After she releases him, he backs away and continues to whirr.

▲ SOMETIMES, as in this case, the male abandons his prospective mate and flies off to safer realms.

◄ PORTRAIT of a female Chinese mantis *(Paratenodera sinensis)*. Her beautiful compound eyes are composed of thousands of tiny lenses, and can change from deep dark wells as shown here to pale translucent gems with only a dark speck in their depths. Between her antennae lie three simple eyes.

▲ TWO FEMALE MANTES in mortal combat. They are cannibalistic, and the fight may end in one of them eating the other. However, they usually prefer smaller and more easily captured prey. *(Mantis religiosa)*

➤ FEEDING a Chinese mantis with a dropper. Mantes must be given water every day if they are kept in the home. You have nothing to fear from the sharp mandibles or thorny grasping legs, as the insects soon become tame.

▼ WHEN FRIGHTENED, a mantis raises its wings and
rubs its abdomen up and down against the lower set,
which are pleated. This causes the whirring noise.

⋏ Egg nests of three kinds of mantes. Left, *Stagomantis carolina*; center, *Mantis religiosa*; right, *Paratenodera sinensis*. The nest is made from a creamy substance secreted from the abdomen and smeared into a froth by paddle-like appendages. This quickly hardens. The female lays the eggs in a definite pattern, all pointing toward an escape ridge along the side of the nest. Afterwards, she lives only a week or two and never sees her young.

▼ A CROSS SECTION of the egg nest. The bubble-like structure is an example of nature's ability to produce insulating material.

▲ THE HATCHING STAGE is a critical time in the life of a mantis. The young insect is not only subject to the ravages of ants but also to attacks from insect-eating birds, like this chickadee.

◄ YOUNG CHINESE MANTES emerging from the egg nest. One after another they wiggle from the nest, each encased in a skin-like membrane that remains fastened to the egg mass by a thin thread. Soon a cluster of tiny mantes forms below- dozens of squirming insects splitting their birth sacs and pulling themselves loose. They sometimes hang 2½ to 3 inches below the nest.

Cave People of Europe

Reconstructed scenes from the life of the past
as portrayed by leading authorities

(Below) A Neanderthal Family of perhaps 50,000 years ago represented at the entrance to the Devil's Tower rock-shelter at Gibraltar. Neanderthal man is believed to have been the first to seize a woman and protect her from animals and other men. He lacked tools for sewing clothing, yet he sometimes endured the climatic conditions of the modern Eskimo. Fires glowing at the mouth of his cave barred animals and cold

Courtesy of Field Museum of Natural History ©

(Right) Members of the Cro-Magnon race which drove the more primitive Neanderthal people out of Europe: a painting by Charles R. Knight for the American Museum, showing early artists at work on the famous Procession of Mammoths in the cave of Font-de-Gaume, Dordogne, France. Light was provided by stone lamps burning tallow

Other articles on the art of prehistoric man will be found elsewhere in this Encyclopedia

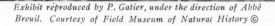

Exhibit reproduced by P. Gatier, under the direction of Abbé Breuil. Courtesy of Field Museum of Natural History ©

(Above) One of our Cro-Magnon ancestors of about 30,000 years ago engaged in artistic endeavor. In the man's right hand is a hollow bone tube through which he blows powdered red ochre around the outlines of his hand to form an imprint on the wall

The Stone That Floats

↗ A PUMICE PIT near Bend, Oregon, one of
the richest regions in this commercially
valuable oddity. Notice that the white band
is at two levels here, owing to the fact that
one section slipped about ten feet past the
other in what is known to geologists as a
fault.

It is lighter than wood, harder than steel, and it serves many uses for our comfort and safety

By Howard E. Jackson

AS a glass, pumice is an odd sort of stone!

That may sound like double-talk, but it isn't. Webster defines pumice as a variety of volcanic glass, full of minute cavities. It is very light in weight and is used, especially in powdered form, for polishing.

You and I think of it as a stone—the kind we cleaned our hands with when we were kids. And we've heard tell that pumice is a rock that can float. A floating stone! While it would take a superman to raise a fair-sized boulder off the ground, an ordinary person can lift an equal-sized pumice stone to chest height.

In addition to being a lightweight glass rock that floats, it also has the rather unusual characteristic of being a hard substance that readily breaks and crumbles away. It's about the hardest rock there is besides quartz. That's why it's such a fine abrasive. It is used in industry on buffing wheels, in restaurants as grill cleaning blocks, and in dental laboratories for polishing teeth. Yet it is so brittle that a child can pulverize a piece the size of a cobblestone in less than five minutes with a toy hammer.

▼ SWIMMERS near pumice deposits sometimes play with stone "lifebuoys."

Durable? Many of the 1500-year-old aqueducts and buildings of old Rome were constructed of pumice blocks. Its durability perhaps exceeds that of any present-day concrete.

The sterling qualities of this prodigal son from the stone family are little appreciated by the average man. Even construction engineers could afford to know it better. Builders in Italy and Germany use pumice oftener than we do in the construction of houses and other buildings. Some U. S. contractors, however, are now using concrete masonry units with pumice as the aggregate, chiefly to reduce weight in construction.

In addition to being a great weight reducer, this lightweight material is an excellent insulator. It keeps a house warm in winter, cool in summer. Ceiling insulation is made of crushed pumice. It is also good as acoustic material, absorptive packing material, and a carrier for catalysts in chemical industries.

Larger pieces of pumice are put to many unusual uses. Since they hold water so readily, they are employed as flowerpots for cacti and rubber plants. Soaked with fuel oil, they make excellent torches for burning brush in the woods.

America is blessed with an abundance of pumice. Central Oregon has some of the finest and largest deposits of pumice to be found anywhere in the world. The entire stretch from Crater Lake to Bend is undermined with it. In one area it is estimated that about 2400 square miles of the stuff lie beneath the surface, unseen, untouched. You drive on roads on top of it for about 60 miles in a north-south direction, yet would never know it is there except that some road cuts have been made through it. Since rain goes right through it, some roadbeds are made of pumice with red cinders on top.

Melting snows quickly disappear where the ground is pumice. Therefore there are no floods, and in the spring you can take off across the desert free of any worry about

being mired down in mud. Natives report that almost anything will grow in pumice, if the crop gets water, but the land must be soaked overnight every two days. They also say that their houses shake when a truck or train goes by on pumice ground, but the vibrations do no damage.

Railroad engineers in pumice country had quite a time with their water supply in the old days. Well water would begin to taste rank. When a man was sent down the well, he would come up with drowned chipmunks. The little animals had bored right through the light material and fallen into the water. After that the railroad men had to haul pure water from springs where it flowed out of the porous rock.

▼ NOTE HOW SMALL the evergreen trees look in this view of pumice cliffs above an oxbow in the Rogue River near Union Creek, Oregon.

⋏ A STEAM SHOVEL loading a truck with pumice. The material is so light that the bucket was enlarged by 65%.

CHUNKS OF THE LIGHTWEIGHT STONE are sometimes imbedded in the ground close to the surface as shown here.

Two Kinds

Roughly, there are two kinds of pumice. The fine kind lies in beds, as far down as 30 feet, covered by an overburden of volcanic or pink ash that is softer than pumice. The dazzling white beds of pumice vary in thickness up to 20 feet. The pumice in these beds is pea-size or slightly larger. You can hold a dozen little lumps of it in one hand. It is mined from pits by steam shovels. When sorted, graded, and sized, it constitutes the bulk of pumice used commercially.

The second kind is the lump pumice, generally found only a few feet beneath the surface. The majority of lumps are about the size of a bowling ball, but some are as big as a bathtub. They are rooted out of the ground by means of a bull-dozer. Many a 'dozer blade has

MINE OWNER Denver Parkes playfully tossing a large piece of pumice into the air.

▲ EVEN A GIRL can lift a good-sized piece of pumice. The stone's porosity makes it useful for insulating and sound-deadening.

been "cut" by the stones it unearths! And where did all that pumice come from? If you are a cook, you can picture it as something like the bubbly fluff atop a pot of boiling applesauce. If you want to make like a volcano and see how the stuff got splattered all over the landscape, put the fluffy applesauce in a funnel and blow a stream of air up through it. A good jet of air will blow the foam off the applesauce and leave the bulk of the mass behind.

That's about the way it happens in volcanoes, only on a much bigger scale. The highly cellular, fragmental volcanic rock is formed in the craters of erupting volcanoes when water vapor and other gases are being released from the viscous lava. When expanding gases reach the surface of the molten rock, they create froth, which solidifies and breaks into pieces. During an explosive eruption, these pieces are expelled from the crater as pumice. While some of the expanded glassy material is blown only a short distance from the crater, the force of the explosion may be great enough to send quantities of it many miles. A supercolossal popcorn machine!

Pumice deposits occur as original beds, laid down as described above, or they may result from the reworking of such beds by wind and water.

Oddly enough, only certain volcanoes produce pumice. In Washington State, for instance, only Mt. St. Helens and Glacier Peak were pumice parents. Famed Mt. Ranier, Mt. Baker, Mt. Adams, and Mt. Tumac spewed none of the frothy stuff. This may not seem to make sense, but perhaps we can't expect every volcano to produce such a pixie as pumice!

▲ PUMICE is so hard that it scores a bulldozer blade. In powdered form, it is a favored abrasive and polisher.

➤ PUMICE BEING APPLIED to a hospital roof in Seattle to help insulate the building from heat and cold.

Howard Staples & Associates

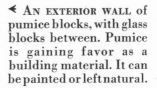

◄ AN EXTERIOR WALL of pumice blocks, with glass blocks between. Pumice is gaining favor as a building material. It can be painted or left natural.

Acme Commercial Studio

Adventures with Big Snakes

In search of the world's largest
snakes in the jungles of Borneo

By HARRY C. RAVEN

Late Associate Curator of Comparative Anatomy,
American Museum of Natural History

THE largest species of serpent in the world inhabits the East Indies. It is the Regal Python, known to science as *Python reticulatus*, and to the Malays, who share its habitat, as Ular Sawa. Ular is their name for snake, and Sawa means a python.

Pythons ceased to be a mere name to me and assumed a semblance of reality even before I started for the East Indies in 1912. I had the pleasure of meeting a Norwegian explorer, the late Dr. Carl Lumholtz, who was also planning an expedition to Borneo, and in the course of our conversation he told me there would be times when I would have difficulty in obtaining fresh meat for food. At such times, he said, if I could get a python I would find its flesh very good, though best of all, he thought, was the liver. This had been his experience, gained years before, when he had visited the tropical part of North Queensland, Australia. As will be seen later, I found that the Dyaks who inhabit the interior of Borneo make a practice of eating the flesh of the python and appear to like it.

◄ A BLACK-TAILED PYTHON OF INDIA: a species closely related to the Borneo pythons described here. The small pit near the nostril is one of a pair of heat receptors used to locate warm-blooded prey in the dark. Some pythons have as many as a dozen on each side. This species exceeds 20 feet in length

In Borneo I met white men whom I questioned about pythons, but few of them had any first-hand knowledge. One told me that pythons occasionally crawled into his henhouse at night, and after devouring some of his valued fowls, they would be so distended as to be unable to crawl out again between the bars. They would then be discovered and killed in the morning. I also met people who said a python was a good thing to have about the house to keep the rats in check. They of course referred to small or young pythons, not over five or ten feet long.

The first python I saw in its native habitat was sunning itself on a horizontal branch of a tree overhanging a river. I was sitting amidships in a dugout canoe at the time. The Malay boy who was sitting in the bow said, "Sawa," reached out with his paddle, and touched the branch, whereupon the python gracefully slid off and disappeared in the dark water.

After shifting about in Borneo, from river to river and from reef to reef, and never getting more than a degree or two north or south of the equator, I crossed the Strait of Macassar in my little schooner and sailed along the north coast of Celebes. Stopping near a mining camp at a place where there was a good harbor, I left the schooner and went inland a short distance to camp on the mountains, which were covered with virgin jungle. The white men at the mine told me of a huge python one of their natives had killed a few days before my arrival, and showed me a very poor photograph of it taken after it had been killed and dragged to camp. Though the print was dull, you could

▲ SWALLOWED BY A SNAKE: a 125-pound wild boar taken from the digestive tract of a 24-foot python in the Philippine Islands

see a man standing on the huge body, which was about a foot thick. The civil engineer told me it was just ten meters (33 feet) long. I asked him if he had paced off its length, but he said, no, he had measured it with a surveying tape. No part of the animal was preserved. It had been rainy weather when it was killed and on account of the dampness not even the skin was kept. I visited the place where the carcass had been cast aside. There was only the odor, and a few little pieces of bone left. Wild pigs, kites, monitors, and maggots were the jungle scavengers that had disposed of it. I greatly regretted not having arrived at this place a little sooner, as I very much wanted a large python and this was the largest one I had heard of.

Much to my surprise, I was told a day or two later that another python of about the same size had been seen not far from the place where the first one had been killed, which was quite near my camp. The mine officials kindly gave orders to the coolies, who were making survey and prospect trails through the jungle, to report to me immediately if they happened to see it again.

One morning several days later a Javanese coolie, almost breathless, arrived in camp to say he had just seen the great python. I picked up my shotgun and some shells loaded with buckshot and followed him down a little valley beside a stream that flowed through the heavy forest. He hurried along ahead of me for about half a mile, then stopped, and, as he looked at the narrow path, remarked in Malay that the python had gone. I could see the place where the snake had been on the path and told my companion we would follow its trail and kill it. He said that he had to go to work immediately or his boss would be very angry, and besides he was afraid of snakes.

I could not persuade him to stay, so as he went off I began cautiously to follow the trail. I had not gone more than a few yards before I realized that I was really on the trail of a giant. I was amazed at the apparent weight of the animal. Where it had moved sideways and pressed against little bushes they were bent flat, and where it had gone over a piece of dead wood, this was broken and pressed into the ground. Every moment I expected to see the fore part of the huge body rise up with gaping jaws, ready to strike at me, but nevertheless, I followed the trail for about 50 yards between rocks and over roots of trees, through twisted masses of lianas and rattans, where I occasionally had to use my machete.

Then the python had turned toward the stream, scraping the moss off the root of a tree as it had slid into the water. It had gone on downstream, sometimes sliding over rocks where I could easily see its marks, or over sand and gravel that looked as if a huge sack of grain had been dragged over them. Here, because the banks in some places were so high and steep, overgrown with ferns and begonias, and because in others the stream flowed under the bank and the projecting roots of great trees, I could no longer follow the trail and had to return to camp, down on my luck for having missed another giant python.

My friend, Mr. Lingard, of Borneo, a nephew of Conrad's Lord Jim, once told me of an experience he had had with some Punan Dyaks and a python. The Dyaks were serving as Mr. Lingard's paddlers on a trip up one of Borneo's beautiful rivers to the interior. He was reminded of this python incident while warning me against Punans as paddlers, for, said he, they never pay attention to their paddling but are always on the lookout for food of one kind or another. They stop paddling to try to catch fish in a circular throw net, or to gather wild fruit from trees along the bank, or again to see what their dogs, which they have released on the riverbank, hold at bay and are barking at. The dogs might be barking at a porcupine, or some sort of

civet hiding in a hole in an old log or under the roots of a tree; they might have treed a wildcat, of which there are many species in Borneo, or a clouded leopard. However, it was more likely to be a wild boar, which they could hold at bay in its muddy wallowing place or between the buttress-like roots of some forest giant. After being worried by some such delays, Mr. Lingard was hoping his paddlers would not see anything more to distract them as they paddled along, a few feet from the bank, when suddenly one of them in the middle of the canoe dropped his paddle, and with an exclamation leaned over the side and grabbed something. It was the tail of a python which had just been sliding off the bank into the water.

In the commotion that followed, the dugout was nearly overturned. The Dyaks kept their heads, however, although all of them, even the one pulling at the serpent's tail, were shouting like maniacs. Several had dropped their paddles and taken out their two-foot, machete-like knives, when out of the water darted the python's head. With a single blow one of them nearly severed it. They then got hold of the great body and made fast to it with rattans. All stopped paddling, and the canoe, tied to the huge, wriggling, bleeding python, drifted downstream. As the natives watched the dead body writhing in the water, they discovered that their victim had recently fed upon some large animal, for they could see the bulge in its sides. It was but a short distance to a bend in the river, where, owing to the low water, a large gravel shoal was exposed. There they encamped for the night and prepared their evening meal. Mr. Lingard said he was disgusted with those Dyaks, for they not only roasted and ate the python, which was about 20 feet in length, but also ate the two half-grown wild pigs they took from its stomach.

About a year and a half after my conversation with Mr. Lingard, which, by the way, took place in his quarters in the rear of a little Chinese shop in northeastern Borneo, I was encamped near some Dyak clearings on the upper Karangan River. Most of the Dyaks had finished planting their season's crop of rice and were preparing to go after wild honey. The preparation consisted of making bark vessels in which to put honeycomb, making torches, or rather smudges, of certain split and dried lianas tied round with rattan, and preparing rice in various ways to take along for food. On honey-gathering expeditions, which are regarded as great festivities, the Dyaks would usually go off in family groups, and camp by a stream or river, half or quarter of a mile from the trees harboring the hives. These magnificent white-barked trees, that usually tower over the rest of the forest, are greatly-prized possessions, each Dyak family having its own particular ones, which are handed down from generation to generation. The men climb up at night and slit open the hives to get the honey and young bees, while the women and childen below make a smudge with bark and the liana fagots. Sometimes there are dozens of hives in one enormous tree. The Dyaks may work at getting the honey all night, having, of course, to be very careful in climbing about in the dark. The children wait below and scramble for any pieces of honeycomb they hear drop, and all in all they have a very good time. At the approach of dawn they hurry away to their camp to avoid being attacked by the bees they have robbed.

During the day, on these excursions, the Dyaks sleep and lie about on their rattan mats, talking and eating honey and larval bees, which are delicious either raw or cooked with honey. They have other food too, such as nice nut-flavored rice, sweet potatoes, bananas, and various fruits from the jungle. On a picnic of this kind they are more apt to have meat than at any other time, for some of the men and boys are sure to tire of lying about the camp and wander off to hunt wild pigs and sambar deer.

It was while hunting pigs one day, that a Dyak boy I knew had a very narrow escape from a python. His dogs, which had been in hot pursuit of a wild boar, had at last apparently got it at bay, and he ran through the forest in the direction from which the barking came. In so doing he naturally followed the trails made by wild pigs, beside which the pythons await their prey. As he ran down a little gully a python struck at him. Fortunately he was crouching low, so it did not get hold with its teeth but hit him with its neck. The boy was bowled over but scrambled on and escaped. He returned to camp so severely frightened that he had fever for several days afterward. The fever was malaria, which manifests itself in most of the Malays and Dyaks of this part of Borneo, though only when their bodies are weakened in some way, as by fatigue or injury. In this case it was mental shock. At first he would not go into the jungle at all and for several days moped about the clearings, spending most of his time in his parents' hut. Later I saw him gathering rattans in company with

➤ THE PYTHON has more vertebrae than any other animal, so far as is known. This reticulated python, 22 feet 9 inches long, had over 400

A.M.N.H. photo

some of the men of the village. This seemed to me to be a stage in his recovery; he would go into the jungle but not alone. At about this time I moved on to another camp, and did not see the boy again. It is probably such experiences as this youth had, or the association with people who have been subjected to such experiences, that tend to make the Dyaks and Malays, who live in the jungles, always go armed.

I have never definitely known of a person being killed by a python. Of course the Malays tell many stories of people who have been eaten by pythons, and there is no reason to believe a large python could not swallow a small man, such as a Malay. The second year I was in Borneo, I had with me a very good Banjerese Malay, who had lived on the east coast of Borneo for a number of years. He had frequently been on excursions into the jungle to gather rattan. On one of these excursions, he told me, he, and three or four companions, spent several weeks gathering rattans in one locality. They had only the one camp during their whole stay, but they wandered to a distance of a mile or more in every direction; consequently they knew the country well, especially as this was not their first visit to the place. Finally they finished gathering rattan and prepared to return home to their kampong. On the morning they were to start for home, one of them remembered that he had one more bundle of rattan to bring down to the boat. Therefore he told the others to put everything aboard, while he went for it. They made ready to depart, but the man who had gone for his rattan did not come. They called, but he did not answer. After waiting a little while, one of them went to look for him. The searcher brought the bundle of

rattan and said there were no signs of their companion having been to it. They then thought he might perhaps have been taken sick and gone back to the camp site. He was not there, and they called and hunted throughout the day until late afternoon. The lost man knew the country better than any of the others. He had been hunting over it every day for weeks. It was impossible to believe he had simply lost his way in going half a mile over country he knew so well. If he had had occasion to go near the river, they would have supposed him caught by a crocodile, but there had been no such occasion. Toward sunset they paddled down to the coast where they met some "Orang Laut" or seafaring Malays. With them, they returned the following day and searched but found not the slightest clew as

W. Henry Sheak photo

to what had become of their companion. They concluded he had been caught by a "hantu" (ghost), or "Sawa" (python). That is the secret of the jungle and, "*Allah sadja yeng tahu*" (God only knows).

New York Zoological Society photo
▲ A 20-FOOT example of the kind of python described in this article

THE END OF A HUNGER STRIKE. Six men held the huge snake while the celebrated reptile expert, the late Dr. Ditmars, administered force feeding

Quartz

It is found almost everywhere and it enables man to defy space, but the pure crystals that are valuable in radio come only from one country

By FREDERICK H. POUGH

Former Curator of Physical Geology and Mineralogy, American Museum of Natural History

Little drops of water
  Little grains of sand
Make the mighty ocean
  And the pleasant land.

ALTHOUGH the familiar rhyme isn't completely true, it does no serious violence to the scientist's feelings to say that little grains of sand make up the earth, and since most of the sand in the world is quartz, it is clear that quartz is one of the commonest of all minerals. It has been known to all peoples through all ages, under a multitude of names. For it has certain properties, obvious ones, which have made it a valuable material to all civilizations.

Its place on our strategic list, however, is not the result of any of its older uses. Quartz is the only mineral that was of little importance in World War I but of crucial importance in World War II. This is largely because of the use of quartz in radio instruments—a use discovered about 1920. Quartz crystals in radio sending sets have made it possible for many stations to operate simultaneously whereas only a few could before. The quartz crystal enables each station to stay precisely on its own wave length or frequency.

◄ A GLOBE OF CUT CRYSTAL calls attention to the one vital source, Brazil

Chemically, quartz is one of the simplest minerals. It is silicon dioxide. By reason of its molecular structure, it is now classed with the silicates and thus belongs to a large group including about one-fourth of the known minerals. The silicate minerals are the principal rock-making minerals, and quartz is an important one of them. Since it is not always present in igneous rocks, it has been made one of the minerals upon which their subdivision is based.

The problem of locating strategic supplies of quartz is simplified by the fact that it is impossible for quartz to occur with certain other minerals. Where you find olivine, for instance, you will not find quartz, because olivine presupposes insufficient excess silica.

Quartz can form in all the classes of rocks—igneous, sedimentary, and metamorphic—, but it is originally an igneous mineral. It forms when deep-seated rocks crystallize after all the other ingredients, such as magnesia, iron, and alumina, have satisfied their silica needs and formed stable compounds. We also get quartz if the still liquid portion of a crystallizing magma is drawn off before all the reactions take place, leaving a final excess of silica which would otherwise have been used up in more complex combinations. This is the present theory of the formation of granitic rocks and is the reason why some minerals cannot occur in the same rock with quartz.

The kind of quartz, however, that is a constituent of granite, while very common, is quite worthless. The strategic variety of quartz is rock crystal, flawless, colorless, and of good size. But even the purest, most perfect looking piece of crystal may still be worthless for radio equipment.

Quartz crystallizes in six-sided prismatic crystals, terminated by six steeply inclined planes which are known as rhombohedrons. These six terminal planes are not all alike, as in beryl, for example, but constitute two sets of three planes each; hence quartz is said not to have full hexagonal symmetry. These two sets of planes are called positive and negative rhombohedrons, and they are important in the radio use of quartz. In addition, quartz crystals sometimes have additional sets of planes, somewhat skewed to the right or left of the ridge between the rhombohedrons, and these determine whether the crystal is what we call left-handed or right-handed. All quartz crystals are one or the other, or both in intergrown combinations, but their nature cannot easily be determined if this third series of faces is not present.

In modern times as in ancient, one of the characteristics of quartz that makes it useful is its hardness and, in the broader sense, its stability under many sorts of conditions. Its hardness is 7 on the mineral scale of hardnesses ranging from 1 to 10, and that is harder than the best grades of ordinary steel, which reach about 6. It does not cleave readily and is a tough mineral under impact. Quartz also resists acids: only hydrofluoric attacks it at an appreciable rate. It cannot oxidize since it is already a stable oxide; and since it does not combine readily with water, it survives the attacks of ordinary atmospheric weathering. The sands of our beaches are good evidence of the hardihood of this mineral, for they are the quartz that has remained in relatively pure form after the other ingredients of the rock have weathered away. The stable quartz fragments remain on the beach, while the feldspars and dark minerals composing the original granites have turned to clays and muds and been washed away into the sea.

One might think that so resistant and clear a mineral would make a good gem, and it does with a single drawback—it is too common ever to be very valuable. There are many gem varieties: rock crystal, citrine, amethyst, and rose quartz, to name a few, and one could go on for half a page. In ancient times it was not realized that clear rock crystal quartz was the same as some of the opaque or translucent varieties like agate, chalcedony, carnelian, and jasper, for these were formed in a different way and look very dissimilar. Instead of being produced from the molten magma about which we spoke earlier, these were formed from aqueous solutions and are very finely, in fact microscopically, crystalline. Much of the silica composing them came from the decomposition of silicate minerals like feldspar, substances which appear to yield their silica into solution more readily than does the primary quartz.

The Greeks and Romans were, therefore, a little hazy about the true nature of some of their gems. They knew rock crystal and called it *crystallus*, in allusion to their belief that it was formed in the Alps from water which was frozen so hard that it could never melt again. Since color was an important distinction to them, they naturally did not associate amethyst, crystal, agate, and jasper as we do today. The general name, quartz, was a miner's word in the Middle Ages, mentioned in Basil Valentine's and Agricola's works.

Large colorless and flawless single

AMNH photos by Coles

⋏ QUARTZ crystallizes in the form of six-sided prisms, terminating in steeply inclined planes. These end planes do not have full symmetry but are grouped in two sets of three planes each, and their different nature must be considered in cutting quartz for use in radio

crystals are in great demand today for use in radio oscillators. The property of quartz that makes it valuable in electricity was investigated by the Curies before their radium work and is known as piezo-electricity (from *piezin,* the Greek word for "to press"). This refers to the habit of the substance to develop an electrical charge upon application of pressure. Conversely, when subjected to alternating electrical current, quartz commences to vibrate, giving off current at the same time. The frequency of the vibration depends upon several factors:

the orientation of the slice selected in the crystal and its proportions. However, for any single slice the frequency is very definite, never deviating from the fixed rate. Thus it can be used in a radio transmitter to fix the frequency of the vibrations and hence the wave length. Of course, the current generated by the single quartz slice is exceedingly small, but this is so amplified by oscillating vacuum tubes that the tiny fragile quartz is able to stabilize the frequency of the whole powerful transmitter.

Many other substances also exhibit

this piezo-electric property—Rochelle salt, sugar, tourmaline, and others. Rochelle salt has a far stronger piezo-electric effect than quartz, and it is used in electric phonograph pickups. The vibrations of the needle cause the generation of an electric current in the Rochelle salt crystal. But this crystal is rather fragile and is sealed into a container in which it operates over a very limited range of temperature. Such pickups are far from sturdy, and radio transmitters in tanks and airplanes must stand considerable abuse and violent changes in temperature and humidity. Quartz is the only substance found so far which is satisfactory.

The cutting of these so-called "radio crystals" is a delicate job, for the frequency of the vibration will change with the removal of each molecular layer. Furthermore, in order to cut a slice that will retain a fixed frequency, it must be exactly oriented in the original crystal. Positive and negative rhombohedron faces must be identified, and the direction of the piezo-electric axes determined. An artificial face is then cut on the crystal at a definite angle to the Z-axis, an angle which must be within a quarter of a degree of the proper inclination. Slices of the flawless crystals are cut parallel to this layer, and they are then etched in hydrofluoric acid, which brings out a complex pattern if the crystal should be one of those complicated combinations of right- and left-handed crystals of which we spoke. If the slice, or a portion of it, is found to be usable, this is then shaped up to definite dimensions, and carefully ground smooth. The final slice is continually tested on an instrument which gives off a howl of varying tone as the slice is thinned down to the desired thickness and vibration frequency. When the instrument becomes silent, the crystal is ready. But so critical is the thickness that the brushing of a finger across the crystal can ruin it and start the howl again.

Several different cuts are used in making these crystals, either for different purposes or because of patents. Sometimes they are sliced singly, sometimes in groups by means of gang-saws. Again, a whole slab may be sliced in a single piece and later subdivided. But these small vibrating wafers are, of course, the final product. Vast quantities—millions—are needed. A single plane or tank may use a hundred or more to be in touch with other planes or tanks and with operational bases. With the vast number of mechanized units being produced today, it is not hard to visualize what a real problem it has become to get the necessary quartz and to turn it into the precisely made slices. In normal times only a few were needed, and a small cutter could turn out all that were required.

All of the quartz for these radio "crystals" comes from Brazil. It occurs in strongly weathered and decomposed veins which are related to the igneous activity in the region. The deposits are very ancient and probably were produced from solutions rich in silica which came off near the close of the magmatic activity. Some of the crystals are found still in place in the veins; others, having been washed down, lie in boulder beds.

The United States has agreed to buy all that Brazil produces, but even this may not be enough. Prices vary according to size and quality, from $1 or $2 per pound up to $15 or $30. Proportionally less is paid for crystals that are badly flawed or twinned (that is, composed of two or more crystals, or parts of crystals, in reverse position to each other) than for ones that permit easy orientation and the slicing of large, pure blocks of usable material.

▼ GROUND so precisely that the brush of a finger will ruin their radio frequency. Quartz "crystals" of this type make it possible for the many mechanized units in a modern battle to maintain contact with one another

AMNH photos by Coles

▼ AN APPARENTLY FLAWLESS crystal section is shown by polarized light to be complexly twinned and hence worthless for radio. Quartz is also used in depth-sounding instruments, ballistic apparatus, periscopes, and gun sights

Drawing by
Matthew Kalmenoff

The Destructive RAT—

Strange By-product of Civilization

It has taken more lives during the last ten centuries than all the wars and revolutions of history

By GARY WEBSTER

MEASURED by almost any standard, the rat is the most important four-legged foe of modern man. A twelve-ounce engine of destruction with built-in disease-carrying features, he easily surpasses all the others in numbers, cost, and menace.

But we've brought it on ourselves. True, rare and scattered clues suggest that rats have been around for many thousands of years. Bones have even been found in association with relics from men of the Stone Age. But the rat has had a very brief career as a major villain.

He has played this role for less than a thousand years—a mere instant of biological time.

The literature of classical Greece and Rome abounds in reference to animals, large and small. There are several allusions to mice, but not so much as a single word about rats. This factor, plus the absence of their bones from excavated sites, indicates they were rare if not altogether missing from ancient cities. Not until late in the twelfth century did any writer make a clear reference to the rat.

Theory has it that wild rats of the Arabian deserts found that they could fare better in villages than among sand dunes. So they moved to town, became dependent on mankind, and gradually spread into more densely settled regions. If this view is correct, they were numerous but not especially important by the time of the Crusades. When Christian warriors returned to Europe, African rats stowed away on their ships and soon established outposts in the new land.

The rat of this era is now known to zoologists as *Rattus rattus*. A skilled and graceful climber, he can easily run along pipes, wires, and ropes. His tail—which is slightly longer than his head and body together—serves as a balance so effective that he can jump from one perch to another almost as nimbly as a squirrel.

Early efforts at control were scattered and ineffective. In some cities, various kinds of bounty were offered. For instance, in the fifteenth-century, Jews in Frankfort, Germany, received special privileges in return for annual tribute in the form of 5,000 rat tails. Professional rat-catchers became so numerous that they were organized into guilds. In Shakespeare's time, a good rat-killer might enjoy considerable honor in his town.

In spite of attacks by professionals and amateurs, the so-called black rat had a field day. Europe was literally over-run. Damage to food and other commodities shot upward at an alarming rate. People grumbled, tried new traps and poisons, passed laws.

They did not even realize that the rat's role as a vandal is the smallest part of its menace. Only in recent centuries have people understood that the epidemics of typhus and bubonic plague in Europe were linked with the invasion of the rat.

Though plague must have existed much earlier, it did not become epidemic until modern times. Plague is transmitted to man by fleas from rats. In the five or six generations before Columbus' voyage, more than 34 million persons died of it. Europe's population was reduced by one-fourth. Spanish armies in Granada lost six men from plague to every man felled by arrows of the Moors. It hit London in 1665; before it subsided, there were 100,000 casualties.

Many persons regard the rat-borne disease as "medieval," of historical interest only. It is true that there have been no major epidemics in the western hemisphere in nearly three centuries. Health authorities have checked it quickly in each U.S. outbreak: San Francisco, 1907; New Orleans, 1914; Galveston, 1920.

Lacking money and equipment, doctors of India have not matched that record. In the quarter-century after 1898, plague killed as many natives of India as there are people in Chicago, Philadelphia, Atlanta, Dallas, Miami, and Los Angeles, combined.

And that's only one facet of the story.

Rats transmit murine typhus through the agency of the lice they harbor. During the four centuries this disease has been epidemic it has claimed millions. Historians generally write the records of nations in terms of kings and generals. As Hans Zinsser has pointed out in his famous book, *Rats, Lice, and History,* rat-spread typhus has influenced western civilization far more than any great man whose name appears in all the history books.

Seventeenth-
century
rat-catcher.

*Bettmann
Archive*

It would be guesswork to estimate the total impact of rat-linked disease and death. Rats rank so high among global killers that most authorities are content with a general statement. In less than ten centuries, experts agree, diseases involving rats as agents have taken more human lives than all the wars and revolutions ever fought.

Plàgue and typhus do not exhaust the list. A rat is a living freighter whose design is just right for transporting a cargo of bacteria. He can digest almost anything; and after a meal in the garbage dump, he may slip into a building for dessert. With feet still wet from a jaunt through his favorite sewer, he will prowl casually over the stock of the corner grocery. His blood stream and stomach harbor disease-producing organisms ranging from those of amoebic dysentery and infectious jaundice to rabies and tularemia.

So far, all attempts to exterminate the rat have failed miserably. Hundreds of inventors have perfected traps—but none are more than moderately effective. Dogs, cats, ferrets, and even weasels are still employed to hunt them, but they seldom do more than thin the ranks temporarily.

Poisons

Long-used natural poisons have about seen their day. Powerful new synthetic compounds of several types have been used with considerable success. One of them, 1080, is so deadly to humans and livestock that only experts are permitted to use it. Another, ANTU, is fatal to brown rats but comparatively harmless to many other mammals. Warfarin, most publicized of new poisons, prevents blood from clotting and causes rats to die from internal bleeding.

A few optimists have predicted that these and other chemical weapons can reduce the rat to negligible importance. Others consider such a view to be wishful thinking. In the known history of rats, they point out, there has been only one instance of a really decisive victory.

It was won, not by man, but by rats. The two main types of rats that live with man are *climbing* rats (such as *Rattus rattus alexandrinus*) and *burrowing* rats (*Rattus norvegicus* and its varieties). The burrowing rats are sometimes called brown

Philip Gendreau

rats, though both brown and black occur in the two main types, and brown is actually predominant in both. History's strangest conquest is believed to have been launched shortly before 1727. In that year, hordes of the unfamiliar "brown" kind were seen scurrying through Russia. When they came to the Volga, the army of migrants plunged into the river. Thousands drowned, but great numbers crossed to the western bank.

Some authorities think this fierce rodent came from Chinese Mongolia. Others believe its original home was somewhere near the Caspian Sea. At any rate, it was unknown in Europe before the eighteenth century.

Once it penetrated new regions, however, the brown rat's advance was sure and rapid. A few specimens reached England in 1728. Popular belief linked the new marauder with timber ships from Norway. Hence

it is now almost universally known as the Norway rat.

The newcomer was short-tailed and blunt-nosed by comparison with the black rat and proved much more fierce. Attacking its well-established cousin, the brown rat won a series of smashing victories. Blacks are still dominant in tropical and subtropical areas throughout the world. But almost everywhere else except in seaports, browns have exterminated their slender foes.

Brown invaders reached North America some time just before or after the Revolution. They spread up and down the Atlantic seaboard within a decade. When miners made their epic dash to California, rats went with them. Working inland from both coasts, they were soon established throughout temperate North America.

Meanwhile, other immigrating rats moved eastward from Europe and set up successful colonies wherever they stopped. Hence they are

**ss of stored crops keeps the farmer
on the warpath against the rat.**

Three Lions photos

Calcium Cyanide is sprayed into suspected places.

⋏ Poisoned pellets must not endanger desirable animals

◄ Vertical traps sometimes fool wary rats

➤ Screening vents helps where original construction was not rat-proof.

now firmly entrenched in regions that make up about half the world's land surface. At the mid-point of the twentieth century, no other mammal except man holds equal territory. The brown rats of the world probably outnumber their hosts; if so, they are the most numerous mammals on earth.

Willingness to eat just about anything has been a major factor in the rat's world conquest. Adults eat about 50 pounds of food a year. Their menu: almost anything they can cut. They've been known to gorge on paint, shoe leather, soap, and rubber insulation from electric wires. Enterprising colonies have cut into the bellies of swine, dug turnips from the ground, even feasted on the oil-rich toenails of sleeping elephants.

No one knows how many rats there are in the world. In the U. S. alone, there are thought to be some 175 million, give or take a few million. This estimate rests on data from many campaigns. In Baltimore, one year of activity by civic forces led to some 460,000 casualties among the city's rats. U. S. Department of Agriculture workers killed 7½ million in a single three-state operation; it took 400,000 traps, carloads of poisoned grain, and about one million pounds of little sausages treated with poison.

According to the best guess of the U. S. Fish and Wildlife Service, direct rat damage in this country ranges somewhere near $200 million a year. World totals soar far into the billions, precisely how far, there is no way to determine.

Actual eating by rats is perhaps the smallest part of their drain on civilization. They destroy many times as much as they cram into their bellies. It is generally believed that their toll exceeds that of all other animal pests combined.

Keep Gnawing or Die

Part of this wholesale destruction rests on a biological base. The incisor teeth of the rat appear eight or ten days after birth. Both lowers and uppers keep growing throughout the animal's life. The incisors advance at the rate of about four inches a year. If one is lost from the rat's upper jaw or is knocked out of line, the one below may push up so high that it pierces the brain cavity and causes death.

Total growth of upper and lower cutting teeth in the normal rat's three-year life amounts to about 29.5 inches. Obviously, if the rodent didn't work constantly at the job of wearing down his teeth, they'd soon become so long he'd go around with his mouth permanently propped open.

This factor may account, at least in part, for persistent life-long gnawing and chewing. Observation suggests that the typical individual uses his teeth at least half his waking hours. When he isn't actually eating, he's ripping and cutting—sometimes, it seems, for the sheer fun of it.

Given a few hours in a warehouse, a single rat may tear holes in dozens of sacks of flour, grain, feed, coffee, or even fertilizer. Instead of dining on two whole potatoes or apples, a hungry fellow is likely to take random bites from a score of them. Rats are said to have slaughtered as many as 1500 baby chicks and 325 broilers in a single foray.

The cutting edges of their teeth

⋀ A TOWN CRIER calling "Bring out your dead," during the London Plague of 1665. The cart in the background is removing the corpses.

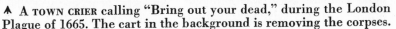

are extremely hard. For no known reason except a remote possibility that water may be their objective, rats sometimes gnaw through lead pipes. Laboratory albinos — weaklings compared with their wild cousins—cut through two inches of foamglass in an eight-night test. Two nights less were required to gnaw a hole in an aluminum sheet a full half-inch thick. Wild rats have been known to cut through four inches of old concrete. They've gnawed holes in dams and started floods, and once threw much of New York into darkness by stripping insulation from wires to cause a major short-circuit.

Though ordinary rats are not such collectors as the notorious pack rat, they do steal small objects and carry them to the nest. Exterminators digging into dens under a tenement have found keys, coins, a belt buckle, a lipstick tube, a shoe horn. Matches are often scattered through such piles of loot.

It is no myth, declare experts, that rats start fires both by cutting insulation from electric wires and by accidentally striking matches. Running to his nest with an ordinary friction match in his mouth, the rat drops it when it happens to strike. If it falls into a pile of litter, there may be another fire of undetermined origin.

Dr. Curt P. Richter, of Johns Hopkins, devoted five years to study of the rat's dietary choices. Given free access to separate containers of minerals, vitamins, carbohydrates, fats and proteins, laboratory animals selected each in proportions making for good health. That, insist some analysts, is more than many humans will do.

Rats can dig their own burrows, but they also are smart enough to take over the quarters of other creatures. They aren't fond of water, but swim when the situation demands it. Sailors have long vowed that rats can tell when a ship is in bad condition. The belief that they will desert a doomed vessel explains the almost universal practice of calling any kind of deserter or traitor a "rat." Bizarre as it sounds, the notion may not be completely unfounded. In old wooden ships, rats would be the first on board to know about new leaks—which may have prompted an exodus at the next port.

Many wild creatures languish in captivity, quickly die. Not the rat. He quickly adapts to almost any conditions in which life can be sustained. Producers making educational movies about rats found that the animals soon ignored intense light. Camera noise was a bigger problem. It was solved by running nonsense sounds continuously at a high volume, masking all minor noises. The four-footed actors went about their business, oblivious of both sounds and lights.

Most exterminators agree that an old veteran, whom they call a "Moby Dick," can master almost any kind of trap. He will kick it around until it goes off, then calmly eat the bait—unless he whiffs poison in it.

One expert vows he has known individual rats that liked music so well they clicked their teeth in applause. That story, which hasn't won general acceptance by scientists, may rank with others which tell of young ones leading the old and blind to safety in time of danger. And there are those who declare they've seen rats steal food by dipping their tails into bottles too small to admit a snout.

Perhaps the most fantastic rat story is the one that explains the way they steal eggs. Though some scoff at it, the tale has been current since the thirteenth century. According to it, rats organize for the purpose of plundering a nest or crate. One grabs an egg in his forepaws and rolls over on his back; another then catches his tail and drags him to their den. Whether that account is accurate or not, *somehow* rats do move eggs considerable distances and over obstacles. Eggs disappeared from one hatchery at the rate of 80 dozen a week. An assault on the dens of the rats revealed many eggs stockpiled in underground store rooms.

Intelligence of Rats

This much is absolutely clear: rats quickly beat every lethal device aimed at them. It is still too early to know whether new synthetic poisons will retain their effectiveness over a period of years. Rats may learn to recognize and avoid them. Albinos studied in the laboratory quickly learned to identify a magazine advertisement for ice cream—then selected it from half a dozen assorted ads. They also proved they could select one letter of the alphabet from a row of mixed ones, or pick a given ink-blot from a display of several different ones.

Some psychologists assert that rats make better scores on five-way choices than on two-way ones. This, they think, is because any simple problem quickly bores them and they quit trying.

Intelligence alone would make the rat a worthy foe. In addition, he is fortified with a biological heritage that enables him to overcome almost any partial victory by his two-legged opponents. Given ideal conditions, a single female can produce ten litters in a year, each with about ten young. Potentially, one pair can have 350 million descendants in three years. Using every known

⋀ THE WHITE RAT of laboratory fame, unlike its unwanted cousin, has helped save millions of lives. These young cannot yet see.

weapon—including cyanide or other poison gas—professional exterminators seldom kill more than 95% of the rats in a region. The survivors can quickly bring the population back to the old levels.

Extermination on a global or even national level is not a real possibility in the foreseeable future. Control is a different matter. It requires three processes. First, use concrete and steel to rat-proof buildings. Second, eliminate open sources of food, such as garbage dumps and waste heaps. Third, wage a continuous war with traps and poison. All three measures must be used. Periodic killing alone is about as effective as treating leprosy with calamine lotion.

Civilization gives the rat abundant food on an all-year basis—plus protection from natural foes. Result: rats have increased greatly in the last few centuries.

Nature offers no rat-cafeterias that approximate the bakery, poultry shop, stable, distillery, feed mill, warehouse, food store, wharf, slaughterhouse, sewer, garbage dump—or even a home where food is constantly on hand. Nor does nature provide spacious shelters from which hereditary enemies are banished. Ferrets, weasels, and skunks consider the rat a choice tidbit, but neither householders nor businessmen encourage such rat-killers to hang around. Nor does man welcome his other allies in the rat war—snakes, owls, storks, herons, eagles, or vultures.

In effect, man has built special rat-havens, which he calls cities and farms. He stocks them with abundant food, which is on hand in wet weather or dry, hot or cold. These life-zones are just right for our planet's most troublesome four-footed pest. To overcome so well sheltered an enemy, it would be necessary to make a major change in some aspect of the man-rat complex. Thus far, only one really effective idea has been suggested: man should put the rat on his menu as a delicacy. Failing this or an equally radical change, it appears likely that "cousin rat" will continue to be man's guest for a long, long time.

HOW A
Rattlesnake

By **Walker Van Riper**
Denver Museum of Natural History
All photographs by the author

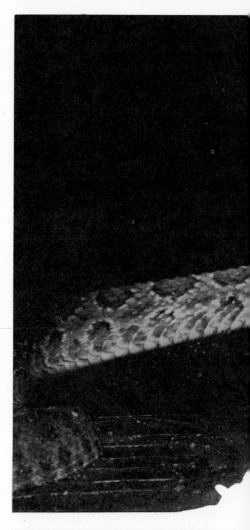

IN both the popular and scientific literature, we are told that when a rattlesnake strikes, it makes a quick bite to embed the fangs. and inject the venom. The bite is said to be essential because the swelling and contracting jaw muscles must press against the venom gland and force out the venom. Further, the strike is often spoken of as being "the fastest thing in nature," or "like lightning." There is also a widespread theory that a rattlesnake cannot strike upward. Strangely enough, all these statements are incorrect, at least for the Prairie Rattlesnake.

A number of years ago it occurred to me that the high-speed electronic flash, invented by Dr. H. E. Edgerton of M.I.T., might be a useful new tool for investigating questions of this sort. A series of experiments that I undertook show quite clearly, I think, exactly what does take place when a rattler strikes.The snake was shown striking a rubber balloon about eight inches in diameter. The

Superspeed photography and a naturalist's ingenuity

clear up three misconceptions that have been current

in technical literature and popular thought

Strikes

⬆ THE SNAKE STABBED the target with jaws spread wide and fangs pointing forward. No bite was shown, but further tests were needed.

high-speed flash apparatus was so arranged that a picture was taken at the instant the fangs touched the surface of the balloon. The photograph showed a pure stab with jaws fully opened, fangs pointing forward. In order to find out whether the jaws closed in a biting action, a picture was also taken an instant after the collapse of the balloon. No

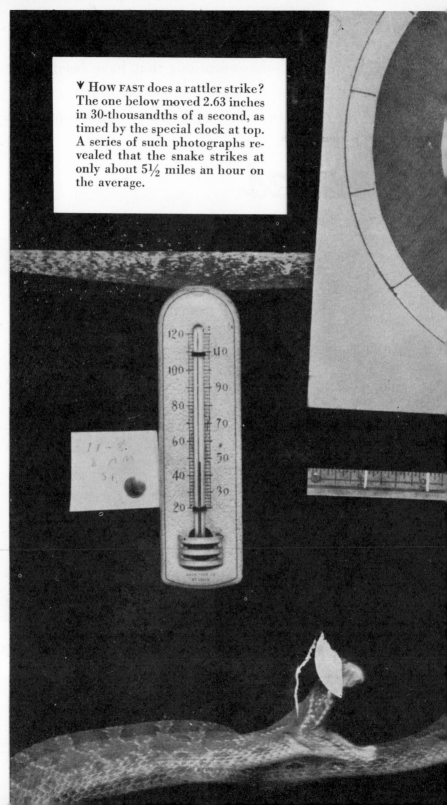

▼ How FAST does a rattler strike? The one below moved 2.63 inches in 30-thousandths of a second, as timed by the special clock at top. A series of such photographs revealed that the snake strikes at only about 5½ miles an hour on the average.

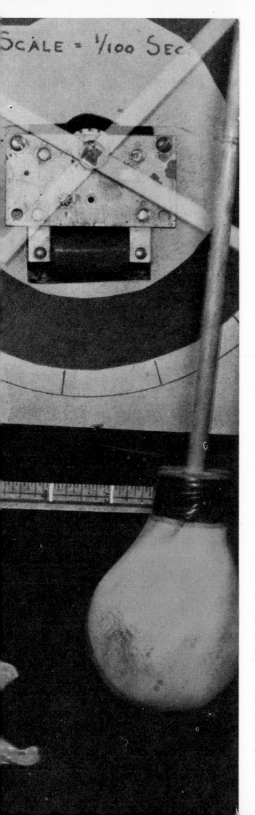

Scale = 1/100 Sec

biting action was revealed.

Some of my friends criticized the experiment, however, on the grounds that the balloon was an abnormal sort of target. They argued that, since it exploded on contact, it afforded nothing substantial on which the snake could bite. I therefore undertook to devise a more solid target and to invent some way to determine whether the snake needed to bite to eject its venom.

The arrangement shown in the first photograph of this series shows the apparatus used. The target this time was a soft latex ball, three to four inches in diameter, held firmly from behind and designed to be as biteable as any normal prey. The timing was arranged so that the picture would be taken not at the instant of impact but *after* the fangs had penetrated the ball and made contact with the material within. To ensure this, the flash was made to go off when the snake's fangs penetrated the mineral wool with which the ball was stuffed.

The electrical current actuating the flash is a vital element in Dr. Edgerton's versatile high-speed electronic flash when used in investigations of this sort. The circuit in this case was made to operate through the snake's body by placing one wire under a damp pad of earth. Though the voltage was high (200 to 300 volts), there was not enough amperage to produce any spark or shock. This was important, because no part of the snake's actions (the expelling of the venom, for instance) should be due to electrical stimulation. Actually, you could touch both contacts to your tongue while the circuit was closed without feeling anything.

Many tests with this set-up showed that the normal strike was a pure stab with no biting action. However, several pictures did reveal an unquestionable bite. Whether this resulted from an idiosyncrasy of the individual snake or from hits on the target a little off center, I was unable to determine, because I could test relatively few snakes. But the records of the pure stab were entirely convincing, and they were further backed up by a large series of delayed and multiple exposure photographs which fully revealed the snake's action during the interval after penetration.

How fast the strike?

Next, the speed of the strike was investigated, by means of a double-exposure arrangement. In the second photograph, the irregular white spot covering part of the serpent's head is not a blemish but was caused by the light actuating an electric-eye. The snake's head is intercepting the beam at this point and setting off the flash. By means of a relay, two high-speed flashes were set off, one 20- to 30-thousandths of a second after the other. The timer at the upper right of the picture indicated the exact length of the interval between the two flashes.

As seen by the six-inch rule, the head of the snake moved forward toward the target 2.63 inches in the 30-thousandths of a second that elapsed between the two exposures. This gives a velocity of 7.3 feet per second. Out of 20 similar records, 13 fell between 6 and 9 feet per second, and the over-all average was 8.1 feet per second, or 5½ miles per hour. This is certainly not "exceed-ingly fast." In fact, in comparison with the speed at which a man can move his hands in swinging a golf club or jab with his fist—about 12 to 27 miles per hour and upward—it is very slow.

The third set of experiments had the purpose of determining whether the rattlesnake can expel its venom without biting. The apparatus was basically similar to that used in the demonstration of the stabbing strike. In short, the circuit was closed only when the fangs penetrated the outer envelope of the target and made contact with the material within. The make-up of the target, however, differed, and this is the critical feature of the experiment. It was necessary to know whether any venom touched the target. I therefore used a double sheet of Kleenex, instead of a latex ball, for the outer envelope and treated it with a dye that would react to moisture. Before assembly, the paper was spread out flat and brushed lightly with finely powdered Brilliant Cresyl Blue. This is highly water-soluble. Then the wad of mineral wool was gathered up in the paper and fastened. The target was thus soft, flexible, and eminently biteable. The paper would tear easily and thus register fang and tooth punctures, as well as any tear made by a biting action or by withdrawal of the fangs. And the least drop of moisture coming into contact with the dye would make a dark blot on the paper.

In order to determine whether or not a bite occurred, the flash circuit was arranged to control two picture-taking flashes, one to record the position of the snake's jaws at the moment the fangs penetrated the target and the other a short interval later. The interval between the first and second flashes could be varied so as to study the action thoroughly.

After recording the strike with the double exposure just described, the snake and the timer were removed and a third exposure was made with the target held facing

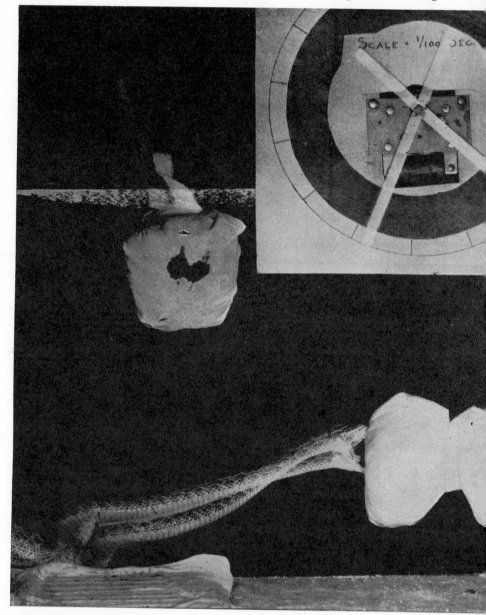

SCALE = 1/100 SEC.

▲ THIS DOUBLE EXPOSURE shows the snake's jaws wide open as the fangs penetrate and still open at the beginning of withdrawal 30-thousandths of a second later. Above, two blots of venom on the specially prepared target clearly showed that the snake had ejected its venom without biting action.

⋏ THE TONGUE projecting from the mouth of the Prairie Rattler in this exhibit is a sensory organ, not part of the venom-injecting apparatus

the camera so as to record the venom blots.

The composite picture shows, at bottom: (1) the strike at the instant of penetration (body of the snake above and in a straight line); and (2) the position of the jaws 30-thousandths of a second later, body sagging, at the beginning of withdrawal. The exposure at top shows two large blots on the target made by the ejected venom. The two extensions of the blot indicate where the fangs entered and were withdrawn. The two small blots below show where the lower jaw came in contact with the target. There is no evidence of a bite, either in the two exposures of the strike or in any tearing of the paper such as would be made by pressure between the jaws.

By cutting out the two blots and extracting the residue in normal salt solution, it was proved that what dampened the Kleenex was really poison. The solution was injected subcutaneously into the back of a rat by Dr. F. E. D'Amour, University of Denver physiologist. The rat was dead the following morning. A similar procedure using the dye alone did not harm a rat.

Twelve pictures of the latter sort were taken over a period of five days, all of the same snake. They differed only in the interval between the two exposures, which ranged from 12- to 40-thousandths of a second. None of these photographs showed any evidence of a biting action. It may be concluded, therefore, that the Prairie Rattlesnake does not have to bite to expel its venom.

The notion that the striking snake must bite seems first to have been proposed by the celebrated physician Dr. S. Weir Mitchell. Starting in the 1850's, Dr. Mitchell worked for 30 years on the venoms of rattlesnakes and other poisonous serpents. In one of his first papers, he reported that the muscles of the head and jaws, in contracting, apparently brought pressure on the venom gland, forcing the venom forward into the duct of the fang.

▼ THE RATTLESNAKE has been thought incapable of striking upward, but in this picture one is seen breaking a balloon directly overhead.

A biting action, he concluded, was therefore an essential feature of a successful strike. This was repeated almost word for word by Noguchi (*Snake Venoms*, 1909), by Ditmars (*The Reptile Book*, 1907, etc.), by Phisalix (*Animaux Venimeux et Venins*, 1922), and numerous other writers on the subject.

That very handy and versatile tool, Edgerton's high-speed flash, has now shown, it seems to me, exactly what does happen.

While taking these photographs, some additional observations were made. It was shown a number of times that the Prairie Rattler, in spite of folklore to the contrary, can hit a target held directly above it. The last photograph shows this action. The balloon is exploding, and the fragments are visible on either side. Here, the contact points controlling the flash were fastened to the surface of the balloon in such a way that when the balloon collapsed, they closed the circuit.

That the rattler will strike at a warm target much more readily than a cold one was first demonstrated by Noble and Schmidt at the American Museum of Natural History in 1937. They showed that the *pit* of the pit vipers (of which the rattlesnake is one) is a specialized organ for the detection of radiant heat. The inference is that this faculty is of service to the serpent in striking its warm-blooded prey in the dark. In my experiments I made it a practice to warm the target before presenting it to the snake. On several occasions, when I failed to do this, my subjects appeared to strike with reluctance. Warming the target made them eager to strike it.

The Rattlesnake's Heat Receptors

A blindfolded rattler will strike at a lighted electric light bulb or any other warm object with remarkable precision.

RATTLESNAKES do most of their hunting after dark and find their prey not by sight but by a pair of heat-sensitive organs. These are so acute as to enable the snake not only to detect the presence of a warm-blooded animal but to strike at it with great precision, as was demonstrated by the late G. Kingsley Noble in the laboratories of the American Museum of Natural History. Having no temperature regulating apparatus as warm-blooded animals have, rattlesnakes are easily killed by too much heat, and they have to spend most of the sunny hours coiled in the shade. The arrow shows where the heat receptors are located.

C. M. Bogert photo

A RATTLESNAKE HEAD, showing the fangs in striking position. They are difficult to see when lying in repose.

Photo by C. H. CURRAN

The Great Barrier Reef

Tiny coral animals are responsible for the largest biologically formed feature on the face of the earth

By ROY WALDO MINER
Late Curator of Living Invertebrates
The American Museum of Natural History

EUROPEANS first heard of the Great Barrier Reef when Capt. James Cook discovered the eastern coast of Australia in 1770. Its existence influenced history to no small extent through its effect on navigation and on fisheries resources. It also has great interest as a natural phenomenon, for it is the largest barrier reef in the world. It extends for more than 1250 miles along the eastern coast of the continent, about as far as from Miami, Florida, to New York City.

The reef is entirely of coral formation; that is, it is built up of the limestone skeletons of coral polyps, the calcareous deposits in the tissues of corallines and other lime-depositing sea plants, the shells of mollusks, wind-blown coral sand formed by ground-up fragments of the above creatures, minute skeletons of semi-microscopic animals, the foraminifera, and, in the shallower warm lagoons, by direct deposition of carbonate of lime from supersaturated sea water. The operations of the reef-building coral organisms are carried on only in warm waters which average at least 68° Fahr., and from the low-tide mark to a depth of not more than twenty fathoms. Hence they are formed only on the shallow submerged margins of oceanic islands and continents within the tropics and usually where they are exposed to prevailing winds and currents. These bring them in greatest abundance the microscopic organisms which form their food, while the boiling surf, dashing upon the outer reef, is well supplied with oxygen. In such exposed situations,

likewise, the growing coral polyps are less likely to be choked by silt and sand. Hence they grow most abundantly on the outer margins of the oceanic shelf and tend to form a living barrier awash at low tide, parallel to the land, and at some distance from it. The barrier is always separated from the mainland by a channel or lagoon, floored by the more slowly growing corals.

In the case of the Great Barrier Reef, this is a continuous waterway, beset, it is true, by complicated shoals, but nevertheless navigable for ocean-going vessels throughout its entire length, provided they are guided by skilful pilots. The Australian government maintains an efficient system of lights and channel markers for the benefit of mariners. The distance of the reef from the coast varies from a minimum of about ten miles at Cape Melville to more than a hundred miles at the northern and southern extremities, where it bends away from the coast. The average distance of the northern half, however, is quite constantly between thirty and forty miles, while farther south it approximates sixty miles, gradually attaining the maximum distance toward the southern end. It is manifest that the lagoon or protected body of water enclosed by this enormous reef must be of considerable area. In fact, Saville-Kent estimates it at more than 80,000 square miles.

The reef itself is not a continuous wall at the water's surface, but is really a series of countless reefs. The outer line of the main reef is broken by channels, while immediately within are numerous secondary reefs forming parallel lines with the outer barrier. At intervals are channels or passageways, a few of which

A.M.N.H. photograph.

ʌ The Great Barrier Reef. The northeast coast of Queensland, Australia, is bordered for more than 1000 miles by a chain of coral islands, lagoons, and reefs. At the southern end of the Barrier lies Heron Island, where the material for this group at the American Museum was collected. The generally flat top of the coral banks is determined by the low tide level, since the coral animals die if exposed long to the air.

The branching and massive corals afford shelter and subsistence to a rich fauna of crustaceans and the small, brightly colored fishes who feed upon them

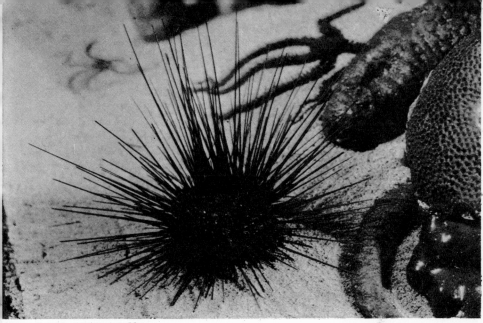

THE SLENDER-SPINED SEA URCHIN: a common inhabitant of coral-reef lagoons throughout the tropical waters of the world. Its needle-pointed spines readily pierce the feet of the unwary wader. In the background may be seen a brittle-star and the elongate, leathery body of a bêche de mer, or sea cucumber.

are well known to mariners as passable for larger vessels.

Occasionally islets of various size occur, formed by coral fragments heaped up by storms until they have projected sufficiently above sea-level to entangle sand and silt and to retain the seeds of various terrestrial plants until a growth of vegetation has been established.

The most valuable products of the Great Barrier Reef from a commercial standpoint are pearls and pearl shell, bêche de mer, oysters, and food fishes.

Australia possesses the most extensive pearl-oyster grounds in the world. The most important fisheries are those of Queensland and Western Australia, said to be of about equal value. The Queensland fisheries have their principal headquarters at Thursday Island, in Torres Strait, which separates Cape York, the northernmost point of Australia, from the southern coast of New Guinea. To reach this strait from the Pacific it is necessary to pass the dangerous ramparts of the extension of the Great Barrier Reef which sweeps northward, nearly to the New Guinea shore. After the reef is passed, the funnel-shaped entrance of the strait is found to be practically choked with thousands of islets and reefs separated by tortuous channels, only a few of which are navigable to large vessels. The safer entrance is by way of the ship channel inside the Barrier Reef from the south, along the Queensland coast. By pursuing this route, after leaving Cooktown, as one sails northward, the vessel passes through the eastern portion of the pearl fisheries grounds, which are practically continuous from here around the peninsula of Cape York, along the entire northern coast of

Australia, and down the western coast to Shark Bay. The fisheries were formerly carried on by Australian natives under the supervision of whites. Later Malays, Cingalese, and Pacific Islanders were extensively employed, while Japanese were gradually brought in increasing numbers, until now they predominate, and, in fact, practically monopolize the industry. This, doubtless, is due to their characteristic efficiency. In 1905, according to Dr. George F. Kunz, the Queensland fishery employed 348 vessels and 2850 men, while the commercial value of pearls and pearl shell harvested was about $675,000; that of Western Australia, about $958,000; and that of Southern Australia (also carried on on the northern shore of the continent), about $125,000.

Thus the entire Australian pearl industry yielded about $1,778,000 in that year. These figures fluctuate and, in recent years, the output has decreased due to the exhaustion of many of the beds.

The Australian pearl oysters belong to three species, of which the largest and most valuable (*Margaritifera maxima*) is known commercially as the "silver lip," because of the silvery white iridescence over the entire inner surface. Next in value comes the "black lip" (*Margaritifera margaritifera*). This is characterized by a dark border around the inner edge of the shell. The third species (*Margaritifera carcharium*) is the smallest and least valuable, so far as its shell is concerned, but yields a higher percentage of pearls than the other two species. The "silver lip"

THE GIANT SEA ANEMONE of the Great Barrier Reef. The huge flowerlike disc is a foot and a half in diameter and is covered with thousands of beadlike tentacles, varying from purple to green in color. These are armed with sting-cells which stupefy fish or other small sea creatures. (From a life-size model in the American Museum of Natural History).

shells yield the largest and finest pearls in the world, according to Doctor Kunz, while the shells themselves form the standard mother-of-pearl of commerce. Their annual value is several times that of the pearls found in them, in spite of the quality of the latter.

The pearl shells were originally secured by employing nude divers, who became very skilful in the very laborious and perilous art of diving, often to depths of sixty feet or more, to return to the surface with one or two shells at a time, or, more frequently, with none at all. The average time spent by a diver under water was fifty-seven seconds to a minute, though some South Sea natives have been known to remain under for nearly three minutes. In some cases, the diver would take a stone attached to a cord as a weight to carry him down more quickly, but in most cases he would dive feet first, turning head downward after descending a short distance and swimming the rest of the way. A few seconds only would be spent at the bottom groping for a shell or two. These would be placed in a fiber basket or secured under the arm, and then the diver would spring toward the surface. As long as he held his breath he would shoot upward rapidly, but if he failed to gauge his time accurately and let his breath go before reaching the surface, he would sink again, and, if not rescued, would be lost. Many such fatalities inevitably occurred during the course of the fishing. More recently, however, diving suits of various types have been employed, and these are now generally used, thus decreasing the danger, and promoting much greater efficiency in collecting the shells. On the other hand, more effective methods and the rapid increase in the number of pearling luggers employed, especially by the Japanese, have resulted in the depletion of the beds, and some of the fleets have been drawn away to the

Philippines and other regions.

The bêche de mer industry is a peculiar but profitable one. These animals, which are also called trepang by the Malaysians, are large sea cucumbers belonging to the family Holothuridæ. As stated above, they somewhat resemble huge sausages lying in shallow pools or lagoon bottoms among the coral reefs. Several species are used, readily characterized by their coloring or markings, or by surface projections of various types. As they are echinoderms, their leathery body is provided with numerous "tube feet," slender appendages terminated by sucker-like discs. These organs are arranged in five bands along the sides of the body and enable the animal to pull itself along the sea bottom. At one end of the creature is a circular mouth surrounded by a fringe of tentacles, by means of which the animal's food is secured. This consists mainly of Foraminifera, microscopic animals possessing a chambered. calcareous shell. The holothurian obtains them by mopping its tentacles back and forth over the sand. These pick up sand and the other particles with which the Foraminifera are entangled, and transfer them to the mouth in ordered succession, returning to the quest again in reverse order. The Queensland natives gather the trepang into sacks, wading in the pools among the rocks at low tide, or diving for them in deeper water. They are then immediately conveyed by a fleet of luggers to curing stations, where they are boiled for a time in large kettles. Next, they are cut open, dressed, and dried in the sun, after which they are transported to smokehouses, where they are smoked on racks of wire netting for twenty-four hours, over a fire of red mangrove wood. They are then in a thoroughly dry, shrunken condition, and are ready to be packed into sacks and sent to the Hong Kong market. They are highly prized in China, where they form

OTHER BARRIER REEFS: A map showing the work of coral animals around the two islands of Raiatea and Tahaa in the Society Group. The reefs are seen fringing both islands and occasionally breaking the surface in the form of small islands. As in the Great Barrier Reef, a channel parallels the reef, but in this case it is much narrower.

the basis of bêche de mer soup. When this is properly prepared it has the reputation of being more delicious than turtle soup. There is also a considerable market for them in Australia, the Pacific Islands, and in American Pacific Coast cities. In Queensland, they form an industry ranking with the oyster fisheries in commercial value.

Several varieties of oysters grow in great abundance in the Great Barrier Reef region. The most important commercial species is the so-called common rock oyster (*Ostrea glomerata*). This forms the basis of an extensive and valuable commercial fishery comparable with that of the Virginia oyster (*Ostrea virginiana*) of the United States, with which it seems to be closely related. The fishery centers about the Moreton Bay district where the mollusks are dredged from submerged beds or are fished from oyster banks exposed at low tide. In the latter case they are also cultivated with success. The bank oysters appear to be the most

profitable. The shells are attached to stones or dead oyster shells as a clutch, or the "spat" (young) frequently settle down on the shell of a species of whelk (*Potamides ebeninus*), which abounds in the neighborhood of the oyster banks. The whelk carries about with it a load of the young oysters, which are thus provided with free transportation to pastures new and advantageous, and therefore thrive exceedingly. As they increase in size and weight, the poor whelk's burden in life becomes overwhelming. Soon it can no longer maintain itself on the surface of the soft mud of the bank and so gradually sinks down to perish, forced into its grave by its thriving burden. Saville-Kent states that frequently the load of oysters borne by a living whelk weighs half a pound, while their downtrodden beast of burden weighs scarcely an ounce. This is so frequent an occurrence that entire oyster banks are known as whelk-oyster banks. There are several other species of oysters found throughout the Barrier Reef area but, for one reason or another, their commercial importance is not so great.

As might be expected, the food fishes of this remarkable and productive region are very numerous and greatly diversified. Even in Saville-Kent's time, the fish fauna of Queensland alone, including fresh-water and marine forms, had reached practically 900 recorded species, of which upward of one-third, or 300 species, are of definite food value. These, as would be expected from the tropical climatic conditions of the colony, largely belong to the Indo-Pacific fauna. Probably the most important commercially are the members of the perch family, of which more than seventy species are of economic food value. A splendid example of this group is the giant perch (*Lates calcarifer*) which reaches five feet in length and a weight of more than fifty pounds. It is an excellent food fish. The gayly colored sea perches of the family Serranidæ are especially abundant in the neighborhood of the Great Barrier Reef, and include at least twenty species, most of which are highly esteemed from a culinary standpoint. Red mullets, sea breams, banded doreys, red rock-cods, tassel-fishes, and jew-fishes are common and, though unfamiliar to American readers, are nevertheless characteristic and important items on the Australian bill of fare. Types allied to our horse-mackerels, barracudas, yellowtails, and bonitos are of frequent occurrence, while flatfishes, herrings, and eels are also well represented in their Australian counterparts. These, and numerous other species render the Australian food fisheries of great economic importance.

The Great Barrier Reef, therefore, is not only a most interesting feature from the standpoint of the zoölogist and geologist, but its 1250 miles of reefs and lagoons form a veritable treasure house of natural resources for the great Commonwealth of the Southern Hemisphere.

Photo by Toshio Asaeda

DR. ROY WALDO MINER descending to examine coral formations in the type of diving helmet he used in various parts of the Pacific, the Bahamas, and elsewhere. Air pumped into the helmet by men in the boat keeps the level of the water below the diver's chin. The outfit weighs 65 pounds in the air but loses its weight underwater.

The ABC's of Einstein's Theory

By CLYDE FISHER
Late Curator of the Hayden Planetarium
The American Museum of Natural History

E ARLY in the present century a new theory of space, time, mass, velocity, and gravitation was presented to the scientific world by a professor of physics in the University of Berlin, whose name has since become a household word. Einstein's Theory of Relativity, although admittedly difficult to understand, has intrigued the layman as well as the mathematical physicist and astronomer.

Soon after Einstein's Theory of Relativity had swept the scientific world, an address on the subject was presented before the American Association for the Advancement of Science, the largest and most important society of scientists in America. This lecture was given by Prof. Joseph Ames, head of the department of physics in Johns Hopkins University, and later president of that institution of learning. In the course of his discussion Professor Ames said: "It has been stated that only a dozen men in the whole world understand the theory of relativity, and I am not one of the twelve." Needless to say I, myself, am not able to increase that select number to a "baker's dozen."

At a dinner given in honor of Sir James Jeans on his recent visit to America, Sir James said that the only conception of the universe that can now be framed is a mathematical conception, and that after you have framed it, only a mathematician can understand it.

Prof. Edwin E. Slosson, in his *Easy Lessons in Einstein*, written soon after the theory of relativity had been announced, has given some encouragement for such an attitude. In a prefatorial dialogue between the author and a fellow commuter, who has just read in his morning paper something about relativity, the following conversation occurs:

THE READER: "Can you tell me in plain language what it is all about?"

THE AUTHOR: "Yes. Just that. I can tell you what it is *about*, though I can't tell you what it *is*."

It is of great interest to observe that the theory of relativity, though radical-ly new, has been accepted by practically all physicists and astronomers of the world. The acceptance of relativity, perhaps not in its present form, but as a principle, is well-nigh universal. There are so few well-known physicists and astronomers who oppose it that one is reminded of the old saying that the exception proves the rule.

Newton considered space and time and mass and force as *absolute*. He looked upon gravitation as a force, but according to the theory of relativity notion must be abandoned. As Bertrand Russell remarked, "Just as the sea does not cause the water to run toward it, so the sun does not cause the planets to move round it."

We have given up the notion of force, since it does not represent anything that is genuinely to be found in the physical world. Although "force" is no longer to be regarded as one of the fundamental concepts of dynamics, but only as a convenient way of speaking, as Bertrand Russell points out, it can still be employed, like "sunrise" and "sunset," provided we realize what we mean. Often it would require very roundabout expressions to avoid the term "force."

The so-called "law of the conservation of matter" and the so-called "law of conservation of energy" of a former generation cannot now be held as true in a strict sense. Matter and energy are interconvertible. Mass increases with speed. Time shrinks or stretches depending upon the velocity.

The name "relativity" therefore is applied to Einstein's theory simply because the primary factors in astronomy such as direction, speed, size, and time are relative. Any one of these factors cannot be reckoned by itself, but only in relation to the others. The reader is referred to the simple examples of the relativity of direction, time, and speed illustrated herein.

For Einstein the old luminiferous ether does not function, and in the sketch that he draws of natural phenomena there is no mention of this hypothetical, imponderable, all-pervasive, and intermediate substance.

In his special theory of relativity (1905) Einstein did not include gravitation (accelerated motion) in his formulae, but after ten years of study

A non-mathematical view of some of the basic considerations, with suggestions as to their importance in understanding the universe

Photograph by Clyde Fisher

Professor Albert Einstein, author of the Theory of Relativity, when he was a member of the staff of the Institute for Advanced Study at Princeton.

Professor Einstein proving the Principle of Equivalence in a lecture before the American Association for the Advancement of Science in 1934 in Pittsburgh. Matter and energy are interconvertible.

Photograph by Keystone View Company

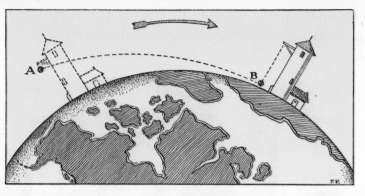

Direction is Relative

From the point of view of an observer in the tower, an object dropped from the top of it appears to fall in a straight line. We know, however, that the earth itself is constantly turning. If observed from a fixed position in space, the object would be seen to travel not in a straight line but in a curve. It might be said to drop straight toward the point on the earth directly under it, but that point is moving. Therefore, the actual path of the object is a curve, illustrated diagrammatically in this drawing by the dotted line from A to B.

The illustration takes into account only one motion of the earth, namely its rotation on its axis.

(1915), he incorporated this phenomenon in his general theory.

Prof. Henry Norris Russell of Princeton has summed up the matter as follows:

"The central fact which has been proved—which is of great interest and importance—is that the natural phenomena involving gravitation and inertia (such as the motions of the planets) and the phenomena involving electricity and magnetism (including the motion of light) are not independent of one another, but are intimately related, so that both sets of phenomena should be regarded as parts of one vast system, embracing all nature."

Eddington in *Space, Time and Gravitation* describes an imaginary experiment in which he supposes an aviator traveling at a speed of 161,000 miles a second relative to the earth. After making allowance for the time of transmission of light, there would still be a retardation in time. His cigar lasts twice as long as one of ours. But here reciprocity comes in because, in the aviator's opinion, it is we who are traveling at 161,000 miles a second past him; and when he has made all allowances, he finds that it is we who are sluggish. Our cigar lasts twice as long as his. Bertrand Russell, who accepts the validity of this supposed experiment, mischievously remarks: "What a situation for envy! Each man thinks that the other's cigar lasts twice as long as his own. It may, however, be some consolation to reflect that the other man's visits to the dentist would also last twice as long."

After correcting Newton, as has been remarked, it remained to correct Euclid, and it was in terms of non-Euclidean geometry that Einstein stated his new theory. According to the theory of relativity, it is believed that no complete description of an occurrence in nature can be made with the three coördinates of Euclidean geometry—length, breadth, and thickness—but that a four-dimensional space-time system must be conceived. Minkowski stated the essence of this conception in the following prophetic words: "Henceforth space by itself and time by itself shall sink to mere shadows, and only a union of the two shall preserve reality."

The question of infinity

Another question connected with the theory of relativity is whether the entire universe is infinite or finite. Twenty-five years ago perhaps most astronomers

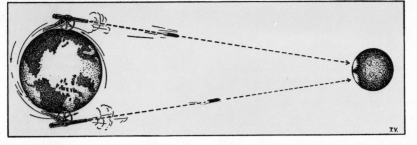

Speed of Light, A Standard in Relativity

Because the speed of light is not altered by any movement of the medium through which it passes or by motion at the source, it serves as a standard of measurement.

In this diagram, two shells are fired at the same instant from a pair of cannons on opposite sides of the earth. Because the earth is spinning, the lower shell travels faster than the upper, and reaches the moon approximately 166 hours sooner.

The speed of rotation of the earth is in one case added to the speed of the shell, and in the other subtracted.

But this does not apply to light. Beams of light sent out from each of the cannons at the same instant arrive at the moon simultaneously, regardless of the movement of the earth. It is because the speed of light is not influenced by motion at its source or by motion of the medium through which it passes that it figures prominently in the theory of relativity.

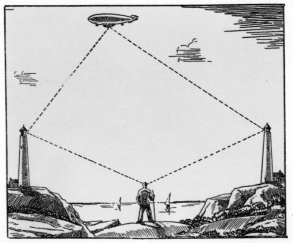

Time is Relative

If lights are flashed from both towers at the same instant, the observer midway between sees the flashes simultaneously. But an observer in the airship overhead, being closer to the lefthand tower, receives the flash from that tower sooner than from the other.

The speed of light is so rapid that the lag could not be detected by the eye; but that there is such a difference is obvious. We are all familiar with the lag between a flash of lightning and the bolt of thunder. The thunder seems to occur several seconds after the lightning, but this is only because the apparent time of their occurrence is relative to the speed of light and sound respectively. Actually they occur in the same instant.

were inclined toward the idea that the universe is infinite. It was said that one could not imagine an end or an edge. And as yet there is no experimental evidence to prove that it is not infinite. Nevertheless, this theory has given the theoretical physicist some difficulty in his dealing with gravitation, and since the advent of relativity, there has been a swing toward the notion that the universe is finite.

The surface of a sphere has no boundary, yet it is not infinite. The universe may be shaped like a huge globe or sphere, and if so, there would be no end or edge. It is conceived as so huge that it would require time of the order of a thousand million years for light to travel around this possibly finite universe. And here is introduced the idea of curved space. There may be no straight lines about which we were taught in our Euclidean geometry. These suppos-

edly straight lines may be arcs of great circles on this huge, though possibly finite, universe. As we know, things are not always as they seem. It may help in some of these apparently contradictory conceptions to recall the principles of perspective. When we look down a railroad track, the rails seem to converge, yet we know they do not.

As shown by Einstein, a finite universe is a necessary condition under the conception of a static universe. Under the modern conception of a non-static or expanding universe, however, he has shown that the universe may, or it may not be finite.

Einstein suggested *three* experimental tests which the astronomer could apply to the theory of relativity:

First—Movement of the perihelion point of the planet Mercury (see accompanying figure). After all the disturbances caused by the attraction of

Movement of Perihelion Point of Mercury

On successive revolutions around the sun the axis of Mercury's orbit turns. Represented diagrammatically, the end of the major axis moves in one year from A to B, in reality a distance of 43 seconds.

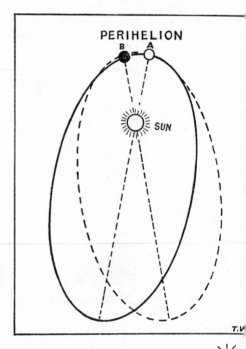

Light Rays are Bent by Gravity

According to one of Einstein's principles, rays of light are bent by the gravitational pull of any large heavenly body close to which they pass. Light rays coming from the star C are bent toward the sun (B) when passing near it. Thus an observer on the earth (A) sees the star in the direction of C' instead of in its true direction.

Speed is Relative

Suppose that in each of these three drawings the submarine is being driven forward at the maximum speed of its engines. Its velocity with relation to the water is consequently the same throughout. But because the water itself may be moving, the speed of the submarine relative to the land is variable.

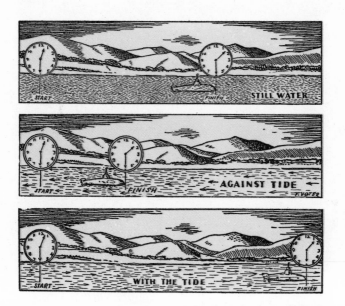

other planets had been taken into account, there still remained an unexplained perihelial movement of the orbit of Mercury. In other words, astronomers had found that the theory of Newton does not suffice to calculate the observed motion of Mercury with an exactness corresponding to that of the delicacy of observation attainable even three quarters of a century ago. In 1859 Leverrier found this unexplained perihelial movement to be 43 seconds in a century. This observation was corroborated in 1895 by Newcomb. The phenomenon had puzzled astronomers until Einstein explained it in 1915 by the general theory of relativity. He found that, according to his formulae, this movement must really amount to just that much. At the time when he published his theory, this was its only experimental verification.

Einstein's explanation accepted

Immediately de Sitter, the great Dutch astronomer, accepted Einstein's explanation and confirmed the correctness of this astronomical test. Einstein stated that Professor de Sitter also contributed to the theory of relativity by showing that observations of the spectroscopic double stars prove that the speed of light is not dependent upon the dynamic condition of the source of light. Einstein stated further that Doctor de Sitter made great contributions in the relativity theory of the structure of space in the great cosmological problem.

SECOND—Bending of the rays of light from a star in passing the sun due to the sun's gravitational pull (to be discussed presently). This can be tested only at a total solar eclipse, when the moon comes between us and the sun and shuts off the overwhelming light of the sun, thus making it possible to photograph the stars in that portion of the sky in which the sun is located.

This effect was first observed under the direction of Prof. Arthur S. Eddington and others at the total eclipse of 1919, and has been observed at succeeding total eclipses of the sun.

Credit in this development has been given to Dr. de Sitter. The Astronomer Royal, H. Spencer Jones, said: "The British eclipse expeditions of 1919, which provided the first evidence in support of Einstein's conclusions as to the

amount of deviation of rays of light in passing near the sun, would probably not have been sent out had de Sitter's papers not appeared." The papers here referred to were three in number, communicated by Doctor de Sitter in 1916-17 to the Royal Astronomical Society, shortly after the appearance of Einstein's paper on the generalized theory of relativity. Surely Doctor de Sitter had much to do with securing the general acceptance of the theory of relativity.

THIRD—The shifting of the spectrum lines of the sun toward the red owing to its own gravitational pull. This is entirely apart from the shifting due to the motion of a heavenly body either toward or from us. In accordance with this latter principle, it has long been known that, when a star is approaching us, there is a shift of the spectrum lines toward the violet, and when the star is receding, there is a shift toward the red. By applying this principle it has been possible to go further and calculate the velocity of approach or recession of a heavenly body. Also, by observing and comparing the shift on one side with that on the other, it has been possible to prove that certain heavenly bodies and systems rotate. This shifting due to

Eclipse Verifies Einstein

The outer symbols represent the false positions in which four stars appear when total eclipse makes it possible to photograph them. The real positions of these stars, determined by photographing that portion of the sky when the sun was not there, are indicated by the inner symbols having dark centers.

the approach or recession of a heavenly body is known as the Doppler effect, and it may be better understood by comparison with a familiar, analogous phenomenon in sound.

The Doppler effect

If one stands by a railroad track when a locomotive is passing with the bell ringing or the whistle blowing, he will note an abrupt change in the pitch of the bell or the whistle as the locomotive passes him. When the locomotive is approaching the observer, the pitch will be higher than when it is just passing him, and after the locomotive has passed by the pitch will be lower than when it was passing him. The slur in pitch as

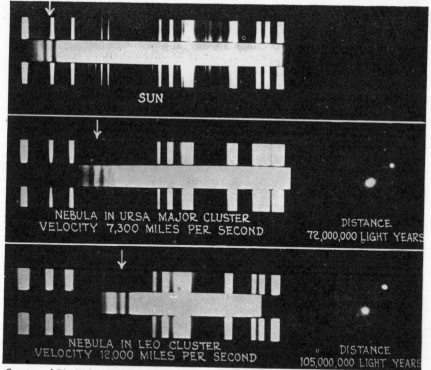

SUN

NEBULA IN URSA MAJOR CLUSTER
VELOCITY 7,300 MILES PER SECOND

DISTANCE
72,000,000 LIGHT YEARS

NEBULA IN LEO CLUSTER
VELOCITY 12,000 MILES PER SECOND

DISTANCE
105,000,000 LIGHT YEARS

Courtesy of Mt. Wilson Observatory

Shift of Spectrum Lines Toward the Red.

The shift of the spectrum lines of these nebulae toward the red is interpreted as due to their motion away from us. This is known as the Doppler effect. According to the theory of relativity, there is an additional shift toward the red in light from the sun and other massive bodies, which is exactly like this in character, due to the gravitational potential of the body.

The Einstein Tower

This Solar Tower was constructed for the purpose of studying the sun. Others like it were built at Mt. Wilson and at Arcetri, Italy. At Potsdam an important objective was the study of the Einstein shift in the spectrum of the sun.

*Photo by Courtesy Astrophysical
Observatory at Potsdam*

the locomotive passes is very noticeable. Since pitch varies with the number of vibrations that strike the ear per unit time, it is evident that this marked change is due to the piling up of vibrations while the locomotive approaches, thus causing more vibrations to strike the ear per unit time—producing a higher pitch—and the stringing out of the vibrations when the locomotive is receding, thus producing a lower pitch after the locomotive has passed.

In the case of light, when a heavenly body approaches, there is an increased frequency of the waves of light, or, in other words, the wave-length is shortened, which causes a shift of the spectrum lines toward the violet; when the body is receding, there is a decreased frequency of the light, or an increase in the wave-length.

Aside from the Doppler effect there is, according to Professor Einstein, a slight shift of the spectrum lines of the sun toward the red. And this has been proved experimentally by the late Dr. Charles E. St. John at the Mt. Wilson Observatory.

And there has been a further confirmation of this effect in the case of the dense companion of Sirius. This star is believed to be so dense that one cubic inch of it brought to the earth would weigh nearly a ton, i.e. two thousand times the weight of platinum, our planet's heaviest known substance. On account of the greater gravitational potential of this exceedingly dense star, it was calculated that the shift here would be twenty-seven times as great as on the sun, and this was confirmed by actual test by Dr. Walter S. Adams, director of the Mt. Wilson Observatory.

The latest confirmation of this test was reported last April before the annual meeting of the National Academy of Sciences in Washington. Dr. Robert J. Trumpler described his six years' work at the Lick Observatory, consisting of observations of Class O stars, the hottest,

Photograph by Clyde Fisher

Dr. Henry Norris Russell, who promoted the general acceptance of the theory of relativity by his lucid discussions, when he was Research Professor of Astronomy and Director of the Observatory at Princeton University.

Courtesy of Wide World Photos

The late Professor Willem de Sitter, the brilliant Dutch astronomer who probably did more than anyone except Einstein himself to establish the theory of relativity. He was Director of the Leyden Observatory.

most luminous, and at the same time the most massive stars in the universe. They reach a mass 180 times that of our sun, and their surface temperatures are 40,-000 degrees Centigrade as compared with 6000 degrees for the surface temperature of our sun.

Radial velocity

Fortunately for the astronomers, many stars of Class O occur in clusters in the Milky Way, Doctor Trumpler stated, and in this investigation he studied nine such Class O stars in six different star clusters. The stars of such a galactic cluster form one physical system and thus all the star members of the cluster must have nearly the same motion. Yet, while all the stars in a cluster have the same true motion, those which have higher luminosity, and higher temperature and mass, show a radial velocity greater than the smaller, fainter, and colder stars in the cluster system.

The excess in radial velocity of the more massive and luminous stars, namely, the O type stars, cannot be due to the Doppler effect, Doctor Trumpler reasoned, since the actual motion of the O stars cannot be greater than the motion of the fainter stars in the same cluster. The excess, therefore, in the observed velocity of the O stars, an excess which reveals itself by a shift toward the red in the spectra, must be due entirely to the red shift predicted by relativity.

All of the three astronomical tests of the Einstein Theory of Relativity were successfully met, and the way was prepared for more extensive explorations into the nature of matter and the universe. Though the complex mathematics involved in these fields of science may prevent a full understanding, it is hoped that these remarks will serve to give the amateur some notion of what it is all about.

Courtesy of Wide World Photos

Dr. Walter S. Adams, who as Director of the Mt. Wilson Observatory, confirmed the Einstein shift toward the red in the spectrum of the dense companion of Sirius.

Photograph by Clyde Fisher

Sir Arthur S. Eddington, as Plumiam Professor of Astronomy and Director of the Observatory at Cambridge University. He directed the first investigation of the second astronomical test of the theory of relativity at the 1919 total eclipse of the sun.

Reptiles

Once the dominant animals on earth, they have evolved through an interesting variety of specialized adaptations to compete successfully with other animals in all three realms —earth, air, and water

By CHARLES M. BOGERT
Curator of Amphibians and Reptiles,
The American Museum of Natural History

REPTILES have the distinction of being the first backboned animals to lay eggs on land. The principal handicap of the early amphibian was its fish-like habit of laying its eggs in ponds or streams. Even today amphibians need moisture at all stages and most of them return to the water to lay their eggs. However, evolution in one sense is the process of overcoming handicaps. And the ancestral reptile overcame its greatest handicap when it finally produced a clutch of eggs that could be incubated on land. It was roughly at this juncture, perhaps nearly 200 million years ago, that a hardy chain-breaking Progressive switched from being an amphibian to become the forefather of the reptiles.

These animals had broken the chain that tied them to the water, but ironically some of them returned to it. The ichthyosaurs, mosasaurs, and other reptiles now extinct, as well as many crocodilians, turtles and sea snakes that survive, began to seek their food in the oceans. The

Photo by James Shackelford, Michael Lerner Expedition, 1939

ichthyosaurs and some of the sea snakes managed to retain their eggs until their young were ready for birth. Other reptiles, notably the marine turtles, now found themselves as securely tied to the land as their remote amphibian ancestors were chained to the water. For even the most aquatic turtles come ashore to deposit their eggs in cavities dug in the sand. Oxygen must be absorbed through the porous covering of the large-yolked egg, and the occupant will drown if the egg is covered with water.

The success of the reptiles on land depended upon other improvements. They developed an impervious skin, later to be covered with horny plates or scales and sometimes underlaid with a bony protective armor. Reptiles branched out into a number of groups, one of which gave rise to the "Ruling Reptiles"— the dinosaurs and their allies—another to the mammals, and still another to the birds. They also gave rise to the turtles, crocodilians, beakheads, lizards, and finally snakes. Lizards and snakes did not assume any prominence until about the time the mammals arrived and the Ruling Reptiles began to fade from the scene.

◄ THE SPHENODON, or tuatara: a living fossil. It is the only creature in one of the five orders into which the 6000 or 7000 living reptiles are divided. In the top of its head it has a pineal body which shows signs of having once functioned as a third eye. Finding security millions of years ago in New Zealand, the sphenodon lived safely up to the coming of white man. The introduction of pigs almost brought its extinction.

Fortunately, at least from the standpoint of naturalists, there are between 6,000 and 7,000 kinds of living reptiles. One is the tuatara, a "living fossil," the sole survivor of the beakheaded reptiles. It too would probably be extinct had it not managed to reach a distant outpost in New Zealand. With two alligators, five caimans, a dozen crocodiles and a couple of gavials, we still have with us a total of 21 crocodilians.

There are fewer than 300 kinds of turtles. Even before the dinosaurs arose, their ancestor managed the difficult feat of getting its ribs outside its limb- and shoulder-girdles, became toothless, and set the pattern followed ever since. Turtles evolved a bony exterior usually covered with horny plates, a shell that is at once a home and a coat of armor. But turtles never gave rise to anything except more turtles. Some of them spent most of their time in streams, ponds, or oceans. Others stayed on land and became known as tortoises. Man eventually joined the host of animals that prey on turtles and applied such names as terrapin, snapper, slider, cooter, and even "canal pullet," to some of the kinds he eats.

Lizards number over 3,000 species and are now at least ten times more successful than the turtles. Lizards sped through most of their evolution after the dinosaurs disappeared. There are lizards that creep or crawl, but some run with speeds up to nearly 20 miles per hour. All of them can swim, and some make a practice of it. The Galápagos marine iguana swims out beyond the breakers, dives down and feeds on the seaweed. Others are climbers. Six-foot tropical iguanas often live in the highest trees. Other tree-dwellers, the "flying dragons" of southeastern Asia, have taken to the air, and glide efficiently from one tree to the next. Still others, occasionally with only vestiges of eyes, are burrowers that have forsaken the surface to search for their insect prey underground or in termite nests. In several instances they have dispensed with limbs. It was some burrower, perhaps a relative of the Bornean "earless monitor," that gave rise to the snakes.

AMNH photo by Charles H. Coles

➤ OLDEST KNOWN EGG with a shell. Its protective covering enabled the animal that laid it to rise above the amphibians, which have to return to water to lay their eggs. This fossil was found in rocks more than 200 million years old, in Texas.

▼ LARGEST KNOWN CROCODILE: a 45-foot Texas giant of some 70 million years ago. It had a three-foot yawn. Dr. Barnum Brown, at left, is recording the measurements of *Phobosuchus'* jaws, which dwarf those of a modern crocodile, shown below. At right are Roland T. Bird who restored the skull, and Dr. Erich Schlaikjer, paleontologist.

The snakes, some of which retain vestiges of limbs, are newcomers, the most recently evolved, and in some respects the most successful reptiles. Snakes are somewhat more tolerant of cold climates than most other reptiles, and one viper has penetrated north of the Arctic Circle in the Scandinavian Peninsula. But species are more numerous in the tropics. There we find all the larger snakes, the pythons in Asia, Africa, and Australia, and the boa constrictor and the anaconda in the Americas. Among nearly 3,000 species, there are numerous burrowers,

Evolution of the Reptiles

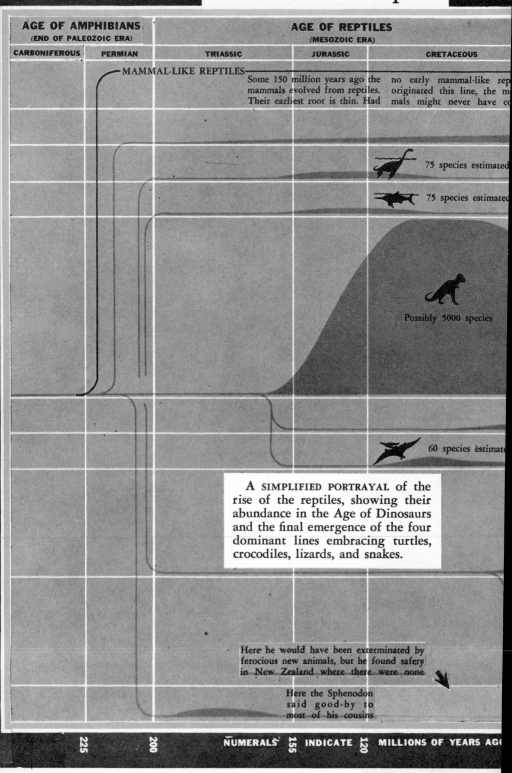

AGE OF AMPHIBIANS (END OF PALEOZOIC ERA)		AGE OF REPTILES (MESOZOIC ERA)		
CARBONIFEROUS	PERMIAN	TRIASSIC	JURASSIC	CRETACEOUS

MAMMAL-LIKE REPTILES

Some 150 million years ago the mammals evolved from reptiles. Their earliest root is thin. Had no early mammal-like rep originated this line, the m mals might never have c

75 species estimated

75 species estimated

Possibly 5000 species

60 species estimate

A SIMPLIFIED PORTRAYAL of the rise of the reptiles, showing their abundance in the Age of Dinosaurs and the final emergence of the four dominant lines embracing turtles, crocodiles, lizards, and snakes.

Here he would have been exterminated by ferocious new animals, but he found safety in New Zealand where there were none

Here the Sphenodon said good-by to most of his cousins

225   200   NUMERALS INDICATE 155 120 MILLIONS OF YEARS AG

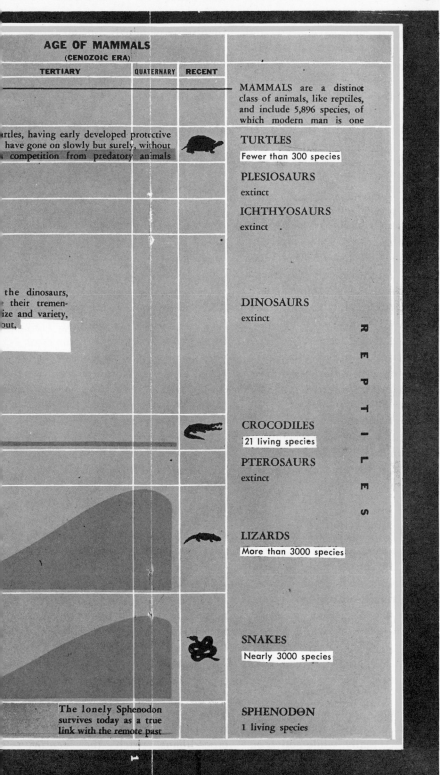

AGE OF MAMMALS
(CENOZOIC ERA)

TERTIARY	QUATERNARY	RECENT

MAMMALS are a distinct class of animals, like reptiles, and include 5,896 species, of which modern man is one

...rtles, having early developed protective ...have gone on slowly but surely, without ...competition from predatory animals

TURTLES
Fewer than 300 species

PLESIOSAURS
extinct

ICHTHYOSAURS
extinct

...the dinosaurs, ...their tremen-...ize and variety, ...out,

DINOSAURS
extinct

CROCODILES
21 living species

PTEROSAURS
extinct

LIZARDS
More than 3000 species

SNAKES
Nearly 3000 species

The lonely Sphenodon survives today as a true link with the remote past

SPHENODON
1 living species

R
E
P
T
I
L
E
S

including one large family of "blind snakes" that may have originated before true snakes evolved. Perhaps the majority of snakes live on the ground, but many kinds live in trees, or forage in the water. Indeed one rather large family, the fish-eating sea snakes, has invaded the Pacific and Indian Oceans.

Turtles, crocodilians, and the tuatara all adhere to the ancestral habit of laying their eggs in a "nest" excavated in the earth or made of vegetable debris heaped on the surface, in the case of some crocodilians. The fully mature hatchling has an "egg-breaker," a sort of horny growth on its snout that it uses to crack or slit the shell when it is ready to emerge. In contrast, lizards and snakes use a razor-sharp tooth, a true tooth that falls off the snout a few days after it has been used to slit the shell to release the occupant. The incubation of reptile eggs depends entirely upon external temperatures, and it commonly requires months, almost a year for the eggs of the tuatara. Live-bearing reptiles are now found only among the lizards and snakes. The eggs are retained within the body of the parent until they are ready to hatch, or in some cases additional nourishment is provided indirectly from the mother's blood stream.

While reptiles gave rise to the mammals and birds, both of which produce heat internally, all reptiles depend on heat from external sources. All of the bodily warmth in a reptile is derived either directly from the sun, or from the ground and the surrounding air. It is not quite accurate to call reptiles "cold-blooded." Actually, while active on sunny days, many of them, particularly lizards, have warmer blood than some mammals. But no appreciable amount of food that reptiles consume is turned into heat. Consequently they require much less food than mammals and birds. While resting at room temperature a lizard requires only about one-fortieth of the energy that a man would need were he the same size. A large python is reputed to have survived for well over three years without food.

Reptiles are inactive for large portions of their life. When their surroundings are either too hot or too cold, they are driven to cover. In climates that have cold winters, they hibernate or remain below freezing levels in the ground. They forage now and then, but much of the time they merely sit and wait, often for hours at a time. They "live slowly" so to speak, but many of them also live for long periods. Turtles hold the record for backboned animals. A tortoise is believed to have survived for over a century and a half; and had it not been killed in an accident, it is believed that it might have reached the two-century mark. A captive tuatara lived for well over half a century, and some lizards may be equally long-lived creatures although the longest authenticated life span is 32 years, recorded for the European glass lizard. The longevity record for snakes is held by an anaconda that lived for over 28 years in an American zoo. Contrary to exaggerated claims of some alligator "farms," the oldest authentic record for a crocodilian is under 60 years, but it is not impossible that some crocodilians reach the century mark.

AN IMPOSING PORTRAIT of a Zone-tailed Lizard, which was actually only 2¼ inches long.

Photo by Charles H. Coles

The larger iguanas, most tortoises, some marine turtles, and a few other reptiles are largely vegetarians. However, all snakes and a good many other reptiles are carnivorous. The tuatara and most of the lizards depend largely on insects for food. Crocodilians subsist mostly on fishes, but young alligators eat crayfishes, shrimps, and insects. As they grow older they devour turtles, snakes, birds and mammals. Large alligators consume mammals at least the size of adult raccoons. Snakes eat lizards as well as other snakes, but small rodents and rabbits are perhaps the mainstay of snakes of average size. Most of the tiny snakes feed on such creatures as insects, spiders, earthworms, and slugs. Big anacondas are said to prey largely on caimans. Pythons in Asia are known to have consumed such sizable morsels as a full-grown leopard and a large boar. The few kinds of snakes that occasionally exceed 20 feet in length have all been known to devour human beings, usually babies or children, though some snakes are certainly large enough and strong enough to swallow a man of average size.

Boa constrictors are often thought of as being the largest snakes. Actually the largest boa known to have been reliably measured was almost precisely eighteen and a half feet long. Numerous statements in print credit anacondas and pythons with lengths exceeding 30 feet, but the fact is that there is meager evidence for the existence of any snake much over 28 feet in length. However, fossil remains of a snake estimated to have been 50 feet long were found in Egypt. The longest venomous snake of our time is the king cobra, which reaches eighteen feet, four inches.

There is a tendency for people to exaggerate, particularly when they lack experience or the equipment to measure or weigh large reptiles. The sea-going leatherback turtle attains a weight of at least three-quarters of a ton, and may reach a ton. But the odds are not good that anyone will capture, weigh, and report one of this size. Weights for really large crocodilians are not on record, but an American crocodile 23 feet long, the maximum accepted by a careful student of the group, might well weigh over a ton. The giant among lizards could scarcely compete. It is the "Komodo dragon," a lizard restricted to four islands between Borneo and Australia. A few indi-

Rhinoceros Iguana. *The Rhinoceros Iguana, the most powerful lizard in the Americas, inhabits the deserts of the West Indian island of Hispaniola.*

viduals around ten feet in length have been captured. The beakheads were never very large and the best that can be claimed for the tuatara is a total length scarcely exceeding two feet.

The largest reptiles probably have few enemies, except man and the parasites that infest all reptiles. Reptiles not only prey on each other (king cobras specialize in eating other snakes), but they get eaten by the carnivorous mammals, and by such birds as hawks, roadrunners, and secretary birds. Even some of

▼ A COBRA in the hands of Grace Wiley, who handled many venomous snakes but was bitten about 40 times, and was finally killed by one.

Photograph   by Newton Berlin

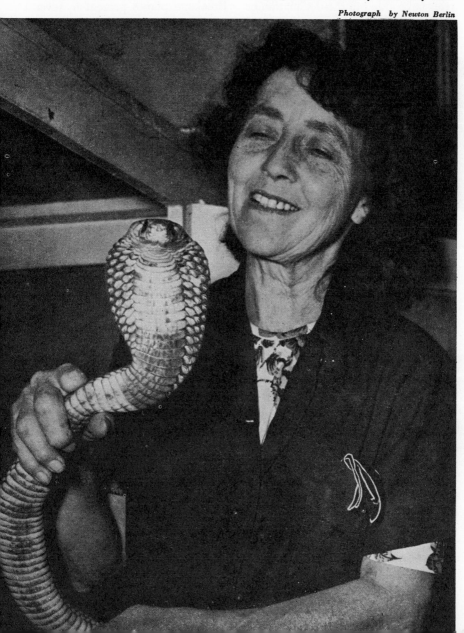

the larger fishes and amphibians occasionally seize and devour reptiles. Reptiles are particularly vulnerable as hatchlings, and their eggs are dug from underground nests and eaten by such lizards as monitors and Gila monsters, or by snakes. Skunks and other mammals, even dogs, dig up reptile eggs, and man's activities as a purveyor of the eggs of sea turtles have aided in the decimation of some species.

Aside from simply hiding most of the time (a simple task for most burrowers), or fleeing as many fast-moving lizards and snakes do, reptiles have acquired armor. The turtles are the outstanding exponents of this mode of survival, but a few lizards are afforded protection by bony plates imbedded in their skin. Breakage planes present in several

VENOMOUS

▲ Water Moccasin or "Cottonmouth." The pit between the nostril and eye marks the moccasin as a venomous pit viper. It is not found west of Texas and Kansas or north of southeastern Virginia, along the Atlantic Coast

HARMLESS

▲ Common Water Snake. Its pattern may be as dull as that of the moccasin, but it lacks the pit, the fangs, and the sheared-off appearance of the snout in profile. It is widely distributed east of the Rockies

▲ Copperhead. Its dark brown cross bands are narrower at the middle, broader at the sides, and extend onto the belly. Facial pits and tubular fangs identify it as a relative of the moccasin and rattlesnake

▲ Common Milk Snake. This harmless snake is more often seen in the East than the copperhead, with which it is confused. The milk snake has a pattern of brownish blotches margined with black, and a checkered belly

vertebrae allow most (but not all) lizards and the tuatara to part with their tail in an emergency. Enemies that seize one of these reptiles from the rear are likely to be preoccupied with the squirming tail while its owner makes good his escape. The powerful jaws of crocodilians and of not a few turtles, lizards, and snakes afford effective weapons of defense. This is particularly true when grooved or tubular teeth for the injection of venom are present in the jaws.

Such specialized teeth or fangs were employed by lizards and snakes well over 20 million years ago. Fossilized relatives of the cobras and of the Gila monster have much the same sort of fangs as their present-day representatives. Roughly one-fifth of the snakes are ven-

VENOMOUS

↑ Timber Rattlesnake, one of 26 kinds in the United States. Other snakes vibrate their tails, but only the rattlesnakes have rattles (at birth a bell-shaped "button"). None reported recently in Maine, Delaware, or Long Island

HARMLESS

↑ Hog-nosed Snake. The hog-nosed snake is harmless despite its ferocious antics and such vernacular names as "puff adder." Its loud hiss and stocky body presumably cause it to be mistaken for the rattlesnake

↑ Eastern Coral Snakes. Venomous relatives of the cobra, coral snakes in the United States have the red bands bordered by yellow, in contrast to the false coral (king) snakes, which have the red bordered by black

↑ The Mountain King Snake of the Pacific Coast has the black snout of the true coral snake, but its red bands are bordered by black as in other harmless ones. The false coral snake of the Southeast also has a red snout

omous, but among lizards only the Gila monster and its Mexican relative have fangs. These are used solely for defense by the lizards, but the venom apparatus of snakes is primarily a food-getting mechanism, used incidentally in warding off predators. Its effectiveness on both scores is shown in the wide distribution of snakes having tubular venom-conducting fangs at the front of the mouth. The Americas have their rattlesnakes, fer-de-lance, bushmaster, copperhead, and cotton-mouth and their allies (all pit-vipers), and the coral snakes. Asia has its cobras, kraits, vipers and pit-vipers, Africa its vipers, mambas, and cobras; and derivatives of the cobra family comprise roughly three-fourths of the snakes in Australia. Most of Europe is inhabited by vipers, and one pit-viper ranges into that continent from Asia. The sea snakes of the Indian and Pacific Oceans are all venomous.

Where other reptiles simply seize and devour their prey, or kill it by

▼ **A DESERT TORTOISE**   *Richard L. Cassell photo*

constriction, as many harmless snakes do, the venomous snakes attack by stabbing or biting to imbed the fangs. The venom is a modified saliva. Many persons do not realize that it not only kills the prey with a minimum of risk to the snake but it also aids in digesting the victim. The fangs of a six-foot Gaboon viper, a thick-bodied inhabitant of African forests, may be over an inch and a half in length, truly formidable weapons. The largest rattlesnakes have fangs nearly an inch in length, approximately the size of those of an average-sized bushmaster.

But fangs, of course, are only part of an extremely complicated and highly perfected mechanism. It

Λ ANACONDA: enough to frighten the timid. This snake's eyes are high, where they serve it well. Being a river snake, the anaconda must look up as well as around in search of prey.

would be an oversimplification to say that nearly 200 million years of evolution among reptiles had culminated in the perfection of a hypodermic needle. We cannot ignore the fact that for nearly 160 million years the reptiles in one sense dominated the land. Even though they declined in both size and numbers 70 or 80 million years ago, today the real measure of their success lies in the existence of over 7,000 species, each with characteristics that allow it to eat and to avoid being eaten.

Monster of the Mist Forests

A heavy pause, a violent snort, a sudden turn, and the massive African black rhinoceros charged through the brush, downing everything in its path. Here, indeed, was nature's counterpart of the Sherman tank

By Ken Stott, Jr.
Formerly General Curator,
Zoological Gardens of San Diego

TANGLED forests clinging closely to the contours of mist-shrouded slopes; ravines of blood-red rock; filmy plumes of water plunging into foaming and tortuous stream beds — this was the stronghold of the monster of the mist forests.

While I waited still and motionless, the guttural chuckle of a colobus monkey echoed through the jungle, and intermittently the throbbing call of a touraco emanated from some hidden perch. From the distance came the sound of the breaking of brush and the muted trumpeting of an elephant. Night was enveloping the East African forest with the rapidity that is typical of the passing of equatorial dusks and dawns.

Suddenly, from up the trail, muffled footsteps advanced, sucking and sloshing in the ooze. A blustering wheeze of uncertainty rent the air. Then a heavy form detached itself from the forest and the increasing gloom.

As it stepped into the clearing, four yards of massive, wrinkled power and two menacing horns became apparent. This was the monster himself—the African black rhinoceros!

Once he had emerged from the forest, he broke into a swaggering trot and made his way to the waterhole with all the grace of a Sherman tank. He stopped on the bank and lifted his head to sniff the air cautiously. Eventually satisfied that all was as it should be, he lowered his head and began to guzzle his evening drink.

The resulting sounds were scarcely indicative of proper table manners. He slurped and gulped like a noisy bilge pump, and then he wallowed.

Gingerly, he waded into the water and lowered himself into the mud, and when half-submerged, he began to thrash with gay abandon. Legs, head, and tail were tossed in every direction as he rolled from side to side on his back.

Then after a moment he stopped, sat up on his haunches, and looked about himself in a most apologetic manner. He rose to his feet and, as daintily as before, tiptoed from the wallow to begin his nocturnal foraging.

It was now quite dark. Only the light from the moon overhead lent a shadowy detail to the landscape.

The rhino, a vague black form, lumbered about the clearing, pausing now and then to nibble at the leaves of some low-growing shrub. In the darkness he resembled an animated boulder, and as such he was not particularly exciting. The time had come to take matters into my own hands.

With a flip of the thumb, I switched on a powerful flashlight, and the rhino stood motionless in a pool of light. Had I been on ground level, this action would have been nothing less than foolhardy, but here in the lofty security of Treetops Inn I had ample reason to feel safe. Treetops, a glorified blind constructed in the branches of a giant jungle fig tree, is an ideal place for even the most timorous of sightseers to view Africa's most cantankerous

Drawing by Museum Illustrators Corps

game without an iota of danger.

After a moment of immobility, the rhino was galvanized into action. He squealed at the top of his lungs and, wheeling frantically, tried to escape this terrifying blaze of unknown origin. All at once he charged, first one way, then another, pausing between charges to squint at the light with his weak little piglike eyes.

Finally, when he could stand it no longer, he barreled out of the clearing as fast as his stubby legs could carry him. With no attempt to find one of the several trails that converged upon the clearing, he merely made his own as he galloped along, pushing down anything and everything that stood in his path. Long after he had disappeared from view, I could hear his panic-stricken squeals and snortings and the violent crashing of brush.

Incredible though it seemed, this mighty beast was scared stiff—the same animal that has been known to derail locomotives and overturn trucks. With my own eyes, I had only a short time before seen a rhino rout a herd of the dread African buffaloes. It was hard to believe and even harder to understand.

The answer came a day or so later from a veteran trapper, Hugh Stanton.

"The rhino's really a very mild-tempered fellow," he told me, and when I appeared skeptical he went on to explain, "He possesses notoriously bad sight. Consequently, the old boy's got to be constantly on the alert, depending almost entirely on his senses of smell and hearing. Any unfamiliar sound or scent sends him into uncontrolled panic. Frequently when he appears to be charging, he actually thinks he's running away from the danger."

"This," I remarked, "must be very comforting to anyone who happens to be in his path."

A.M.N.H. photo

Stanton ignored my sarcasm. "Of all the animals I've collected for zoos," he continued, "I'd call the rhino by far the most responsive. I've found it possible to tame a full-grown rhino within a month of his capture. It's all a matter of mutual understanding. Treat him gently and quietly and you'll have a perfectly reliable pet."

All of Mr. Stanton's opinions may well be true (and I for one would hesitate to contradict them), but a rhino remains a formidable adversary in the bush. Rhinos are most active during the hours from dusk to dawn, at which 'time they are difficult to discern and thus avoid, being as dark as the night itself. During the day, they usually retire to the depths of the forest or, if they are plains-dwellers, into the densest thornbush thickets. Once they have

▼ A POINTED upper lip used for grasping leaves and twigs and two extraordinary horns make the black rhinoceros one of the strangest looking animals of Africa. The black is the most common rhinoceros throughout most of Africa south of Abyssinia and the Congo. The rhinoceros sees poorly with his small beady eyes and has to depend more on the sense of smell.

entered the vegetation they become almost invisible. The nondescript gray of their leathery hides serves as excellent camouflage. Thus, an innocent traveler can stumble upon a rhino before detecting its presence, and in the resulting encounter it is sometimes difficult to convince the beast that one's intentions are harmless.

The black rhino is found in a variety of habitats: the lowland deserts, the upland bush and plains country, and even in the forested mountain ranges; but he is commonly looked upon as a denizen of the first two only. This may be due in part to the fact that game photographers, because of the nature of the forest habitat, have been forced to limit their activities to the other two, where the light and climate are better. But even fairly authoritative natural history texts sometimes dogmatically restrict the distribution of the black rhinoceros to the drier, open terrain of Africa south of the Sahara. Regardless of the cause, the black rhino, as far as the layman is concerned, has erroneously emerged as a creature of bush and desert only. Nonetheless, it is in reality every bit as much at home in the densest of East African mountain forests, and in some such areas it is extremely abundant. Hunters maintain that the mountain-dwelling rhinos develop longer horns than their lowland kindred, but otherwise they differ neither in appearance nor habit.

Wherever it occurs, the black rhinoceros is primarily a browser. It feeds on succulent aloes and euphorbias, as well as on the leaves of acacias and other scrubby trees. It is innately fond of wallowing, perhaps because of the hordes of insect parasites that dote upon it. Even the omnipresent tickbirds seem utterly incapable of coping with the situation. Although the rhino is a great wanderer, it is seldom found far from water; and according to native lore it possesses a remarkable memory for local geography, which guides it unerringly from one watering and wallowing place to the next.

Sociologically speaking, the black rhino is essentially a lone wolf. Only during the breeding season does one rhino customarily join forces with another. In but a single instance was I privileged to observe more than a solitary bull or a mother and calf at one time. In this case, a father rhino apparently wished to have a hand in the rearing of his offspring.

The scene was in Kenya's northern desert, near Wamba, and I watched it from the vehicle of Hugh and Jane Stanton, who were conducting me on a brief tour of the Northern Frontier District.

They made a tender sight, this rhino family. Mother, father, and half-grown baby stood testing the air suspiciously about three hundred yards away.

Stanton howled gleefully, "Now for some real sport!"

Somehow, I didn't quite like the sound of that. I had a very uncomfortable feeling that Stanton's idea of "real sport" might differ from mine.

He started the car, turned it around, and headed toward the rhinos. They stood their ground for a minute, snorted audibly, then scattered as we drove into their midst. We stopped and they stopped, one on each side of us and the third in front. Once again we began to move,

and when we started, they started, this time converging upon the car. It was the beginning of a wild game of tag among the "four" of us, and it was one in which I did not care to be "it."

The three leathery, armor-plated monsters presented a thoroughly unpleasant picture as they rolled toward us from their separate directions, and the thought of the picture our vehicle might offer if they reached us was even worse. Apparently Hugh considered the same possibility. for he slammed his foot on the accelerator with a vengeance.

Off we went, with the rhinos on our tail, about a hundred feet behind us. Finally, they appeared to be thoroughly tired and stopped short in their tracks. Wheeling the car around, Stanton drove toward them again. At about eighty yards, he turned the car sharply to the right and, slamming on the brakes, switched the motor off.

"There's a picture for you!" he shouted.

I had completely forgotten about the camera in my hand and, at the moment, taking a picture was the last thing in the world I wanted to do. The rhinos, snorting and pawing the ground, were obviously on the verge of a charge.

"Let's get out of here. The heck with photography!" I yelled back.

Stanton shook his head firmly. "Not until you've taken your pictures."

I swore at Stanton, I swore at the rhinos, and I swore at the camera, but apparently I had no choice in the matter. I pointed the camera at the rhinos and without the slightest hope of getting a decent exposure (and caring not in the least) I began snapping pictures. Then all at once, the rhinos charged!

Mr. C. B. Perkins, one of my co-workers at the San Diego Zoo, has often sarcastically observed that I create the impression of existing in a perpetual state of imminent danger, regardless of where I am or what I am doing—and perhaps he is not without some justification. I wish, however, that on this occasion

he might have shared in the adventure (and I vaguely remember wishing it at the time). Even now I do not like to imagine what might have happened had our engine failed or had we dropped into one of the all too numerous pig holes.

The rhinos throttled toward us like a trio of jet-propelled steamrollers, and I held my breath while Stanton ground on the starter. After a hysterical sputter, the car jerked

Photograph by Hugh R. Stanton

⋏ THE MENACING HORNS of the black rhino are more dependable than its eyes. Notoriously bad sight keeps the animal on the alert, and any unfamiliar sound or scent will send it into uncontrolled panic

A WALLOWING in the mud is great sport for the rhino—and possibly great necessity. The hordes of insect parasites that dote on the beast seem unable to cope with this activity

into motion and away we went at a speed of nearly thirty miles an hour. The rhinos followed close behind, with their wicked horns aimed at our rear bumper. We veered to the right to miss a boulder and swerved to the left to avoid a thicket, all the while heading for the road. The rhinos meanwhile had begun to slow down and, just as we reached the road, they lost interest in the chase and dove into a thicket.

As we resumed a normal speed, the color (or lack of it) on Stanton's face gave me a certain degree of comfort. Mrs. Stanton, who had remained tensely silent throughout the entire episode, now patted her brow delicately with a handkerchief and said, "Wheeeu! There was a moment there when I thought about pig holes." A moment! I concluded that any remarks I might make would be better left unsaid.

There is no more dutiful a parent than a mother rhino. She sometimes keeps her baby with her for several years—long after it is quite capa-

ble of fending for itself. Only a very young rhino is in danger of being preyed upon by other beasts and then only by lions. But the mother rhino looks upon her child as a precious but completely helpless infant, even when it is almost as large as she. Any cause for alarm, and she moves in front of the baby, daring the intruder to come one step nearer her beloved charge.

Other than man, the black rhino has few enemies. However, one notable exception, or so legend has it, is the elephant. Professional big game hunters insist that the two are deadly foes and that the elephant invariably emerges victorious from any conflict between them. A rhino, it is said, will never remain in the presence of an elephant. This seems open to question since on several occasions I have watched specimens of both species drinking from the same small water hole without the slightest indication of incompatibility.

The reactions of a rhino to other

forms of animal life is entirely un-predictable. Sometimes it may drink or forage amidst a group consisting of several different species of ani-mals and yet appear oblivious to their proximity. On other occasions it obviously wants the area all to itself and makes no bones about the matter. Whether this contradiction in attitudes is due to individual va-riation in disposition or merely the momentary state of the mind of the beast, I do not know.

One evening I watched a rhino charge directly toward a herd of buffalo, scattering them in all direc-tions; and in another instance, a female rhino and calf sent a group of ten giant forest hogs scrambling away from a water hole. The rhinos were not content to drink until the forest hogs had entirely abandoned the clearing in which the muddy pool was located.

Numerically, the African black rhinoceros occupies a regrettably precarious position, and it has dis-appeared altogether from regions in which it was once common. That its numbers have dwindled so rap-idly is due in part to the ravages of trophy hunters, in part to the inevi-table encroachments of civilization, as well as to systematic slaughter of game of all types in the current and perhaps misdirected campaign to control sleeping sickness.

It is not inconceivable that the day will arrive when the black rhino has been entirely eradicated in the more open and accessible parts of its range, surviving only in the tan-gled mountain forests, which now constitute but a small part of its native haunts. Barring the removal of the jungles themselves, the black rhino may survive there almost in-definitely—a relic of the distant past, an awesome and incredible monster of the mist forests.

▼ THE BLACK RHINO is essentially a lone wolf, and only during the breeding season is it customary for one rhino to join forces with another

Photographs by Hugh R. Stanton

THE FIRST
White Rhino
IN CAPTIVITY

Martin Gibbs photograph

THE 75-POUND BABY was only two
weeks old when found and taken
to the Pretoria Zoological Garden

With only about 200 of the rare white rhinos remaining in Zululand and about the same number of the Upper Nile variety, the capture of a baby for the zoo in Pretoria was an important event

By ROBERT BROOM

Transvaal Museum

THE so-called White Rhinoceros or, as it had better be called, the Square-lipped Rhinoceros, was discovered by William John Burchell in 1812 in the region to the north of the Orange River in what is now called Bechuanaland.

Large numbers of this huge rhinoceros lived in this section during the middle of the last century. It

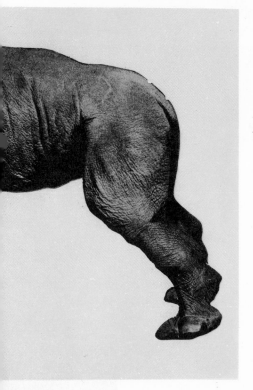

differed from the Black Rhinoceros in being considerably larger and having a square upper lip instead of a pointed prehensile lip such as is seen in the Black Rhino.

As civilization advanced, the number of White Rhinos was rapidly reduced, so that by the end of the century fears were expressed concerning its survival. Fortunately it was learned in 1894 that a few had still survived in Zululand. Then in 1899, small herds of a variety of the White Rhino were found in the Lado district of the Upper Nile. These northern herds contained an estimated 150-200 individuals, and it is thought probable that about this number still exist.

The baby rhinoceros whose picture appears here became separated from its mother shortly after birth on one of the preserves in South Africa. When the mother did not return, Dr. Bigalke of the Pretoria Zoological Gardens was notified. He acted with the greatest promptness and sent a motor lorry with a well-padded crate through the night 400 miles to Zululand.

The little rhino, a female, was brought safely to Pretoria. It was estimated that she could not be more than two weeks old when the picture was taken. Her height was 2′6″ and her weight 75 lbs. She began at once to drink a gallon of milk a day. By the age of two months she weighed 105 lbs.

As will be seen in the photograph the head is relatively large and the legs well developed. When stand-ing drinking out of her bottle, she holds much of the weight of the body on the front toes, the lateral toes being off the ground.

A.M.N.H. photograph

⋏ WHITE RHINOCEROSES of the Upper Nile variety, as exhibited in a habitat group in the American Museum of Natural History. Attaining a length of 15 feet, it is second in size only to the elephant among living land animals. Its formidable horns are neither tooth nor bone, but are compacted hair. Its eyesight is of limited service in detecting a possible enemy, but the nose and ears are acute. The white rhinoceros is much less prone to charge than is the black, which can at times become dangerously aggressive. Not actually white as the name might imply, this inhabitant of the Sudan is only slightly different in color from the darker gray of the so-called black rhino. The main difference is in the head and par-ticularly in the muzzle, which is square rather than pointed

Herbert Lang photo

⋏ WHITE RHINOS are rare today. Two hundred are estimated to be living in Zululand, with perhaps the same number of the upper Nile variety in the Lado District

∨ THE WHITE RHINO is considerably larger than the Black Rhino, but its whitish skin is the result of mud-wallowing. The two are actually very similar in color

Herbert Lang photo

◄ Unhulled rice kernels of the variety known as Blue Rose

▼ Cultivated Rice

Photos from U. S. Dept. of Agriculture

Rice

One half of the people of the world consider rice their chief food. To examine its role in human life is to travel far back along the corridors of history

By Clark Wissler
Late Curator of Anthropology
The American Museum of Natural History

RECENTLY two articles appeared in this Magazine stressing the importance of wheat and corn in the development of civilization. We now look at rice, the chief crop in the third great cereal area of the world. When the New World was discovered, corn characterized one such area as shown on the accompanying map. In the Old World we find two fairly distinct areas, a central area dominated by wheat, and a southeastern area devoted to rice. Wheat seems to have been first domesticated in Asia Minor, a dry upland country, whereas rice originated in a tropical, rainy, marshy country. The cultivation of each spread abroad rapidly about as far as its growing habits permitted.

The area devoted to the cultivation of rice is evidence of its importance to man. The number of people who depend upon it for food is even more impressive. Almost everywhere in Southeast Asia, rice ranks as the main food. Because of the density of population in that part of the world, it is estimated that one half of the human race lives upon rice. The other half of the world's people occupy a much greater area, but for the most part they are bread eaters (wheat, barley, rye, and corn).

When we think of rice, we think of China, but in India rice plays an even larger role. British India alone, with a population of about 300 million, produces annually about 600 million bushels of rice. We have no good statistics for China with its 400 million people, but it is estimated that she produces less rice than India. Hence, it would be a mistake to rate China as a whole as being fully dependent upon rice, though rice is the chief food in the southern provinces.

In a region like the Philippines, native life is largely organized around the production of rice. Its importance is shown by the special rituals that accompany almost every phase of its cultivation and processing. It is the only food recognized by such ceremonies in the Philippines. As the well-known anthropologist A. L. Kroeber puts it, "The native point of view is clearly that if the success of the rice

▼ Cultivated rice in the field

Photo from U. S. Dept. of Agriculture

is assured by the necessary magical and ceremonial means, other crops will automatically take care of themselves. When plant food is offered to the spirits in any connection, it is almost invariably rice. In short, the Filipino not only eats rice, but thinks in terms of rice, and if his civilization is to be described in a single phrase it can only be termed a rice culture."

We have noted that there is still some difficulty in identifying the wild ancestors of wheat and corn, but cultivated rice seems definitely to have come from a single species, *Oryza sativa,* native to the East Indies. All rices grown are regarded as varieties of this species, and they are surprisingly numerous. According to some writers, about a thousand varieties of cultivated rice are known in India alone, all of which are special strains, adapted to local differences in soil, temperature, and rainfall. In the main, however, a tropical or at least a subtropical climate is required. The plants are annuals and reach a height of two to five feet, with panicles (seed heads) roughly resembling oats.

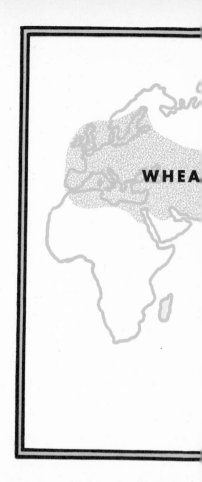

WHEA

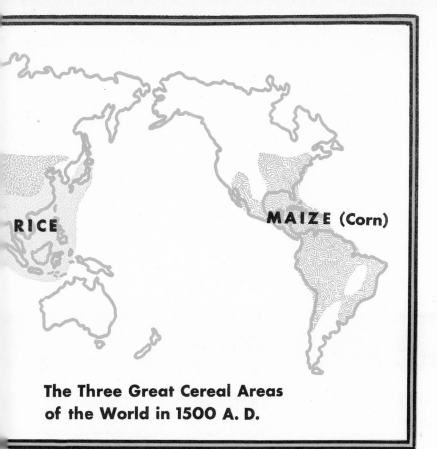

RICE

MAIZE (Corn)

**The Three Great Cereal Areas
of the World in 1500 A. D.**

The original wild species required low ground that was flooded at least part of the year. The cultivated varieties known as "hill," "upland," or "dryland" rice can be nursed through the growing season without flooding, but the yield is less and the grains smaller than in the aquatic varieties.

Methods of rice farming

One of the regions often chosen to best exemplify aquatic rice-growing is the Malabar coast of southwest India. This coast receives torrential rains in May, June, and July, followed by a period of moderately heavy rains in October. The dry season is from December to March. The lowlands of the coastal belt vary from 30 to 50 miles wide and are thickly populated by rice-growers. There are 1000 to 2000 inhabitants to the square mile. Originally these lowlands were covered with dense deciduous forests,

◄ CULTIVATION OF RICE apparently came later in history than wheat. But wild rice was probably eaten in the East Indies long before the plant was domesticated. The only implements the first rice-growers used seem to have been digging sticks and wooden spades. Only after the cultivation of rice spread to the Asiatic mainland and contact was made with people who grew wheat and millet were the plow and draft animals adopted. "Dryland" rice, as distinct from that grown in flooded fields, was probably developed through watching wheat farmers at work

which were later cleared for rice growing. All the land that can be flooded by impounding rainfall and river water is devoted to rice. Sixty to 120 days are required for a crop, depending upon local conditions. Harvest time is usually in September.

Before the rains begin, a simple pointed plow is used to scratch up the surface of the ground. Water buffaloes are preferred to oxen and are yoked to the plow either singly or in pairs. Cattle dung is spread over the plowed surface, which after the first rains is plowed once more, and the earth is finally smoothed by dragging a log back and forth.

When all is ready, the banks, or dikes, surrounding the field (paddy) are repaired. If the timing has been correct, the rains now begin, and as soon as the ground softens up, the rice seed is sown broadcast, sometimes trampled into the mud, sometimes not. The plants begin to grow in the water-covered soil. At intervals during the growing season, men and women wade into the rice paddy to pull out the intruding weeds. Finally, the water is drained from the paddy

▾ WHEN the field is dry and the rice mature, knives or sickles are used to harvest it. A scene in Bali

Photo by Lionel Green, from Frederic Lewis

A.M.N.H. photo

▲ TRANSPLANTING RICE. Sometimes the seed is sown broadcast, sometimes it is trampled into the mud. Here the young plants are being replanted, near Baguio in the Philippine Islands

▼ MULTIPLE SCARECROW: an arrangement of lines extending to all portions of the field and jerked as needed from a central tower. This device is used frequently in Hawaii. Constant vigilance is necessary to save the rice crop from birds

Sevda Studio photo

◄ TREADING RICE IN THE PHILIP-
PINES: the aboriginal method of
threshing the world's staple food
grains
(Fenno Jacobs photo, from Three Lions)

➤ HEAVY WOODEN PESTLES
are sometimes used in hulling rice in the Philippines

*Theodore Roosevelt, Jr.
Collection, A.M.N.H.*

to permit the ground to harden. When
the rice is mature, the heads are cut
from the stalks with various kinds of
knives or sickles. Immediately thereafter, millet, pulse, or sesame is sown.
Water buffaloes, a few cattle, and
sheep and goats are herded upon the
wastelands and are fed in part upon
rice straw, chaff, and other crop foods,
such as millet, oil cake, etc.

Turning from the Malabar coast-
dwellers to Asiatic and insular rice-
growers in general, we find that
wherever the growing period is short,
rice may be sprouted and grown for a
time in flooded beds and then transplanted by hand to flooded rice fields.
This naturally adds to the labor of
rice production.

When the rice grains begin to mature, the fields are raided by seed-
eating birds, often in such numbers
as to leave but a small harvest. A
common method of keeping the birds
away is to stretch a number of strings
across each paddy, with streamers or
pennants attached to them. These
flap about when the cord to which they
are fastened is jerked vigorously. Small
platforms or towers are erected so as
to enable a single watcher to guard
four plots. This is no small task, because the flock, when disturbed,
merely takes wing to descend at another location.

Processing the crop

Threshing rice involves two operations. As in oats, a hull or husk firmly
encloses each grain, and this must be
removed by rubbing or gently beating
the grain in a mortar or upon a mat.
The most primitive way is to tread
barefoot upon the unhulled grain.

The next step is to separate the detached hulls, or chaff, from the grain
by winnowing. The usual way is to
scoop the trampled mass into a shallow basket and toss it into the air
above a mat or sheet. The heavy grain
falls straight down, while the chaff is
floated to one side by the gentlest of
air currents.

For the most part the hulled grains
of rice are not white but are covered
with a coat of brown, which can be
removed by rubbing or beating, a
process called "polishing." However,
many native rice-growers dispense
with this procedure and eat "brown
rice" instead. The food value of rice
is decreased by polishing, yet custom
regards white rice as preferable.

▲ THE LABOR of tending hillside rice terraces like these and of keeping the dikes in repair can easily be imagined: a scene in Ifugao Sub-province, Luzon, in the Philippines, where human life revolves about the growing of rice

Theodore Roosevelt, Jr. Collection, A.M.N.H.

In the Philippines, as in many other parts of the rice area, hillsides are utilized by the construction of terraces, or walled-in shelves, extending horizontally one above the other. These are flooded with water in the rainy season. The magnitude of these terraces, covering the landscape from valley to hilltop like a gigantic series of hanging gardens, is impressive. The prodigious task of keeping them in order means that the owners make rice-growing their chief concern. Hand labor prevails, with the simplest mechanical appliances, — little more than digging sticks, crude wooden shovels, and the bare hands. The plow, first developed by wheat farmers, seems to have been introduced by the Spanish conquerors of the Islands.

Fenno Jacobs, from Three Lions

▲ BEATING RICE to separate the kernels from the husks, in the Philippines

▼ AFTER the rice is hulled, it must be winnowed.
The kernels fall to earth and the chaff floats away

Alfred T. Palmer photo, from Black Star

Three Lions photo

▲ A JAPANESE RICE GARDEN

Since 1500 A.D. the cultivation of rice has been introduced into many tropical and semitropical areas, such as southern Europe and North Africa, and parts of west Africa, southern United States, certain localities in Mexico, Central and South America, and many Pacific Islands, including Hawaii. The annual production of rice in the United States is about 70 million bushels, or about one-fourth the barley crop. This amounts to about one-half bushel per capita, but since cooked rice expands 300% in bulk, the amount is of some importance.

North American wild rice

Our story would not be complete without some account of wild rice in America. This is a different genus of rice, *Zizania aquatica* and *Z. milicea*. *Aquatica* grows in single stems, five to ten feet tall, with panicles about two feet long. The glumes (husks) are about an inch long, containing long slender grains, of a dark slate color when ripe. The plants can adapt themselves to quiet water, two to eight feet in depth, preferably the margins of ponds, lakes, or flood plains of rivers with mud bottoms. Early in June the shoots appear above the water. They mature about August 1st, and the grain is ready for gathering in September. The early French explorers speak of this wild rice as wild oats, Indian oats, etc.

The plant is an annual and seeds itself, since the ripe grains are heavy and sink to the bottom when they fall. The main habitat of *Z. aquatica* is the part of the United States and southern Canada east of the 100th meridian west, an area roughly east of a line passing through Pierre, South Dakota, Dodge City, Kansas, and Abilene, Texas. The Indians who made the most use of wild rice were those of eastern Canada around the Great Lakes and Winnepeg drainage areas, tribes speaking Algonkin and Siouan.

A similar Asiatic species, *Z. latifolio,* has been observed in Siberia, Japan, Formosa, and part of eastern China. Although *Z. aquatica* is reported from the West Indies, it is not known in South America.

None of the North American Indians seem to have *sown* wild rice until after contact with white people. Since 1800, some of them are known to have stocked lakes and ponds when necessary, but once the plant was introduced, it needed no cultivation.

The only attention the early Indians gave the crop was to tie the rice heads in bunches to protect the crop from birds and to prevent the wind from shattering out the grains. For this, they made twine of basswood bark fiber. Each woman, or family, used a slightly different tie and accordingly claimed ownership of the ripening rice.

The rice was gathered from canoes, poled or paddled among the rice stalks, the bunches of heads being bent over and the grain beaten off into the boat, as shown in one of the illustrations. The earliest accounts of rice gathering (1689) mention tying the heads but make it clear that much of the rice harvested was not tied but merely bent over the edge of the canoe, as shown in the drawing by Eastman. When a canoe was filled, it returned to camp, where the load was spread upon drying-frames.

The grains had then to be hulled by treading or beating. According to tribal custom, there were varying stages in these processes, since the drying frames might be smoked, the grains parched in a kettle, etc. The wild rice you purchase from your grocer has a smoky flavor if prepared in the Indian way.

Note that the main procedures in preparing wild rice closely parallel those for cultivated rice in the Old World. The two important differences are that in Asia rice is not tied in bunches to protect it from birds as was wild rice in America, and it is not smoked. On the other hand the American grain is not polished. In both areas the laborious processes are harvesting, hulling, and winnowing the grain. Like the Asiatics, the Indians almost never ground their rice but ate it boiled, usually with meat of some sort and frequently sweetened liberally with maple sugar. The Indians did not plant and weed their crops, but the labor of making twine and tying their rice was by no means

▼ THIS VIEW in a Chinese shop in the town of Pishan shows a method of hulling rice that has been in use for centuries

Alexanderson (C N S), from Guillumette, Inc.

a light task. Gathering the basswood bark and preparing the twine by hand occupied the spare time of the family during the winter months. We have estimated that from two to six miles of twine were needed by each family, the number of bunches tied ranging from 400 to 1600.

A world view of man's plant foods

The plant foods of man are embraced under a few main classes, as (A) cereals, (B) root crops, (C) fruits, and (D) vegetables. The cereals, or grains, head the list: wheat, barley, rice, rye, oats, the millets, and maize. All are the seeds of grasses. It appears that the period during which man merely gathered the wild foods that nature offered at the time and place, without cultivating the plants, was by far the longest span of time in human existence. During this long primitive period man overran all the habitable parts of the earth and met up with almost every variety and species of seed-bearing plants. The opportunity for experiment was almost boundless. In turn, the habitats of these grasses were spotty and highly localized. By trial and error, man probably came to recognize the most important species of seed-bearing plants in his habitat and sought to devise more and more convenient ways of gathering, processing, and cooking them.

Even from the first he seems to have been a *gourmet*, putting himself to a bewildering routine of trouble and toil to improve the raw products offered by nature. His fellow creatures were content to take seeds as they found them, but not he, as in the words of the most ancient of sages, "He prefers to earn his bread by the sweat of his brow." Even the way of the savage is the hard way. Hours and hours of patient toil are given to the preparation of what is eaten in a few minutes.

Fortunately for us, not all peoples of the earth became civilized at once. The understanding of our subject is made possible by comparing the ways of the nonagricultural peoples with the civilized. Thus in the United States we can still observe Indians gathering seeds as they did centuries ago, particularly in the semidesert lands of Arizona, Utah, Nevada, and southern California. The Paiute tribes, armed with simple ingenious basketry devices, strip seeds from many species of wild grasses, winnow out the chaff, and store the tiny seeds for grinding into meal and eventually baking in cakes, or more frequently for thickening soups. Seeds of more than 50 species were gathered by the Paiutes alone, which about exhaust the list of local wild grasses. Civilized men and women will not bother themselves over such small returns for the labor involved.

In a large part of semiarid Australia, where there is sparse vegetation and grasses, it is not surprising that the natives recognize the food value of even the smallest seeds. They carefully gather and conserve them, grinding them between stones and making cakes with the meal. It should not be overlooked that arid lands also bear numerous root plants whose bulbs are dug out with digging sticks. This is true in Australia as well as in the habitat of the Paiute Indians. Thus the popular contemptuous name "Digger Indians" is said to have been applied to many tribes west of the Rocky Mountains because they were so often seen digging in the ground for food. Some Australian explorers have written that the ground around a native encampment was so upturned as to suggest that a drove of pigs had been rooting up the place. Even Captain Lewis (of the Lewis and

Clark Expedition) found the Nez Percé Indian women who were camped along the Columbia River so busy pounding roots that the noise reminded him of a nail factory.

But we are now concerned with cereals or seed grasses. We have reason to suspect that a long period of experimentation with wild seeds was necessary before success was achieved in producing the world's three great staple foods — bread, (wheat, barley,

▼ WILD RICE, native to North America, was an important source of food to many Indians. It flourished without cultivation in the margins of lakes and on the muddy floodplains of rivers and was harvested in September. (Potomac River)   *Fish and Wildlife Service photo*

Courtesy of the Bureau of American Ethnology

▲ CHIPPEWA INDIAN in boat, tying wild rice. To protect the rice from birds and wind, the Indians laboriously tied the heads in bunches. Ducks of every variety, geese, and birds of all sizes and kinds found millions of acres covered with this pleasant food, while the Indians could gather but a small quantity, according to Mrs. Eastman, who described the aboriginal scene in 1853

▼ A NARROW BED of wild rice tied in bunches or sheaves

Photos courtesy of the Bureau of American Ethnology

▼ THE BINDING TWINE was threaded through rings attached to the jacket the woman wore when tying wild rice. From two to six miles of twine are estimated to have been needed by each family for tying one season's wild rice. Customarily the twine was made by shredding out long slender ribbons of basswood bark fiber and tying them together (From the Chippewa Indians)

Eastman's Aboriginal Portfolio

and rye), hominy (maize, hulled by boiling in wood ashes), and a bowl of boiled rice. Partly because of the large role that grasses have played in providing food for man, the semiarid lands are more often thought of as the place where agriculture began. Many root crops seem to stem from forest flora, but not all of them do. Tree-crops are chiefly of forest origin, but man probably planted grains before he planted anything so slow-growing as a tree. Plants of aquatic origin, including rice, tend to have forest homelands, but grains of the millet-wheat group seem to have been native to uplands tending toward aridity. Further, their cultivation appears to have been more ancient than rice. It is therefore most probable

▼ WHEN THE WILD RICE was ripe for harvest, the grain was beaten into canoes as shown in this drawing by General Seth Eastman, dating from the middle of the last century. To quote from Mrs. Eastman, the girls from an Indian village made quite a frolic of it

▼ A SEED-GATHERING BASKET AND BEATER from the Paiute Indians of
Nevada. The basket is shaped so that the edge can be held low and the
grass stalks bent over it and shaken by the beater. Again, the beater
may be used to catch falling seeds and transfer them to the basket

A.M.N.H. photo

that the cereals and civilization developed in favorable spots in a semiarid environment and that the development of rice was stimulated by the
successful exploitation of wheat. These
assumptions are at least consistent
with the locations of the earliest
known civilized towns of any size.
Civilizations are not conceivable with-

out relatively dense populations, which
in turn depend upon agriculture.

The archaeology of agriculture

The archaeology of plant foods,
wild and domesticated, is only beginning to unfold, but the world is
awakening to its importance and there
is promise of new knowledge, like the

twilight before a glorious dawn. Within another decade or two those who survive us will write a thrilling account of this new chapter in the science of man. Even now scraps of information are worth citing. We recall one of the latest contributions to the knowledge of plant foods of early man. Most of you have heard of that famous cave in China in which were found the remains of Peking Man. Embedded in the debris of that cave were masses of cracked shells of seeds which botanists have identified as hackberry (genus *Celtis*). A modern form, *Celtis occidentalis* var. *crassifolia,* still grows in western United States, especially in semiarid districts. Similar hackberry seeds are found in deposits of the Pleistocene or Ice Age in South Dakota and in north China. The mere presence of the cracked seed shells in the cave does not prove that they were eaten by man. Rodents could have carried them into the cave. However, Ralph W. Chaney of the University of California sought to solve this problem in a scientific way. He offered modern hackberry seeds to rodents and monkeys of several different species. Most of the rodents ignored them, but the few that ate them merely gnawed small holes into the shells to extract the kernels, whereas the shells in Pekin Man's cave were crushed to fragments. The monkeys chewed the seeds and spat out the shell fragments, which were similar to those in the cave, but there is no archaeological evidence that monkeys lived in the vicinity of the cave when Peking Man was there. Since even modern Indians in western United States eat hackberry seeds, Professor Chaney gathered information from them. He found that their method was to crush the seeds between stones to secure the kernels and that the resemblance of these fragments to those from the cave approached identity.

We do not know whether Peking Man chewed the seeds or crushed them between stones, but since he used simple stone tools, it seems fair to assume that he gathered hackberry seeds and carried them home to crack at his leisure.

Diggings by archaeologists almost everywhere have brought to light the charred remains of grasses and seeds, and botanists have usually been able to identify them. In the other articles on wheat and maize we have

▼ THE PROCESSING OF WILD RICE in America was in many ways similar to that of cultivated rice in the Orient. Here we see a Chippewa Indian treading rice in the familiar manner to remove the husks, but with two railings to take some of the weight off his feet

Courtesy of the
Bureau of American Ethnology

mentioned such findings. In the submerged remains of Swiss lake dwellings were found charred and natural remains of many cultivated plants, including wheat, barley, rye, oats, millet, celtic peas, and carrots. By such finds it has been possible to distinguish between the horizons of agricultural and nonagricultural peoples.

In the New World we now find special published articles on the prehistory of cotton, beans, peanuts, sunflower seeds, gourds and squashes, tobacco, maize, etc., each a fascinating chapter in the unwritten history of the world. One conclusion to be drawn from such data for the United States is that other kinds of agriculture were practiced in Kentucky, Tennessee, Missouri, and Arkansas long before maize was introduced into that region. In fact, the last crops to appear were maize and tobacco. Long before they were grown, sunflowers, squashes, gourds, and seed plants were a part of the agricultural economy of the tribes. A recent publication by George F. Carter tells how the new data resulting from preserved seeds and fragments of the *Cucurbita* (gourds, squash, pumpkin, etc.) suggest that their cultivation in southeastern United States long preceded maize in the same area and that they found their way in pre-maize times into New Mexico and Arizona. In general, this new information fully justifies the belief that agriculture in the New World was developed independently and without influence from the Old.

Our younger readers can look forward confidently to the time when a much more complete story of man's achievements with plant foods can be written.

▼ ALL of the world's modern production of wheat, corn, and rice has grown out of the primitive occupation of collecting grass seed. Today we can still see this elementary activity among the naked, hungry Australian "blacks," as shown in these drawings. For thousands of years, primitive women have thus gathered food—a seed or two here, another there—at great cost in toil and patience and with a return so trifling as to transcend belief

▼ ILIAWRA women in Australia collecting grass seed from ants' nests

▼ TREADING the grass seed to husk it

WINNOWING the husked grass seed

drawings by
ula Hutchison,
om photographs

▲ WILD RICE from the country of the Ojibway Indians:
above, threshed but not
hulled; below, hulled and
ready for storing or cooking

A.M.N.H. photo

THE SIMPLE but exacting routine of
converting grass seeds to food is
everywhere the same: (A) find the
ripening seed, (B) strip the grain
from the stem, (C) hull it by treading, (D) winnow out the chaff, (E)
pulverize the seeds, (F) combine
with water to form a paste, (G)
bake or toast on a fire

Getting Down to the Roots

(Below) CYPRESS KNEES: natural ventilating systems. These peculiar conical growths sprout off from roots that are in water or soil low in oxygen. Their bark is spongy and filled with air spaces. Thus they can convey oxygen to submerged portions of the tree and enable it to grow even in swamps charged with harmful gases

U. S. Forest Service photo by B. W. Muir

A single root system can penetrate miles of soil, but its most important part is the first quarter-inch. Where this "nose" will lead it—whether into the air, along the ground, or deep into the earth—depends on the often astonishing individuality of the plant

By WALTER HENRICKS HODGE

Longwood Gardens

PHOTOGRAPHS BY THE AUTHOR, UNLESS OTHERWISE CREDITED

MOST roots are reticent things. Even the first young root of the sprouting seed pushes out furtively and dives to spend a mole's life beneath the ground. The result of this habit is that we know considerable about all other plant organs— leaves, stems, and flowers—, but our knowledge of roots is comparatively small.

To be sure, anyone who has ever tried to dig up even a small tree knows what a tough job it can be and how strongly the roots attempt to fulfill one of their principal functions—to support the tree. And again, when one's Oriental poppies die after transplanting, the importance of roots in a plant's life is only too strongly brought to mind.

Primitive peoples probably knew more about the kinds of roots than do their civilized descendants. This is to be expected, for in early times the ability to recognize this or that kind of root went a long way towards solving problems of meals and medicine. Certain early Greek physicians derived their title from these subterranean plant organs: they were the "root-cutters," the rhizotomi. These folk believed that all the healing properties of plants were limited to the roots. Today we see the hang-over of such early beliefs in the common names of many familiar plants, such as: bloodroot, cancerroot, and snakeroot.

Roots still influence the life of man to no small degree and form important portions of his diet in most parts of the world. Just go down to the corner market and look at the familiar beets, carrots, turnips, radishes, parsnips, and sweet potatoes, and you will realize what a meal would be without roots. In the tropics yams, cassava, and countless other root vegetables play a still greater part in the daily diet All these cultivated roots have been developed from wild ancestors and in some cases have become so changed that their origin would hardly be suspected. The wild carrot, for instance, commonly known as Queen Anne's lace, is the direct ancestor of our cultivated garden carrot, yet its root in the wild form is generally small and stringy. Some roots find their way into the arts and crafts, yielding valuable dyes and materials for basketry.

Modern plants show many different types of roots, but their distant ancestors did not. A period existed, far in the past, when no plants had roots. Indeed, there was no need for them when all life was aquatic. Those were the days when the stuffs from which plants manufactured food could filter from the water into any portion of a submerged plant's body. And those were also the days when the lowliest of plants —the algae—were the rulers of the world. Even today if you want to see plants totally undifferentiated into organs of any kind, examine the simpler algae. Some of them, like the rockweeds and giant kelps of our coastal waters, have "holdfasts" which certainly mimic roots, but the similarity is superficial and ends right there. In construction and purpose these nonassimilating, fastening organs are still far removed from real, honest-to-goodness roots.

But evolutionary progress on dry land required roots both for support and as a means of tying and cementing vegetation to its prime source of raw materials, the earth.

Of course you have seen a seed germinate. The very first thing to pop out is not stem, not leaf, not flower, but root. No matter what is the position of the planted seed, down goes the root, answering the gravitational urge just as surely as Sir Isaac Newton's apple. The snaky youngster almost seems to know what it's after. It is seeking, above all, moisture, and the mineral salts dissolved in moisture. Unless it gets both of them fast, it will fail to make a success of life. A ticklish period, germination—a period when the success of an infant root marks the line between the life and death of the plant.

The most important part of any root is its tip. This is the portion we seldom see, for when a plant is yanked out of the ground most of the finer roots with the tiny tender tips are broken off. It is in the tip—the first quarter-inch of a root's length—that all its powers are located, for if one slices off this segment the root is helpless. The tip is the center of growth—of elongation. Here are located the root's "nose" and "sense of touch," which enable it to turn towards the greatest moisture, the best food, the

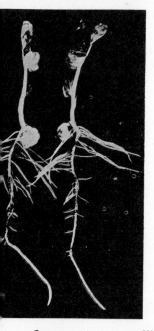

most favorable temperature, or on the other hand, to avoid toxic substances and to creep around phys-ical impediments. Such a control center ought certainly to be well protected, and it is. Creeping onward in subterranean growth, root-tips are forever running against the abrasive action of soil particles. They would soon be worn completely away were it not for the thimble-like cap or calyptra protecting them. New layers are continually added from within to replace all outside wear and tear. The root-caps of most plants are tiny—hardly visible to the naked eye—, but on aerial roots of certain large tropical species you will be surprised to find them prominent and easy to examine.

Back from the root-tip one meets the older portion of the root, just as in the aerial skeleton of a plant the trunk is older than the twigs. Like the trunk and branches, roots of shrubs and trees grow thicker with age and lay down a corky bark. Roots don't have to be big to be strong, and when they meet soil obstructions they frequently perform miracles, split-

SPROUTING pea seedlings make their critical all-out dive for moisture and dissolved minerals. Unless they get both, death is certain

ting boulders and causing sidewalks and pavings to careen. There is a case on record where the root of a birch tree entered a rocky crevice and in the interval lifted a boulder weighing 20 tons. This feat flattened out the root into a ribbon, but it at least made some room for itself.

As far as water is concerned plants are the heaviest drinkers this world has ever known! Most of this liquid passes off through the leaves into the atmosphere but all of it has to be absorbed by the roots. It has been shown that in hot summer weather a single birch tree with 200,000 leaves gives off 700 to 900 gallons of water a day, and most plants give off a daily quantity of water equal to their own weight. You can see what a task roots have, to supply such tremendous quantities of water, and all of it comes from the soil. No wonder lawns and gardens become dried out when rain fails to come.

Roots are efficient. In order to get plenty of water-absorbing surface many of the cells close to the growing root-tip push out to form root-hairs. These

ANCHORS as well as feeders, roots delve deep, losing their strong grip only under such force as the hurricane blast that felled these trees.

HOLDFAST OF A GIANT KELP:
This crude mimic of the full-fledged
root is purely an anchor. It has none of
the nutritional functions of a land root.

THE TIP is the business end. It is the
center of a root's growth, the "nose"
and "sense of touch" which enable it
to dodge impediments and find the best
food

TO PREVENT wear and tear of abrading
soil on these vital probes, Nature has
equipped them with special protective
caps called calyptra. In the picture at
right one of these thimble-like devices
is being removed, exposing the sensitive tissue beneath

act as a pumping system, sucking up all available moisture and relaying it to stems and leaves. Unfortunately the task of the root is not as easy as it sounds; for if moisture in the ground is not abundant, the root-hairs have to fight with the soil particles for what is available. But when water is finally absorbed it goes into the root proper and thence upward to the leaves via the plant's woody cylinder.

Root systems are long,—longer than most people realize, for this underground ramification is always larger than the part of the plant growing above ground. If it doesn't look so when a garden weed is pulled up, it is only because all the finer rootlets have been broken off. The root system of a single oat plant, though occupying but a cubic yard of soil, was found to measure well over 450 feet in length. At that rate the roots of a giant sequoia would have to be measured in miles!

Normal roots, the familiar underground type, take two forms. The many fine roots of grasses are known as fibrous roots. But many plants put all their faith in a single large organ or taproot, like that of a parsnip, which has but few laterals. Most taproots, particularly those of the common root vegetables, not only take in water and raw materials but have also expanded their facilities so that they may serve as storehouses for food. Certain of these plants can boast of roots that reach an enormous size, such as those of the "man-of-the-earth" *(Ipomoea leptophylla)* of the Western Plains. This bushy relative of the sweet potato, with an erect stem only two to four feet tall, has a taproot that often attains a weight of 100 pounds. Such a reservoir of food and water enables the "man-of-the-earth" to thrive in a region where rains may be extremely limited.

The normal life-span of any plant is directly related to the life-span of its roots. So-called annuals have roots whose duration is but a year; whereas perennials can live almost indefinitely. In between these two are the biennials—plants like the carrot—which live for only two years. Length of life of the root is evidently controlled somewhat by climate, for the castor bean is perennial in its native tropics, but acts as an annual in temperate regions. Wheat that is planted in the fall (winter wheat) acts like a biennial, but always as an annual when it is planted in the spring (spring wheat).

Agriculture capitalizes on root structure, and growers who own dry farmlands well know that certain crops like alfalfa, because of deep roots, can exist where others would fail. On the other hand,

tap-rooted plants are useless on loose soils which,
always susceptible to erosion, need tying down. On
such soils the fibrous root is the answer. Thus for
stabilizing wind-blown dunes nothing is better than
a grass, as you can see on any sandy seacoast.

Variety in roots is endless, especially in the group
called "adventitious." The thing we think of first
about roots is that they live underground, but there
are many which have the strange habit of originating
on leaves or stems. On these adventitious roots is
based the whole foundation of plant propagation by
means of layering and cutting. In this way the housewife "slips" a new geranium or begonia and thus
short-cuts Nature. Actually she is merely copying
Nature, which has long followed such practices.
Many a shrub—forsythia, raspberry, or blackberry
—arches its branches in such a way as to permit rooting at the tips. Similarly strawberries send out rooting
runners, and the walking fern anchors its frond tips
in terra firma. Certain bizarre plants, such as live-
forevers *(Bryophyllum)*, actually form plantlets,
complete with roots and leaves, suspended on the
aerial portions of the parent. This type of adventitious root-formation, of course, supplements seed
production by enabling plants to reproduce without
flowering, and many a pernicious weed is such because of this free rooting behavior.

Not all abnormal roots are for reproduction, however. Native Indian corn, though husky enough
above ground, is invariably top-heavy, being supplied
with a rather weak main root system. But Nature
comes to its aid by early sending out peculiar roots
as props. Palms, screw pines *(Pandanus),* and many
another tropical plant with a heavy crown that is
freely tossed about by the wind, have to develop so-
called "prop roots" of this sort as stabilizers or shock
absorbers. Such roots commonly spring out from the
stem above the ground and then penetrate the surrounding soil, burying themselves at a 45-degree
angle. Special fibrous tissue is developed in prop roots,
and this is arranged in such a way as to resist powerful strains caused by the wind. At the same time the
tissue is so highly elastic that in any kind of breeze
its spring-like, supple resilience is sufficient to force
back the bending plant into its correct vertical position. Prop roots are more common in the tropics,
especially in regions where very wet soils make normal roots precarious.

At maturity plants like pandanus have, indeed,
nothing but prop roots, the main trunk having died

(Left) AN "UNDERGROUND" view of a root system. These labyrinths of fiber belong to corn plants growing in nutrient solution. Fibrous root systems are amazingly long. That of a single oat plant which occupied a cubic yard was found to measure well over 450 feet in length

(Above) A "LIVE-FOREVER." This bizarre plant (Bryophyllum crenatum) actually originates plantlets, complete with roots and leaves, high up on the aerial portions of the parent. Here is a spectacular example of adventitious root formation which enables plants to reproduce without flowering, a method employed by many of our pernicious weeds

(Left)   SHOOTING down into the ground at an angle, the innumerable prop roots of the palm Euterpe strengthen it against the winds that freely buffet its head about

away. Most famous of all prop-rooted plants are the widespread mangroves *(Rhizophora)*, which have the habit of sending out multitudes of freely branching stilt-roots. The formation of these is so rapid that the mangrove trees might almost be said to walk through the shallows upon their interlacing stilts, which hold in their grasp all the litter of the tidal flats. Land inundated by shallow seas is thus reclaimed. In southern Florida hundreds of "keys" owe their origin to the reclamation work of mangroves, whose rootstalks can resist the undermining action of wave and tide.

Another form of root that serves as a prop is not cylindrical, but flat, and resembles the great flying buttresses of continental cathedrals. Indeed, these roots serve the same purpose, for they hold up the main columns of Nature's cathedral spires—the heavy, cumbersome canopies of giant forest trees. "India rubber" trees *(Ficus elastica)*, when fully developed in their homeland, have tremendous boles which are supported by amazing tabular roots, looking like so many massive planks running out in all directions from the main tree trunk.

The banyan *(Ficus bengalensis)*, a first cousin of the India rubber tree, solves the support of its heavy crown not with buttresses, but in still another fashion. It props each heavy branch with so-called "pillar" or "columnar" roots. Unlike true prop roots these are extremely resistant to bending. In youth pillar roots grow out first as stringy chandeliers, which dangle nearer and nearer to earth until they finally root in the soil. Thus when the parent limb most needs help she can depend in a human fashion on her offspring for ample support. The columns continue to grow throughout the whole life of the parent (which may be upwards of a thousand years), and a really old banyan with all its many pillars, resembles not a single tree but rather a forest of trees. At Calcutta is a lusty youngster of 100 years, whose main trunk is 42 feet in circumference and which possesses 232 additional pillar root trunks, some attaining a girth of ten feet. Tradition states that Alexander the Great camped 7000 men under a banyan whose leafy crown today measures 2000 feet in circumference and is supported by 3000 "trunks."

When left to themselves these giant trees fail to develop great numbers of columnar trunks, because under the dense leafy canopy of the mother plant the soil is usually too dry and hard for hanging roots to penetrate. The banyans of "Indian figs," known as the *asvhatta (Ficus religiosa)*, are sacred to the

OTHERWISE TOP-HEAVY, the pandanus plant sends out prop roots from the main stem which are able to support it. So zealously do the prop roots perform their function that at maturity the main trunk has died away, leaving no other support

FLYING BUTTRESSES support the main columns of Nature's forest temples much as they are used in the Gothic cathedrals of the Old World. The tree above is the giant tropical species, *Sterculia*

THE SILK-COTTON tree of the West Indies likewise boasts a set of buttress-like ridges which can see it through many a hurricane season. This is the tree which in its cultivated state yields the fiber known as kapok. It has large pods filled with cotton-invested seeds

Buddhists, who assist Nature by steering the descending roots into hollow protective bamboo poles and thence into well-broken and moistened soil. At Dena Pitya on the island of Ceylon there is said to be an old *asvhatta* tree whose canopy shelters a village of 100 huts.

By means of roots many kinds of plants are enabled to climb. Certain so-called "ivies" possess roots of this category, in particular English ivy, poison-ivy, and the trumpet creeper. A close look at the stem of any of these three plants will reveal tiny, stubby outgrowths on the shaded side of the stem, which attach themselves to a wall or other support with such strength that the weight of the vine scarcely ever breaks them loose. Climbing roots never gather food, but are only for attachment. Indeed, if they fail to grasp or to touch their "ladder" they quickly shrivel and die.

The so-called "air plants," which grow upon other plants instead of in the ground, possess attachment roots which hold them tightly to their aerial seats. Many of these epiphytes absorb all their nutrients from the air. Others, collecting vegetable debris among their rosette leaves, send out peculiar adventitious feeding roots from the stem into this happenchance "soil." Epiphytes are not always small plants, but are sometimes actual trees. The tropical clusias start life as youngsters high up in the crotch of a tree, where their seeds have been deposited by some bird. Then in order to get enough food to grow they eventually find it necessary to tap the principal storehouse of supplies, the ground, and they send down long aerial roots as pipelines. These cables are as tough and as pliant as a rope and make fine ladders or swings for the plant explorer who needs to climb in tropical forests. Unfortuntely clusias and their cables have a habit of fusing together around the trunk of the supporting tree, and as more and more of these festooning ropes amalgamate, the host finds itself encased in a living strait jacket, which over a period of years eventually strangles it.

The tropical orchids boast the queerest root modifications among epiphytes, for besides acting as binding organs the roots of the aerialists have a most peculiar blotter-like covering, velamen, which spongelike, can soak up atmospheric moisture. In addition some orchid roots even function as leaves and manufacture food—an unheard of feat in the realm of normal roots. Chlorophyll-bearing roots of this type reach their most spectacular development in *Taeniophyllum,* an epiphytic orchid which

Most FAMOUS of all prop-rooted plants are the widespread mangroves *(above)*, builders of the Florida Keys. On a multitude of interlacing stilt-roots, the mangroves wade out through shallow water. The tangled roots gather all the tidal litter and thus build up land where once was water

(Above) FOR stabilizing wind-blown dunes, nothing is better than a grass. This fibrous-rooted family has the ability to tie soil together, thus playing a great role in land reclamation and conservation

1   Young banyan trees use pillars rather than buttresses to solve their architectural problem. Rigid roots grow down from the heavy branches to the ground. The banyan is a first cousin of the India rubber tree

2   Appearing first as stringy "chandeliers" somewhat resembling Spanish moss, these pillar roots continue to grow throughout the tree's life, which may last 1000 years or more

3   Pillar roots, firmly fixed in the ground. Unlike true prop roots, they are extremely resistant to bending. As dutiful children, they support the parent banyan when it most needs their help

4   Mature pillars. A really old banyan tree with its many offspring resembles a whole forest. One such titan boasts a leafy crown 2000 feet in circumference and is supported by 3000 pillars

1

2

3

4

EPIPHYTES cling aloft without ground roots. Unlike parasites, their attachment roots do not impoverish their host. (*Anthurium palmatum*)

is "all roots" and has no leaves and stems at all.

The layman frequently confuses epiphytes with parasites. The latter actually draw upon the supporting plant for nourishment. This is an easy mistake, for air plants certainly look like parasites when growing on their treetop perches. However, an examination of their root system shows that the epiphytes' lack any penetrating sucking apparatus. Parasitic plants always possess this equipment, and life would be impossible to these jackals of the plant world without it. Their root adaptations are remarkable.

The mistletoe is as typical of the parasites as any. Birds distribute the sticky seeds. Upon germination on a tree limb, these seeds sink the queerest of roots into the living tissues. Their root system resembles a many-tined rake, each tooth or sinker of which represents a sucking organ that can tap those pipelines in the living tissues of the host, through which are pulsing the foods so laboriously manufactured. As this rake-like affair develops in size so does the external green foliage of the mistletoe, until a time is reached when there is no hope of eliminating the parasite,—for every time the exposed part is hacked away, the roots send up a half dozen different new plants to take the parent's place. Even more degenerate than the woody mistletoes are the herbaceous dodders—those orange twining vines that are so common along country roadsides. Total inability to manufacture food—as is shown by the lack of green chlorophyll—makes it even more necessary for the young dodder plant to contact a life-giving host. Look at a mature dodder and you will see how its penetrating knob-like roots enable this parasite to siphon the life-juices of any herb so unfortunate as to be grasped in its octopus-like grip.

Like all living things, plants need and breathe oxygen in order to live; and every portion of a plant takes in oxygen, even the underground root. When soils become too compacted or if water stands upon normally well-drained soils, plants develop poorly

PECULIAR FEEDING ROOTS creep out into the debris in the rosette base of *Anthurium bookeri*.

TINY, stubby climbing-roots of English ivy.

TREETOP CLUSIAS send these aerial pipelines to earth for food. Sometimes they strangle the host.

and are apt to die. The roots have been drowned. But some trees, with which many of us are familiar, cannot be drowned. Like divers they possess air hoses which keep their submarine growth-activity continually supplied with fresh air. The bald cypress *(Taxodium)* of our southern swamps has just such an apparatus, enabling it to live in soil and water low in oxygen and often charged with deleterious gases. From the muck of their swamps, cypress roots sprout off and send up peculiar conical outgrowths known as "knees," which stand well above the water level. The bark of these natural ventilating systems is spongy and is filled with air spaces which allow oxygen to pass freely to the submerged portions of the tree. Black mangroves *(Avicennia)*, living in salty tropical swamps, have similar organs which, though much smaller, are more numerous than cypress knees. These stick up like so many fingers in the shallow tidal water.

Roots are as variable as Nature herself. When they form a normal underground system they act as the plant's support and assure it of a constant water supply. As migrants out of their natural earthy element they may prop, climb, bind, parasitize, or fend for themselves. They may even set up natural "air conditioning" systems.

(Below) BLACK MANGROVES, with their finger-like aeration roots growing out of a salty tropical swamp. These roots supply oxygen to submerged sections of the plant and prevent drowning

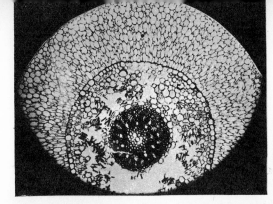

(Left) WHITE blotter-like velamen covering the aerial roots of an epiphytic orchid. Above is a cross-section showing the loose outer cells which can soak up moisture from the atmosphere. Some orchid roots even function as leaves and manufacture food—an unheard of feat in the realm of normal roots.

Below, by contrast, is a true parasite, the octopus-like dodder vine, siphoning the life juices of a jewelweed by means of penetrating knob-like roots

By Ewing Galloway, N. Y.

Rubber

A great industry has been built on a product of nature discovered by prehistoric Americans

By HAROLD N. MOLDENKE
*Director of Trailside Museum,
Watchung Reservation, New Jersey*

THE sources of rubber are many. Hundreds of plants are known to produce latex. The late Thomas A. Edison studied thousands of American plants for their rubber potentialities. A dozen or so have proved commercially practicable under certain conditions.

However, the most important source of rubber is the Pará rubber tree (*Hevea brasiliensis*), a member of the spurge family and native to the Amazon. Some 300 million wild trees are estimated to grow there, and they could produce 50,000 tons of this "black gold" annually.

However, Brazil's rubber industry has been dormant for decades, because of the development of rubber plantations in the East Indies, capable of supplying 90% of the world's needs. In 1876 Henry A. Wickham unwit-

◄ LIFEBLOOD of progress along man's rough road: a young Malay boy gathering latex, the elastic sap that smooths the way for a civilization on wheels

▼ A TYPICAL SCENE in a rubber plantation in the Straits Settlements

Burton Holmes from Ewing Galloway, N. Y.

➤ A PANEL-LIKE CUT is made in the bark of the tree, severing the latex vessels, which are in the innermost part of the bark. Above the fresh cut an old tapping scar is seen in this photograph. The bark renews itself in six or seven years

tingly struck his devastating blow to the American rubber industry by obtaining 70,000 seeds of the *Hevea* tree and smuggling them out of the country to England. These seeds became the ancestors of nearly all of the 8,000,000 acres of *Hevea* rubber trees in the East Indies and Malaya, from which the United States obtained 93 percent of its rubber supplies in recent years.

When the Japanese invasion cut off the East Indian sources of rubber during World War II, vigorous efforts

Severin from Three Lions

⋏ TREES that will mature faster and yield more rubber are produced by a delicate grafting operation. A flap of bark is carefully cut away near the base of the sapling

▼ THE BUD TISSUE from a high yielding tree
is inserted, and the bark is pressed back over it

Boury from Three Lions

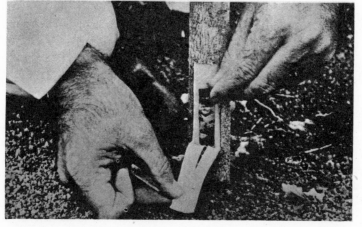

▼ FINALLY the bark covering the bud is spirally bandaged
with paraffin tape, which is removed after a period of from
18 to 35 days. Growth of the bud provides vigorous sap production on the already established root system

Severin from Three Lions

were made to revive the rubber industry in Brazil and other tropical American countries. In 1940 and 1941, about 15 million rubber trees were planted in Latin America. So important was the transportation of rubber tree seeds and seedlings that the Army furnished bombers to carry them from Liberia and Brazil to various distribution centers.

This will be understood when it is realized that airplane tires require 33 to 100 pounds of rubber each; a supply truck uses 100 to 500 pounds; a medium-size tank 1700 pounds. The bulletproof gas tanks of big bombers take 1250 pounds. A battleship uses 75 tons—the equivalent of 17,000 automobile tires. It is essential in gun carriages, pontoon bridges, antiaircraft guns, barrage balloons, scout cars, and pneumatic rafts, to mention only a few military uses.

The operation known as tapping, by which the latex is obtained from a rubber tree, is in reality a form of bleeding. A downward 30-degree panel-like incision is made in the bark of the tree, sufficiently deep to sever the latex vessels which are in the innermost portion of the bark. Tapping begins when the tree has a circumference of about eighteen inches three feet above the ground, a girth it usually attains in six or seven years. The tapping cut usually extends half way around the tree, and its upper end is always to the left as the tapper faces the tree. Shallow vertical grooves are made at both ends of the cut—on the upper end to indicate where tap-

▼ THE "BUCKET BRIGADE" wades the Rewa River in Fiji, carrying latex from the plantation

Burton Holmes from Ewing Galloway

Screen Traveler, from Gendreau

⋀ THE STUFF from which rubber is made leaves the tree as a milky fluid, as seen here in a Sumatran plantation. The ancestors of most of the rubber trees throughout the East Indies grew in America. A devastating blow to American rubber industry was unwittingly struck in 1876 when 70,000 seeds were smuggled out of Brazil.

ping is to begin and on the lower end to provide a channel down which the latex can run by way of a spout into a collecting cup. When tapping begins on a new panel, several cuts are made to remove the bark gradually before the latex-bearing cells are. reached. Thereafter only one cut is made at each tapping, and tapping is done on alternate days. On each tapping day after the first a thin shaving of bark is taken from the lower edge of the previous tapping cut. Thus the bark is gradually removed as the position of the tapping cut moves slowly down the panel. The thickness of the shaving removed each time is about a thirteenth of an inch, and a careful

By Ewing Galloway, N. Y.

worker, tapping every other day, will move downward over the surface at a rate of about an inch a month. If tapping is so deep that the wood is exposed, wounds will result and it will be difficult (if not impossible) to re-tap the same panel. In about three years the tapper will have progressed down one side of the tree to near the ground level, and then he begins on the opposite side of the tree. Thus, 6 or 7 years are allowed for the tapped bark to be renewed before tapping is repeated on any given side or panel.

Second in importance in the rubber industry is the Central American rubber tree (*Castilla elastica*), belonging to the mulberry family and native only to southern Mexico. Some 9 other species of the genus, however, extend from Mexico to Bolivia, Brazil, and Peru. Common names in Central America and Mexico are *hule* and

caucho. Wild *Castilla* trees are found in open forests and on the margins of dense jungles. The largest trees attain a height of 150 feet and a trunk diameter of five feet. The trunks have buttressed roots when old and rather smooth, thick, light gray-green bark. Trees can be tapped two or three times a year without serious injury and with a fairly good yield each time. Trees under ten years of age give very inferior yields, and 20 years must elapse before tapping becomes really practical. Early tappers in the Amazon area used to cut down the giant trees and obtain up to 50 pounds of rubber per tree. This practice accounts for the relative scarcity of large trees today. The value of *Castilla* at the present time lies not so much in new slow-maturing plantations, but in wild trees and in plantations established many years ago and later abandoned.

In Ecuador about 2,000,000 *Cas-tilla* trees were planted before the First World War but were neglected after lower-cost plantations in Malaya and Java flooded the American and world markets. Rubber from these trees once sold for as high as $3 a pound, but the price dropped to two and one-half cents a pound in the world collapse of commodity prices from 1929 to 1932. Two species, *C. elastica* and *C. panamensis,* are being cultivated in Haiti. In Ecuador's Oriente region rubber is harvested from a wild species of *Castilla* by the Yumbo Indians. These natives have no need of money but will tap the trees for colored beads and such useful domestic articles as cloth, thread, needles, fishing-lines, scissors, salt, machetes, rifles, cartridges, etc. Beads, once quoted at eight cents a pound, now bring $17 a pound at Quito, the usual payment being four pounds of beads for 100 pounds of latex.

Experts state that Panama has more

◄ SHEET RUBBER in a drying shed at Singapore, the crude rubber capital

▼ A MACHINE resembling a clothes wringer is used to press the congealed latex into sheets, near Moeratembesi in Sumatra

Philip D. Gendreau, N. Y.

By Ewing Galloway, N. Y.

Castilla trees in proportion to its size than any other Caribbean area. As in the case of South American forests, the problem of getting out this rubber is one of manpower and transportation. The average *Castilla* tree yields from 1 to 3 pounds of latex at each tapping. By cutting down the tree more rubber can be obtained at one time, but the productivity of that tree is naturally ended. The Canal Zone is now supplying "scrap rubber," which is the hardened milky juice that collects at the base of the *Castilla* trees after they have been tapped in herringbone fashion—a lower grade of rubber than the smoke-cured sheets prepared from more carefully collected latex.

Before the turn of the century *Castilla elastica* was one of the three trees that were close rivals in the production of the rubber, fast becoming important as a commodity of commerce. In some countries it was the favorite; in others the Pará rubber tree took precedence; while in Java the Assam rubber tree (*Ficus elastica*) was most popular. Environmental conditions which seemed to be the most suitable for one species in a given country were not satisfactory for another, and so

◄ A PRIMITIVE CART rattles wearily toward the waterfront of Singapore, carrying the stuff that permits an automobile to travel 60 miles an hour as though on air

▼ TREASURES OF THE EAST: rubber and tin ready for export from Penang, Straits Settlements

By Ewing Galloway, N. Y.

▲ DOCK COOLIES handling crude
rubber at a Singapore wharf

different species were chosen for cultivation. Plantation practices varied
greatly, and many different methods
of extracting the rubber were employed. Then, in 1897, a new method
of tapping *Hevea* trees was discovered.
This method enabled harvesters to tap
the trees without injury at intervals
of one, two, or three days throughout
the season, instead of only a few times
as had been done before. This is essentially the method still employed today
and results in an annual yield from a
Hevea tree far exceeding that from
either of the other trees, which can be
tapped only a few times each season
without serious damage to the tree.

Physiological and anatomical differences in the bark prevent the same
method being employed on the other
trees.

In Mexico and Central America
the *Castilla* tree was always the most
popular. Its latex had provided the
natives with rubber before Europeans
first set foot on American soil. Indians
of Mexico made large rubber balls
for playing a game like basketball, in
which rings were used as goals, set
high on the walls of a specially constructed court. They also used rubber
for waterproofing and to tip drum-
sticks. In 1872 about 100,000 trees
were planted in Chiapas alone, and

▼ TOASTING wild rubber sap into balls fo
transportation from the jungle
(Kurt Severin, from Black Star)

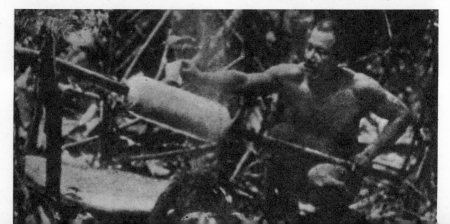

(Photo by Gilbert L. Campbell)

⋀ NEW IMPETUS to a type of rubber cultivation inactive since the East Indian boom: a "plantation" of *Castilla* seedlings at the experimental station of the U. S. Department of Agriculture at Coconut Grove, Florida

⋁ PLANTING small rubber seedlings in the Fordlandia rubber plantation in Brazil: part of a long term plan to make the Western Hemisphere independent in this vital product
(Kurt Severin, from Black Star)

▲ A COSTA RICAN WORKMAN, supported by shoe irons and rope, taps a *Castilla* tree

(Bureau of Plant Industry, Soils, and Agricultural Engineering, U. S. Dept. of Agriculture)

▼ LOADING RUBBER into a plane in the Amazon country: rapid transit for a scarce commodity which formerly traversed the long, lazy cargo route from the East

Three Lions

by 1910 Mexico had 135,000 acres of *Castilla* plantations and exported over 8000 tons of rubber. About this time, however, production of *Hevea* rubber was increasing tremendously in the Far East, where labor costs were lower and yields higher. The price of rubber consequently dropped. Mexican and other American plantations were gradually abandoned, and since 1928 less than one ton of *Castilla* rubber has been exported from Mexico annually. The same story was repeated in other Latin American countries.

▾ COOKING RUBBER in Brazil

Severin photo from Black Star

Largest Star Ruby

The Edith Haggin de Long Star Ruby, at the American Museum of Natural History, is the largest and finest gem of its kind known in the world. Its color is a peculiar milky crimson, which can best be described as "orchid red." The beautiful six-rayed star results from a myriad of tiny hollow tubes which are distributed throughout the crystal wtih great regularity, parallel to its six sides. This gem was discovered in one of the ruby mines of Burma. It is unique among star rubies and is larger than any other even remotely approaching it in quality.

AMNH photo

Sahara Canyon

Evidence of extensive erosion by water in the Sahara, though known to scientists, surprises many persons who have pictured the great desert as an endless succession of dunes.

By B. Douglass Harris

The accompanying photograph shows an extremely large canyon in the middle of the Sahara Desert. Because the photograph was taken at an altitude of approximately 10,00 feet, the canyon is probably larger than it appears. As nearly as can be estimated, the plateau at this point is about 4000 feet above sea level, and the canyon bottom about 1500 feet less.

The canyon is approximately at the mid-point between Kano, in northern Nigeria, and Tunis.

▼An aerial photograph of the canyon in the middle of the Sahara Desert, taken at an altitude of about 10,000 feet. The plateau itself is estimated to lie at an elevation of about 4000 feet

Photo by the author

MYSTERY OF
Singing Sands

One of the strangest tales of the desert happens to be true—sands that roar so loud one has to shout to be heard! A yet unsolved riddle of Nature

By E. R. YARHAM

THE two explorers, Mr. Bertram Thomas and Mr. H. St. John Philby, the only white men ever to have crossed the Great Desert of the so-called "Empty Quarter" of Arabia, both describe how they were startled by the phenom- enon known as "singing sands," the exact causes of which have long been debated by scientists.

Mr. Thomas and his party were in the heart of the vast desert, floundering along through heavy sand dunes, when the intense si-

lence was suddenly broken by a loud droning of a musical note. One of his Badu companions pointed to a steep sand cliff about 100 feet high and shouted, "Listen to that ridge of sand bellowing!"

All the explorer could see was a filmy wisp of sand being carried up the gentle windward slope to spill like smoke over its top. On another occasion, Mr. Thomas was similarly startled by a curious note emitted from the sand as his camel trod on it, but the tribesman at his side, a Murri who was quite familiar with the phenomenon, could only give as an explanation some dark activity in the uppermost of the seven underworlds. The Arabs, as a matter of fact, attributed the sounds to the spirits of the sand dunes talking.

Ewing Galloway

In Mr. Thomas' case, the note continued for about two minutes, ceasing as abruptly as it had begun. When Mr. St. John Philby experienced a similiar thing a few months later, it was set up artificially, although accidentally. He, too, was in the heart of the Empty Quarter, and he heard the noise in the afternoon, at about the same time as Mr. Thomas had heard it. The explorer was resting in his tent when his attention was arrested by a deep, musical, booming sound. Looking out, he discovered that it had been set up by one of the party walking up the steep sand slope of the dune encircling the camp.

The traveler's own description of what he heard and saw is worth quoting: "Quite suddenly the great amphitheatre began to boom and drone with a sound not unlike that of a siren or perhaps an aeroplane engine—quite a musical, pleasing, rhythmic sound of astonishing depth. . . . The conditions were ideal for the study of the sand concert, and the first item was sufficiently prolonged—it lasted perhaps about four minutes—for me to recover from my surprise and take in every detail. The men working at the well started a rival and less musical concert of ribaldry directed at the Jinns [desert spirits] who were supposed to be responsible for the occurrence. . . . I realized that the key to the situation was Sa'dan, seated on the top of the slope. It was evident that the music was being engendered by the sand sliding down the steep slope from under him."

Mr. Philby followed Sa'dan's example and found that he, too, was able to produce the same sound by setting masses of sand in motion down the side. The noise commenced with a grating sound and was gradually increased into a musical booming, which just as gradually decreased until it died away. He experimented by pushing a bottle into the singing sand, and as he withdrew it there followed a wail like that of a trombone. At another time he plunged into the moving mass of sand halfway down the slope, and it appeared to throb beneath him like a great organ.

These singing sands of southern Arabia have only become known to science this century, but it has been truly said that there is nothing new under the sun. The phenomenon was known to the Chinese at least a thousand years ago. One of their writers left an account of an area in the province of Kansu where it had been noted in the ninth century. The document speaks of the "Hill of Sounding Sand," which was 500 feet high in places. According to the author it possessed strange, supernatural qualities: "Its peaks taper up to a point, and between them there is a mysterious hole which the sand has not been able to cover up." The writer said that in the height of summer this hill of sand gave out sounds of itself, but if trodden by men or horses, the notes could be heard for long distances. The manuscript also spoke of a queer custom which was followed at the time to induce the singing. The account runs, "It is customary on the tuanwu day (the Dragon Festival on the fifth of the fifth moon) for men and women from the city to clamber up to some of the highest points and rush down again in a body, which causes the sand to give forth a rumbling noise like thunder. Yet when you come to look at it the next morning the hill is found to be just as steep as before. The ancients called this the Hill of Sounding Sand; they deified the sand and worshipped it there."

The Misses French and Cable, well-known missionaries in inland China, have also recorded their observations of the phenomenon in Chinese Turkestan. The City of Sands (Tunhwang) takes its name from the ranges of sand dunes that lie to the south, stretching out into the great desert of Lob. These sand hills possess the property of "singing" when the sand is moved. Before the desert gale blows, a sound like the rattle of drums is heard, but at any time the hills can be induced to voice their curious song by those who will pay the price of climbing their steep slopes. Visitors do this and then slide down the sharp incline from the knifelike edge of the highest point for the sheer fun of hearing the great vibration, which seems to spring from the very center of the mighty hill of loose sand.

It is to the deserts that one must turn to hear the finest exhibitions produced by singing sands, because the immeasurable quantities of sand which characterize them offer ample opportunities for the production of the sounds. But it should be noted that a similar phenomenon has been reported from beach sands. The little island of Eigg, in the Scottish Hebrides, for instance, is a spot unique along Scotland's western shores, for in the Bay of

Laig are found sands that sing. The honor of the first discovery of similar sands in England appears to go to Mr. C. Carus-Wilson, who found them about 60 years ago at Studland Bay, on the coast of Dorset. They have also been recorded on the coast of North Wales; and in the United States two observers have reported them at 74 places on the Atlantic coast alone.

The sounds produced by desert dunes certainly vary, for travelers have compared them to a ship's siren, a throbbing organ, the beat of drums, a trombone, and the twanging of a monster harp.

Writing from Egypt a year or two ago, Lieutenant Colonel de Lancey Forth spoke of the following experience in the great sand dune country to the south of Siwa, Egypt: "I found, after a strong westerly wind had blown throughout the day and had banked the fine drift sand high up on the knife edged tops of the dunes, that sometimes in the evening, when the wind had died away, leaving a deep stillness in the air, this fine drift sand slid down in streaks over the coarse big-grained red sand which forms the steep slopes of the solid part of the dunes, and the friction of the one rolling over the other gave out a noise like distant rumbling thunder with a deep musical note as that of a 'cello in it."

Mr. Bertram Thomas, too, noticed the noise late in the afternoon, when the heat of the day was fading. Apparently, another factor also favors the close of day. During the day the wind blows the fine drift sand to the tops of the dunes, and toward sunset, when the wind usually dies down, it be-gins to roll down the slopes. Dryness seems an essential factor, for the ancient Chinese manuscript states that the Hill of Sounding Sand gave out notes only at the height of summer; and Mr. Philby likewise testifies that early in the morning, when the air was cool and the sand somewhat moist, he failed to elicit any response from it. And a few weeks later when there had been a little rain, there was no music in the sands.

Examination of the sand has not revealed any peculiarity linking the whistling sands of the beach with the booming sands of the desert. Samples from the dunes do not reveal any distinguishing features. The grains are no more uniform in size than those of many silent sands; and though clean sand sometimes seems to sing best, R. A. Bagnold heard it in a desert region where the sand was dirtier than usual and was wetted appreciably only once or twice in a decade.

A. D. Lewis found that when singing sand was taken from the Kalahari Desert to Pretoria, it lost its "voice" unless kept in airtight containers. But the quality could be restored by heating it to about 390° F.

Scientists generally agree that the sounds are caused by the rubbing of grains against each other, but as yet there is no real explanation of the mechanism by which they are produced. When further critical studies are made, the answers may be forthcoming. Meanwhile, when you are in the desert. keep an ear open for one of the strangest concerts ever to come from nature's versatile music box.

Your Unknown Friend
The Sardine

Millions welcome him on the menu, but few can carry on a conversation about him.

By LORUS J. *and*
MARGERY J. MILNE

Department of Zoology
University of New Hampshire

WE MAY be on familiar terms with sardines laid neck to tail in olive oil, but the living fish, complete with head, insides, and particularly scales, in its home in the sea —that is a creature with which few are acquainted.

When a Maine fisherman, minding his own business, sees a whale spout a few hundred yards from his boat, he doesn't shout, "Thar she blows!" He doesn't even yell. He just says: "Must be sardines yonder." For sardines make good whale food, and the sight of a finback may mean that sardines by the million are rushing away at top speed. Indeed, they live in schools that number upward from three billion individuals to populations of nobody knows how many.

Above the whale you may see herring gulls, which recognize the turbulent water stirred up by the sardine schools. In they plunge, to rise with fish in their beaks.

Almost everything in and over the sea eats the sardine, if big enough to do so. The Atlantic sardine along the Maine coast is a herring, *Clupea harengus*. Each mature female lays about 30,000 eggs each year, but so many fall victim to other creatures or perish through various natural causes that an average of less than 2 survive to repeat the cycle. On the fluctuation of this average rests the rise and fall of sardine populations in the sea.

Some sardines reach a length of eighteen inches. These may be 20 years old and are multiple grandparents. But those that a man or a gull prefers — five inches or less in length — have not reached their first birthday. A ten-inch herring has reached reproductive age and is usually about three years old.

To survive so many successful attacks by enemies, sardines themselves must find plentiful food. Each of them is equipped with a sort of sieve in the gill region, which effectively strains out food particles from the water. The particles are microscopic algae and other minute plants in the upper levels of the sea (where sun energy can penetrate), plus the hordes of barely visible crustacea and various animalculae. Collectively these are known as plankton, and the sardine is a plankton feeder. Of all the small creatures on which herring thrive, almost the only one to have a common name is a tiny crustacean belonging to the genus *Euphausia*. It is known to fishermen as "red seed," because it becomes so abundant as to color patches of the sea. Sardines take both the algal plankton on which these crustaceans feed and the crustaceans themselves.

The eggs of the Atlantic herring are heavy; they stick together and sink to the bottom. The most valuable sardines of international trade, however, start out in no such fashion. They are the French sardines—luxury tidbits that gave the common name to the whole group of little fish, because Sardinia, in Mediterranean waters, was where this delicacy abounded. And a French sardine comes from a buoy-

NETS filled with the sardine catch are emptied into a small boat, which will transfer them to the fishing fleet. In New Brunswick waters

R. Gates photo from Frederic Lewis

ant, floating egg—one of 60,000 each mature female lays through the summer. Properly these fish are *Clupea pilchardus,* and if not caught as yearlings to be canned in the familiar manner, head to tail, they may attain a length comparable to that of the Atlantic herring. In Norway there are two kinds. The Grade A sardines are known as *brisling* and are *Clupea sprattus.* The others are called *sild* and are *Clupea harengus.*

The word "sardine" has fallen into confusion. As popularized, the term has come to refer to any small fish that can be canned. To a Californian the word signifies what he calls a pilchard, *Sardinops coerulea,* caught at a size where two cleaned fish may fill a fifteen-ounce can. Such pilchards are caught in purse seines to an annual total of between 250,000 and 500,000 tons, and their market value amounts to at least 19 million dollars. Such fishing methods miss the small individuals and commonly take fish after they have reproduced at least once. Maine sardines, sought close to shore in smaller sizes, are all immature fish. Four to a dozen of them go into a 3½-ounce can; and those that are marketed annually in this way total only slightly over 40,000 tons, but they have a market value about equal to the total output of the California "sardine" industry. With the exception of cod, haddock, menhaden, and rosefish (redfish), more weight finds its way to the fish markets from the herring family than from any other source. Only salmon and tuna exceed the sardine and herring fisheries in value.

Atlantic sardine fishermen usu-ally seek out regions where the fish breed in large numbers and then trap the young as they roam in schools. With so many mouths in a single group, there must be a tremendous demand for food, and sardines are apparently very sensitive to the taste of nourishment diffusing through the water. They will swim toward bait made of the salted roes of cod and other fishes, and they may be induced ("toled" is the word) into traps built of branches driven into mud flats. These are "brush weirs" such as are used extensively in the region around Eastport, Maine, at the Canadian boundary—the center of sardine catching and processing for the Atlantic coast. In a sense, a brush weir is a net made of interwoven plant materials, but the important feature is that it extends into the bottom, and through that bottom the fish cannot escape. In deeper water, a similar enclosure may be achieved through use of a pound net, whose sides are continuous with the bottom. The name refers to the impounding of the catch. Pound nets for sardines are often supported by a circle of floats, and the mesh is fine enough to limit the catch to useful sizes.

Wherever sardines are held captive, the surface of the sea takes on a curious, glittering appearance from countless minute scales. These fish have a poorer hold on their overlapping armament than most, and the mere brushing of one agitated animal against another serves to scrape loose the light-reflecting, tough transparent flakes. Often the scales, like sequins on a dark sea, are clues along the Maine coast to

Acme photo

HOMEWARD BOUND: well loaded with sardines, the purse seiner leaves the fishing area and heads for port

the arrival of a sardine boat—a floating factory more bulky than a finback whale and more destructive to the fish. Sardine boats can be anchored wherever sardines are abundant. Each boat is ordinarily equipped with a special boom from which a funnel-shaped net can be lowered into a passing school of herring. A huge pump on board then inhales a continuous stream of water from the funnel through a six- or eight-inch hose and sucks in sardine and sea together. Both emerge into a pound net on the opposite side of the vessel, the fish to be dipped out and processed at leisure.

Right on board, the fish are finally cleaned and sorted for size. Sea water rinses away the loose particles before the sardines are raised from the tanks on screens to drain. When almost dry, the fish and screens in vertical layers may be lowered into boiling cauldrons of oil—olive oil for high-grade small fish, cottonseed or peanut oil for poorer quality—and when cooked enough they are raised again to drip. Packing in cans requires hand labor, but the work proceeds with amazing speed. The waste parts, meanwhile, are dried as fish meal or manure. The canned fish go to the sardine boat's hold, while bags of fish meal are piled on deck. When sardines are running, several families may live on a single boat for weeks at a time, lending hands for the work and amassing a valuable cargo.

The season must be right for a French sardine to have the proper flavor, and cooking them becomes an art if you wish to preserve the full savor and texture of the meat. Similarly, the herring along the New England coast can only claim membership in this class of delicacy when quite small. Thereafter, if they escape to live to larger size, they come to the market fresh or dry as "red herring" or slightly salted and smoked as "kippered herring" or "snacks." When larger still, and strongly salted and smoked to cure the meat, *Clupea* becomes a "bloater." Thus modes and methods differ around the world, as do the fish that bear the general name "sardine."

Animals of the Sargasso Merry

Ever since Columbus plucked a crab from its mass of seaweed, this sea within a sea has stimulated romantic and fanciful legends

By MYRON GORDON

AWAY from the main trade routes of America, owing to the dangerous coral reefs, many of which can be seen from a boat only at low tide, and far away from the centers of human population, the coral reefs and islands of the Dry Tortugas—a series of islands about 90 miles west of Key West, Florida—have remained a virgin biological territory, practically untouched by advancing civilization.

Every summer scientists from all parts of the country come from universities, biological laboratories and medical institutions and settle there on Logger-

head Key. Under the paternal supervision of the Carnegie Institution of Washington, they work in its camp-like Marine Biological Laboratory in a South Sea setting, except that there are quarters for bachelors only. The wives, if any, are left at home.

On one brilliant June day, Doctor W. H. Longley, leader of the colony, invited me to join him in an excursion to the Sargassum weed drifts in the Gulf Stream. As we walked down to the dock to board the Institute's yacht, the *Anton Dohrn*, the tropical waters were so calm that our view of the ship did not stop

o-round

All photos by
Myron Gordon

at the water's edge. Its image was repeated in reverse in the mirrored surface of the sea and it ended in the fleecy clouds that moved across the watery sky.

Once started, we headed directly for the Gulf Stream, only a short run from our laboratory base, but so small and low were the coral islands of the Dry Tortugas that we soon lost complete sight of land. From the view about us we might have been in mid-ocean, and from the sight of the floating Sargassum seaweeds, we might have been in the heart of the Sargasso Sea.

Over the side of the *Anton Dohrn* I saw a Portuguese man-of-war drifting in the sweep of the Gulf Stream, accompanied by its constant piscine retinue, the broad-banded, blue-black man-of-war fish (*Nomeus*) and the fine-striped yellow-jack (*Caranx*). About fifteen fishes milled slowly within the protective veil of the long, curly tentacles that hung down several feet from the transparent, pearly-white, floating balloon of the jellyfish. Not all fishes

(*Above*)ONE OF THE STRANGEST CREATURES inhabiting the enormous seaweed-strewn Sargasso Sea: Pterophryne (pronounced ter-o-FRY-nee). It is camouflaged to match its seaweed background and can change its color.

If you think the fish is perplexing when removed from its environment, look at the other photograph, in which Pterophryne has climbed aboard its weedy wagon. Note how perfectly its golden brown sides and markings blend with the branching fronds and gas-filled bladders of the weed.

know their way around the jellyfishes' stinging tentacles. The Sargassum pipefish (*Siphostoma pelagicum*), a cousin of the famous sea-horses, has repeatedly been seen hopelessly entwined in their treacherous clutches.

The notion is still wide-spread that

the Sargasso Sea is a forbidding region of the tropical Atlantic and is cluttered with wrecked and rotting ships that are held in one enormous mass by the entangling jungle of seaweeds. Honest sea-captains, intent solely upon legitimate trade, supposedly shun "the port of missing ships, the graveyard of the sea," as they would a plague-ridden country. Novelists and motion-picture directors have gone on mental treasure-hunting expeditions into the Sargasso. Their imaginative, blood-curdling romances are but mild modernizations of age-old legends told by sailors of Columbus' day.

In reality, the Sargasso is a region in the southern Atlantic characterized by the presence of great quantities of seaweed that slowly, almost imperceptibly, rotate; they support a floating world of strange sea-organisms. The Sargasso Sea is mysterious in origin, prehistoric in age, and unique in the perfect fraternity of its bizarre plants and animals. So close is this organic fraternity that it is often difficult to tell its animals, judging by their shapes alone, from its plants. There are many things about the Sargasso and its Sargassum weed that are still as unfathomable today as they were in 1492 when Christopher Columbus discovered them 30 days before he discovered America.

Dr. Longley promised us a grand show when we were within hauling distance of the Sargassum weed rafts, and in preparation for it, we set up a stage in the shape of a large basin of water. The magic show began with our grasping portions of the bladder-tasseled seaweeds and shaking them vigorously over the basin.

We found not only weed-like fishes in the Sargassum, but weed-like crabs, weed-like slugs, and a host of tiny creatures that cling to the fronds so closely that at first glance they seem to be an intimate part of their algal surroundings. Small shrimps, in tones of rust and browns, row their curved shells cleverly through the tunnels formed by the interlacing weeds. Bryozoans, that look more like mosses than the animals they really are, have a perfect background for their colonial homes. Hydroides, the stay-puts of the jellyfish order, are so numerous, yet so small, that the Sargassum fronds appear fringed. Only by use of a lens can one definitely satisfy oneself that the fringes on the weed are not of vegetable but of animal origin.

Even the lowly worms build their spiral igloos of lime upon the wandering weeds. The annelids keep their bottom parts safely tucked away in their houses while the front-ends look out upon their floating marine world with flaming head colors. When disturbed in their monotonous routine of waving their food-gathering tentacles, they pull in their groping head feathers like a signal man retiring his gags after the end of his message.

From a clump of Sargassum I picked up a strange, blubbery mass about an inch in diameter. It was a tiny octopus. As it spread its tentacles and clung to my hand, I felt its strong, clammy, sucking power. It gave me an unpleasant inkling of what a man-sized octopus could do. But in this instance, I am sure that the less than pint-size octopus was more frightened than I. It first turned exceedingly pale; then it started to flash its signs of distress in many colored signals. From its variously hued pigmented cells, tiny discs of red, yellow, green and black enlarged and diminished in a series of pulsations. The flashing on and off of the many colored chromatophores seemed like the blinking of a multi-colored Broadway electric sign. I wanted to let the little cuttlefish go but it clung tenaciously to me for a while before making off like an animated umbrella.

The floating seaweeds make up a marine nursery, probably the very first cradle of the deep. Many species of fishes lay their eggs within the protective folds of the Sargassum; there the young hatch and spend their infancy. In the 1870's Louis Agassiz, one of the world's most famous naturalists, startled the world of ichthyology by announcing the discovery of the nest of the Sargassumfish in a clump of Sargassum weed, that was held together by elastic, beaded threads. The beads, Agassiz thought, were the eggs of the Sargassumfish, but when William Beebe in 1932 watched the hatching of such eggs, out came embryo flying fish (*Exonautes*) instead. And Charles M. Breder, the director of the New York Aquarium, repeated the hatching of flying fish eggs when he explored the Sargasso Sea in 1934, and provided the final explanation of a 70-year-old Sargasso Sea biological mystery. Were it not for the eggs' anchorage on the floating Sargassum, Breder said, they would sink into the abyssmal depths of the Sargasso, in several miles of cold dark waters. From these depths flying fish embryos would never arise.

Where the eels breed

Yet from the depths of the Sargasso some fish do arise. Eels arise. Every fresh water eel that is seen in a creek, river or inland lake was born somewhere at a great depth between the oceanic floor and the surface of the Sargasso Sea. Doctor Johannes Schmidt, the great Danish ichthyologist and oceanographer, sailed and combed the Atlantic Ocean for eighteen years before he found the breeding grounds of eels. In the international waters near the Bermuda Islands, a thousand feet down, the American and European eels, in two separate camps meet and breed. When the eggs hatch, the young eels look no more like their parents than a crawling caterpillar looks like a fine-scaled, winged butterfly. The larval eels are thin, flat, ribbon-like; they look like open cigar-bands made of cellophane. The European and American

eels cross one another's paths on the way back and forth, to and from their native continents; they never lose their way. The waters of the Sargasso may be the meeting grounds of eels, but they are no melting pot of nationalities; the American and European eels never interbreed.

But the first naturalist in the Sargasso Sea was its discoverer, Christopher Columbus. His journal records the finding of a crab, swimming in and out of the thickly entangled Sargassum weeds. The crab was regarded as having great significance and Columbus caught and pre-

This strange seaweed-strewn section of the Atlantic Ocean varies in distribution and density with the seasons and under the influence of local weather conditions. In August, it embraces an oval area about 2000 miles by 1000 miles. It rotates slowly; it is mysterious in origin and prehistoric in age.

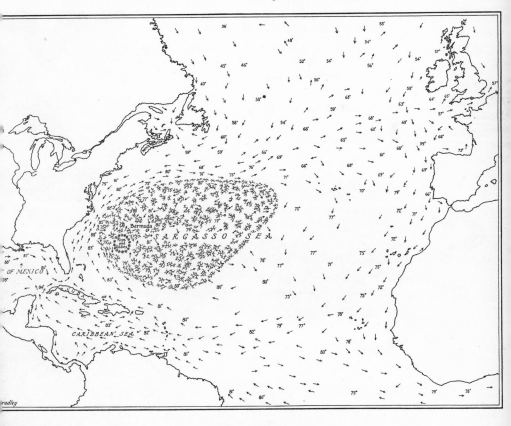

served it. To him, the crab and the surrounding weed meant nearness to land and to outflowing rivers, for both the crab and the weeds were thought to have been of fresh water origin. Little did Columbus know that the Sargassum weeds and the crab were perfectly at home on the high seas.

Carcinologists and oceanographers think that Columbus' Sargassum crab was either the little wanderer (*Planes minutus*) or the drifting crab of the sea-god (*Neptunus pelagicus*), for both are found abundantly in the floating vegetation of the Sargasso. Columbus must have had a keen eye to spot the tiny crab, for it is hardly distinguishable from the weed upon which it clings.

A voracious crab

A modern Columbus of 1867, Cuthburt Collingwood, traveled through the Sargasso and told the readers of the *Intelligent Observer* (a Review of Natural History, Microscopic Research and Recreative Science) his story of the animal life he found there. He says that Neptunus is a splendid swimmer. It can rest leisurely, motionless, near the surface of the sea or upon the drifting weeds. But its chief occupation is the pursuit of game. It is a veritable shark among the crustaceans, for it is swift, certain, and deadly; it is graceful and tiger-like in its movements: it never tires in preying upon the Sargassum community of animals.

The seemingly innocuous sea-slug (*Scyllaea pelagica*), a member of the slow and meek fraternity of snail-like animals, has taken on belligerent habits of life. The sea-slug may appear soft on the surface, but in its little insides it hides a wicked, rasping gizzard, equipped with bands of hard, horny, sharp-edged plates, bristling with spines. And its tongue is covered with thirteen tooth-like cutting edges. Every spine points backward, directing the victims down a dark, one-way path.

The Sargassum sea-slug, apparently, is

CHRISTOPHER COLUMBUS discovered the Sargasso Sea and recorded finding a crab swimming in the thickly tangled weed. It may have been this type. A glance at the other photograph shows what a good observer Columbus was to see the crab in its concealing weeds.

no sluggard. It is a terrible carnivore that has fully earned its scientific name, *Scyllaea*, for Scylla was a mythical she-monster with six heads, twelve feet and the voice of a yelping dog. She dwelt in a cave by the sea and snatched sailors from passing ships.

The sea-slug bears a remarkable resemblance to the color and shape of the weeds it frequents. Its brown colored body is covered with large round, dark edged circles that look like the air bladders of the Sargassum. Folds and flaps of skin extend from an otherwise chunky body, producing the effect of a clump of thickly tangled weeds. It clings to Sargassum so tightly that an early naturalist believed it was permanently attached to the weed. When it swims, Collingwood says, Scyllaea's club-shaped tentacles are thrown back. In this attitude, it bears a most grotesque resemblance to a small four-legged animal ·with large ears—a Scotch Terrier perhaps.

In the Sargasso, where everything seems to be unusual, you may expect the water-fleas to be peculiar, too. They differ strikingly from the cute, elephant-faced Daphnids that aquarists catch from inland fresh water pools to feed to their tropical fishes. Some Sargasso water-fleas have huge eyes, so large that they dwarf the rest of the body, while other members of the cladoceran clan are completely blind.

A mid-ocean hitch-hiker

The Sargasso supports one creature that seems to be totally out of place in mid-ocean; it is an air-breathing insect that lives, not in the sea, but on top of it. It is *Halobates*, the oceanic water strider. This outlandish insect runs over the surface of the sea by means of its six long hairy legs; it is often found thousands of miles from land. The hemipteran hitch-hiker often uses the floating Sargassum as a temporary means of conveyance. The Sargassum world moves as though it were a colossal merry-go-

round, but the little bug apparently does not mind because, like most of the animals of the Sargassum community, it is born and bred on the high seas. Halobates' eggs are found firmly attached to floating feathers of pelagic birds. Beebe picked up a number of feathery rafts of eggs and hatched out a swarm of Sargasso bugs in mid-ocean.

In the process of sorting the wealth of animal types picked up in Sargassum weed rafts I shook a bunch of the seaweeds over the basin; I felt and saw something fall to the water below. It looked like a weed fragment but plants do not move of their own volition and this Sargassum-like matter did move. While I was debating whether it was vegetable or animal, the ragged chunk of brown stuff turned sidewise, and I saw that it was one of the most fantastic of fishes, the famous Sargassum fish. The technical name for it, *Pterophryne* (I learned to pronounce it Ter-o-fry-nee), was bestowed upon the fish by one of America's greatest ichthyologists, Theodore Gill, the man who built the wonderful collection of fishes at the Smithsonian Institution at Washington. To keen-eyed Gill, the little fish with the large head and the many flaps looked like a finny toad, and its name, Pterophryne, is an allusion to these bold features.

Many fishermen of the tropics call Pterophryne the frogfish and some, even in the days before the fame of Walt Disney, called it the mousefish because of its curious antics, but to me it will always be known as the Sargassumfish because of its remarkable resemblance to the weed and because it is found only in closest partnership with it. When Pterophryne boards its algal trailer, it merges its animal identity with that of a low vegetable. This may appear to be a descent in its social level, but actually it is a definite step forward. When it graduates to the Sargassum status, it gains all the rights, privileges, and immunities pertaining to that status. In this biologic world Pterophryne may be difficult to see, but it sees everything. When live food in the shape of a juicy shrimp or marine worm, passes by innocent of danger, Pterophryne approaches it, not in the dress of a fear-inspiring, ferocious predator, which in reality it is, but in the guise of an innocuous vegetable.

Pterophryne has the golden brown color of Sargassum. On its golden sides

are broad, irregular, brown markings that resemble the branching fronds of the seaweed; and the round gold patches on the fish resemble the gas-filled bladders. Sprinkled over the darker brown parts are many white dots that simulate the white encrustations of tiny animals upon the fronds of the Sargassum.

Like an old-fashioned shawl, Pterophryne is fringed from head to tail. Tiny tabs of skin grow out from its head ornaments, its fins, and its body. And this fringed appearance of the fish matches the fringes and scalloping that arise from the Sargassum stems, fronds, and bladders. Curiously, the weed's small filaments are not part of the living substance of the weed, but are, in reality, colonies of small animals that have made their homes there. Pterophryne has matched not only the appearance of the weed but the weed's tenants as well.

The Sargassumfish makes the most of its concealing coloration; it has been practicing the so-called modern art of camouflage for centuries—certainly long before man rediscovered its effectiveness during World War I. Not only does Pterophryne have protective colors and deceiving shapes, but it practices the third and most difficult trick of the camouflage art—the trick of changing its skin coloring to match the background of its changing environment. And in this department of the art, the much-vaunted chameleon is a lubber in comparison with the speed of the Sargassumfish.

If some power of decay strikes the Sargassum home of Pterophryne and as a result the weed becomes deeper and deeper brown in color, the skin color of the fish is adjusted to a corresponding shade. And if the weed disintegrates, Pterophryne deserts it for a younger, healthier branch and again assumes the lighter color of its new home surroundings.

Driven far from home

Pterophryne, like all ocean-going, wave-riding creatures, becomes a helpless victim of violent oceanic disturbances. When unusually strong southerly winds prevailed along the Atlantic seaboard early in 1897, they sent large rafts of weeds far north of their usual beat; later during the summer, off-shore winds of unusual force and persistence blew huge patches of Sargassum and their living cargoes inshore from the Gulf

Stream. That year Hugh Smith, one-time chief of the United States Bureau of Fisheries and adviser on fisheries problems to the Government of Siam, caught twenty-two Sargassum-fish in Vineland Sound off Woods Hole, Massachusetts, by simply dipping up pieces of Sargassum with a net. In all, 100 Pterophrynes were rescued from derelict weed rafts, but how many fish were carried further north by the wind into the sphere of influence of the cold Labrador Current that sweeps down the coast of Maine from Arctic regions, nobody knows.

Often Pterophryne have been swept to uncongenial ports. Their journey's end has been recorded as far north as Norway. Outside the warm charmed circle of the Sargasso, neither the weeds nor their dependents can long survive. When the Sargassum floats are projected tangentially from the outer fringe of the Sargasso Sea, they are embarked upon a one-way ride. William Beebe's word picture captures the spirit of the sad

▼ The Sargassum Sea-Slug. This member of the meek fraternity of snail-like creatures may appear soft on the surface, but in its insides it hides a wicked, rasping gizzard, bristling with spines. The spines all point backward and direct its victims down a dark one-way path.

Folds and flaps of skin extend from the sea-slug's body, giving it the appearance of the seaweed in which it lives.

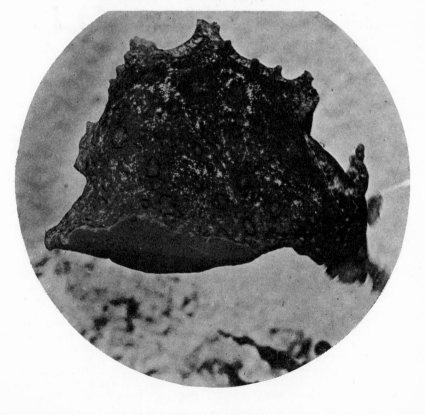

exodus: "Bravely the fronds float along, day by day the hundred little lives breathe and feed and cling to the drifting home. But soon the gas berries decay and the fronds sink lower and lower as the current flows northward and the water becomes colder. Crabs move less rapidly, the fish nibble less eagerly at the bits of passing food. Soon a seahorse lets go and falls slowly downward to be snapped up at once or to sink steadily into the eternal dusk and black night of deeper fathoms. Soon the plant follows and like its chilled pensioners dies."

Fins of most fishes have many rays which stiffen them; when the fins move, they move as wholes, like open fans or paddles with perhaps a rhythmic ripple toward their tips. Pterophryne is one of the few true fishes that can close its flexible fins over objects, and this maneuver indicates a high rating in the scale of fish evolution.

Finger-like fins

Wilfred S. Bronson, the artist and author, who has studied the anatomy of Pterophryne, describes its fins, not in a text-book, but in a delightful children's book, "Fingerfins": "These marvelous fingers did not work the way our fingers do. In each of ours there is a cord which pulls to make it bend. We can bend each finger by itself. But the fingers of this little fish had to bend all at once because he had only one cord in each hand. It passed through the bottom of each ray or finger and when it pulled, they all closed together just the way a bag shuts up when you pull the cord at its neck."

Beebe has seen the Sargassumfish assume a score of unfishlike poses in as many minutes, swinging from frond to frond, hanging upside down, and generally giving a piscine imitation of a monkey in a jungle. But even a monkey has only five locomotor appendages. Pterophryne uses its two "arm" fins and two "foot" fins to hang on to its sea-jungle weeds; and when necessary, the top, bottom, and tail fins serve as props to keep it securely anchored to its ever-changing wind- and wave-swept weedy hammock.

In getting about in the water, Pterophryne frequently moves by a series of thrusts caused by the rhythmic jets of water being ejected from small round gill openings, one under each "arm." Its fins move gently in guiding its swimming movements which are relatively slow. It therefore relies largely on being able to approach its prey without detection. Strange, but true, fish-story teller E. W. Gudger saw a Pterophryne in stalking its living prey of alert fishes and quick shrimps, "with closed mouth draw near, and, opening its mouth suddenly, take in its prey with an instantaneous gulp."

A Pterophryne gulp is no ordinary gulp. When this fish opens its mouth to catch its victims, its jaws open so suddenly, so widely and powerfully, that a forceful current is created; the unfortunate prey is sucked down a capacious throat. Sometimes it uses the quick gulping technique for self-defense. If it is attacked by a larger fish, Pterophryne throws open its jaws, swallows water as it is on the point of being devoured, and instantly pumps itself up to an unexpected size. Thus the swallower is forced to cough up the swallowee.

Reluctant but fierce fighters

In its native haunts, Pterophryne is a strict individualist. It avoids intimate association with its fellows and will not tolerate their approach. If two Sargassumfish meet, they keep a respectable distance between them like two ships that meet at sea. But if two Pterophrynes are placed in an aquarium, a fight is sure to start. If they are of the same size, the battle goes on for days. The fish follow no wrestling code; no holds barred. As they bite and tear each other, their fleshy head and body ornaments are ripped to shreds. Their hand-like and foot-like fins become frayed and their delicate fin-rays protrude like broken bones. With their body adornments stripped from them, they look like fish on their way to an aquatic nudist colony.

If a small Pterophryne is placed with a larger brother, the larger takes the smaller, not to its bosom, but into its stomach. Even the special trick of quickly swallowing water is of no avail in family quarrels. On one occasion, Hugh Smith saw a six-inch Pterophryne stealthily approach his four-inch relative, and then pounce on it, swallowing it at one gulp. If you stand sixty inches tall, can you imagine the task of swallowing your forty-inch baby brother, bones and all?

I wondered whether there was room for the newcomer in the larger fish's stomach. Smith assures us that the bigger fish "did not seem particularly incommoded thereby."

Beebe has a story of Pterophryne cannibalism on the Sargasso Sea. On his ocean laboratory, the *Arcturus*, he kept his Sargassumfish in a jar: "There had been three, sized like the three bears, but after half an hour we found that an inverted magician's trick had been performed—to my astonishment, where there were three, was now but one—a Pterophryne, very fat and gulping uneasily. The awful truth dawned upon us, but we never settled whether it was a case of Japanese boxes, each within the other, or whether the big cannibal had in turn engulfed his spiny and much tentacled brethren."

Family life unknown

The thought of Pterophryne's ferocious pugnacity toward its kin fish-folk is disturbing. We know that they must establish some kind of family life, for their young populate the Sargasso Sea. What psychological change takes place within their brains that calls a truce on belligerency for the period of their mating season? Is a parental instinct hormone released from their diminutive glands to calm their cannibalistic natures?

We do not know too much about Pterophryne's personal habits of life. Some of the Sargassumfish kept in aquaria by Smith at Woods Hole and by Gudger at Beaufort spawned. A ripe female Sargassumfish, only three to four inches, liberates a gelatinous string in which thousands of eggs are imbedded. The egg mass absorbs water and swells ten times in volume and becomes jelly-like, quivering when touched. This is similar to the egg-laying habits of its close relative, the anglerfish (*Lophius*), which lays an egg mass called a "purple veil" that becomes 40 feet in length, although the fish itself is only about four feet.

Strangely enough, no one had with certainty ever seen a male Pterophryne until 1954, when Carol Mosher discovered a male of the species, placed a pair together, and watched them mate and spawn.

So the legendary Sargasso Sea, scene of many fantastic and romantic tales, is still yielding secrets to scientists.

▼ YELLOW-JACK *(Caranx)*, a frequent traveler in the Sargasso merry-go-round. When young, it hides in the weeds. When older, it sometimes associates itself with the Portuguese man-of-war, finding protection from enemies in the long, stinging tentacles.

Sawfish

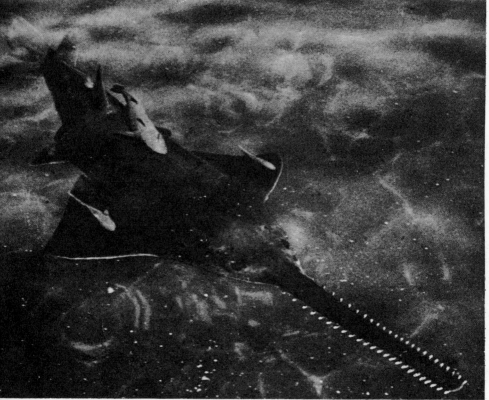

Photo by Hugo H. Schroder

Richard Harrington photo

This fifteen-foot sawfish had five remoras, or shark suckers, attached to its upper side. These marine hitchhikers usually attach themselves to the under side of a fish, but since the big sawfish frequently rested on the bottom of the oceanarium, they attached themselves inverted.

◄ THE SIZE of the armored snout of the sawfish is impressively shown here. The specimen is being displayed by an Australian boy of Arnhem Land, where it was caught.

Saw-whet Owl

Smallest among the owls of north-eastern United States, the Saw-whet reaches a length of only about eight inches. Because of its smallness and its nocturnal habits, it is not often seen, though fairly abundant and absurdly tame. It is possible by approaching cautiously, to catch full-grown adults in the hand. Bird banders sometimes use this technique, thus avoiding the use of a trap. Capture is facilitated if their notes are imitated and if a second person distracts them. Saw-whets nest in old woodpeckers' holes, laying five or six white eggs. Their range is from southeastern Alaska and across southern Canada, south to Maryland, and Indiana. They winter somewhat farther south and are also found in Arizona and southward to Guatemala.

Austing-Koehler photo

The Truth about Scorpions

By WILLIAM H. CARR

Photographs by MARVIN H. FROST *unless otherwise credited*

Intimate facts about creatures that have
been shunned since Biblical times

IT is true that a scorpion has no backbone, but if you should have the misfortune to step on one while wandering about without your shoes, you would be willing to believe that an animal does not need a vertebral column in order to fight back. A friend of mine who operates a large cattle ranch in the foothills of the Santa Catalina

a ENCOUNTER between a Giant Hairy Scorpion and a tarantula. The scorpion arches its back and brings its stinging apparatus into readiness as the tarantula approaches

Mountains near Tucson, Arizona, had just such an experience one night last summer. While crossing his living room floor, barefooted, he suddenly felt a sharp pain in his foot. Quickly switching on the lights, he discovered that a scorpion some two inches in length had, as he put it, "nailed him." The creature lay dead upon the floor, but it had succeeded in repaying its slayer before pressure of the man's foot had taken its life.

To the rancher's surprise there was no mark to show where he had been stung, and no swelling came at the point of contact. He went to bed but found it impossible to sleep. He arose a number of times during the night and was alarmed to learn that the poison had affected his optic nerves so that it was difficult to see any object distinctly. He also experienced distressing pains in the region of the chest. From the symptoms, it was certain that he had been stung by one of the two most harmful kinds of scorpions known in America. Regardless of a restless and uncomfortable night, he somehow managed to carry on his strenuous work

b BOTH have moved to a new area, and the tarantula is again drawing near. The scorpion holds firm with its rear legs and raises its weapon. It has struck the spider once

the next day, riding far out on the range and actually roping several calves.

In three days he felt nearly normal, and the scorpion sting, though still a bit annoying, did not cause him any further marked trouble. "It's a strange thing," he said, "but nobody seems to know very much about scorpions. Once in a while someone gets stung or sees one and kills it, but still we don't know about 'em. There are different kinds, too, and I guess they live in a good many states."

Some persons who have had encounters with the dangerous species of scorpions have not been as fortunate as the rancher. More than 40 deaths have been authentically recorded in Arizona in a recent 10-year period. In all these instances children have been the victims. Many adults have been hospitalized. Regardless of this, scorpions have never been known to go out of their way to injure a human. They journey about at night in search of food, mostly spiders and insects. The scorpion seizes its prey with its lobster-like pincers and either subdues it through the "squeeze" system or poisons it by means of the needle-sharp stinger or spine at the very tip of its body.

The business end of scorpions may be operated either in self-protection or in offensive action, with lightning-like rapidity or slowly and deliberately as the occasion demands. The curved spine projecting from a bulbous base, is brought up over the scorpion's back to strike, unerringly, any insect or other prey

C THE TARANTULA now closes in. It has been struck several times by the scorpion, apparently with no ill effect. Note the piece of spider "hair" remaining on the stinger

held firmly in the pincers. It is not correct to say that the puncturing device is located on the end of the "tail," because the alimentary canal continues right to the base of the poison-injecting apparatus. In effect, scorpions have no tails. The venom is developed in two glands just below the stinger. Thanks to the fact that the long, thin, stinger-tipped section of the body is jointed in more or less ball-and-socket fashion, the scorpion is able to turn its weapon in practically any direction and thus strike within a wide radius.

Scorpions are not insects. Among other differences they possess eight legs while true insects have only six. They are close relatives of the spiders, belonging to the same scientific "class." They breathe by means of small, whitish lung sacs, which you can see if you care to examine the under surface of the scorpion. Incidentally, when one of these creatures is turned upon its back it rights itself within a split second.

The ferocity of scorpions has been very much exaggerated, as has been that of most animals possessing poison in any degree. The creature's principal effort, whenever approached, is to run off and hide as speedily as possible, waving its efficient pincers in an effort to ascertain the nature of its aggressor. In fact, it sometimes fails to use its poison attachment even when cornered. It is wise to shake off a scorpion that may accidentally fall or otherwise land upon one's person. If one's hand is brought down

d THE TARANTULA tried to bite the scorpion but caused no damage. Neither creature showed signs of injury after the encounter, and both were alive more than three months later

upon it or if it is too rudely brushed aside, it is very apt to retaliate, with unfortunate results.

I once observed a scorpion that had grasped the leg of an exploring tarantula. When the large spider endeavored to pull away, the smaller creature released its grip, not once employing its stinger during the encounter. Scorpions possess from 2 to 12 eyes, yet their sight is so poor that about all they are able to distinguish is the difference between light and dark. The pincers are used as "feelers." Scorpions traveling about, undisturbed, remind one of a blind person groping in the dark with arms outstretched to avoid and identify objects in the path.

In order to sense the nature of its surroundings and objects over which it may pass, the scorpion also uses small, comb-edged projections, located upon the lower surface of its body. This auxiliary tactile equipment is kept in constant motion as the creature progresses over the ground.

Scorpions exist the world around in warmer climates. More than 600 species are known. In our own country they are found particularly in the southern states from coast to coast. Various kinds are found in 30 of our states, ranging in size from less than an inch to some eight inches in length. In general, the northern limit of scorpions in the United States roughly follows the southernmost advance of the ice sheet during the last glacial period. None have thus far been reported from New England.

Of the more than 40 known species of scorpions in the United States only two are of any serious danger to mankind. These two varieties have caused numerous fatalities among children, since the early days when the first pioneers entered the regions of cactus and thorn, for the particularly venomous species live in Arizona, California, and possibly Texas. They are known, scientifically (and jaw-breakingly) as *Centruroides sculpturatus* and *Centruroides gertschi*. No acceptable popular name has been adopted for these dangerous scorpions. As one scientist remarked, "They just never will be popular anyway!"

Both varieties are rather innocent in appearance, in striking contrast to some of the larger, more startling-looking types. They are slender and grow to a length of about two inches. The one known as *gertschi* possesses black stripes running down its straw-colored or yellowish back, while *sculpturatus* lacks this patterned decoration. Both scorpions may be darker in ground color depending upon age or other natural causes of discoloration. Their identification is not easy for the layman.

Unfortunately they live in close proximity to man, hiding in the daytime beneath boards, stones, bricks, rags, or rubbish, especially where a bit of dampness exists. The creatures have been known to seek the protection of sheets and blankets upon beds, a highly unwelcome trait. It is well to remember that scorpions that burrow in the sand are not of the lethal kind.

Dr. Herbert L. Stahnke, a specialist in poisonous animal research in the State College at Tempe, Ari-

➤ ONE of the two worst
kinds of scorpions found in
the United States: *Centruroides sculpturatus,* Ewing.
This scorpion is about two
inches long

▼ THE OTHER of our two most dangerous scorpions,
male and female: *Centruroides gertschi.* The 40 or
more other scorpions are considerably less poisonous

Photo by Herbert L. Stahnke

zona, has devoted many years to the study of scorpions, with the aim of learning their behavior and discovering means of combatting their poison. He points out that the sting of the two dangerous species of scorpions may cause death in from 45 minutes to eleven hours, and the suffering meanwhile is considerable. The venom of *sculpturatus* and *gertschi* produces a reaction upon the nerves, an effect that is general in character. The stings of the more innocuous types, on the contrary, result in local inflammation and swelling, somewhat like a wasp or bee sting. With this fact in mind it is well to recall that the more harmful injection of poison does not result in swelling or discoloration in the area first affected.

Recoveries among children are numerous, and fatalities among adults are extremely rare. Dr. Stahnke advocates an ice water treatment for the limbs, or crushed ice packing for body stings, the idea being to localize the venom as much as possible. It is also advised that a tourniquet or stricture be applied immediately to prevent circulation for a brief time and isolate the venom. The tourniquet should be released within five minutes and not replaced. Under no condition should hot packs be used. Patients who have had the latter treatment have survived in spite of it—not because of it. Heat causes the poison to spread rapidly, whereas cold delays it. Children should have medical aid at once, the ice or ice water treatments being continued meanwhile, despite any inconvenience or discomfort caused

by the cold.

The Mexican Department of Public Health developed a serum to offset the harm caused by the venom of scorpions. Dr. Stahnke secured a small amount of this life-saving liquid in 1935 and found it quite effective. However, he learned that there were too many legal difficulties surrounding the transportation of the serum across the Mexican border. Furthermore, it could not be secured in any appreciable quantity. Consequently, he commenced research of his own to produce an American serum to combat the damage to nerve tissues caused by scorpion venom.

In an effort to become better acquainted with scorpions I have kept some five different species in roomy glass cases in my home. Their marvelous adaptation to their peculiar mode of existence is certainly noteworthy. One large individual proved especially tractable and repeatedly demonstrated his ability to act in public. He was about four inches in length and belonged to the less harmful group of scorpions. When touched with a wire or otherwise molested, he would seldom strike with his poison barb. Instead, he would try to side-step the object, crablike, or else back away. While walking about he constantly waved his pincers and kept his stinger raised, arched and ready, with his body well off the ground. At times, when attempting to avoid the offending wire, he would behave like a sedate performer of the stately minuet.

His ability to dig was amusing as well as interesting. If a dog had eight legs, it would dig as this scorpion did. Using its pincers as a support in front and its hindmost pair of legs as a rear anchor, the creature would work in spurts, very rapidly, employing its forward legs, scooping up the sand at a great rate, and throwing it at least ten inches out between its hind

▼ NEWBORN SCORPIONS clinging to the mother's back. Popular superstition has it that young scorpions feed upon the tissues of the mother, but this is not so. The sting of this scorpion, *Vejovis spinigerus* Wood, is said to be no more dangerous than that of a wasp

Photo by Herbert L. Stahnke

▼ NOT a cactus plant but the jointed hind portion of a Giant Hairy Scorpion, showing the stinger projecting from its bulbous base

legs. Finally a small mound of sand would accumulate, whereupon the scorpion would back up and literally kick the pile out of the way so it would not impede further digging operations. Speed and energy were the watchword as the nocturnal animal struggled to bury itself. Occasionally it would stop to clean its pincers, using its front legs in the process. Our scorpion was as smooth and glistening as could be—truly well-groomed. No doubt frequent burrowing in the sand would favor the creature's shining appearance. In addition, scorpions are known to use secretions from their mouths to aid in keeping their bodies clean.

Whenever the scorpion did bring its weapon into play, it would strike with such rapidity that one's eye could not follow the movement. The hind end would dart forward, bringing the barb into contact with the wire or stick, so swiftly that the action seemed over before it had started. After the creature had had an exciting bout with the long-

▼ HEAD-ON VIEW, showing the mouth parts of the Giant Hairy Scorpion, located between the two pincers

▲ A TYPICAL EXPLORATORY POSE: the Giant Hairy Scorpion, *Hadrurus arizonensis* Ewing, approaching the top of a rock, with pincers reaching forward. Scorpions have poor eyesight

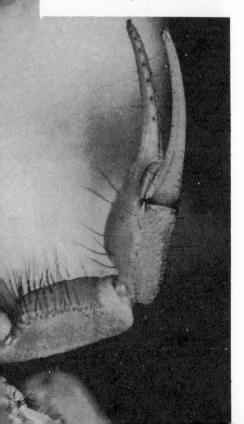

stemmed tweezers that were used for handling it, it would relax and rest. At this time the stinger would be permitted to droop over to one side as the scorpion settled down upon the floor of the cage.

The life history of scorpions is imperfectly known, but much has been learned about their way of reproduction. Eggs are developed within the mother's body and hatch very quickly after they have been deposited. The female hovers over them meanwhile, maintaining actual contact until the thin membranes open, sometimes a matter of seconds, and the young climb upon her.

Contrary to popular belief, young scorpions do not feed upon their mother's body. They are endowed with a "yolklike" substance that supplies nourishment until they are able to fend for themselves. The strong plates upon the mother's back are much too resistant to be pierced by the relatively delicate mouth parts of her young. Bob Ripley, in his "Believe It or Not" column, once declared that the female scorpion was "the finest example of maternal sacrifice. She feeds her young with her own body." This, however, is not the case. No, the mother carries on quite well after the offspring have departed, unless overtaken by some misfortune. The infants cast off their first skin or outer covering while they are still upon the mother's back, and this causes her to appear quite disheveled in the region where the young are, or have been, ensconced. No doubt this has caused some observers to believe that harm has come to her through the activities of her young. When departure takes place the little scorpions wander off by themselves and are fully able to become self-supporting.

Another fable has it that scorpions, when hard pressed, will sometimes commit hara-kiri by stinging themselves. There is one main fallacy in this conclusion, and that is that the creature's poison has not been observed to have any fatal effect upon it. It is quite possible that, when engaged in active combat or otherwise excited and striking viciously, the scorpion may accidentally receive a jab from its own barb.

My interest in the animal with the poison sting ultimately led me to visit Dr. Stahnke, who, in connection with his work as a leading authority on scorpions, is host to some 500 of his subjects. Many kinds of scorpions in bottles, jars, open-topped glass boxes, and test tubes are to be seen on the shelves and tables in the specialist's laboratory. The more harmful varieties are "milked" of their poison to provide a "venom bank," used in the production of serum. Dr. Stahnke has the distinction of having been the first to name twelve species of scorpions, and he is classifying sev-

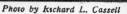

Photo by Richard L. Cassell

▲ A HIGHLY ENLARGED photograph of
the mouth of the Giant Hairy Scorpion

eral other unnamed kinds at present.

Despite the fact that scorpions have been despised and wholeheartedly shunned, they nevertheless have the singular distinction of having been selected to designate one of the great constellations of stars and to represent one of the signs of the zodiac, the symbol for the month of October. There are several references to scorpions in the Bible. They were named as one of the terrors of the wilderness of Sinai, where they still exist. More than ten species are known in Palestine. They were also believed to be a symbol of desolation and were depicted as divine scourges. Indeed, they sometimes were a tribulation in certain areas, yet it is amazing how few persons have taken the trouble to observe their ways.

A man with whom I come in almost daily contact has lived in a section of Arizona where scorpions are especially prevalent. His child had actually been stung twice by the most objectionable type of scorpion and had nearly succumbed, yet his knowledge of the animal was surprisingly scanty, and the information he did possess was a combination of folklore and faulty observation. He had believed that scorpions stung with their pincers and also that they deliberately sought out humans to sting. Dr. Stahnke has labored long and hard to inform persons about scorpions but is quick to say that a great deal remains to be done to provide the public with essential natural history information. It is almost as important to quell unnecessary fear as to engender a healthy respect for the creatures. It seems a pity that people's enjoyment of the out-of-doors is impaired

⋏ IF THE HIND PART of this Giant Hairy Scorpion were straightened out, the creature would measure about four inches in length. Some scorpions in the United States are approximately eight inches long, others less than an inch

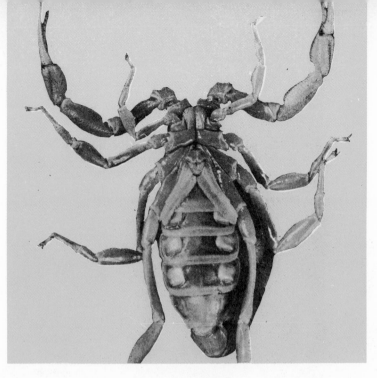

↑ Small, comblike projections on the undersurface of the scorpion help it to sense the nature of the ground over which it is passing and are kept constantly in motion. Just behind these, the two rows of whitish lung sacs can be seen

through needless worry about the imagined dangers of animals large and small. Only through intelligent efforts can thousands who are uneasy in the open learn to be at home in the woods and deserts and gain an uninhibited appreciation of some of America's outstanding scenic marvels.

It should be a comfort to many that in the vast majority of our states scorpions are not of the virulent kind. By the same token, people who live in the restricted areas where *sculpturatus* and *gertschi* occur are grateful for knowledge of protection against, and treatment of, scorpion stings. Dr. Stahnke has learned, incidentally, that the newly-discovered chemical repellent "DDT" can be used very successfully in ridding dwellings of scorpions. He cautions against turning over boards and stones in infested regions and states that no one, "who uses his head" and observes a modicum of caution where caution is advisable, need fear scorpions during an outing anywhere in America. However, he does believe that being forewarned is a good preventive particularly where dangerous varieties of scorpions exist, for, as the Bible tells us, in Revelations 9:3, "the scorpions of the earth have power."

▼ A BEACH LIKE this, where the depth of the sand may
shift as much as six feet during the year, provides an ideal
home for the sea anemone *Anthopleura elegantissima*

THE BIG

STRETCH

By

WOODY WILLIAMS

Photographs by the author

When this hardy inhabitant of the tidal rocks wants to multiply, it simply divides

ONE of the first creatures to set up housekeeping on rocks newly exposed by the shifting sands of the beach is the anemone known as *Anthopleura elegantissima*. It is perhaps the commonest anemone along the coast of northern California.

This hardy invertebrate thrives where the surge swirls the sand off

↑ THE ANEMONES give the rocks the appearance of giant brain corals. Not many creatures can survive such extremes of moisture as this sea anemone. The changing tides daily subject it to immersion by the sea and the drying effect of wind and sun

the bottom. The rocks rapidly become mantled with the squushy anemones, whose convolutions, when the creatures are contracted at low tide, suggest the patterns of giant brain corals. Sometimes the masses are camouflaged by pieces of rock and shell held to the anemones by tiny suction cups. Sometimes an investigator drops wearily upon one of these rocklike surfaces only to find in a very short time he has made a wet and cold mistake.

Underfoot the polyps huddle together, secure in their great numbers against destruction by rain, fog, sun, and wind, to which they are periodically subjected during the daily low tides. The rapid growth of these communities is perhaps explained by the ability of *Anthopleura* literally to tear itself in two.

The "big stretch" begins when an anemone changes from a circular pattern to an elliptical one. The central mouth stretches so that a section of it and part of the internal anatomy are contained in each end. The parent end holds fast while the opposite section slowly creeps off on its sticky base. The

> A SEA ANEMONE beginning to divide by stretching into an oval disc. This photograph shows the adhesive foot of *Anthopleura elegantissima* clinging to the aquarium glass, while the upper end pulls away

V THE ANEMONE continues to stretch apart until the tissue connecting the two halves suggests a piece of rope. One strand breaks at a time

▲ ONLY A NARROW cord holds the two sections together. A slight jar will break this tissue. The ends will then jerk back and there will be two anemones in place of one

connecting link stretches until it resembles an unbraided rope, whose strands part one by one. After perhaps a week or more, only a single thread of tissue remains to connect the two sections. A slight jar separates the offspring, and a new anemone is released into a turbulent world along the edge of the sea. The parent and offspring may slowly move away from each other.

Gradually they repair the ruptured edges of their discs, until two complete anemones are formed, each with a radiating crown of tentacles.

As these tentacles are armed with stinging capsules, the anemone has few enemies, except a large sea slug of a type called "eolid," which makes anemones its exclusive dish. In some cases, the sea slugs have been known to ingest the stinging

◄ Now ON ITS OWN, the offspring is attacked by an eolid, a sea slug that dines only on anemone colonies

▼ THE ATTACK of the eolid leaves the anemone in poor condition. Larger anemones, however, often recover and may indeed survive a number of attacks by sea slugs. The slug consumes the internal structure of the anemone, but the anemone can rebuild the organs consumed by the slug

capsules and to incorporate them
into their own body as a useful defensive mechanism. The stinging
capsules are lodged in the tips of
the plumes on the sea slug's back.
These plumes are hollow tubes with
respiratory and digestive functions.

The slug eats out the internal
structure of the anemone and
leaves it a crumpled sack. But the
anemone has a remarkable ability
to restore order from a torn mass
of tissue, and it can quickly rebuild
organs consumed by the slug.
Larger anemones can survive several attacks by the sea slug. The
sea slug, for its part, has chosen a
dinner plate which, like something
out of mythology, is never empty.

Anthopleura also offers a home
for certain one-celled algal plants,
which thrive within the tissue and
give the anemone its green color.
Sometimes these anemones live in
caves and under wharves. In such
locations, there may not be enough
light to support the photosynthetic
activity of the algae. Then the anemones revert to their natural color
of white with pink-tipped tentacles.

These elegant and delicate-look-
ing anemones are some of the
toughest marine creatures on the
West Coast. Where the waves
pound, they live on rocks in the
upper tidal zone exposed to drying; and in the estuaries, they inhabit silt-laden water often polluted
with sewage. In the bays, we do not
see the dense aggregations found
on the outer coast. Instead we find
individuals with their stalks elongated deep into the mud, where
the bases adhere to buried rocks or
ancient pilings.

▲ THE PARENT ANEMONE slowly repair
the ruptured section of the disc until
regains a symmetrical crown of tentacle

➤ AN AGGREGATION of anemones differe
from the kind shown in the precedin
photograph but related, probably *Anth*
pleura artemisia

The Curious Life Habit

For centuries naturalists mistook the male sea horse for the female because of a strange reversal in the reproductive functions.

By RENÉ THÉVENIN

ALL THE ILLUSTRATIONS IN THIS SERIES ARE FROM THE FILM BY JEAN PAINLEVÉ

I T IS easy to understand how a type of fishes so singular in appearance as the *Hippocampi* or sea horses should formerly have been thought of as a group far apart from all others.

The French scientist, Georges Cuvier, created for them (and for their cousins the *Syngnathi* or sea needles) the order of Lophobranchiata. As the name implies, the distinction depended upon the structure of the gills, which in the sea horse grow in the form of tufts instead of in comblike formation as in most other fishes.

Unusual characters

Today it is known that this characteristic of the respiratory system is also found in other fishes in various stages of development. Likewise, the armor of the sea horse which protects its body and which replaces the scales is not absolutely unique. But in spite of these later discoveries which minimized somewhat their strangeness, the *Hippocampi* still deserve special interest because of their unusual appearance and also on account of their life habits. I have the good fortune to illustrate this article with photographs taken from the extraordinary film of my compatriot, Jean Painlevé, which traces in a most expressive manner the principal events in the life of the sea horse.

Sea horses are primarily inhabitants of the warmer seas, though a few representatives may be found in comparatively cold waters. In Europe, where we studied them especially, they occur as far north as in the Channel. But they begin to be rare in these latitudes, while they are very common in the Mediterranean Sea.

of the Sea Horse

THE SEA HORSE does not swim about much but spends considerable time motionless, attached to some marine plant by his prehensile tail. His pectoral fins help him to stay in a vertical position, a most unusual attitude for a fish.

The most abundant varieties do not grow larger than about two inches, but the tropical forms sometimes attain much greater size. In the Australian Seas and also near Japan large specimens occur. The largest are possibly two feet in length.

Like the "knight" in chess

Their appearance also varies, but in general they justify fully the popular name "sea horse." The head of these fishes closely resembles that of a horse, or, even more exactly, the "knight" in the game of chess. Their skin shows no scales but instead a "skin-skeleton," similar to that of the insects. The plates which form this skin-skeleton are connected with each other in rings that give the body of the animal the shape of an irregular polyhedron. One can count fifty-odd such rings from the neck to the lower end of the body. The shields which ride on the back of the fish like the tiles of a roof produce a crest on the head, the neck, and the back. In certain varieties, especially those of the warm seas, these appendages are elongated, overgrown and branched in the most extraordinary fashion, and seemingly for camouflage resemble the marine plants among which the creatures live.

One of the peculiarities of this family is that unlike all other fishes its members swim in a vertical position. And the tail is not used for propelling the animal at all, but only for gripping a more or less solid support around which it curves itself like a spiral. This support is usually a plant of some sort, but any other object might serve the same purpose. It is easy indeed to have a sea horse clinging to one's finger in an aquarium. To bring this about, it is only necessary to touch its caudal extremity gently. One notices in this instant how much gripping power the little tail of the fish has; it could be compared to that of a small child's hand. The sea horse is the only fish aside from the closely related Nerophis that has a prehensile tail. Nerophis, of which at least two species are known in Europe only, belongs to the same family as the sea horse.

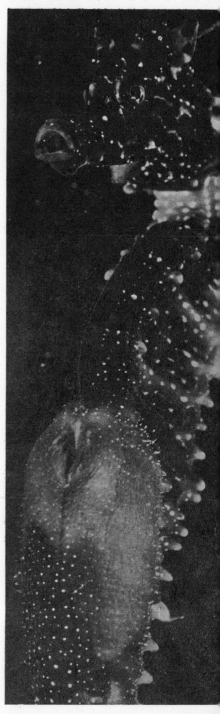

MALE SEA HORSES. In this photo graph, the observer can see the inc

A vertical posture

The tail is restricted to this use and does not serve as a fin. The anal fin is also reduced to the simplest form and apparently no longer has any function. The fins that are normally found in pairs on the bodies of fishes are represented only by those farthest forward, namely, the pectoral fins, which are placed just behind the gills. They are used to maintain the vertical position and the equilibrium of the body in the water. The only really active fin is the dorsal fin, which oscillates in a rapid, rhythmic manner, reminding one almost of a propeller.

The sea horse does not swim much. Hooked to a bunch of seaweed, it remains motionless in its vertical position; if it does not discard its support it has no exercise at all.

The structure of the head is extraordinary, too. It ends with an elongated snout which opens and closes with a rapid movement. One can distinctly hear the faint smacking sound it makes when it snaps at its prey.

All these characteristics may easily be observed in an aquarium, where sea horses can be kept alive without any difficulty. This at least applies to our native (French) varieties, especially *Hippocampus antiquorum* which is the variety discussed here.

This animal certainly accustoms itself easily to changes in temperature, as well as to changes in the salt content of the water—even to a change of diet. Its food consists, in captivity, of little shrimps, worms, and even small pieces of meat, which the sea horse catches by a very quick movement of its head the instant they come near its mouth. It is in this moment that one can hear—when listening carefully— the sound produced by the opening of the mouth. The prey is swallowed quickly without being chewed.

In the act of catching its prey the animal is greatly aided by the mobility of its eyes. They are placed on the sides of the head, and are independent of each other. Their way

ation pouch into which the female
ill deposit her eggs.

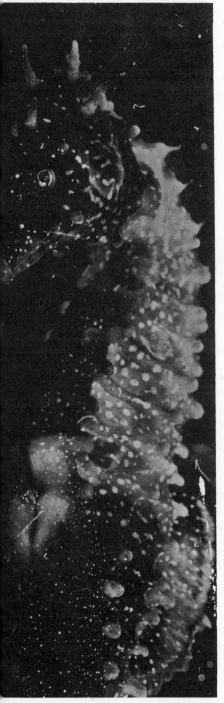

of working reminds one of the eyes of the chameleon. The eyes of the sea horse appear to sense very slight changes of form and illumination.

Light apparently has also an important influence on the general coloration of the body. The color varies not only with the species, but also with the surroundings in which the specimens are found. The commonest color is a dark gray, almost black. But reddish, greenish, and silverish colors are also found; quite often the body shows very brilliant spots. Male specimens sometimes show the dorsal fin rimmed with yellow; the coloration of the females is less pronounced.

When these dark colors turn to a greenish-yellow or even to white, it is a sign of bad health, and the animal usually dies very soon afterward. At the same time the sea horse abandons its vertical position and begins to swim on its side. Sometimes bleedings occur, accompanied by losses of skin which may lead to the loss of parts of the tail. Most frequently all these signs of bad health do not show before it is too late to interfere.

Ascending and descending

When the sea horse descends, it curves its neck and rolls its tail in; when it wants to float upward, it straightens itself out almost completely. It can also creep on the bottom by little movements of body and tail.

The breathing is done, as has already been stated, by means of pufflike gills. In the moment when the water is inhaled the tongue bones or hyoid bones are erected and poke out the skin from the inside, producing the semblance of little horns.

The rigidity of the skin-skeleton makes it exceedingly easy to preserve the bodies of the dead sea horses. The mummified little forms are picked up on the shores of the Mediterranean by the children—especially in Naples—and constitute the stock of a minor trade, or, more exactly, an excuse for begging.

Reproduction

But the most interesting thing to observe in sea horses is their manner of reproduction and their way of caring for the young.

In the adult state the female carries about two hundred eggs. When the time has come for mating, the male and female approach each other and begin to make movements which may be compared to a dance.

The male is equipped with a ventral pocket or pouch which extends from the twelfth to the eighteenth ring and has its place underneath the pelvic bone. To be exact, there are two pockets in the skin, right and left, which join in the middle in the adult, leaving only a small slotlike opening.

The female inserts her cloacal appendix into this slot and projects in that way her eggs into the male pouch; while passing the slot they become fecundated. This brings to a conclusion the duties of the mother, and thenceforth the father performs the rôle of a mother—a unique reversal of the usual habits.

When the pouch of the male sea horse is not occupied, it is lined with conjunctive tissue, which is only slightly wrinkled. But from the moment that the eggs are deposited a considerable change takes place. The tissue begins to swell and to grow, it becomes spongelike and the capillary blood vessels enlarge and multiply. In short, _lacentation is occurring. Interesting speculation surrounds the question as to how the male may have developed this complex function.

Soon after the eggs have entered the pouch each one produces a localized excitation; little holes form, the whole tissue takes on the appearance of a quadrangular network, and each compartment engulfs one egg. In addition, a wall begins to grow from the bottom of the pouch and approaches the seam of the outer skin of the pouch so that it is divided into two parts. Thus two additional surfaces are created which give the remainder of the eggs a chance to secure a place on the pseudo-placental tissue. Those that do not succeed in finding a place where they can develop, degenerate.

The successful eggs start to develop at once, and as they grow they embrace more and more tissue.

The shell, or rather the skin of each egg splits open inside the pocket, but the embryo is

FEMALE SEA HORSE. Here we see the peculiar shape of the head, the spiral of the prehensile tail, the

covering of the body, and the cloacal appendix with which the female puts her eggs into the male pouch.

not yet expelled. It rests in the pseudo-placental tissue and remains in this position usually until its yolk is used up almost entirely. During this time it has the curved position of many embryos and does not straighten itself out until it is finally projected into the water.

Sometimes it happens, however, that a few embryos are expelled which are still in possession of a fairly large yolk sac. It is to be noted that these are handicapped in the struggle for existence. The young ones best equipped to meet the dangers of life are those that have freed themselves completely from the natural reserves of the embryonic stage. These also swim in the vertical position at once, the position customary for the sea horses. They even show the adult tilt of the head at once.

Further proof that the connection between the young ones and the father is a very close one can be observed in the fact that the male suffers considerable difficulty in the act of expulsion. He can be seen writhing on the soil, rubbing his body, and struggling energetically. At the same time his eyes are wide open and move convulsively in the rhythm of breathing. Finally, with considerable force the male ejects its burden of young sea horses, the residue of the eggs, pieces of tissue, and many bubbles of gas.

The pouch does not empty all at once. There are several expulsions which may extend over a number of days in the form of consecutive spasms. Even when the pouch is finally empty, the contractions continue for a time, slowly becoming less violent. Finally the pouch is deflated, its slot, wide open during the expulsion, closes again. The tissue in the pouch returns to normal, the network of blood vessels becomes more ample.

Possible accidents

A few accidents may happen during this period. The pouch may close over a comparatively large amount of gases not ejected together with the embryos. These gases, of course, disturb the buoyancy of the animal. In the aquarium it is easy to catch the specimen and to insert a narrow tube or cannula into the pouch and allow the gas to escape, pressing gently against the sides of the body to expel it.

After the young sea horses can no longer draw from their father or their reserves of yolk they have to seek their nourishment independently by the normal means. Their appearance at this time still varies even with specimens of the same variety, according to the conditions of their birth. Those that are "born" prematurely still carry the burden of their vitelline sac, swimming awkwardly in a horizontal position. In spite of the yolk sac which tends to drag them down to the bottom, they swim near the surface, probably because their still highly developed swim-bladder keeps them afloat.

Physical characters of the young

Their eyes are still very large and remind the observer of the eyes of the embryos still in the egg. On the other hand, the snout is very short and so to speak flattened out over the face. The face looks vaguely like that of a Pekinese dog. The body is still more or less transparent and one can see the tiny heart beating. But soon the first spots of pigmentation begin to appear here and there, in a strange pattern. Slowly the distribution of these spots becomes more regular, and they begin to look like stars. The blots unite and cover the whole surface of the body, which becomes opaque and takes on the coloration of the adult.

Though normally it should occur at the time of birth, sometimes the snout does not protrude until an advance date. But finally the head assumes the adult position at right angles to the body and the animal begins to swim in the vertical position. At the same time the little animal descends deeper into the water and begins to look for a water plant as a support. Quite often, the young ones, misled by limited experience, try to attach them-

UNITED. In the European climate the couples begin to unite in the spring. The female carries approximately 200 eggs. She deposits them into the male pouch during a period

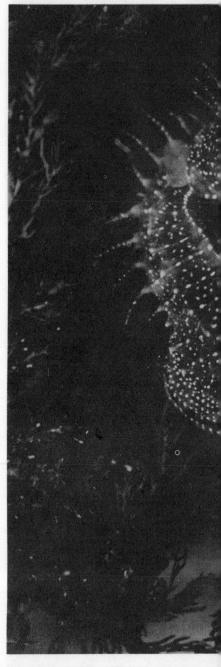

f from 24 to 48 hours. Thenceforth
ie father takes on the duties of the
iother. It is his task to bring forth
ie young.

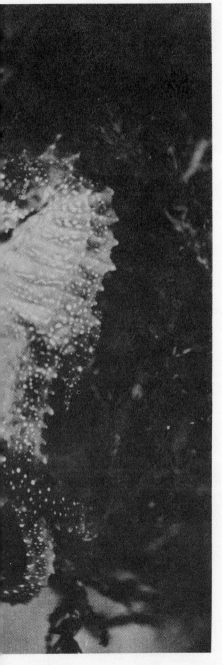

selves to non-solid objects such as air bubbles
that come from the plants or float on the surface of the water.

The sexual characters do not appear before
several months have elapsed. It is not before
that time that the forming of the male pouch
and the female appendix can be observed.
Generally speaking, the animal is not ripe for
reproduction before the following year. In
our European climate the couples begin to
unite in spring, and the events we have described take place sometime in the summer,
according to circumstances. The expulsion of
the young ones takes place forty to fifty days
after fecundation.

These are the curious life habits of the sea
horse—life habits which have been known to
naturalists for hardly a century. To be sure,
the incubation pouch was long ago mentioned
by classical authors, but quite naturally it
was attributed by them to the female, and
careful observation by scientists was necessary
to reveal that the opposite condition existed.

The final achievement in elucidating the
life habits of the sea horse should perhaps
be accredited to Monsieur Jean Painlevé, for
it was his skillful studies with the motion picture camera that made it possible for the man
in the street to observe and understand them.

Early records

The first person to observe the intertwin-
ing of sea horses in the act of transferring the
eggs was probably Dufosse, a Frenchman, in
1854. He published his description in 1874;
and in the same year Fanzago, in the zoö-
logical station in Naples, observed the same
process. In 1867 Lockwood, an American,
saw the delivery of the young.

Huot, another Frenchman, published in
1902 a paper in which he showed sections
through the egg pouch, and showed that the
epithelium makes nests surrounding each egg
and that the network of blood vessels supplies
nourishment to the eggs by osmosis. Cohn extended and confirmed Huot's observation.

THE INCUBATION POUCH of the
male is here distended with its burden of eggs. From 40 to 50 days are
required for the eggs to develop.

A GREATLY MAGNIFIED VIEW of
the embryos embedded in the tissue
of the incubation pouch of the male.

DETAIL of the incubation pouch,
charged with eggs, which will mature during the period of the "male
pregnancy."

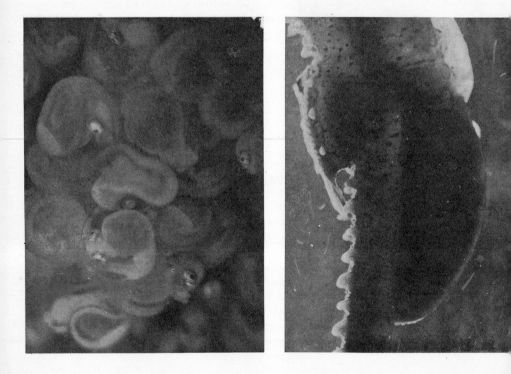

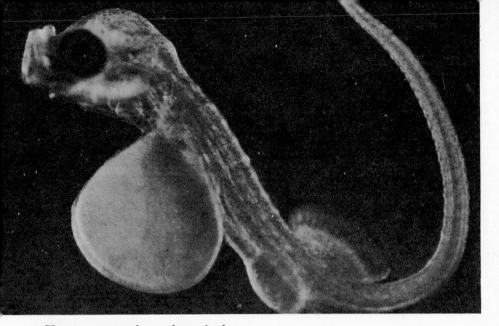

▲ THIS IS HOW the embryo looks when it is still in the pouch of the male. If by chance it is born prematurely at this stage, it must overcome handicaps in the struggle for existence, for it still carries the burden of its vitelline sac.

▼ THE MALE SEA HORSE, with pouch inflated to the limit, suffers great difficulty in expelling the young at birth.

↑ A YOUNG SEA HORSE just after its birth. The yolk has been absorbed and the tail is already curved. However, the little fish still maintains a horizontal position. Note the short, flattened snout, also the large eyes, reminiscent of those of the embryo still in the egg.

A VIEW OF THE OPEN POUCH, showing the embryos embedded in the tissues.

AFTER EXPULSION of the young, the tissues of the inside of the pouch return to their normal condition.

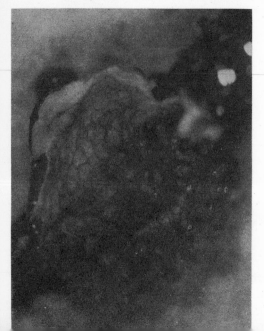

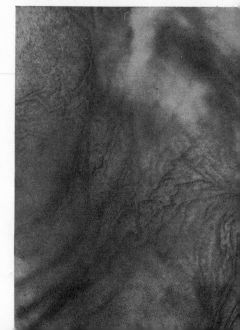

➤ AS THE YOUNG SEA HORSE grows up, the spots of pigmentation enlarge, become more regular, and begin to look like stars, as seen here. In the adult stage, they finally cover the whole body.

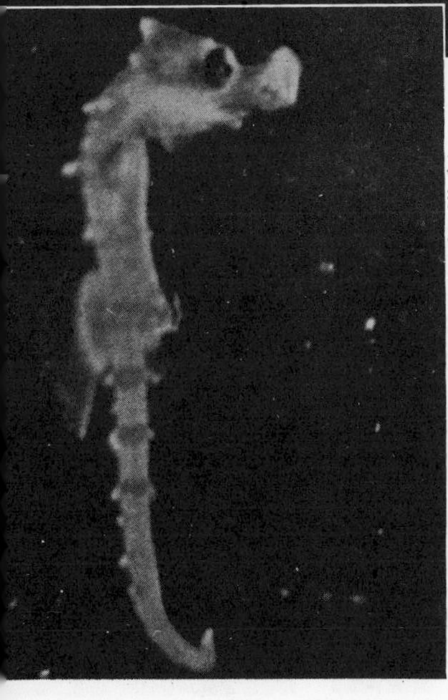

⮝ WITHIN ONE WEEK after birth the snout has become prolonged. The color is deeper and more evenly distributed, and the head has begun to form an angle with the body. However, the fish still swims in a horizontal position.

⮜ THIS LITTLE SEA HORSE has just reached the point where it can swim vertically.

The Kingdom of the Tides

By ROY WALDO MINER

*Late Curator of Living Invertebrates
The American Museum of Natural History*

W HEN we look at maps and charts, we see the boundary between land and sea marked by a definite line, but if we search for its exact location as we stroll along the beach, we cannot find it. The incoming waves rush up over the sands until they flatten out, lose their momentum, hesitate, and stream back into the flood whence they came. As the tide rises, the sea gradually advances farther inshore, but finally a limit is reached at high water. At certain seasons, and at times of storm, a greater area of land is covered, but the recession always takes place and the territory won by the ocean is abandoned, until, at the very lowest ebb, a strip of sea-bottom, in turn, is conquered by the land.

The strand slides under water at th same general slope, and, though diversifie by sand bars and shoals, the sea-botton sinks at a uniform rate, until, at a greate or less distance offshore, at a depth c about six hundred feet, it dives at a mor rapid gradient into the depths of the sea Here, at the edge of this steep slope, is th first indication of a line of separation. I is said that, ages ago, the real boundary c the land was to be found here, and th continents were much larger. Now th seas have flooded over the edges of thi ancient land, forming a comparativel shallow border or rim, varying in widt from thirty to one hundred miles, whic we call the continental shelf.

This shallow area, well lighted by th sun, and warmer than the oceanic deeps is the real theater of the life of the sea bottom. In the sunlight the sea-plants, c algæ, abound, and feeding among ther are myriads of small oceanic creature which, in turn, form the food of the large inhabitants of the sea.

Here are gathered living hordes o

Sea Shore Warfare

The five pictures at the right show, first, a colony of oysters on a mud flat. The second picture shows a mass of in-vading mussels which, in the third photograph, are pictured after they have overwhelmed the oysters. The fourth view depicts the mussel colony be-ing invaded, in turn, by barnacles which, in the fifth view, are shown completely victorious

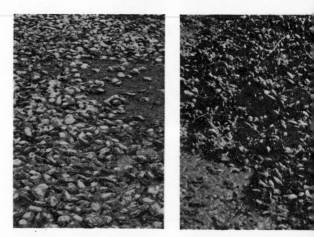

Some of the Creatures One May Find along the Shore Line of New England

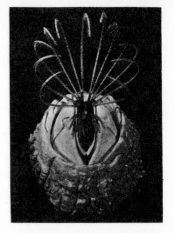

A barnacle extending its feathery feet from its lime-stone wigwam

ishes, mollusks, crustaceans, sea-worms, echinoderms, and the lower forms of life. From this shallow zone, in the course of time, many species have invaded the deeper waters and have become adapted for the dark abysses beyond the edge of the continental shelf. Myriads of others have crowded into the warm, sun-lit shallows near the shore and have even sought the intertidal stretch which is laid bare twice daily by the ebbing tide.

As we walk along the shore at low tide or wade in the shallows, we invade the edge of this teeming world of sea-creatures and see many signs of their activities. Along our coast from New York to the Bay of Fundy, the aspect of the ocean margin presents many contrasts. Long Island and Connecticut are characterized by stretches of exposed sand beaches, sheltered mud flats and sand spits. Here and there may be found out-croppings of rocks or tide-rips where glacial bowlders have been laid bare, but the chief character of the coast is low and free from rock. This condition becomes intensified as we reach and round the curving arm of Cape Cod, which is nothing but a huge sand spit. North of Massachusetts Bay and Boston, bold headlands of rocky cliff jut out into the sea, as at Nahant, Marblehead, Gloucester, and Cape Ann generally. Along the coast of Maine, high, rocky cliffs become the rule, lining and limiting deep bays, sown with jagged islands, and hemming in the estuaries of great rivers.

The height to which the tide may flow

shows great variation. Along the exposed sandy shores of southern New England it ranges from two to five feet in height, except where the incoming seas are forced into narrowing bodies of water like Long Island Sound, where it rises six to seven feet, as at New Haven and Bridgeport.

High Tides and Low

On the outer side of Cape Cod, the rise is but two feet, but the masses of water that crowd into Cape Cod Bay reach nine feet at Plymouth. North of Boston this height continues, becoming gradually increased along the Maine coast. The Gulf of Maine is a huge, curving and tapering funnel, guarded by Cape Cod to the southward and the peninsula of Nova Scotia to the northeast.

The tides entering this huge gulf are shunted along the hollow curve of the Maine shore line and Bay of Fundy, rising at high water eighteen feet at Bar Harbor, twenty-eight feet at St. Andrews, New Brunswick, and the enormous height of forty-five feet during spring tides at Amherst and Truro, where, at the double apex of the funnel-shaped Bay, the Nova Scotian isthmus ties the peninsula of that name to the mainland of North America.

Naturally the combination of high, swift-running tides and rocky coasts has a far-reaching effect on the animal and plant life inhabiting the impetuous waters of northern New England, compared with the low-lying, quiet, sandy and muddy coasts of the more southerly portions.

The temperature of the waters in the two regions also is of great influence. Southern New England is washed by spurs from the warm waters of the Gulf Stream, especially in the Cape Cod region which, with the outlying Elizabeth Islands, as well as Marthas Vineyard and Nantucket, juts boldly out into the sea. But farther north, the cold Arctic Current pushes its way in close to the shore, and creatures which, in southerly waters, are

found only in the deeper, colder seas here occur near the surface and are able to live in shallow waters near the rocky shore

If we could stroll along the entire New England coast in a few hours, we should find ourselves passing over regions continually changing in character, and the species of animals populating the shallow waters around the low-tide limit also would be seen to vary in harmony with the changing environment. The forces of inanimate nature sift out all individuals that invade regions to which their bodily structures and habits are not adapted.

As it is out of the question to cover so much territory in one journey, let us transport ourselves in imagination from place to place and sample a number of contrasting typical localities to become acquainted with the shallow-water animals characteristic of them.

An Exposed Sandy Beach

The white sand stretches out before us for miles, heaped high into dunes at our left or extending over into broad flats covered with beach grass and low shrubbery. At our right, the surf breaks thundering on the shore, washing to our very feet and bringing quantities of loose sand along with it. Here and there, with a rattle and a roar, the waves bombard the coast with masses of rounded pebbles spreading them over the strand in assorted sizes ranging from gravel to bowlders.

We pick up dead and empty shells on the beach, many of them broken and beach-worn. Ruffled fronds of kelp are washed up and other flotsam from the sea, but, for the most part, life is conspicuous by its absence, and the sand shore seems barren indeed. This is not to be wondered at. The shifting sand gives little opportunity for harboring animal life which otherwise might burrow within it, and the force of the waves transforms into grindstones the pebbles and rocks which, in quieter waters, would give

Creatures
of the
Sandy Beach

(Below) Two pictures of *Natica*, the sand collar snail, which hides in mound-shaped burrows or crawls over the sand, pushing its fleshy apron before it. Next comes a lady crab up to her eyes in sand; a "sand bug" preparing to "dig in"; a rock crab, and finally another lady crab showing its paddle-shaped hind legs

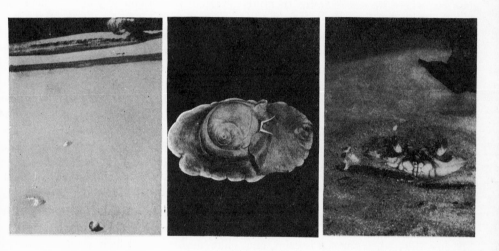

shelter to all sorts of sea-creatures. The siliceous sand grains are barren of food material and could support no life even if any could find foothold among them.

Nevertheless, at the upper tide limit, long lines of beach wrack mark the boundary of the ocean's surge, and as we stir up the decaying and drying fragments of seaweed, swarms of beach-fleas (*Orchestia agilis*) come to life and jump hither and thither in clouds. If we are quick, we can capture them and put them into a glass jar, where we can examine them at leisure. They are olive green in color. Now, as we look closely at the sand not far from the high-tide mark, struggling forms emerge from tiny little holes that are almost invisible, and go leaping about, their grayish, sand-colored bodies closely resembling their environment. They, too, are sand-fleas of two different species (*Talorchestia megalopthalma* and *longicornis*) somewhat larger than their green brethren and distinguished by unusually large eyes and long feelers, respectively.

The Lady Crab

At low tide, when the sea is calm, one may wade in the shallows with a water glass and find other evidences of life. Yonder a lady crab (*Ovalipes ocellatus*) goes swimming by sidewise, waving its paddle-shaped hind legs over its back as a means of propulsion. A short distance away it settles down on the sea-bottom, raises its stalked eyes, and regards us warily. We approach with stealth, to get a good view of its carapace gayly spotted with irregular purplish pink dots, and the sharp pincer-like claws, striped also in purple and pink, which wave menacingly toward us. It is all a bluff! For as we cautiously wade nearer, the crab shoves the hinder margin of its carapace down into the sand, and rapidly digs itself under till only the frontal edge, the ends of the stalked eyes, and the waving, threadlike antennæ are visible.

The rock crab (*Cancer irroratus*) is also abundant here, scuttling over the sandy floor, as it has no paddles to swim with like its more fortunate cousin. We catch glimpses of the slender almost transparent boatlike bodies of the common shrimp (*Crangon vulgaris*) darting here and there like phantoms.

Sand-collar Snails

A number of sand-collar snails of two species (*Natica heros* and *duplicata*) have started a settlement yonder where the sandy floor is nearly level and is laid bare only at the lowest tide. Low, rounded mounds scattered over the wet sand betray their habitat, and, as we watch, there is a disturbance in one of them which is still under water, and we see a round, almost globular shell, about as large as a tennis ball, break through. A fleshy foot protrudes itself from the shell opening and extends forward and back over the sand until it seems impossible that so much animal could be packed so tightly within the spire of the shell. Now it begins to travel forward, pushing before it an apron-like flap, above which waves a pair of antennæ, each with an eye-spot at its base.

As the creature slowly progresses, a transparent, jelly-like ribbon emerges from under the right side of the apron and is slowly pushed around the lower margin of the shell, where it is overlapped by a fold of the broad, fleshy body. Soon it completely surrounds the shell like a border. The snail continues to creep forward and leaves the transparent ribbon behind it on the sandy sea-floor. The sand washes against it and sticks to it. We pick it up and find it is a delicate little collar-shaped arrangement, open in front and slightly ruffled at the lower margin. The sand which has stuck to the outer surface covers it in a single layer, giving it an appearance of fine sandpaper. If we examine the under side with a hand lens we find that it is entirely lined with a

Tidal Water
and
Marsh Grass

In settings such as the one shown at the top of the page, fiddler crabs dig bur-rows among the grass roots. The sectional view above at the right shows a fiddler-crab burrow, together with a starfish pre-paring to feed on an oyster. Marvelously adorned seaworms dig in the mud, as well. In the circle the ornate worm (*Amphitrite ornata*) spreads its delicate tentacles; in the center rectangle a fringed worm (*Cirratulus grandis*) extends its threadlike filaments; at the left is pictured the head of a plumed worm (*Diopatra cuprea*). Except for the view at the top, these photographs are of models at the American Museum

delicate layer of transparent eggs, each like a tiny bead of jelly, all closely set together in a finely wrought mosaic. As the collar dries in the sun, it becomes so fragile that it crumbles to sand in our fingers.

We now turn our attention to the snail itself and see that it is rapidly creeping through the shallow water toward a group of little flattened sticks standing up from the sand at an abrupt angle. The snail seems much interested in them. As we examine them with attention we see that their sides are formed of two long, narrow, slightly curving shells which somewhat suggest the size and shape of the old-fashioned razor handle. We recognize the razor-shell clam (*Ensis directus*). The shells stand half-buried in the sand, showing the ends of their short siphon-tubes at the top bordered with fringelike papillæ. Apparently they are aware either of us or of the approaching snail, for suddenly first one, then another, shoots down into the sand until the siphon-openings are barely even with the surface. They are great diggers, for their lower end is equipped with a powerful curved and tapering foot, which is used as a very efficient digging organ.

These inhabitants of the exposed sandy beaches, together with certain others, such as the soft clam (*Mya arenaria*), the surf clam (*Spisula solidissima*), the "sand bug" (*Hippa talpoida*), the sand dollar (*Echinarachnius parma*), and a few sea-worms, are able to endure the difficult conditions of exposure to the open sea. Most of them also occur in the more sheltered regions described below, but they are the hardy explorers of the shallow seas, and form the scattered population of a region which is otherwise without abundant visible life.

Sheltered Sand and Mud Flats

As we walk along the beach, we may find our progress stopped by an inlet through which the tide flows into more sheltered waters. In such places the currents wash the sand and mud away from the bowlders embedded therein and much of the mud is carried into the sheltered waters of the bay, to be deposited upon its floor, mingled with sand to a greater or less degree.

Among the Eelgrass

This mud is filled with nutritive material in which eelgrass grows readily and which also provides sustenance for all sorts of burrowing sea animals, and many others which lurk among the weed. Hosts of tiny creatures grow on the eelgrass blades, hide under the stones in the bottom and edges of the tidal channel, and cling to the seaweeds growing in such places.

Depending on the amount of exposure to the open sea, the soil grades from gravel, through sand, sandy mud of various degrees of admixture, and pure mud, abounding in inhabitants which thrive best in each special environment as well as those ubiquitous creatures which range over the whole field.

The little hermit crabs (*Pagurus longicarpus*) are among the latter. These may be seen scuttling back and forth in shallow water. They are small shrimplike creatures with a pair of heavily armored, formidable claws and four spiny walking legs, but with a soft, tapering abdomen which is their weak point and is entirely unprotected. Attached to this are a few pairs of small holding claws. To make good their deficiency, the hermit crabs appropriate abandoned snail shells, backing their soft abdomen into the spiral chamber of the shell, into which it neatly fits. They hold the shell in place by gripping the central columella of the spire with their weak abdominal claws, and then boldly run around with their castles on their backs. If assailed by an enemy, they retreat within the shell, closing the opening with one of their large claws. However, certain species of fish eat them, shell

A Ripple-Marked
Mud Flat

Prolific sea worms make their homes and dig their subways in the tide-washed mud.   In the circle, a clam worm (*Nereis*) appears to be attacking an opal worm.   At the upper right a trumpet-worm model is shown, surrounded by the sand grains that it has built into a home.   The center rectangle shows a model of the head of a "beak thrower," pictured also in the circle "throwing its beak."   Below at the left the head of an opal worm is shown, gleaming with iridescent hues. The tracks shown crossing the ripple marks in the bottom picture have been made by black mud-snails

Photograph by
M. C. Dickerson

and all. The hermits are the scavengers of the shallow seas and always gather together in great numbers to feast upon dead and decaying plants and animals. On muddy bottoms they are joined by the black mud snails (*Nassa obsoleta*), whose progress over the mud can be traced by their undulating groovelike trails.

A Populous City on a Shell

The hermit crab is also interesting, because, in many cases, the dead shell that it carries may become covered with a soft substance appearing at first glance like the pile of coarse velvet. If we place such a crab in a small dish of sea water and look at it under a magnifying glass, this covering resolves itself into a city of tiny hydroids (*Hydractinia echinata*), little flower-like creatures with slender tube-shaped bodies, some of them with terminal mouths surrounded with grasping tentacles; others with no mouths but carrying quantities of egg-producing organs looking like tiny clusters of grapes; and still others near the edge of the shell with no mouths, but with their heads crowned with beadlike batteries of sting cells. Obviously this is a community of specialists, some members of which are the feeders for the colony, others, the reproducers and nursemaids, and the rest the fighters. Each has its special work to do. All the individuals are connected by a network of tubes, so that food may be supplied to the members that have no mouths by those which secure and digest it.

Larger species of hermits (*Pagurus bernhardus* and *pollicaris*) hide in the eelgrass, where also may be found the great whelks (*Fulgur canaliculata* and *carica*), which bear large, coiled shells on their backs with a pointed siphon in front. The females of these whelks manufacture egg-strings, two or more feet in length, looking like strings of spiny, yellow pill boxes, in which the eggs hatch into baby snails with tiny shells like those of their parents. After a time the little snails emerge from a hole in the edge of each pill box and take up an independent life. The whelks prowl around, in the hope of capturing one of the scallops (*Pecten gibbus*) which abound in the eelgrass. This is a game of stalking, for the latter possess a hundred or more gleaming, steely blue eyes around the edge of the mantles, and, when alarmed by a shadow, will spring up in the water and flit out of the way, opening and closing their shells rapidly as a means of locomotion.

The green crab (*Carcinides mænas*), conspicuous with its bright green, yellow, and black markings, and the blue crab (*Callinectes sapidus*), familiar to us in the markets, frequent the sheltered mud flats in shallow water, while the small mud crabs (*Panopeus herbstii* and *sayi*) with their black-fingered claws are everywhere at the water's edge. The large spider crabs (*Libinia emarginata* and *dubia*), with their long legs and small, spiny, rounded carapaces, hide in the eelgrass and are hard to see on muddy bottoms.

Oysters and Mussels

On mud-flats laid bare at low tides one may chance upon occasional oyster beds, though these are usually cultivated at some depth. More frequently huge flats may be covered with edible mussels (*Mytilus edulis*). These black mussels are a potential article of food, now much neglected, but, when properly prepared, they rival the succulent oyster and littleneck clam in delicacy of flavor and nutritious value. On Marthas Vineyard Island, literally acres of mussels are laid bare at low tide. They multiply so rapidly that, if by chance they come in contact with a bed of oysters, they will overspread it and completely smother it. The rock barnacles, in turn, reproduce even faster than the mussels, and, by sheer force of numbers, given an opportunity, will invade a mussel colony and overwhelm it,

Above: A giant whelk pursues a scallop, which swims by opening and closing its shell

Below: The "velvet" on the hermit crab's appropriated shell is shown, in an American Museum model, to be made of three types of tiny hydroids—fighters, feeders, and egg producers

Above: A hermit crab in his borrowed and "velvet"-covered shell

Below: The familiar edible blue crab

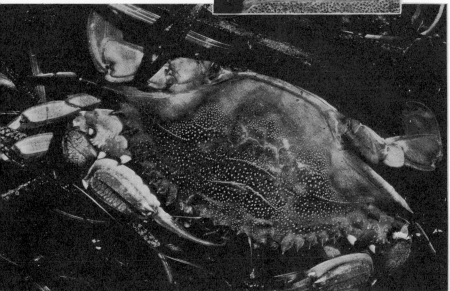

Photograph by M. C. Dickerson

thus rendering poetic justice to the former conquering horde.

Enemies of Mollusks

These beds of shellfish, of course, attract the enemies of bivalve mollusks in great abundance. The most important of these are the oyster drill (*Urosalpinx cinerea*) and the common sea stars (*Asterias vulgaris* and *forbesi*). The former bores neat little pinholes in an oyster shell, and sucks out the contents, while the latter mounts the oyster, applies the pneumatic disks of its tube-feet to the two valves, and, bracing the tips of its arms against surrounding objects, pulls the shells open by main force and proceeds to devour their contents.

The oysters are not naturally found in muddy localities, but have been transplanted there by man, by spreading shells to form a "clutch." They belong more properly on a rocky bottom.

The animals most typically associated with more or less muddy regions are the sea worms. Burrowing in the soil everywhere, they construct tubes of greater or less consistency, or, in some cases, no tubes at all. They hide under flat stones, or dig among the roots of eelgrass. In localities rich in mud the fringed worm (*Cirratulus grandis*) burrows in great abundance, its reddish body adorned with a multiplicity of long, threadlike, breathing organs on the forward third of its body, each filament of golden yellow with a brilliant red thread of blood showing through the translucent walls. The plumed worm (*Diopatra cupræa*) constructs tough, parchment-like tubes in sandy mud; showing like chimneys above the sea-bottom, to which bits of shell and seaweed are cemented. The worm has a bluish iridescent body equipped on the forward part with marvelous blood-red plumes with spirally arranged branches. The ornate worm (*Amphitrite ornata*) builds tubes of sand and mud. It is a wonderful creature with three pairs of intricately branched gill-plumes on its shoulders and numerous flesh-colored tentacles extending in all directions from its head. Its body is beautifully marked with reddish brown, and a broadly tapering upper lip is colored from rich rose to violet. The opal worm (*Arabella opalina*) has an orange head with four eyes, and a long, slender body composed of brilliantly opalescent rings. The trumpet worm (*Pectinaria belgica*) digs with a pair of golden combs and constructs a trumpet-shaped tube of neatly matched sand grains arranged in a delicate mosaic.

Scores of other species occur, all remarkable for beauty, grotesqueness, or strange habits, but it is impossible to mention them all here. Needless to say, the sheltered mud- and sand-flat is one of the most fruitful fields for the study of the strange creatures of the sea.

Rocky Shores and High Tides

Let us now transport ourselves to the north shore of Massachusetts or the coast of Maine. We are on a rock-bound coast, hemmed in by high cliffs, against the base of which the incoming tide breaks in masses of foam, which scour through every crevice and rush back into the sea. The tide rises and falls nine feet or more, according to the locality, and, farther north, several times that distance.

At low tide the vertical walls of the cliffs are seen to be broken into shelving terraces, draped and festooned with rockweed, bordered above with a long frieze of white barnacles. The basin-like hollows on the rocky terraces are filled with water, even when the tide is at its lowest, and each one glows with submerged colors like an aquatic sea-garden. There is no soil for burrowing like that on sand- and mud-flats, and all animals having no adequate clinging organs, or requiring a soft substratum for burrowing are eliminated here by the force of the elements, and yet

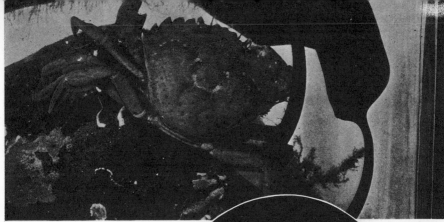

Photographs,
M. C. Dickerson

Above: The green crab above is not
edible, but is a pugnacious fighter

Below:
A spider crab, which has camou-
flaged himself by plucking tufts of
Bugula and placing them on his back

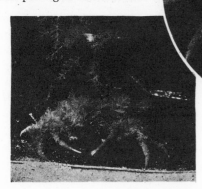

A rough-spined
spider crab, which
has lost one claw

Below: A lady crab is shown swimming vigorously in an attempt to escape from a lobster

certain creatures familiar to the southern shores adapt themselves to these trying conditions and survive.

Black Mussels and Purple Snails

The same kind of black mussel (*Mytilus edulis*) that covers the mud-flats of the southern coast to so great an extent, clings to the rocks in broad bands below the barnacle zone and underneath the rockweed, but, in exposed situations, the shells are always very small, for when they reach a size to present resistance to the force of the waves, the silken strands of their tough byssus threads give way and they are stripped from their anchorage by the rushing water. They also must dispute their territory with the purple snails (*Thais lapillus*), which cluster in numerous colonies and feed on the little mussels. These snails derive their name from the fact that they exude a purple fluid, allied to the Tyrian purple of Mediterranean snails. Their shells, however, are gayly banded with red or yellow spirals, or the entire shell may vary from white, through orange, red, and brown. They lay their eggs in little pink or yellowish vase-shaped capsules, which stand on slender stems and are grouped together in small patches in the crevices of the rocks.

At low tide multitudes of sea stars familiar to the southern shore (*Asterias vulgaris*) but varying greatly in color from purple, through blue, crimson, and yellow, feed on the mussels and on the little green sea urchin with the long scientific name (*Strongylocentrotus droebachiensis*), which is very abundant here. Another sea star characteristic of rocky coasts is a small, deep-red species (*Henricia sanguinolenta*), bright yellow beneath and at the tips of its curving arms. The Jonah crab (*Cancer borealis*) is very common, crouching and hiding in rocky dens. It is larger and with much rougher carapace than the rock crab of Southern New England (*Cancer irroratus*), which also is

found on the northern coast, but more sparingly.

The tide pools on the terraces show remarkable concentrations of sea life. As the sun slants through one of these flooded basins at low tide, it lights up tangles of rich brown, brilliant green, purple, pink, and red algæ, their graceful fronds clustering and overarching miniature vistas, in which acorn snails (*Littorina litorea*), green crabs (*Carcinides mænas*), and tiny red or variegated chitons (*Chiton ruber* and *apiculatus*) creep about amid fairy clusters of pink-hearted hydroids (*Tubularia crocea*), gray-green chimney sponges (*Halichondria panicea*), and pink finger sponges (*Chalina oculata*).

Sea Anemones and Seaweeds

Sea anemones (*Metridium dianthus*) expand their broad, flower-like, fringed disks and cylindrical bodies, brown, pink and white, and bright orange in color. Even the rocky basin itself is enameled with encrustations of red-purple *Melobesia* and brick-red *Lithothamnion*,—calcareous seaweeds, that spread thin, stony layers of color over the underlying rock. Clusters of huge horse-mussels (*Modiola modiola*) covered with purple and red bryozoa, open their shells slightly, exposing their orange-colored mantles.

It seems impossible that there should be such an abundant association of living forms in so small a space, but the secret lies in the flood of aërated and food-laden waters that twice a day overwhelms these tidal pools and brings the inhabitants everything on which their life depends.

These associations of the animal life of the seas, whether on sandy shore, mud flat, or rock-bound coast, are but glimpses of an almost infinite kingdom of creatures under the rule of the tide, which sweeps over the great oceanic shelf, bringing life or death to its subjects, depending upon how they adapt themselves to its laws.

Left: The only coral (*Astrangia danaë*) of the New England coast is shown growing over a rocky bottom

Photographs, M. C. Dickerson

In the small rectangle a common starfish (*Asterias vulgaris*) is portrayed. *Below:* A starfish is shown attacking a small fish. The "tube-feet" are equipped with sucking discs by means of which the fish is dragged into its attacker's central mouth

Above: A sea anemone (*Metridium marginatum*) expands its feathery crown, which is armed with sting-cells with which it slays small fish for food

The rocky coast at low tide.
The white band is made up of
barnacles. Below these, fes-
toons of rock weed partly
cover crowded masses of mussels. In the water, starfish
and green sea urchins abound

Right: The little red sea star
(*Henricia sanguinolenta*),
which is abundant in the tide
pools of rocky coasts. Photograph by M. C. Dickerson

Below: A view looking
through the clear water of a
pool replete with Irish moss,
coralline dulse, kelp, rockweed,
and sponges

Seaweed drapes the rocks of a beautiful pool at Nahant, Massachusetts. In these clear, quiet waters are displayed a magnificent sea garden in which the observer may find a rich field for observation

Left: Purple snails (*Thais lapillus*) are shown feasting on mussels. These snails produce a beautiful purple dye similar to the ancient Tyrian purple. A cluster of eggs is also visible

Below: A corner of the Nahant pool showing green sea urchins, sea stars, and green crabs on the coralline covered rocks

An especially attractive specimen often makes a
nice wall decoration in the library or game room.

How to Collect Seaweeds

By EDWIN WAY TEALE

The delicate
and artistic forms of seaweeds
lend themselves
to a fascinating hobby

WHEREVER the sea meets the land, all along the 21,862 miles of the United States coastline this fascinating hobby can be enjoyed. The great variety found among seaweeds and their artistic forms when mounted to form a collection make this pursuit among the most attractive of seaside diversions. Published information on how to mount and preserve seaweeds has been so scarce that most people do not realize how easy it is.

Anyone living within visiting distance of the shore, whether among the rocky headlands of Maine or along the sandy beaches of Southern California, will find a surprising variety of forms to include in his collection. And because comparatively few persons have taken up the hobby, amateurs are able to mount specimens that have scientific as well as artistic importance.

During the past five years, one collector on Long Island, Edmund

➤ EDMUND MORGAN collecting at the tide line. Whole, full-grown specimens should be gathered whenever possible: foliage, stem (the so-called stipe), and holdfast. If they are muddy or sandy, they should be washed out. After a gale, many deep-water specimens not ordinarily found will be picked up. The pail must be kept about half full of salt water which should be changed from time to time. It should be placed in the shade so that the temperature will not rise above about 50 degrees F. Smaller specimens deteriorate rapidly in warm water. Heavier rockweeds can be stored temporarily in a sack that is kept wet.

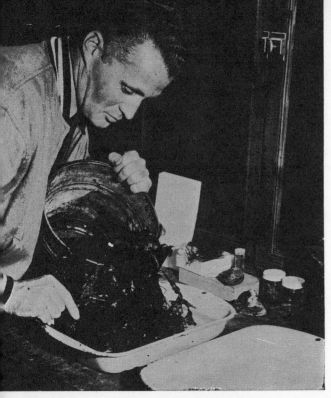

➤ THE SMALLER, more delicate red seaweeds should be separated from the heavier green and brown sorts. All specimens should be placed in fresh water for about half an hour before mounting. Excess salt might prevent them from drying thoroughly.

Morgan, has added more than 6,000 mounted specimens to his collection. He is the Curator of the Tackapausha Museum, Nassau County's natural history center at Seaford, N. Y. Many of his mounts represent the same kinds of algae growing under different conditions, but there is never any lack of variety in shapes. How the specimens are collected and mounted is shown pictorially in this series of photographs.

A pail and a few accessories are all that are needed in order to start a collection. An incoming tide is best for floating seaweed. Since the specimens should be taken from the water rather than from dried or decayed pieces thrown up on the shore, bathing or wading togs are in order. When working among rocks, sneakers with heavy rubber soles can be worn. In cold water, the collector will find hip boots more comfortable.

➤ THE FIRST STEP in mounting the specimen is to slide the paper or card beneath it in the pan of water. The gelatinous nature of the seaweeds causes them to stick to the mounting paper when dried. Larger specimens may require strips of adhesive mounting paper or drops of a clear mounting plastic. Normally two sizes of mounting paper are used, 5 x 8 inches and 11 x 16 inches. For permanent collections, paper with at least 25% rag content should be used. Beginners will find sheets of a large loose leaf sketching pad suitable or large white filing cards. The base of the seaweed is held with one thumb while the branches are arranged with tweezers or a needle.

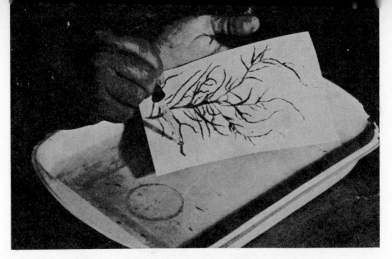

▲ DELICATE FEATHERY SEAWEEDS, such as this red specimen, need to have their fine hairs separated out by allowing water to flow gently from a medicine dropper. Otherwise they will mat together. After the specimens have been floated onto the mounting paper and drained, it helps to lay them on a slanting board so that they can be drained thoroughly before putting them in the press.

▲ THE MOUNTED SPECIMEN is placed face up on an herbarium-press blotter. A piece of white, unsized, unbleached muslin is laid on top of it. Otherwise the seaweed will stick to the next blotter as well as to the sheet of paper. Waxed paper is sometimes used instead of muslin, especially when dealing with wiry specimens. Cloth is used on the more delicate and slippery seaweeds. Some people use a folded newspaper page in addition, to avoid direct contact with the blotters.

Filing and Learning

The sheets are filed and stored in the same manner as the more familiar herbarium specimens. Spring-back binders are better than loose leaf notebooks. If you file them loosely in a file drawer, prevent friction from damaging delicate specimens by affixing a cover sheet over each one.

Some seaweeds float freely, others are anchored to the bottom by sucker-like discs. The green forms usually grow nearest the shore, whereas the brown ones range from the low-tide mark to a depth of 50 or 60 feet. All seaweeds belong to the division of plants known as algae, and they reproduce by producing spores or by the union of eggs and sperms.

Those interested in further infor-

▲ A SECOND HERBARIUM BLOTTER is then placed on top of the waxed paper or muslin. When many specimens are being prepared in one press, they are stacked between blotters, one on top of another. The lattice-work wooden top is then placed on the stack and weighted down. The blotters should be changed from time to time during the process, as they absorb much water. This is especially necessary to avoid mold in the case of the heavier brown and red seaweeds. Removing the blotters requires only moderate care. As the specimens shrink slightly while drying, the pressure in the press should be gradually increased. When finally the cloth is removed, it must be stripped away slowly and gently so as not to damage the specimen.

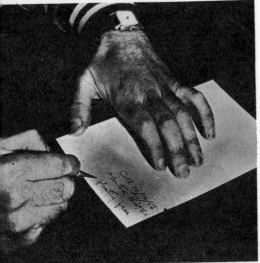

mation about seaweeds and the hobby of seaweed collecting will find a valuable reference book in William Randolph Taylor's *Marine Algae of the Northeastern Coast of North America* (University of Michigan Press). Although it deals primarily with the seaweeds of the Northeast, it contains general information that will be helpful in other parts of the country as well.

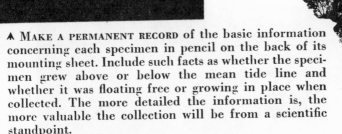

▲ MAKE A PERMANENT RECORD of the basic information concerning each specimen in pencil on the back of its mounting sheet. Include such facts as whether the specimen grew above or below the mean tide line and whether it was floating free or growing in place when collected. The more detailed the information is, the more valuable the collection will be from a scientific standpoint.

▼ TRANSFERRING some or all of the information to a label at the lower righthand corner of the mount is the last step in preparing a specimen. The scientific name can be added when positive identification is possible.

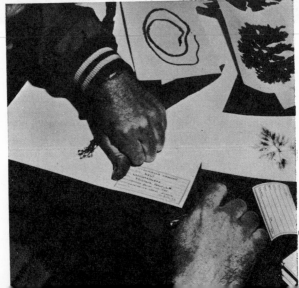

▲ THE MOUNTED SEAWEED with the label attached
should be stored in darkness. The colors will fade
if subjected to much sunlight but will remain
unchanged for years in darkness. Pressed seaweeds are not subject to the attacks of small
beetles and therefore do not need to be treated
with insect repellent as do other herbarium
sheets. However, they tend to be brittle and
should be handled carefully to prevent damage.
With reasonable care, they will remain in good
condition for many years.

How Nature Plants her Flowers

The many ways in which flowers and trees scatter their seeds; how the wind aids some, how birds and animals carry others, and how some help themselves

"THE LONG BROWN   PATH"

By Clyde Fisher
Late Curator of the Hayden Planetarium
Photographs by the author

THE love of beauty seems to be innate. There seems to have been born in every human mind a love of the beautiful in one form or another, and surely in most persons this embraces our wild flowers in their great variety of form and color and fragrance. Some of these flowers are to be looked for along roadsides and in cultivated meadows, others in marshes and bogs, others in shady woods, and still others on mountain tops. Some plants grow only in acid soil, while others are to be found only in limestone regions. But wherever they occur, they attract our attention because of their beauty.

For some reason, perhaps not easy to explain, our early associations strongly influence our appreciation of wild flower and birds and other objects of nature This significant fact is a plea for arousing and cultivating an interest in the outdoor at an early age. Burroughs speaks of the "memory-stirring" note of the meadow lark.

Plants live as animals live. Many lower forms have powers of locomotion highly developed. Some plants, for example the wheat-rust, a parasite, seen to migrate in a way analagous to the seasonal migration of animals. The insectivorous plants entrap insects and digest them as some animals do. Here belong the pitcher-plants, the sundews the butterworts, the bladderworts, and Venus's fly-trap. Some plants, like the

DANDELION'S SPHERE OF PARACHUTES
After the flowers fade and while the seeds are ripening, the hollow stalk grows longer, thus lifting the ball of seeds with their parachutes so that they may be more effectively wafted away on the breeze

slime molds or myxomycetes, have a plant phase and an animal phase. In fact, some biologists consider these organisms animals and call them mycetozoa. This recalls a fascinating essay by Huxley on the borderland between the vegetable and animal kingdoms.

Many of our conspicuous flowering plants have extended their range, have traveled far in historic time. Most of the so-called weeds of our roadsides and cultivated fields in eastern United States have been introduced from the Old World. This is true of yarrow, dandelion, daisy, bouncing Bet, butter-and-eggs, corn-cockle, shepherd's-purse, Queen-Anne's lace, viper's bugloss, and many others. Occasionally one has come from the western United States, as black-eyed or brown-eyed Susan, and occasionally one comes from South America, as *Galinsoga*, a small weed with inconspicuous, composite flowers.

This habit of traveling, which is universal among plants, is obviously an advantage to the individual species, for if all the seeds produced by a given plant would fall straight down to the ground and were allowed to remain and to germinate there, the resultant overcrowding can easily be imagined. Of course, this does not occur in any absolute sense, although there are some approaches to it. In practically all cases, however, there are means of scattering the seeds far and wide. In many instances clever devices astonishing in their effectiveness have been developed by the plants themselves. In other cases there seem to be no special devices. It is doubtful whether it is generally appreciated that myriads of seeds are moved, and to long distances in the aggregate, by the water that falls as rain, while it is flowing over the surface of the earth before it has collected into the recognized brooks and larger streams.

One of the commonest and most frequently observed methods of seed-dispersal is that dependent upon the wind, and there are at least three different devices for the accomplishment of this. First, are those with *flying-hairs*, for example, the dandelion. Every one is familiar with the wonderful little parachutes, one attached to each seed, and all arranged in a ball on the scape that previously bore the head of flowers, which is known to the child as the dandelion flower.

> *"The dandelion's coin of gold*
> *Anew is minted on the lawn."*

But how many of us have observed that the scape or stalk of the dandelion grows much longer between the time of flowering and the ripening of the seed? This lengthening serves to lift the head of fruits or the ball of seeds with the parachutes up above the grass and other surrounding plants, so that the wind may waft them away more effectively.

Similar to the dandelion's flying appendages are those of colt's-foot, and perhaps most astonishingly complex an beautiful of all flying devices of the dande lion type are those of goat's-beard an salsify.

We find flying-hairs of a different typ in willows, milkweeds, goldenrods, aster thistles, and very greatly developed i cotton. The lint or fibers of cottor which are woven into cloth, are the flying hairs from the cotton-seeds.

Just as dependent upon the wind is great group of plants whose fruits c seeds have *wings*. Examples of these ar the maples, the elms, the ashes, trumpet flower, cross-vine, and ailanthus. On has only to toss up a handful of mapl seeds or ailanthus seeds when a breeze i blowing to observe how the wings func tion.

The *tumble-weeds* and tumble-grasse constitute a third group of plants whic depend upon the wind to scatter thei seeds. All of the tumble-weeds are mor or less globular in shape, and have th habit, when the seeds are nearly ripe, c

TROUT-LILY BESIDE THE BROOK

John Burroughs referred to this spring flower as the trout-lily or fawn-lily, because of the mottled o
spotted leaves. An additional reason for the former name is its frequent habit of growing along trou
streams

TWIN-FLOWER OF THE NORTH WOODS

'he European form of this flower, *Linnæa borealis*, was named for the great Swedish botanist, Linnæus.
He admired its modest, retiring habits, and its delicate fragrance

A BEAUTIFUL MEMBER OF THE CAMELLIA OR TEA FAMILY

Mountain Stewartia, a shrub whose large, showy flowers with cream-colored petals attract attention
along the mountain streams from Kentucky to Georgia

GRAY SQUIRREL BURYING A NUT

The seeds of many of our nut-bearing forest trees are without doubt transported and planted by mice, chipmunks, and squirrels

WATER-HYACINTH

This floating plant is often blown about on lakes or slow-moving streams in Florida, where it has been a nuisance to navigation

TOUCH-ME-NOT OR JEWEL-WEED
The touch-me-not has explosive fruits, the turgid capsules bursting open and the valves curling up with sufficient energy to throw the seeds a considerable distance

breaking loose from the ground. These light, rolling masses are then blown across the prairies or fields by the wind. Not all the seed-capsules are opened at once, but they are opened gradually, thus scattering the seeds as the plant tumbles along. Besides the common western tumble-weed, there are several close relatives, such as the ghost-plant or white pig-weed. A relative of the Indian-turnip of the Great Plains, and the Russian thistle, and several grasses are tumble-weeds that scatter their seeds in this way.

The coconut, which is cultivated around the world in the tropical regions, is a classical example of a *water-borne* seed. The outer fibrous husk with a water-proof coat on the outside makes this possible. So often this tree overhangs the water along the borders of islands or other tropical shores, and this habit makes the method a practicable one in nature. Many of our local aquatic plants, such as arrow-head, and the white water-lily, have their seeds transported by water. We do not include the many plants whose seeds are washed considerable distances by rain-water, as mentioned above.

Some plants depend upon both the *wind* and the *water* in an interesting way. Examples are the Egyptian lotus and the native American lotus. In the lotus the flower is borne on a stiff stem that projects a foot or so above the water. The seeds, which resemble acorns, develop in depressions in the flat upper face of an enlarged top-shaped receptacle. The flower-stalk later supports this receptacle, holding it firmly above the water. The seeds cannot fall out of the receptacle because the cavities open upward, and they are only released when the wind blows hard enough, with the aid of the waves it causes, to shake the receptacle violently enough to throw the seeds out. In this way it works like a certain type of boy's sling-shot, and the seeds are thrown quite a distance.

Many plants have *explosive fruits*, and there is great variety in the ways in which this is accomplished. In the witch-hazel the seed-capsule bursts open and the two seeds are thrown some distance. In the

Virginia knotweed there is a cushion of elastic cells at the base of each fruit, which throw the ripe fruit or seed a distance of several feet when the hook, formed by the dried style of the flower, is pressed. In the squirting cucumber the fruit becomes very turgid upon ripening, and finally the pressure is great enough to push the stem out, leaving a hole through the rind. The seeds, which are held in suspension in the liquid contents of the fruit, are squirted out with the liquid through the hole at the stem-end of the cucumber.

The violets, the wild geraniums or crane's-bills, and many members of the bean family have explosive fruits, and for different reasons.

Plants, whose seeds are *carried by animals*, may be divided into several groups.

FIRST: Fruits or seeds with hooks, as in burdock, cockle-bur, stick-tights, Spanish-needles, tick-tre-foil, hoarhound, sand-bur, and many others. Everyone is familiar with the way these burs or hooked fruits are carried on the clothing of human animals, in the mane and foretops of horses, in the wool of sheep, and on the coats of fur-bearing animals.

SECOND: Seeds of plants are carried long distances on the toes of migrating waterfowl, as Darwin proved in an experiment which he described.

THIRD: Fleshy fruits containing seeds, which are indigestible, are eaten by birds and animals, and transported far from the parent plants. Probably many of the wild black cherry trees which spring up along our fences, came from seeds carried in this way. Robins and starlings carry not only cherry-seeds but also the seeds of the flowering dogwood, and other trees and shrubs.

FOURTH: Certain birds store away or hide seeds,—for example the blue-jay hides or puts away acorns in various places, sometimes in abandoned birds nests; the tufted titmouse hides or places pine seeds in the chinks of bark of trees the California woodpecker regularly stores acorns in holes which it drills in tree-trunks or in posts. In many cases these seeds are eaten by the birds, but there is no doubt that some of them reach the soil, perhaps by being washed down by rain and germinate.

FIFTH: Many rodents store up nuts for

BUMBLEBEE ASLEEP IN THE FLOWER OF A HOLLYHOCK
Photographed on an autumn morning before the sun had warmed the bee into activity

BROWN-EYED SUSAN
The brown-eyed Susan, or black-eyed Susan, has been introduced from the western United States

QUEEN-ANNE'S LACE
The flat-topped umbel of Queen-Anne's lace or wild carrot usually has in the center an aborted flower, brown in color. By the time the seeds are ripe the umbel has become concave and dense, closely resembling a bird's nest

PARTRIDGE BERRY
This may be called the Siamese twins among flowers, for two flowers develop into one berry having one stem and two blossom-scars

WIND-BLOWN PODS OF THE MILKWEED
The seeds of the milkweed are scattered by the wind

food in positions well adapted to lead to planting. One of the best examples is the gray squirrel which buries many nuts each autumn,—one nut at a place. After a gray squirrel has buried fifty or one hundred nuts, let us suppose that the squirrel comes to some tragic end,—he may be shot by a hunter or killed by a dog. Then what is likely to happen to the buried nuts? They are in excellent position for germination. In case the squirrel were not killed, it is altogether possible that it would not find and dig up all the nuts it has buried. Those not found would be in fine position to grow.

It is believed that squirrels and mice have a great deal to do with transporting and planting the seeds (nuts) of forest trees.

In this brief article only a few of nature's methods of scattering seeds can be mentioned or described. There are many others, and every one is interesting.

"Happy is he who understands the causes of things."

A PARENT CEDAR AND ITS CHILDREN

The overcrowding due to the lack of efficient means of scattering the seeds is well illustrated by this old red cedar and its offspring

In the Days of the Giants

By DONALD CULROSS PEATTIE

WE made a prompt start that morning, for we were going to visit giants in the earth. Of all that has survived from the Mesozoic era, which began 200 million years ago and ended about 60,000,000 B. C., Sequoia is the king. It is so much a king that, deposed today from all but two corners of its empire, superseded, outmoded, exiled and all but exterminated, it still stands without rival. And from all over the world, those who can make the pilgrimage come sooner or later to its feet, and do it homage.

In Sequoia we see the heroic age of plants, the age of conifers. This is best thought of as the High Middle Ages of plant life, just before its Renaissance when the world literally burst into bloom. In zoological terms, it is the age of dinosaurs, when birds and mammals and the higher insects were just beginning.

Of Sequoia there are two species left, though once they were as various and abundant as are today the pines, their lesser brothers. One is the coastal redwood of California, which is the tallest tree in the world, and the other is the Big Tree of the Sierra Nevada, which is the mightiest in bulk. These two surviving species were here before the last glacial period. But as a genus or clan of species Sequoia has its roots in a day of fabulous eld. This noble line knew the tyrant lizards; through its branches swept the pterodactyls on great batty wings. As they saw the coming of the first birds, crawling up out of lizard shapes, so the forebears of our Sequoia witnessed the evolution of the first mammals when these still laid eggs, when they were low-skulled opossum-like things, when they became scuttling rodents that perhaps, gnawing and sucking at dinosaur eggs, brought down that giant dynasty from its very base.

Sequoia as a tribe saw the rise of all the most clever and lovely types of modern insects—the butterflies and moths, the beetles and bees and ants. Yet since there were then none of the intricate inter-relationships that have developed between modern flower and modern bee, Sequoia sowed the wind. It had flowers of an antique sort, flowers by technical defi-

This article is a chapter from a book on botany for every man by Donald Culross Peattie, published by G. P. Putnam's Sons.

Five thousand years of living, 12 million pounds of growth out of a tiny seed, and no one has ever known a Sequoia to die a natural death

nition, at least; petals and scent they had none. But their pollen must have been golden upon that ancient sunlight, and the communicable spark of futurity was in it. For Sequoia towers still upon its mountain top, and I was going there.

Journey to the past

The way back to this reef out of the Mesozoic is over the coastal ranges and across the Great Central Valley. And that, in early summer, is a blue and gold wide basin of drowsy heat. You sweep from the hills into its sparse and arid range lands upon a long hot breath. Wheat and willows border the irrigation canals that lead the scanty thaw of Sierra snows out on this burning plain; here is a geography like Egypt's, perhaps like that of Mars. The playas glisten with the salt and gypsum left behind when the lake waters dried. Maybe when all our seas are shrunken to intensely salty sumps, when our air is thinner and earth is very old it will bear a vegetation like this, of tumbleweed and salt-bush, greasewood and short grass, with tule rushes and cottonwoods hugging the last of the marshy grounds. By noon—if the start was early—one is deep in the fertile bosom of the Valley. Green alfalfa or golden wheat, vineyards and orchards go by with the shining hours. A sweet stupor blows in one's face. And then at last the first ground-swell of the coming mountain breakers lifts under the car.

It is a long climb still through the foothills of the Sierra. But now I sit up, with a lifted face. Beyond, higher in the east, portent is gathering. It takes shape, cloud-colored, gleaming with a stern reality where the sun smites a rocky forehead. Then appears that eternally moving miracle—snow in the summer sky. Sierra Nevada.

If the flora of the alkaline flats has perhaps the look of things to come, the foothill flora is all today's. Swift sprung, swift fading, shallow of root and delicate of bloom, bulbous or annual, it fits its hour. It is plant life as the dominant plants of the temperate zone must be to meet the terms of a planet with marked seasons, alternating rains and drought. It can face the diminishing forests, the advancing encroachments of man. Light freight of earth, these poppies

and blue sage, these lupine and mariposa lilies are sure to please, were never meant to last, turned out to meet a season's need, destined for the blades of the reaper.

Trees are thickening, among bigger boulders. Maul oak and black oak fall away behind, and dusty Digger pines, as vanguard. Greater things are coming; they send their breath ahead, a scent of rocks and resin, of damp and fern. It demands a deeper inspiration than the heavy valley air; it reaches to the bottom of the lungs, and braces a man for event.

The forests march upon the car; the ruddy soaring trunks of the sugar pines close around in escort. One hundred and two hundred feet overhead, their foliage is not even visible, screened by the lower canopy spread by western yellow pines which are giants in themselves. Groves of white-fir, smelling like Christmas morning, troop between the yellow pines. Aisles of incense cedar with gracious down-sweeping boughs and flat sprays of gleaming foliage invite the eye down colonnaded avenues, fragrance drifting from their censors that appear to smoke with the long afternoon light. It grows darker with every mile, darker and deeper in moss and lichen, dim with the dimness of a vanished era. We have got back into earliest spring, at this altitude, and the blossoming dogwood troops along, illuminating the dusky places with a white laughter.

With each breath, I feel as though I gained in stature. This aroma seems health itself. The further men get, I think, from pines, the worse for them. Life, if we had never left them, might be plain and hard, and men would not stop fighting or even murdering because they lived in such a place as this—history dispels any such illusion. They might suffer bodily pain and know great weariness. But they would not toss with insomnia, or doubt till they could no longer act. Men to match these trees might raise the devil but they would never for one moment believe in the sicklier saints. You could hardly be small here. You might, sometimes, have a noble thought.

Geologic in scale

For now, as the land of sunny levels has fallen remotely out of sight, there is a prescience in the cold air, of grandeur. We have climbed into the shadows; the drifts of snow are thicker between great roots,

and richer grows the livid green mantle of staghorn
lichen that clothes all Sierra wood in green old age.
The boles of the sugar pines, which are kings, give
place before the coming of an emperor. The sea sound
of the forest deepens a tone in pitch. The road is twisting to find some way between columns so vast they
block the view. They are not in the scale of living
things, but geologic in structure, fluted and buttressed
like colossal stone work, weathered to the color of old
sandstone. They are not the pillars that hold up the
mountains. They are Sequoia. The car has stopped,
and I am standing in the presence.

Centuries of fallen needles make silence of my
step, and the command upon the air, very soft, eternal,
is to be still. I am at the knees of gods. I believe because I see, and to believe in these unimaginable titans
strengthens the heart. Between 3000 and 4000 years of
living, 12 million pounds of growth from a tiny seed.
Three hundred vertical feet of growth, up which the
water travels every day dead against gravity from
deep in the great root system. Every ounce, every inch,
was built upward from the earth by the thin invisible
stream of protoplasm that has been handed down by
the touch of pollen from generation to generation,
for a hundred million years. Ancestral Sequoias grew
here before the Sierra was uplifted. Today they look
down upon the plains of men. Neither insects nor
fungi seem able to destroy a Sequoia utterly. Lightning may smite it dead—a fit ending, one may say for
such a godly tree. But Sequoias seem to have no old
age; while one part of the tree is ancient, another
part may be as young as the day before spring.

Aerial world

In their uplifted hands they permit the little
modern birds, the passerine song birds, vireos and
warblers, tanagers and thrushes, to nest and call. I
heard, very high above me in the luminous glooms,
voices of such as these. I saw, between the huge roots
that kept a winter drift, the snowplant thrust through
earth its crimson fist. A doe—so long had I stood still
—stepped from behind the enormous bole and, after
a long dark liquid look, ventured with inquiring
muzzle to touch my outheld hand. Bright passing
things, these nestle for an hour in the sanctuary of
the strong and dark, the vast and incalculably old.

That day I stood upon a height in time that let me
glimpse the Mesozoic. It followed the Coal Age, the
age of the fern forests, and it was itself the age of
Gymnosperms. Sequoias are Gymnosperms. So are
the pines, the larches, spruces, fir, yew, cypress, cedar

—all that we call conifers. Though there are other Gymnosperms that do not bear cones.

The Gymnosperms are, literally translating, the "naked-seeded" plants. For their seed is not completely enclosed in any fruit or husk, as it is in the higher modern plants that truly fruit and flower. Neither is the Gymnosperm egg or ovule completely enclosed in an ovary, as in the true flowers. To make an analogy, you could say that the Gymnosperms are plants without wombs, while the Angiosperms, the true flowering plants with genuine fruits, are endowed with that engendering sanctuary.

But though the seeds of the Gymnosperms are naked, they are seeds, and the seed is mightier than the spore. For the seed contains an embryo. Spores are very many and very small; they blow lightly about the world and find a lodging easily. But the seed is weighted with a great thing. Within even the tiniest lies the germ of a foetal plantlet, its fat cotyledons or first baby leaves still crumbled in darkness, its primary rootlet ready to thrust and suckle at the breast of earth.

Wood out of earth

This vital secret was inherited from the seed-ferns, back in misty days when the ferns were paramount. The conifers bore it forward; the true flowering plants were to carry it on and spread it in blossoming glory. Of that there was little hint in the Mesozoic forests. They must have been dark with an evergreen darkness, upright with a stern colonnaded strength. For they developed the power of building wood out of earth, not the punky wood of the tree ferns, but timber as we know it.

But they can be replenished. They can be grown

"LIVING ANCESTORS" of the lonely Sequoias were discovered surviving in the interior of China in 1944. These Dawn Redwoods (Metasequoia glyptostroboides) are restricted to a section only about 30 miles long. Unlike the redwoods, they shed their leaves seasonally.

and cut as crops, and they yield a profit on poor sandy and rocky soil, or in swampy lands where no other crop could be hopefully tilled. Thrifty, fertile, tough, industrial, they are of all trees the most practical. Ancient in lineage beyond all others, they rise tall and straight in the pride of their aristocracy. Sea-voiced, solemn, penciled against the sky, their groves are poetic as no leafier places. Conifers stand in the sacred temple yards of Japan, where, with venerating care, their old limbs are supported by pillars. They line the solemn approaches to the tombs of the Chinese emperors at Jehol. Solomon sought them in the peaks of Lebanon for his temple. But in all the world there are none like those upon our western coast of the Pacific.

And it was in the Black Hills of Wyoming that a fragment of the Mesozoic lay hidden till the days when the West came to be called new country. Miners on their way to Deadwood, cowboys riding herd found strange stone shapes, and broke off fragments. What lay in those calloused brown fingers, turned over curiously, ignorantly, was once sprung in the Gothic glooms of the Mesozoic forests. These were cycads, which must have formed the undergrowth of those prehistoric coniferous woods, hundreds and hundreds of species of them. A few linger today, scattered thinly over the tropics of the world. Some call them fern-palms; they have an antique look, stiff, sparse and heavy; crossed in pairs upon a coffin, they impart a funebrial dignity. Cretin of stature for the most part, growing sometimes only six feet in a thousand years, they are beloved in the Japanese dwarf horticulture, cherished in family pride there, since a cycad of even moderate size may represent a long domestic continuity.

What pride, then, and what a ring of age was there in the first set of fossil cycads from the Black Hills rim to reach the men of science at the National Museum in 1893! Professor Lester Ward hastened to the field, and what he found there, besides the bones of a great dinosaur and the petrified logs of old conifers, were not imprints but complete petrefactions. Atom by atom the living tissue had been replaced by stone. Here were hundreds of fruits, all the leaves a gloating paleobotanist could desire, perfect trunks, every detail of wood structure preserved, and dozens of species, some dwarf, some colossal.

Protection

Ward took back with him what he could. Other students hurried to the find; Yale and the Universi-

Moulin photos from Save-The Redwoods League

SEQUOIA SEMPERVIRENS (Coast Redwood)

Two distinct trees comprise the sequoias— the redwoods and the big trees. They are restricted to quite different areas as shown here

CALIFORNIA

SEQUOIA GIGANTEA (Big Tree)

ties of Iowa and Wyoming have great collections from Deadwood, and the government museums, too. Tourists carted away entire specimens, and what remained might have been utterly scattered and destroyed, had not Professor G. R. Wieland saved the last rich tract in the Black Hills. Close to the mountain where Borglum carved his heroic profiles, the scientist filed on the area under the homestead laws, and then presented his claim to his country. It has since been made Cycad National Monument.

These cycads, when the world was young and they were flourishing, must have brought into the dark monotony of the evergreen forests the first bright splashes of color. For the seeds of cycads are gorgeous scarlet or yellow or orange, borne on the edge of the leaf or commonly in great cones. They are sweet and starchy to the taste, and perhaps Archaeopteryx, that first feathered bird in all times, crunched them in the teeth that he still kept, reminder of his lizard ancestry. So, it may be, the earliest animals came to aid in the dissemination of plants, as squirrels do today, and birds. Somehow, at least, the cycads over-ran the world. Their reign had grandeur, but its limits narrowed. There is evidence that some of the Mesozoic cycads flowered only at the end of their immensely

Pictures, Inc.

long lives—a thousand years, perhaps. Then, after
one huge cone of fruit was set, the plant died to the
very root. A hero's death, but a plan ill fit to breed a
race of heroes. In the cupped hand of the future lay
other seeds, with a fairer promise.

Winter and summer the giant trees defeat the onrush of time
and stand as man's oldest living link with the geologic past.

Patterson photo from Save-The-Redwoods League

How the

Sequoias got

their name

◄ SEQUOYA with his syllabary.
From a painting made in 1828.

Photographic reproduction by Hodson

By HARRIETT WEAVER

It is altogether fitting that our most famous
trees should bear the name of a lonely, half-
breed cripple, for he was an artist, scholar and
statesman who devoted his life to the welfare
of his people—the American Indians

FOR whom are the Sequoias named? The usual botanist? No, not this time—nor for two of history's most illustrious generals, though their names were proposed. The distinction went to an American Indian, as gigantic in spiritual stature as the towering trees. His greatness of soul merits, now and forever, the tribute of mankind. This was Sequoya, the Cherokee.

Sequoya was born about 1760 (some say 1770) to an Indian woman of mixed blood, the daughter of a chief. His birthplace was the Cherokee village of Taskigi, Tennessee. His father, a white trapper, had tired of life among the Indians and gone his way, never to return. The young mother was blessed with extraordinary intelligence and did well in raising her son alone. In her company Sequoya found better companionship than among the braves of his own age, especially after he injured his leg and could no longer be active.

Rejected by his contemporaries because he was permanently crippled, Sequoya escaped within himself and too early began brooding over the oppression of his people by the white man. It was a heavy load for a small boy's shoulders, but it was fortunate for the Cherokees that he shouldered it, because there was need of sober thinking at this critical period.

As he reached manhood, Sequoya made a journey to the American Colonies. While he was there he beheld the wonders of the silversmith's craft. This he must learn so that he could fashion ornaments to delight his tribesmen! But how would he ever take the knowledge of tools, workshop, and techniques home with him? He had no way of writing all this down because he was illiterate. The Cherokees only spoke their language. There was just one way. He must store each detail in his mind.

This he did, memorizing the craft so well that when he reached his village he was able to set up shop, make the tools, and go to work. The silver ornaments he created have never been surpassed in beauty of design and workmanship by any other eastern American Indian. His tribesmen, who had always pitied him, now came from far and wide to watch him and to stare in wonder at his skill. Great was their admiration. Soon they looked to him for strength and leadership, and even found themselves consulting him on matters of state. He began to feel that the welfare of the Cherokees was his personal responsibility.

In desperately seeking a way to better the tribe, he remembered something he had seen while visiting the Colonies. The people there were speaking to each other on paper. They made little marks on this "talking leaf" as he called it, and, afterwards, whoever looked at the leaf knew what had been said. One man had many leaves tied together, to which he often referred. There seemed to be a brotherhood among these men who could speak in this manner. Sequoya then became convinced that the Cherokees must meet the white man on his own grounds — with quick wits born of unity — and never again, futilely, with bows and arrows.

So at the council fire Sequoya spoke his thoughts and presented a plan to the chieftains. He proposed that the Cherokees create a nation with a governing body that would pass laws and endeavor to raise their standard of living, while he, himself, would give up his profitable silverworking business and devote his entire time to making a written language for the tribe. These things he felt would unite the Cherokees against the continual persecution by the white man.

At first the idea was almost beyond the vision of the high men of the council, but finally they ceased trying to dissuade him, and at the age of 49 Sequoya laid aside his beloved tools and began a task of such colossal magnitude that scholars of today look upon it with awe.

The English alphabet, as we know it, has come down to us through 30 centuries of development, from Egypt, Phoenicia, and Greece. Almost overnight the entire Cherokee Nation was to become enlightened after this one selfless man dedicated twelve years of his life to the making of a syllabary.

All through these years, Sequoya worked alone and friendless, scoffed at by everyone, even by his own family. He was thought to be bewitched because of his endless and strange carvings on the tree bark. No one would have anything to do with him lest they, too, might become possessed of evil spirits. Yet he labored on, often working into the night by the light of a burning pine knot.

At the end of the third year, he had thousands of symbols—one for every word of the Cherokee language. Realizing that this would have no practical use, Sequoya then destroyed everything he had done and, undaunted, started all over again.

In the years following, he listened to his people as they spoke and so began to break down the words into sounds and units of sounds, or syllables. When he had finished, there were only 85 symbols—some of his own design and some that were English characters taken from an American newspaper he found beside a trail. His Herculean task was at last finished. Sequoya was ready to teach the writing to the Cherokees.

But no one would have any of it—not those mysterious signs—the workings of a demented spirit. The alphabet appeared to be doomed. And then two cocky young braves volunteered to be taught, though not sincerely to learn. They merely wanted to prove what everyone already thought—that Sequoya was mad. Much to their surprise, however, they discovered that the writing would work and that they actually could speak to each other on the leaves. On winged feet they sped back to their villages and spread the word. The redskins began pouring in from every direction.

Life for the Cherokees now took on new meaning. Learning to write became a passion that was even more intense than their religious zeal. All things were put aside while they mastered their written language — and within a few months, as a nation they were completely literate!

Parts of the Bible were translated into Cherokee in 1824, and the *Cherokee Phoenix*, the first Indian newspaper, made its appearance four years later. The tribal Congress meanwhile, had passed laws forbidding drinking but advancing agriculture, so that it became common for an Indian to own a large herd of livestock. Loads of grain and tobacco were shipped down the Mississippi to market on flatboats; cottons and woolens were manufactured on a grand scale. It was the Golden Age for the Cherokee, and to climax it all, the White

Cherokee Alphabet.

D_a	R_e	T_i	δ_a	O_u	i_v
S_ga O_ka	F_ge	y_gi	Λ_go	J_gu	E_gv
ᵛV_ha	P_he	ϑ_hi	F_ho	Γ_hu	ꝺ_hv
W_la	C_le	P_li	G_lo	M_lu	ꓬ_lv
ꝉ_ma	Cl_me	H_mi	ꝷ_mo	y_mu	
Θ_na t_hna G_nah	Λ_ne	h_ni	Z_no	ꝺ_nu	O_nv
T_qua	ω_que	P_qui	V_quo	ω_quu	ε_quv
U_sa ω_s	4_se	b_si	ꝉ_so	ε_su	R_sv
L_da W_ta	S_de L_te	J_di J_ti	V_do	S_du	ꝺ_dv
δ_dla L_tla	L_tle	C_tli	ꝺ_tlo	ꝺ_tlu	P_tlv
G_tsa	V_tse	Ir_tsi	K_tso	J_tsu	C_tsv
G_wa	ω_we	Θ_wi	θ_wo	ꝺ_wu	6_wv
ω_ya	B_ye	ꝺ_yi	f_yo	G_yu	B_yv

Sounds represented by Vowels.

a, as a in *father*, or short as a in *rival*.

e, as a in *hate*, or short as e in *met*.

i, as i in *pique*, or short as i in *pit*.

o, as *aw* in *law*, or short as o in *not*.

u, as *oo* in *fool*, or short as u in *pull*.

v, as *u* in *but*; nasalized.

Consonant Sounds

g nearly as in English, but approaching to k. d nearly as in English but approaching to t. h.k.l.m.n.q.s.t.w.y. as in English. Syllables beginning with g. except ꝺ have sometimes the power of k. ꝺ.S.ꝺ. are sometimes sounded to. tu. tv. and Syllables written with tl except ꝉ sometimes vary to dl.

▲ THE CHEROKEE ALPHABET is the unique accomplishment for which Sequoya is known best. With its 85 characters, it provided a means of written communication for the Cherokee Nation. Parts of the Bible were printed with these strange symbols as well as a weekly newspaper, the *Cherokee Phoenix*, which first appeared in 1828.

Father in Washington asked that a representative from the Cherokee Nation be sent to his Council Fire. Sequoya, of course, was chosen, and was received with honor and respect.

The Invasion

And then came tragedy. Gold was discovered in Cherokee country, and a horde of prospectors and settlers swarmed over the land, killing and plundering. Stock was stolen, grain was burned in the fields, Indian men were shot down in cold blood if they attempted to protect their families. The White Father was no longer friendly. His soldiers drove 13,000 Cherokees from their native soil to lands across the Mississippi in Oklahoma. Four thousand of them died on the way, and the survivors found themselves unwelcome intruders among kinsmen who had migrated there years before. Sequoya tried desperately to secure harmony, and he did unify them for a time, although their numbers were decimated and their spirit crushed.

Sequoya was well past 70 by now and wanted to live out his remaining years quietly, enjoying his hobbies. But a lifetime of service was too strong in him, and he began to dream of uniting all redmen in a common language. One summer day in 1843 he laid aside his garden tools and with the fire of a vision burning brightly within him disappeared into the unknown western wilderness, accompanied by a young brave. If they could just visit every tribe, listen to the talk, and make a written language that every Indian could understand! Wherever Sequoya went, the In-

dians received him worshipfully and did their best to give him the elements of the language they spoke so that he might try to forge a universal tongue.

On and on Sequoya and the brave plodded, across the plains and the Rockies, through blistering sun, and wind and sleet, camping first in grassy lowlands and then among the crags of alpine peaks. It was too much for the youth. Somewhere along the way he gave out. Sadly Sequoya buried him and stumbled on his high trail alone.

No doubt sensing that he was on his last trail, the grand old man kept going, determined to find the lost band of Cherokees that had disappeared into Mexico long, long ago, when he was a boy. He wanted to find them and re-unite them with their brothers.

But what he sought was beyond all human endurance, and at last Sequoya became too weakened from old age and his indescribable hardships. Far away, in the Mexican Sierras he came to the end of his journey. Beside his campfire that night he listened in a half dream to the song of the coyotes on a distant skyline, and watched the smoke of his campfire curl lazily toward the stars. Reluctantly, the flame of his spirit flickered and went out, even as his campfire. The wind and the sands of time covered his earthly remains but left no marker on his resting place.

And yet—most magnificent of all monuments to the memory of a man's devotion, is the giant Sequoia, the living proof of life eternal, dedicated to an ideal which, like the great trees themselves, will surely live on through the ages to come.

Creatures of th

Most visitors to Sequoia National Park are so spellbound

by the Big Trees that they do not notice these other

denizens, upon whom the giants depend for their existence.

By JOHN L. BLACKFORD

All photographs by the author

IN the shadows, upon furrowed trunks, on needle-padded forest floor, and in the towering evergreen-top of the most stupendous grove in the world lives an elfin community of wildlife without which the Sierran giants themselves would perish. Here in Sequoia National Park, as elsewhere in nature, the marvelous and complex interweave of life pattern and habitat shows every winged and four-footed "forester" playing a part in relation to all the rest.

This famous Park, continuing and enlarging upon the concept of natural areas to be set aside in perpetuity for all of us and our descendants, was the second National Park to be so dedicated, and it is noteworthy that it was established to protect and preserve *living* things.

The idea of National Parks, first inspired by the scenic wonders of Yellowstone, has spread over the globe. But it was the Sequoias that brought the realization, after centuries of exploitation, that life in other forms than man can be beyond price.

Standing literally like columns in the Temple of Time, the immense sequoias of Giant Forest rival or surpass the life spans of all other living forms. Yet these Big Trees of the Sierra, which stood and prospered in matchless grandeur while civilizations rose and fell, are intimately dependent upon their associated plants and animals. They cannot live without the infinitely smaller winged, furred, and bacterial lives that flourish with them— or that perish when their habitat is materially disturbed.

It is this vital story of nature's delicate balance—of the interdependence and interrelationship of all the plants and animals making up a distinctive *life community*— that the sequoias of Giant Forest can tell us. It is because of biological harmony and adjustment between every living form in this mighty forest that the Big Trees maintained health and strength through the millenniums and attained their venerable age of around 4000 years. Here, too, in these cathedral corridors of Time, is the secret for human happiness—for man cannot achieve lasting security until he again finds a harmonious

Giant Groves

> THE GOLDEN-MANTLED
GROUND SQUIRREL refor-
ests many a rockslide with
his "planted" seedlings.
He looks and acts so much
like his striped cousins as
to be called the Big or
Golden Chipmunk. But
his colorful stripes reach
only to the shoulder in-
stead of to the end of his
inquiring nose, as with the
true chipmunks

> BLUE - FRONTED JAY: an alert watchman of the woods, who warns many creatures of danger. Occasionally he becomes a predator. All life in some way holds other species in balance. When the crested jay hides acorns in the soil, he becomes a forester. An eater of wild fruits, he sows their seeds. He carries cones about and distributes the evergreens. He is a clown, a wit, a servant of the forest, a thrilling adventure in wild beauty

< RED-SHAFTED FLICKER. This handsome, friendly woodpecker is familiar to most of us through his jovial *wicka-wicka* and his engaging presence about our dooryards. In the Giant Forest he seems a different character, as he darts among the tremendous red-brown boles of *Sequoia gigantea* or plunges arrow-like into the vast canyons of the Kaweah. As feathered ant-eater, grasshopper, hunter, acorn gatherer, and wild-berry harvester, his impact upon his environment is a most beneficial one

relationship with his natural environment.

Modern man's most successful attempt to understand and reveal biological relationship—the science of ecology—is more than a science; it is an exciting adventure into the living world. In Sequoia National Park, a few steps from pavement, you are lost in that world. The varied Sierra Montane Forest broadly girdles the mid-elevations of California's Sierra Nevada. Islanded in this expanse of Ponderosa, Jeffrey, and Sugar Pine, White and Douglas

Fir. Incense Cedar, and Black Oak are the occasional massive groves of sequoias. Half of them, perhaps 5000 Big Trees, are preserved in Sequoia National Park; and nearly half of these tower together in Giant Forest. Their burly crowns thrust 300 feet into the Sierran blue. Paleobotanists say their kind are survivors from the remote ages of giant reptiles and mammals.

Such is the home of Sequoia's varied and intriguing wildlife, the furred and feathered foresters of this mighty Montane wood.

⋏ No TIMBERLAND could long endure
without the constant check placed upon
its teeming insect population by hungry
birds. A professional in this class is the
Northern White-headed Woodpecker,
strikingly marked guardian of all the
mighty Sierran conifers. He is a characteristic Sequoian, frequently seen in flash-
winged flight among the huge pillars of
the forest

⋖ HART OF THE SEQUOIAS: a handsome California Mule Deer buck
with new horns in the velvet, reclining at the buttressed base of a
colossal Big Tree in the Giant Forest. What part does a deer play
in a sequoia's lengthy life? His browsing controls the undercover
beneath which Big Tree seedlings take root. Nor is there any member of a life community that does not, in life or death, in some way
affect the organic chemistry of its living associates

▼ THE SIERRA CHICKAREE, a geographical race of
the Douglas squirrel. This spunky little "forester" clings to the bole of an incense cedar as he
"steals" nuts and acorns from the cameraman

▲ PICKER AND SEEDER of wild berries and fruit, this female Sierra Grouse helps maintain the floor and understory of the montane wood. Her precocious downy brood place a heavy check upon fast-multiplying insect life. The budding of conifers by wintering grouse thickens the new growth—just as does a nursery man's budding and pruning. No game bird should be "harvested" to the point where it cannot fulfill its vital role in the delicately balanced natural world

▼ THE CREEPER, whose days are passed in specialized work upon the tree trunks, is an obscure but important life-link in the chain of arboreal survival and growth

◄ BLACK BEAR. His tearing apart of old logs and stumps in search of beetles, grubs, and ants hastens forest decay. The soil is "cultivated" during his digging for roots, bulbs, and burrowing animals. In return for these and many other services in Nature's scheme of things, he enjoys an unexpected pleasure in the forest. The "Bear's Bathtub," a rain-filled cavity hollowed by fire from two huge sequoias joined at the base, is patronized regularly by an approving ursine clientele

▲ AMONG the intricately interwoven life patterns in the Giant Forest, the Stephens Fox Sparrow specializes in the efficient inspection of forest duff and surface topsoil. His kicking legs and sharp eyes unearth and detect countless creeping and squirming forms. His appetite controls their numbers. To those who know them, the loud rich songs of the Fox Sparrows spell the inexpressible lure of the wilderness

▼THE ADAPTABLE WESTERN ROBIN is a familiar Sequoian, and his carols are inseparable in our memories from the montane groves. Extensive range, abundance, varied insect diet, and frequent broods of young—all make him an important control agent here, as in any of the widely differing biotic communities where he is at home

➤ THUS the trails leading into the sequoias disclose a magnificent forest wildlife society. Its delicate balance has been achieved through the adaptations of many creatures and thereby perpetuated for untold thousands of years

The Goliath of Seeds

By WALTER HENRICKS HODGE

Longwood Gardens

RESIDENTS of temperate climes are generally unfamiliar with large seeds. When we plant our garden vegetables, we know that a handful of average-sized vegetable seed should suffice for a row or two. In comparison, a horse-chestnut seed is really something to marvel at, as is shown by their popularity among small boys. Yet the seed of the horse chestnut is a puny thing compared to a coconut, and a coconut in turn is puny, too, when set down beside a Seychelles nut, or coco de mer. For the Seychelles nut is the largest true seed that grows and is to the plant world what an ostrich egg is to the animal world. In short, it is the Goliath of all seeds.

For centuries prior to about 1600, gigantic hard-shelled nuts, two or three times the size of an average coconut, were sometimes found washed up upon the shores of India and other lands bounding the Indian Ocean. These enormous seeds looked like oversized coconuts, yet no one knew their origin other than that they were brought in by the sea, and so in this way the name coco de mer (sea coconut) fell upon them. Such marvelous flotsam was rare and, as was common in those days, its rarity was supposed to give it wonderful virtues.

At first, people were not sure whether the great floating objects were plants, animals, or minerals. Before long, and typical of the times, a number of wild tales had been invented to explain the source of these sea-deposited objects. One had it that the nuts grew on submerged trees near the island of Java. Yarn-spinning sailors reported that on diving to pick these under-sea seeds, the trees would mysteriously disappear. Another story related that in certain parts of the tropical ocean the trees, growing above the surface of the water, harbored a griffin, or vulture-like bird, which was accustomed to fly to the nearest land, where it fed, of all things, on tigers, elephants, and rhinoceroses! Unwary sailors were also devoured by the flying monster if their ships were inadvertently drawn in by the giant waves that, supposedly, surrounded the tree at all times.

Seeds obtainable only after passing such hazards must certainly be as valuable as the mythological golden apples. It is little wonder, then, that kings and other potentates of the Orient coveted the strange nuts and even passed decrees that these peculiar objects could be acquired only by persons of high rank. Apparently the nut's chief virtue was as an antidote to poison, and in a day when royalty was under constant threat of poisoning, the possession of a coco de

The largest seed that grows was shrouded in mystery until its island home was finally determined

Photo by Hugo Schroder

▲ THE HUGE Seychelles nut resembles a coconut in some ways. But it weighs upwards of 40 pounds, and its "meat" becomes as hard as vegetable ivory

Photo by L. H. Bailey

▲ SECTION through a dehusked Seychelles nut, showing the peculiar two-lobed design

mer was almost a necessity for a successful and continued rule. Obviously, no sum was too large to pay when a charmed life itself could be thus ensured. In those days the nuts must have been hollowed out to form tight receptacles, for it was believed that poison, however violent, would be ineffective when added to water that had been stored in one of these containers. As the coco de mer became more widely known, it grew in virtue to such a degree that it came to be considered a general panacea, which accounts for the new name, *nux medica*, which was given it in

the sixteenth century.

All the aura of mystery that veiled the coco de mer in its early contacts with civilized man was finally lifted in the middle of the eighteenth century. About that time Praslin Island, one of the 29 islands included in the Seychelles group (lying in the Indian Ocean northeast of Madagascar) was discovered, and in its extensive forests of palms was found a curious species of palm (*Lodoicea maldivica*) bearing a giant nut. The source of the coco de mer was at last known.

Despite inroads by agriculturists and curiosity-seekers, groves of *Lodoicea* are still to be seen on this tiny isle of palms. The trees love their own company and form extensive colonies on the slopes and intervening valleys. Like many another interesting palm, it has wandered at man's behest far from its home, and quite a few distant tropical gardens—a number of them in our own hemisphere—can boast living specimens of this famous species.

The Seychelles nut palm is oversized not only in its seed but in most other respects. The straight, tough trunk, said to be "as upright and unyielding as an iron pillar," sometimes attains a height of 90 feet and bears at its summit giant, rigid, fan-shaped leaves that often measure 25 feet from the tip to the base of the leaf stalk. A peculiarity of the palm is a queer protective, socket-like bowl into which the bulbous base of the trunk snugly fits. As tough as the hard shell of the nut and apparently made of the same substance, the curious bowl is extremely resistant to decay, and half a century or more after one of these palms has been cut down, its socket may be found perfect in every respect.

But today, as in the past, it is the fruit that is the most spectacular feature of *Lodoicea*. In its homeland a female palm usually attains an age of at least 30 years before it produces its first crop of nuts, and even then the tree is hardly out of its youth and may not yet possess a true trunk. Clusters of the great nuts, which require about five years to mature, resemble somewhat the common coconut in all except size (a single coco de mer may weigh upwards of forty pounds!), for they have a similar smooth, tough outer coat or husk

Photo by L. H. Bailey

▲ YOUNG at 40 years: a male Seychelles nut tree growing in Jamaica. It is not yet old enough to have a true trunk

which overlies the same sort of fibrous layer that one associates with the coconut bought at the corner market. The big difference lies under the smooth outer husk, for the giant Seychelles nut is, unlike a coconut, bilobed, a fact accounting for the misnomer "double coconut" often met with in discussions of this palm. In its youth the jelly-like interior, or endosperm, is edible like that of a green coconut, but at maturity most of it is as hard as vegetable ivory. The edibility of this bizarre nut may thus be transient but not its fame, which firmly rests on its size, making it the Goliath of all seeds.

Hitchhiker of the Sea

The fish that rides free to its meals lends itself

to one of the strangest fishing methods known

By N. J. BERRILL
Professor of Zoology,
McGill University

WHEN Columbus returned to the Caribbean the year after his first voyage of discovery, he was in less of a hurry to get back to Spain and took more time to explore. He found Cuba to be a lovely island, and it was during a leisurely voyage among the islets off the south coast, which he called the Gardens of the Queen, that Indians came in a canoe to hunt turtle with a fish.

The Admiral himself watched while they fastened a cord to the tail of a curious fish and let it go down into the sea with the line held to the canoe. The explorers who were with him recorded their observations as follows: These fish "have a large mouth all full of suckers like a cuttlefish, and they are very daring, as ferrets are here. And when they are thrown into the water, they go to fasten themselves on some fish; of these they do not leave hold in the water but

only when they are pulled out . . . they had one of these fish fastened on the bottom of a large turtle, and they waited to get it into the canoe." The description is not quite accurate, for the suckers are not in the mouth but on the top of the head. And while Columbus was not familiar with the fish, it is one that was well known to the ancient civilizations of the Mediterranean.

The fish was the Remora (pronounced REM-o-ra), otherwise known as the Shark-sucker. Its peculiarity is that its dorsal fin, which starts life like the dorsal fin of most other fishes, changes into a complex sucker or adhesive organ shaped like the sole of a shoe and divided into many compartments. The fish uses the sucker to hitchhike from one place to another. By means of suc-

New York Zoological Society photo

➤ REMORAS attached to a Sand Shark. They
will share the shark's meal when he finds it

tion it attaches itself to any convenient large swimmer of the seas,
whether it be a shark, turtle, porpoise, or even the manatee, which
Columbus called the mermaid. This
is pure laziness, for what the remora gets is a free ride to a free
meal. It attaches by the back of its
head to the lower side of its traveling companion and hangs on till the
meal is reached. Then it drops off
long enough to join in the feast,
after which it reattaches and goes
for another ride. And there is little
doubt that the hull of a ship looks
as good to the remora as the belly
of a shark.

There is a very old legend that
the remora can slow down sailing
vessels and even stop them altogether. We repeatedly find the idea

in medieval and classical literature,
and the fish was often drawn on
Greek and Roman vases. In fact,
the death of the Emperor Caligula
was attributed indirectly to a remora, which was supposed to have
fastened to his great galley and
held it back while the rest of his
fleet escaped. Its scientific name,
Echeneis, itself means "holding
back," and older writers usually referred to it as the Ship-holder. The
remora is never big enough to exert
much force against a moving boat.
One kind reaches a length of about
sixteen inches, and another about
three feet. There is little doubt,
however, that a rowboat or small
sailboat would be slowed down by
one of these underwater hitchhikers, and several of them might make

their presence known to the oars-men of a larger boat. Mark An-thony's delay and defeat at the battle of Actium was also supposed to have been caused by the attach-ment of many suckerfish to his galleys. Perhaps any excuse was better than none, especially when Cleopatra may have been the real reason.

The remora fastens itself very tightly. It has been reported, for example, that when one is at-tached to the glass of an aquarium, it will hold so firmly that the sucker is left attached to the glass, and the fish is so injured that it dies.

Another old name for the sucker-fish is the "Reversus," from the mistaken idea that the fish swims on its back. It does give that im-pression, but it actually swims in the normal manner.

According to reports left by Co-lumbus and his companions, the Caribbean Indians caught these curious fish when they were young and raised them in pools. Before and after a hunting trip below the sea, the Indians would talk to the fish, cajoling and praising them as though they could understand.

There is something very strange in the widespread use of this method of fishing. It reflects either the wanderings of mankind or the tendency of men throughout the ages to use their ingenuity in every possible way to obtain food be-yond their reach. There is no doubt that man is inherently lazy and will make someone work for him if he can. But is it not surprising that the remora is employed to hunt fishes, turtles, and other sea ani-mals, with a cord fastened to its

tail, not just in the West Indies but in Malaya, China, the Spice Islands, and northeastern Australia? Chin-ese, Polynesians, Melanesians, and Australian aborigines isolated from the rest of the world for thousands of years, as well as Carib and Lucayan Indians of the West In-dies, all use or have used the same fish in the same way. It does seem more reasonable to believe that the statement "Great minds think alike" accounts for this widespread practice, rather than that the method was discovered only once and was then carried over so large a part of the world.

The aborigines of the Barrier Reef angle for suckerfish with hooks made from pearl shell or bone fastened to woven bark lines. Then they fasten the fish by the tail and keep it in shallow water until it is time to hunt for turtles. In leashing the fish, a hole is made at the base of the tail fin by means of a turtle bone, and one end of a very long piece of string is inserted and made fast to the tail. A short piece of string is also passed through the mouth and out the gills, securing the head end, and the fish is slung over the side of the canoe. When a turtle is sighted, the short piece is pulled out of the mouth, and away the remora goes. As a rule, just before the fish is re-leased, the disk and shoulders of the sucker are scrubbed with dry sand to remove the slime and ex-cite the fish.

So long as the line is kept taut, the remora cannot let go of any-thing it has caught, and the size of the turtle or fish that can be cap-tured is limited only by the strength of the line and the breaking strain of the remora itself. Turtles up to 100 pounds have been hauled to the surface in this way. But when the turtle is very large and clings to the bottom (and green turtles can weigh several hundredweight!), the natives dive overboard and follow the line down to the turtle to secure it with a rope.

One little difference stands out between the customs of the aborigines of Australia and the gentle Indians described by Columbus. Whereas the Indians endowed the remora with intelligent understanding and treated the fish humanely, the Australian aborigines at the end of a day's fishing eat the remora, too.

◄ THE DISC by which the shark sucker attaches itself is a greatly modified fin. Suction is created by the many slits

▼ THE REMORA appears to swim upside down, but the suction disc is really on the top of the head. The fish at right was photographed while clinging to the glass of a tank

New York Zoological Society photo

Woody Williams photo

How to Collect Shells

Tips from an expert on a hobby that will bring you beauty, knowledge, and adventure at the small price of perseverance

Condensed by special permission from the book *American Seashells*, by R. Tucker Abbott. (D. Van Nostrand Co., Inc.)

▼ BEACHES up and down the land attract thousands bent on discovering rare and beautiful specimens

Ace Williams photo from Black Star

By R. TUCKER ABBOTT
*Associate Curator, Division of Mollusks,
U. S. National Museum*

SEASHELLS and man have been closely associated since the dawn of civilization when primitive people gathered snails, oysters, and other kinds of mollusks along the seashore for food, implements, ornaments, and money. In modern times, thousands of people have become interested in collecting shells purely for their aesthetic beauty and their educational value. Their beauty and permanence make shells an ideal thing to collect, and the infinite variety of their form and color proves an endless source of gratification not only to the collector himself but to his friends.

Collectors of fancy seashells are constantly in search of specimens of outstanding quality. A number of species are well known for their high value or unusual beauty. Perhaps the classic example is the Glory-of-the-Seas, of which only twenty-three specimens are known. In addition to these twenty-three specimens, three were destroyed during World War II and eight, formerly known to exist, are missing. A search in grandmother's attic or along some East Indian beach will doubtless bring others to light. But there is a wide range of personal taste in shells, and it is not only the so-called rarities in museums that are worthy of note. The man who covets a brilliantly patterned Olive Shell of rich golden-red colors may see little in a tiny white shell that another collector treasures for its intricate snowflake sculpturings. For many shell collectors, desirability is gauged by the top price that a specimen may bring. For others, the important judging point is the scarcity of the species in nature or perhaps its rarity in collections.

Instructions for collecting seashells are much akin to revelations of the secrets of good cooking. Everyone has his favorite methods. There are, however, a number of fundamentals that will help guide the collector in obtaining a representative series with the least trouble.

The most successful collectors mix together four ingredients to obtain what appears to most of us "unusual luck" in finding good shells. These are knowledge of the habits of mollusks, a familiarization with the physical conditions of the ocean and the seashore, a sensible choice of collecting equipment, and, perhaps most important, a large proportion of perseverance. The first three can be learned from books and from veteran collectors, but only keen observation and many hours of trial collecting will develop satisfactory techniques.

Fred G. Koeth photo from Frederic Lewis

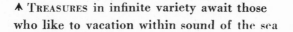

⋏ TREASURES in infinite variety await those
who like to vacation within sound of the sea

Low tide is obviously the best time to collect, and most collectors make long-range plans to catch the spring tide, consulting the Coast and Geodetic Survey Tide Tables to plan in advance for the lowest tide of the month. Tide Tables for the Pacific and Atlantic coasts may be obtained for a fraction of a dollar from the U.S. Department of Commerce, Washington 25, D. C. Since the rise and fall of tides are caused by the attraction of the moon, and to a lesser extent by the sun, a good simple rule is to plan your collecting for the time of new and full moon. Low tide lasts for about fifteen minutes, but profitable collecting may be done one hour before or after. It is useful to know that the tides are about 50 minutes later each day. Beware of the dangers of rising tides, especially if you have waded a long distance out to some small isle at low tide. Tide currents can be extremely strong at the narrow mouths of inlets, and swimmers are urged to familiarize themselves with local conditions.

Most species that live between the tides reveal themselves more frequently about half an hour after the tide has begun to rise. A great number of species are more active a few hours after dark, while others are content to wait until early morning before starting on their foraging missions.

Certain seasons are most favorable for certain collecting. September seems to be the best time, for instance, to gather shells on the Carolina strands. During late April and early May there is more likelihood of the Purple Sea Snail *Janthina* being washed ashore on the east coast of Florida. After winter gales, some New England beaches may be strewn with large surf clams, *Spisula*.

If one were to use all the collecting equipment that has been recommended by friends and books, he would certainly resemble a Christmas shopper in full knightly armor. Crowbars, bilge pumps, shovels, rakes, sets of screens, hammer and chisels, even water wings and miner's caps have been suggested. It is true that these and many other pieces of equipment are ideal for specific and limited purposes, but for general collecting, simplicity and lightness of gear are most important. Streamlined collecting in the intertidal areas when it is calm calls for little more than a pair of canvas shoes, bathing suit, and a few small cloth bags. Guard against sunburn. Most shells can be picked up by hand, and the more fragile ones can be put in matchboxes or thumb-sized vials.

When a breeze is disturbing the surface, it is impossible to see the bottom, and many collectors use a glass-bottomed bucket or a diving mask floated on the surface to clear

▼ THE FACE MASK is valuable for shallow diving

U. S. Navy photo

U. S. Navy photo by Abbott

↟ TRUE SONS of Triton who don't mind a pounding do their searching where the surf breaks

the view. A square or oblong bucket about a foot each way and ten to twelve inches deep may be made of light wood. The glass is set in the bottom and held in place with a thin layer of white lead and strips of molding or quarter rounds. Paint the inside dull black to avoid reflections on the glass. The water bucket is useful to those who enjoy diving for shells. It not only serves as a friendly support between dives but may be used as a collecting receptacle. Diving masks or water goggles are indispensable for collecting many shells that are normally found in waters down to twenty feet in depth.

A fine-mesh wire screen bought in any kitchen utensil store can be put to excellent use in sandy or muddy areas, where many interesting small shells live. Screening for mollusks is a favorite pastime with many collectors. Copper mesh can be used if you plan to screen over a period of a few months. Forceps are sometimes useful in getting small shells out of rock crevices, but in general it does not pay to search individually for minute shells. Mass screening or taking a large bagful of bay bottom or beach drift home for leisurely sorting brings richer rewards. Shaking clumps of seaweed over the screen often gives encouraging results, for many uncommon species are found nowhere else. Breaking apart coral blocks often yields interesting rock boring clams.

If you have yet to collect your first live Olive or Terebra shell, wade along the shores of a sandy bay on a quiet, moonlight night and with the aid of a flashlight follow along the trails in the sand. A dozen daytime visits to the same locality will never compare to that hour of night collecting. Not only are sand-dwelling mollusks on the move, but in rocky regions the cowries, mitras, and murex shells are out from under their hiding places and traveling along in full view.

Overcollecting is to be avoided in some localities, particularly if certain species have taken several seasons to build up their population even to a moderate size. By leaving at least most of the mature specimens and perhaps one or two adults you will assure yourself of good collecting at the same spot later. While it is unreasonable to expect people to roll back the rocks they have overturned, some collectors do this in order to obtain additional specimens on their next visit. Once destroyed by sunlight and air, the protective algae and the sponges need many months to grow back. However, the blame for the extinction of many beautiful mollusks at Lake Worth, Florida, and in many other places rests not with greedy collectors but with superdrainage experiments, city pollution, and construction work.

Keeping accurate information with your collection is essential. Many private collections are eventually left to museums for the enjoyment and use of future generations. Today's crowded museums must rightfully dispose of specimens that have no data and are therefore of no scientific value. Large and beautiful collections representing much time and cost would have been of inestimable value to science had someone only taken the time to record where each specimen was collected. "Australia," "Hawaii," or "California," is not enough. A good entry would read: "North end of Captiva Island, Lee County, Florida. Leo Burry, collector. July 4th, 1952." Many careful collectors add interesting notes concerning the depth of water, type of bottom, abundance, and so forth. A rare shell in perfect condition, correctly identified and with accurate information, is almost worth its weight in gold.

The beauty and value of a collection depends largely on the manner in which specimens are cleaned and the methods in which the shells are arranged and housed. The majority of snails and clams can be cleaned of their animal soft parts by merely boiling in fresh or salt water for about five minutes. The meat can then be extracted with a bent safety pin or an ice pick. Shells having a highly glossed or enameled finish, such as the cowries and olives, should never be thrown directly into boiling water. Start them in warm water, bring slowly to a boil, and then let cool gradually. Any rapid change in temperature will crack or check the polished surface. Save the horny operculum, or trapdoor, when it is present. A plug of cotton will hold it in the aperture after the shell is dry.

Many shells are difficult to clean even when the boiling system is used. Usually the tip end of the animal's body remains in the shell of such genera as *Terebra, Vasum,* and *Xenophora.* Vigorous shaking or syringing with a powerful blast of tap water will get most out. Filling the shell half full of water and setting it out in the shade for a day or so with an occasional

syringing will help. If odors still persist, a few drops of formaldehyde in the shell, plus a cotton stopper, will eliminate the objections.

In the Pacific Islands, most collectors bury their shells alive a few inches under soft, dry sand. In a few weeks they are dug up and washed. The sand must be sifted for smaller shells and for the opercula. Some people who do not ob-

▼ A BEACHCOMBING FAMILY examines their day's haul, which happens to include a lot besides shells

Nolan Patterson photo from Black Star

ject to flies set their shells upside down in the sand and allow blowfly larvae or maggots to clean out the meat in a week or so. Vigorous rinsing of the shell is then all that is necessary.

Many delicate shells, including most land ones and small fragile clams, may be placed in fresh water overnight and then syringed or picked clean. The shells that are composed of two halves hinged together are usually the easiest to boil and clean. Allow the pairs to dry in the flat or "butterfly" position as this will permit ready inspection of the hinge teeth for identification purposes.

Many tiny shells obviously cannot be boiled and picked clean. Shells less than a third of an inch may be soaked in seventy per cent grain alcohol and then placed in the sun to dry thoroughly. Isopropyl alcohol may be used, but it is best to use this at fifty per cent strength. Never use formaldehyde (or formalin) to preserve mollusks. The shell will turn soft, lose color, and often crumble away in a few months.

Most shells are ready for display in their natural state. However a large number of gastropods, whose beauty is hidden by coral and algal growths, need a certain amount of "face lifting." A stiff brush, soapy water, and diligence will usually suffice. Many collectors soak specimens in a strong chlorine solution for a few hours to remove part of the unsightly growths without damaging the shell. If you have several similar specimens, however, it is best to keep at least one in its natural state.

Very few expert collectors use acid in treating shells, since this often gives specimens a very unnatural, although colorful, sheen. It is used occasionally to remove limy deposits and to brighten up old specimens. Commercial dealers dip the Pink Queen Conch, for example, for five or ten seconds in a vat of one part muriatic acid to four parts of water and then rinse in fresh water. Shells can be dipped with forceps in full strength oxalic or muriatic acid for two seconds and then immediately put under cold running water. This may be repeated until the desired effect is obtained, but it should be pointed out that any acid treatment ruins most shells for scientific study.

Polishing abalone shells and cutting cross sections of larger shells require special equipment such as electrically run burring wheels and circular diamond cutters. A visit to a shell factory will be of profit to those wishing to undertake this interesting hobby.

Although seashells are easy to keep since they do not deteriorate and generally do not fade in color like many insects, they present special problems in housing because of their many sizes and shapes. There are three general types of collections—the knickknack shelf, the display arrangement, and the study collection.

The first of these is usually the result of a summer's random beach collecting by the novice. Many important private collections have started in this manner.

The display collection for museums, libraries, clubs, or even the home is limited by the pocketbook and by the type of secondhand display cabinets that can be afforded. Little more is needed than common sense to secure good artificial lighting, attractive but neutral backgrounds, neat labeling, and the proper spacing of wisely selected specimens. The exhibit should be designed for its eye-appeal as well as for its interest. One has a wide choice of themes—a selection of local shells, of mollusks of economic or medical interest, shells of odd habits, or examples of colors and patterns. Miniature display boxes with cotton background and glass or cellophane covering

are very popular. If of uniform size, they can be neatly stacked in a closet when not in use. The labels should give the scientific and common names and the geographical range.

The name "study collection" may sound ominous to some, but this type of housing can actually bring more joy and less work than any other system. It is not only neater, more compact, and just as attrac-

▼ SOME MAKE LAMPS and other decorative objects from shells

Carroll Seghers photo from Black Star

tive as the display type, but it also permits the collector to locate any specimen quickly and add new material with the least rearranging. The choice of cabinet and style of drawers for this collection will be limited, of course, by the collector's pocketbook. If the cabinet is oblong and about table height, additional cabinets can some day be set alongside for desk space. Pine, basswood, or any of the whitewoods can be used. It has been reported that certain oaks have a detrimental effect on shells that have been stored away for years. The cabinet door should swing all the way open but permit the drawers to be pulled out when it is only open ninety degrees. Some students prefer removable doors. The ideal cabinet is 40 inches (or 80 inches) high, 22 inches wide, and 32 inches deep. Runners for the drawers are 30 inches long. If wooden, they can be ½ x ⅜ inch and set 2¼ inches apart; if of galvanized sheet iron, 2½ inches wide and bent along the midline to form an L. The inside measurements of the wooden drawers would be 20 inches by 30 inches and 1⅝ inches deep. No runners or handles are necessary on the drawers.

All cardboard trays to hold specimens should be ¾ inch in depth and all of their other outside dimensions should be multiples of the smallest type of tray. In other words, if you start with 1½ by 2 inches, the next larger tray is 3 inches by 2 inches, then 3 inches by 4 inches, then 4½ inches by 6 inches, and the largest of all would be 8 inches by 9 inches. Five sizes is enough. Odd-sized trays prevent neatness. Cardboard trays covered with glossy-white enamel can be purchased in any large city, or you can make them, holding the corners together with adhesive tape or butcher's tape. The labels should be pasted on the lower left corner of the lid. A duplicate label or a slip of card bearing the catalogue number should be placed in the box. Some people can afford to have glass-covered boxes. Smaller specimens are kept in small glass vials without necks. Use cotton for plugging them; corks are expensive and eventually deteriorate.

A catalogue is most essential to prevent loss of valuable locality data. Each specimen should bear the same number, written in India ink with a fine pen, as the label and catalogue entry, for identification in case of accidental spilling. Run your catalogue numbers from one on up in a thick ledger about 12 inches by 8 inches and give more space to "locality" than any other section. Do not experiment with mystical letters indicating the locality or other information or waste time with a card catalogue. Keep shells that are too small to number in vials or covered boxes with a small slip bearing the catalogue number.

Your collection should be arranged in biological sequence, that is with the first drawer containing the primitive abalones, followed by the limpets, and on up to the specialized bubble shells (*Bulla*). You may want to place your unassorted or unidentified material in the last few drawers.

Exchanging is an ideal way of sharing your local rich hauls and obtaining species beyond your collecting sphere. A list of the many hundreds interested in exchanging is published in several directories of conchologists and naturalists. Some people make up elaborate exchange lists, which they send around to other collectors. Exchanging is worth while and exciting, but it is time-consuming, and you must be careful not to let your main collection suffer.

Shells mailed or expressed up to 20 pounds in weight will travel safely protected by loose newspaper and packed in cardboard cartons obtained from the grocery store. Mailing tubes are good for small lots. It is better not to try to send living snails through the mail.

If you start collecting shells, you'll meet a lot of people you never would have known otherwise, and if you get too expert on the local shells, you'll be plagued with requests for help in identifying specimens. So while you are learning, have a heart. Ask first whether the identifier is willing to help you, and never send more than five species at a time. Photographs are not satisfactory for identification. And remember that one of your own shells may prove a welcome gift to your identifier.

▼ THE ULTIMATE in accessibility and educational value is attained by the collector who builds up a study collection

Courtesy Ralph Humes, Miami, Florida

Beauty and Variety in Shells

A Study in Shell Photography

BY ROY WALDO MINER

Late Curator of Living Invertebrates
The American Museum of Natural History

THE soft-bodied animal known as a mollusk acquired the habit of manufacturing carbonate-of-lime to form a protective shell at a very early age in the earth's history. This faculty was already well developed at the beginning of the Cambrian Era, for the rocks of that time contain abundant fossils of mollusk shells buried more than 600,000,000 years ago. Doubtless, this shell-forming habit accounts for the fact that so many species of mollusks have survived extinction from their enemies to the present time. In fact, more species of mollusks are in existence today than of any other group of animals except insects, about 90,000 species having been recorded by scientists.

Since the mollusk shell is of hard substance, and the animal outgrows it, enlargement must take place by addition to its margin to keep pace with the tenant's requirements. This function is performed by the soft mantle, a thin membrane that encloses the entire creature. Most of the shell enlargement is due to lime secreted by the relatively thick edge of this structure.

The shell, therefore, is actually a record of the mollusk's past life and an expression of all its activities. The periodic cessations of growth are marked by concentric lines representing the edge of the shell's aperture each time that growth stopped. Flaring lip-spines, due to more or less frequent exuberances of shell formation just before certain of these waiting periods, are completely preserved, when growth is resumed, as conspicuous sculptural features. Colored pigments deposited by special glands at the lip-margin remain, as the mollusk shell grows, to form the elements of a beautiful pattern on each whorl.

Thus, shells may be beautiful or they may be grotesque, but they are always interesting. Even when picked at random from a collection they are sure to fascinate both student and artist, whether the latter be a painter, sculptor, or photographer.

The remarkable and often surprisingly variable forms of shells and the contrasts of light and shade presented by their sculpture are especially irre-

➤ A WELL-PROTECTED OYSTER. Not all bivalves (two-shelled mollusks) are devoid of sculpture. The Thorny Oyster *(Spondylus Americanus)* is abundantly equipped with long, flattened spines, curving outward in menacing fashion, gayly colored with rose, orange, and yellow. It inhabits tropic seas, where its rich hues blend with the multicolored setting of the coral reefs.

It is usually attached to coral rocks by one of its valves, and thus cannot skip about like the Deep Sea Scallop to avoid its enemies. Hence the need for its formidable armature to repel invaders.

sistible to the skilled camera artist, as illustrated in this series of photographs, so well executed by Miss Bernhard. Incidentally, the pictures provide an opportunity for commenting on some interesting features of the various species of shells which she has selected for portrayal.

Photographs by
RUTH BERNHARD

◄ SOUTH MEETS NORTH in shell sculpture: a study in contrasts. The Lace Murex *(Murex florifer)* of Florida, ornate with branching spines, and almost Gothic in its shelly architecture, is shown in close juxtaposition with the Puritan simplicity of the New England edible Deep Sea Scallop *(Pecten magellanicus).* The Scallop is protected by streamlined paired shells of purely utilitarian aspect.

The *Murex* belongs to a large family of coiled sea snails, many of which are noted for their elaborate spiny ornamentation. They include the species from which the ancient Tyrians extracted their famous purple dye, which afterwards became the royal purple of the Roman emperors.

In contrast to this almost grotesquely sculptured creature, the plain valves of the scallop waste no superfluous shelly material to enclose their soft-bodied inhabitant. The scallop is one of the most active of mollusks. Aided by its powerful muscle and an elastic ligament in its hinge, it alternately and rhythmically opens and closes its shells with spasmodic rapidity, shooting out a stream of water from between them, thus' propelling itself in irregular flight through the sea depths.

▼ VERSATILE SNAILS. The Swamp Apple Snail *(Pomacea paludosa)* is so called because it is about the size, shape, and color of a small green apple. It inhabits the swampy regions about the tributaries of the St. John's River in Florida, while other members of the family are found in fresh waters of the tropics in both the Old and New Worlds

THESE MOLLUSKS are quite amphibious, for they breathe with gills when submerged. The gills are found in a large, partly enclosed chamber, which enables them to retain moisture when out of the water or during dry seasons. At such times they breathe air, often for months. Thus they are said by some authorities to represent a transitional stage in the evolution of land mollusks.

▲ RED HELMET, also called the Bull's Mouth, because its aperture has a red flaring upper lip and a rolling lower one. The slitlike orifice with wrinkled modeling, narrowed in the center and slightly expanded at the ends, is indeed very suggestive of a bovine mouth!

The orange-red spire, when standing with the aperture downward, is helmet-shaped. This is one of the commercial cameo shells often seen carved into bas relief by skillful artisans.

This shell is well known as a household ornament, often used as a doorstop. It is sometimes equipped with an electric light for use as a table lamp, the wonderful coloration of the shell being brought out by the light shining through it.

This species is common in the Indian Ocean, especially off the coast of Zanzibar.

◄ A STUDY IN SYMMETRY. The remarkable Heart Cockle of the Mediterranean Sea, *Glossus humanus,* is a bivalve with shells that display a most unusual symmetry. The umbos of the two shells match each other perfectly as they curve to their peaks in a faultless spiral, and as seen here they present a striking heart-shaped figure, from which this shell derives its name. The Heart Cockle lives in cool waters at depths of from 15 to 450 feet.

◄ INTERNAL ARCHITECTURE. A shell of the Giant Whelk (*Busycon canaliculatum*) has been broken open to show its interior, and, incidentally, to reveal the story of the shell growth. When newly hatched, the whelk possessed only the little knob-like shell which still shows at the summit of the spire. As the animal grew, it built the shell larger in a spiral course to fit its growing body. The outer curve of the spiral formed the expanding outer shell surface. The inner side was squeezed compactly, resulting in the more or less solid columella, or central spiral stem, the main mechanical support of the shell. This is shown clearly in the photograph.

This is one of the largest mollusks found along our Atlantic Coast. It devours oysters and other bivalves with the aid of the hard, rasplike teeth of its proboscis. It pries the helpless bivalve open with the edge of its shell and its strong muscular foot.

Ψ FOR A SEA-GODDESS'S TRESSES. Venus's Comb (*Murex tenuispina*) is an appropriate name for this species, after the goddess who was born of the ocean foam. The graceful shell entitles it to be called the most beautiful of the Murices. The slender, tapering canal is equipped with three rows of long, curving spines, alternating with three other rows of short ones, all arranged in parallel series, strongly suggesting a most unusual type of comb.

The conical spire, at the right, is adorned with alternating rows of large and small finely set ribs. The shell aperture or "mouth" is a perfectly arched, lenticular opening. The color of the living shell is soft brown, often tinged with bluish.

This mollusk lives in the Indian Ocean, ranging also to Japan and Australia.

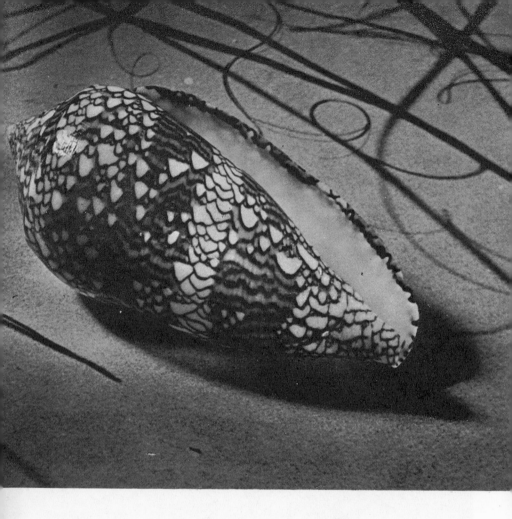

↟ A PRINCE AMONG SHELLS. The cones may be considered the royal family of shells. The Cloth-of-Gold Cone (*Conus textile*), shown here, is dressed in princely garments, richly patterned in chestnut brown, gold, and white, in contrasting zig-zag stripes crossed by broad revolving bands composed of pure white mosaic triangles outlined in brown.

Four hundred species of cones are found in tropical seas throughout the world, but especially in the Pacific Ocean and the Far East. Most of these exhibit gorgeously contrasting patterns, adding greatly to the colorful reefs where they are found.

They prey voraciously upon worms and live fish by means of their harpoon-like teeth.

Their needle-like teeth are supplied with a venom and are capable of dealing a vicious wound to the careless hand that picks them up.

These shells are much esteemed by natives of the South Seas, one species being used for money, while another is reserved as a symbol of chieftainship. The rarest of all, the "Glory of the Sea" (*Conus gloria-maris*), is much sought after by collectors. Not more than twelve specimens of this shell are known in collections.

▼ A WEIRD CONFERENCE FROM COAST TO COAST. Here, two American shells, one from the Atlantic Coast the other from California, are apparently trying to impress each other with their relative grotesqueness.

At the left, the common Worm Shell (*Vermicularia spirata*), which looks like a worm but is a mollusk nevertheless, started off in life as a perfectly respectable sea snail, as may be seen from the close spiral of the coils at its tip. Then, apparently, its shell-building activities got out of control, for in the latter part of its existence the shell wandered aimlessly in loose coils all over the sea bottom. It is often found, with others of its kind, in great coiling masses, perhaps for mutual protection.

At the right, the Three-cornered Trophon (*Trophon triangulatus*), from deep water off the California coast, displays its fragile, spiny shell. The photographer has posed it with its spire downward, buried in the sand, and with its round aperture facing the Worm Shell, doubtless to enhance its weird effect. Its delicate drab or soft brown coloration and exquisite sculpture make it one of the most attractive of sea shells. It is quite unusual to get a perfect specimen, because of its great fragility.

> ➤ SEA SNAIL AND BIVALVE. These shells typify two of the main classes of mollusks, the Pelecypoda, or bivalves, and the Gastropoda, or snails.

The Pelecypoda have two nearly equal shells, hinged together at the top, while the Gastropoda possess a single, spirally coiled shell.

They are represented here, respectively, by the common Hard Shell Clam (*Venus mercenaria*), familiar on our Atlantic Coast as one of our most welcome table delicacies, and Triton's Trumpet Shell (*Charonia tritonis*) of the South Seas and East Indies.

The Hard Shell Clam, common though it is, possesses a special beauty of its own, because of the graceful, symmetrically equal shells, with their evenly developed concentric growth lines. The closely locking internal hinge and two powerful muscles keep the shells tightly closed against the opposing action of the membranous elastic ligament, which causes the shells to open when the muscles are relaxed. This ligament shows conspicuously in the photograph, as an external feature at the upper part of the shell junction.

Triton's Trumpet is beautifully marked with brown, yellow, purple, and red arranged like lines of overlapping scales along the whorls. The Polynesian natives use it for a pot, the horny operculum (not present here) serving as a lid. The spout is formed by the curving canal which terminates the shell aperture at its base. Sometimes a hole is made near the apex of the spire, and the shell can then be blown like a trumpet. It is one of the largest of the sea snails, often reaching a length of sixteen inches.

➤ A CASTLE OF PEARL. The Chambered Nautilus shell (*Nautilus pompilius*), famed by poets and artists, sought after by collectors and merchants of mother-of-pearl, is the habitation of a noble mollusk of unbelievably ancient lineage, reaching far back into geologic times. Scientists call it a "living fossil," because its primitive make-up has persisted to the present time with little change.

The graceful spiral is conspicuously patterned with reddish brown stripes, alternating with cream color. There is a large black blotch at the center, near the shell-opening.

The lining, and, in fact, the entire thickness of the shell beneath the thin colored surface, is composed of iridescent mother-of-pearl. The interior of the coil is divided into a succession of chambers by concave pearly partitions, gradually increasing in size from the central chamber outward.

The animal, a relative of the squids and octopuses, lives in the outer chamber, and, when grown too large for it, seals up its former home and constructs a new one.

It is particularly abundant near the Philippines, Fiji, New Caledonia, and neighboring islands.

▼ THE GROTESQUE IN SHELLS. That shells may be weird as well as beautiful is shown by the Spider Shell (*Lambis rugosa*). First cousin of the West Indian Queen Conch (*Strombus gigas*), the adult shell, instead of developing the widely flaring lip characteristic of the latter species, expends the momentum of its shell-forming energy in producing the six long, curving and tapering spines, which sprawl in various directions from the lip margin. These spines are hollow when first formed, but they finally become solidly filled with shell material. The young shell can hardly be recognized as the same species as the adult, for it has a perfectly ordinary smooth lip. Later, flat budding projections appear, which develop into the extraordinary adult condition.

The Spider Shells are found in the Pacific and Indian Oceans.

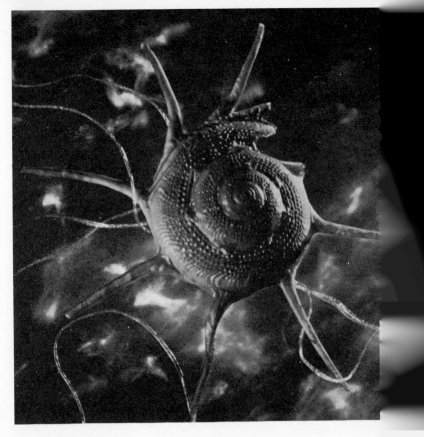

➤ A DANDY AMONG FROG SHELLS: the Frilled Frog Shell *(Biplex perca)*. It is one of the strangest of Japanese snails. The frills appear on only two sides of the shell, thus giving it a flattened appearance. Japanese fishermen net this species in large numbers and use the shell for jewelry. There are three other species of *Biplex* in the Indian and Western Pacific oceans, but this is the largest. It sometimes reaches a length of 3 inches. The smallest *Biplex* is from the South Pacific, where it lives in shallow water on coral reefs. It is less than a half inch in size and has a vivid mauve mouth, or aperture.

◄ THE JAPANESE STAR SHELL. This fragile Star Shell *(Guildfordia yoka)* of the Sea of Japan is phantom-like in its delicate spiral symmetry. Around the flattened spire and body whorl radiate slender tapering spines. The shell is relatively common within its region. It is about two inches or more in diameter. While this particular species is of comparatively limited range, other shells of the genus *Guildfordia* are widespread in tropic seas, but none occur in the West Indies. Many are characterized by a tendency to produce more or less flattened spires and radiating spines or tubercles. The filaments in the photograph are not parts of the shell, but are threadlike seaweeds.

Shells, Their Growth an

BY WILLIAM K. GREGORY

*Curator Emeritus of Fishes
and of Comparative Anatomy,
The American Museum of Natural History*

THE kingdom of beauty is free to all who can enter it, but only those who have eyes to see can find their own way to its inner temple. Many will be content merely to glance at a sea shell and say that it is pretty before placing it to their ears to "listen for the sound of the waves."

Some prefer to keep the mysteries unsolved and take for granted whatever beauty they may find in Nature's patterns, but experience shows that the more we can learn about the origin and unfolding of a natural design, the more deeply do we feel its beauty.

In natural designs a profusion of details often tends to conceal a few simple and easily grasped principles. But while the principles have a wide application, any particular case always represents the end result of an age-long history. This must be deciphered at least in its main outlines before the facts of the present can be properly interpreted against the background of the past. And since a part of the remote past does live on in the present,

(Below) ONE STYLE, from infancy to aldermanic girth.
The swelling contours of this worthy clam
Are here engraved upon his ample shell.
Each growth ring spells one feast, each line one fast.
One feast, one fast, and thus his life ran on
Through many a varied year until the storm
Stopped short the life, but left the shell unharmed

All AMNH photos by Coles

Evolution

Full appreciation of form and color among clams and conchs is gained through an understanding of how Nature unfolds their complex patterns from simple beginnings

it is necessary both to keep open before us the fossil records of ancient life and to compare the living with the dead in order to learn which traits come from the older heritages and which are of later date.

Now there are many thousands of species of fossil and living shell-bearing mollusks, so it might seem at first to be a hopeless task to learn much about them even in a long lifetime. Fortunately, however, the molluscan world is one which permits itself to be surveyed and mapped in great detail. Through the coöperative and mutually corrective labors of many students, it is now divided into classes, subclasses, orders, families, genera, species, subspecies, and individuals, in descending order. If we constantly keep these "maps" (or classifications) before us, we may in even a few years gradually build up some knowledge of the territory as a whole, especially if we study our individual specimens as representatives of the larger groups.

As in the human world, fashion designs for clams and conchs involve both form and color. Although the clam tribe is by no means ancestral to the snail-like mollusks, the history of its shells is in some respects easier to interpret and yields many striking examples of our present theme. If we look at an ordinary clam, we can see that the outside of each of its shells bears a concentric series of evenly curved lines. Each one of these lines records a former stage in the growth of the shell, so that the most recent zone is on the outer edge, while the tiny baby shell is usually preserved at the top. This habit of carrying on its back a nearly complete set of

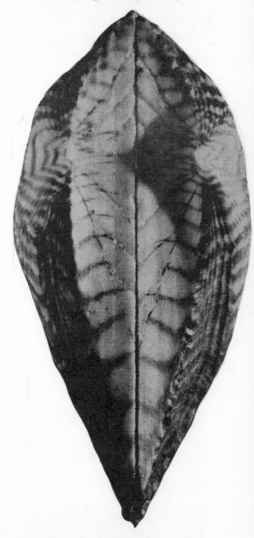

(*Above*) MEDIEVAL ART or natural design? In this Florida "turkey-wing," as viewed from above, the growth forces have wrought a brilliantly balanced symmetry. The "wings" on either side start from the umbo or growth center. The straightness of the median hinge line records the even balance of the opposing growth forces

(Above) THE WORLD'S FASTEST CLAM? With its long, thin, stream-lined shell and sharp-edged foot, the razor clam would seem like a sure winner in the Clam's Day sweepstakes. Its cousin the Tellina clam *(upper row, right),* although far less successful in reducing "waistline" and adding to "length," yet seems to represent the rangy type from which the "razor" has been bred

growth stages from infancy to old age is useful to the clam because its armor is thus automatically enlarged to suit the size of the animal within.

The shells of most other mollusks, both bivalves and snail shells, grow in much the same general way, that is, by building out the shell along its outer edge, next to the gape, or open-ing.

The material of which the shell is made consists mostly of calcium car-bonate, which oozes out from many small glands that lie along the outer edge of the growing mantle or apron. We can readily understand that if all

(Right) WHERE flounces are required. The stony folds built up by the mantle of the spiny oyster may have a protec-tive value against starfishes

(Below) THE CONTOURS SHIFT, the plan alone remains: diverging propor-tions among mussel and oyster shells. In the most primitive stage *(lower row, left)* of the horse mussel both length and height are but moderately devel-oped. Increasing height in the wing shell and pearl oyster culminates in the excessively high and narrow hammer oyster *(far right).* Increase in length alone produces the pen shell *(top, left)*

the little shell glands secrete their material at equal or nearly equal rates, the shell will grow larger evenly in all dimensions so that an old clam will be very like a young one. If you ask me what makes all the little shell glands work together so evenly, I can only say that a racial or hereditary tendency in certain kinds of clams causes all the little shell glands to be as much alike as peas in a pod and to behave far more alike than do the famous quintuplets.

There is a convenient technical name for any such series of similar units. Some years ago I invented for them the term *polyisomeres,* from the Greek stems meaning "many equal parts." I may say now that polyisomeres of one kind or another form at least the background of all natural as well as human designs. And if clams could sing, even their vocal patterns would involve polyisomeres of several kinds.

The most primitive of the clam tribe have their right and left shells, or valves, nearly alike, and the hinge line along the back is long and straight. Thus if we look at the "turkey-wing" shell, we see a symmetrical design with its rights and lefts disposed toward each other as the so-called "mirror image" is to the original.

Every student who has seen models of the development of the frog's egg

(Above) AN ANGELIC ABACUS. The angel wing's amazing system of radiating ridges and nodes record the intersections and resultants of two sets of growth forces, one radial the other zonal

(Below) COLOR DESIGNS in the clam tribe. The widening rays of the sunrise shell have been laid down along the edge of a steadily widening mantle; the dark wedges of Chione follow the strong folds which the mantle secretes at regular intervals. In the turkey-wing *(lower row, right)* the wavy bands are due to unequal growth rates

will recall that after the spherical stage is reached, the cells begin to heap up along either side of a notch which eventually lengthens out in a fore-and-aft direction. In this way a spherical body is transformed into an elongate animal, with "mirror image" (or bilateral) symmetry. Something of the same sort has happened in the remote ancestors of the familiar long and narrow razor clams, in which the fore-and-aft length of the shell has come to be many times greater than its height. This change took place so long ago that even the oldest known fossil representatives of the razor clam

family already resembled their modern descendants in general plan; but certain members of the family are much less elongate than others, and in the not distantly related family of the Tellina clams we find shells of intermediate proportions that seem to lead back to a more normal clam type.

The razor clam, as we have seen, owes its peculiar form to an extreme emphasis of its length. And so does the giant pen shell.

The opposite case, in which the vertical diameter has become excessively great, is seen in the high, narrow hammer oyster. Both extremes may have been derived in remote geological times from a more primitive and central form, illustrated by the horse mussel, in which both length and height are moderate.

Thus when certain parts of an evenly growing series become accelerated or retarded, equality, or monotony, gives way to emphasis or accentuation. In technical terms, polyisomeres give rise to *anisomeres,* or unequal parts.

When certain equally spaced units are selected for emphasis, the surface of the shell may be covered with nodules, ribs, flounces or spikes. In the ornate spiny oyster, such more or less regularly spaced outgrowths have a double aspect: they are polyisomeres in so far as they resemble each other, but they are anisomeres in comparison with the less emphasized units which they have outdistanced in growth.

In this case the spines may be useful to the owner because they would make it difficult for a devouring starfish to wrap its arms around the shell in order to pull the two valves apart. So a natural design which happens to have a certain aesthetic value to the human eye may have a purely utilitarian value to its owner.

The color patterns of bivalves are doubtless just as much a result of spa-

(Below) FASHIONS in hat shells. Seen from the underside these diversified limpet shells seem made for heads of varied shapes

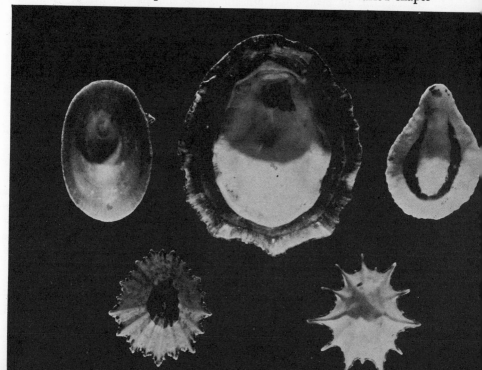

(Above) A WARNING TO PINOCCHIO: shells that start out as respectable little turrets but lose control of themselves and soon turn into a tangled mass of "worm" tubes

tial arrangements of growth forces as are the forms of the shells. Pigment-producing cells are located in the edge of the mantle just beneath the under surface of the horny outer covering.

When a man is called a "pinhead" he is supposed to be deeply insulted, but to a clam such an epithet would be not only a compliment but the equivalent of an honorary title, for a clam has literally no head at all. Whether a clam has even a tiny brain is partly a matter of definition. He has at least a network of sensory and motor nerves which are connected with several small receiving stations called ganglia, which serve to coördinate his simple activities. Thus he does pretty well in the game of life. He lives snugly in a streamlined movable house, and if danger threatens, his plow-like foot can pull his shell quickly into the yielding sand. The countless clams and other bivalves might be compared to the flocks and

herds of peaceful herbivorous animals on land. The typical sea snails, on the contrary, play the part of the carnivorous animals and live by killing and eating the weaker citizens of the molluscan world.

A typical sea snail is a much more complicated animal than a clam. It has a real head and a very complex feeding machine, including a long bandsaw or flexible, strap-like rasp set with countless teeth. With this it can make neat circular holes in the shells of its victims, who may belong either to the clam tribe or even to its own species, for in the sea snails' age-long code of morals only might makes right. The sea snail can hunt for its prey, creeping about on its muscular base or foot. The snail's viscera are coiled up like a Chinaman's queue and they are tucked away inside of the shell which rides like an elephant's howdah on the animal's back. This shell is like a fool's cap which has been twisted into a spiral horn. On top of the foot,

behind the shell, is a stout oval or circular shield. When stimulated the snail squeezes as much water out of himself as is necessary and pulls himself into the lower whorl of the shell. The last part that rolls into place is the oval shield or operculum, which serves as a trap door and completely closes the aperture, forming a stout front door to the snail's castle.

A real knowledge of the evolution of form and color in the world of clams and conchs can hardly be gained without reference to questions of their respective origins on the Tree of Life. Clams and snails are exceedingly different creatures, and their lives have been distinct almost since the beginning of the fossil record; yet both are shell-secreting mollusks with many

(Above) THE TOP SHELLS go in for stripes or zigzags. The pigment-secreting cells all follow the "stop-and-go" system but by varying the times and rates produce a wide variety of patterns

fundamental characters in common, so it is probable that at some exceedingly remote period they had a common ancestral source. What was this source?

The best scientific opinion considers that the snail type is the older. Its original ancestor was a slug-like animal with a shell shaped like a pointed cap on its back as described above. This was manufactured by a glandular fold

(Below) THE ABALONE'S "MOUTH" is big, because his foot's so large! Scientifically speaking the aperture of the shell widens to keep pace with the growth of the foot which fills it. The curlicue in the left-hand shell is all that remains of the primitive spire

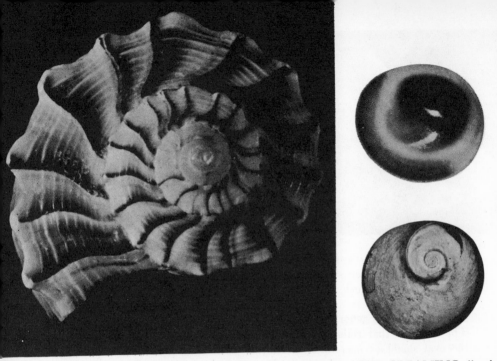

(Above) THIS SPIRAL goes the "wrong" way. And the pattern goes with it

(Above) THE GLEAMING "cat's eye" (at top) guards the sea snail's castle. The spiral growth of this unique form of trap door is shown on its inner side (below)

of the outer skin known as the mantle. When in the course of time this cap became twisted it tended to become one-sided and assumed the peculiar spiral form typical of snails as we know them. At some remote period before the twist of the shell became developed, certain groups of snails were evolved with a split mantle which produced two nearly equal shells, and thus the bivalves or clam-like mollusks arose.

On the other hand, among the fossil relatives of the clams the ram's-horns (Chamidae) actually succeeded in developing secondarily a coiled snail-like shell out of their left valve, while their right valve gave rise to an operculum-like structure. But these snail-like clams are only pseudo-snails, for the true operculum of real snails is not developed by the mantle.

The embryology of the clam and snail tribes shows only that they both belong to the primary grand division of the animal kingdom that includes the annelids and crustaceans.

In most shells after the baby stage is passed, the growth tendencies, whatever they may be, continue to become more and more pronounced but do not change their general character and direction, so that the young shell is much like the old shell except for its smaller size. In some shells, however, there is a marked change in the direction of the growth after the shell has attained a certain stage. In the erratic worm shells, for example, the baby and early child stages form normal and respectable little turrets, but afterward the shell-secreting mantle seems literally to get out of touch with the inner coil of the shell. It pauses, loses its sense of direction, and then wanders wildly first on one side, then on the other, until a tangled mass of stony tubes results.

Although the color patterns of the sea snails attain greater complexity than those of the clam tribe, the basic principles are the same, especially that color patterns are first of all dependent upon the growth pattern of the shell itself. Thus it seems reasonable to suppose that the more primitive types of shell-forms would also bear the more primitive color patterns. Among the more primitive top shells, for example, we find vertical zigzags or wide stripes set obliquely to the spiral axis; finally, as in the New Zealand tiger shell, they may break down into vermiculated streaks on a dark background.

That the structural spirality of the shell itself plays an important part in the arrangement of its surface pattern is well illustrated in the reversed whelk shell, in which the radial bars are tangent to the spiral.

In the cat's-eye turban of the tropical Pacific the excessive pigmentation which is common in tropical shells has produced a rich brown background

(Below) TURBANS are always in style. These swirling coils suggest the glittering court of an Indian prince

(Below) IN THE "BLEEDING TOOTH" shell the "teeth" serve as part of the hinge for the trap door

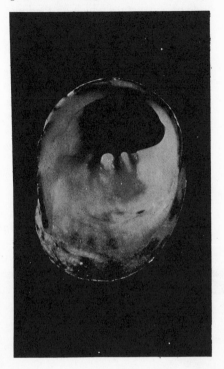

relieved by **U**-like marks and bands. Since the edge of the mantle is a bit like a slowly moving recording cylinder, we may conceive that a horizontally-placed **U** results from a vertical bar which has been bent forward by growing faster at either end than in the middle.

The remarkable "cat's-eye" which is seen on the lid of certain turban shells has been developed on the outer side of a structure which on the inner side plainly shows its spiral mode of growth. A trace of this underlying spirality may be seen in the cat's-eye itself. The circular or zonal appearance of the cat's-eye pattern may be due perhaps to the slow spread of an oily spot of pigment outward from the center in a spirally-growing, thick lens of pearly substance.

Comparison with the large eye-like spots in the wings of certain butterflies, or with the eyes in the tail feathers of the Argus pheasant is likely to be misleading, for each of these has arisen in its own peculiar way. Nevertheless in every such case which I have as yet examined, it is possible to trace a progressive series leading from a simple alternation of dark and light to an eye-like end result; and all such cases exhibit a contrast of light and dark which we may provisionally think of as an expression of polarity

(Below) A SIMPLE THEME with endless variations. The immortal Bach might well have been an ardent admirer of the volutes and olives, because they too learned the secret of extensive repetition with varying emphasis. Their patterns are all built up on the wavy or **V** plan

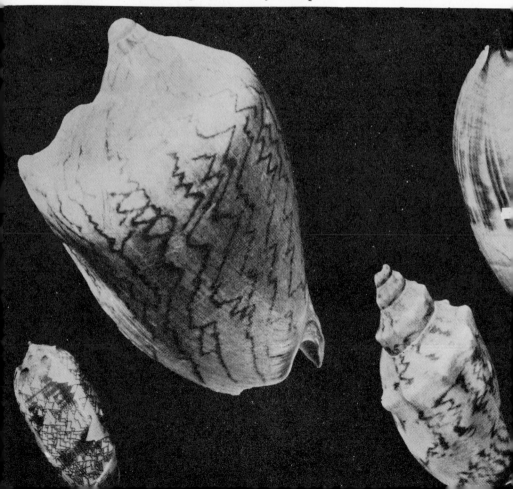

(Right) THE SEA SNAIL with the "magic girdle." In a sea snail's beauty contest this pert little columbellid might win first prize away from more stately rivals

(Below) MOST MOON SHELLS *(Natica)* and neritids *(upper row)* like to be inconspicuous. Some moon shells, however, wear pretty bands *(lower row, right)*

(Below) THE MUTTONFISH deserves a better name. On its back this shell bears one of the most beautiful of all the designs in the world of sea snails

or repulsion between chemical substances of opposite characters.

The question whether the cat's-eye pattern of the turban shell may be of any particular value to its owner in the struggle for existence, is not easy to answer. The cat's-eye is really more like the eye of a large fish. It may be visible from above when the snail is crawling along under water. It might conceivably scare off small fishes which otherwise might be bold enough to nibble at the snail itself. But it is doubtful whether it could be seen by the giant conchs, which may be supposed to be the principal enemies of the turban shell and which rasp a circular opening in the shell itself.

(Below) **TWO MITRES and an auger. Solomon and all his pomp are gone, but these more splendid gifts remain**

The *Shoestring* FERN

Found southward from Florida, it fools people everywhere.

By Edwin Way Teale

ON THE Florida Keys, along the coast, and in the hammocks of the Everglades, a curious fern grows on the palmettos and other rough-trunked trees. Anchored to its support, it hangs down like a mass of round green shoelaces. It seems formed of a cluster of stems without leaves. Natives call it the shoestring fern, the beard fern, or the grass fern. Botanists know it as *Vittaria lineatta*. All the year round, the string-leaves of these ferns produce spores in immense quantities.

Rarely found more than a few feet above sea level, the shoestring fern ranges south from peninsular Florida through the Caribbean islands into tropical America.

As early as 1753, pressed specimens of the fern reached the herbariums of Europe from the island of Santo Domingo. Thirty-five years later, in 1789, the pioneer botanist Andre Michaux first discovered the plant on the North American mainland during his explorations in Florida.

Our slaughtered shorebirds sound a warning for other forms
of wildlife that are threatened

enjoy them

WHILE THEY LAST

▼ RUDDY TURNSTONES. In the days of abundance, the Boston market offered
turnstones at 10 cents a dozen

Allan D. Cruickshank from National Audubon Society

By BEN EAST

UNLESS you are an old man, you were born too late to witness the great autumn flight of the shorebirds over the dun marshes of Cape Cod, the rush beds of Lake Erie, or the prairie sloughs of the Dakotas.

Fifty or one hundred years ago, massed legions of curlew and plover, yellowlegs and snipe, wheeled and dipped above the salt meadows and mud bars in the bright blue days of September, in numbers that challenge the imagination and defy description. The shorebird flight then deserved a place among the truly great wildlife spectacles that graced this continent. But it was gone before our time, sacrificed to the greed and short-sightedness of a generation that had neither understanding nor the will to practice restraint, dissipated by men to whom the sagging game bag was the only measure of a successful day afield.

AMNH photo

⋏ THE ESKIMO CURLEW (*Numenius borealis*) can now be seen only in a museum. Of the many shorebirds decimated by market gunners in the late nineteenth century, it suffered most severely. It is now practically extinct.

"Are you ready?"

A disputed shot

General view of the tournament grounds

Chasing
and killing wounded birds

These drawings from 1881 show the conflict between a shooting organization that called itself the New York State Association for the Protection of Fish and Game and Mr. Henry Bergh, founder and president of the American Society for the Prevention of Cruelty to Animals. In this tournament at Coney Island, 201 contestants shot at 2000 live pigeons for prizes valued at $1490. During the shooting, men and boys cruised the field with sticks to kill wounded birds. A sensation was caused when small boys distributed a pamphlet by Mr. Bergh urging American citizens to "abolish this cruel and unsportsmanlike pastime."

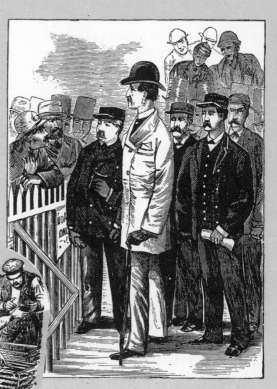

Mr. Bergh
was refused admission to the grounds

The victims of the day's sport

▲ BIRDS like the sanderling might have shamed the hunter by their size alone, but they stood high on the "game" list

Much the same thing is happening, many conservationists believe, in Alaska at the present time. And the same alibis are being given. We are told that bald eagles are destroying the white sheep, that caribou have taken new migration routes, and that the moose are simply falling victim to the wolves. So the tales run, echoing the selfsame theme as the stories men told 50 years ago to account for the tragic decline of the flights of plover, curlew, and yellowlegs in the United States.

Today the shorebird legions are a tattered remnant. Of all the clan only one, the woodcock, remains on the legal game list for hunters in the United States. And charming, wily gamester that he is, he is so unlike the others of the tribe, both in his way of life and in the kind of shooting he affords, that for practical purposes he should hardly be ranked as a shorebird.

Of the rest, the Eskimo curlew has probably gone beyond the help of protection. A specimen was taken in Labrador in 1932, but although we have had reasonably reliable sight records within the past few years, practical conservationists fear that this bird may have joined the ghostly company that includes the great auk, the passenger pigeon, and the heath hen.

The others—the plovers and yellowlegs and Wilson's snipe—missed the same fate by a margin too narrow for comfort. Depleted by a slaughter that has hardly a counterpart for wantonness in the history of American field sport, they won respite from the guns only when their numbers had shrunk to the danger point and beyond, when they had dropped so far that it has taken years of protection to produce signs of a comeback.

Even if these birds returned to the full carrying capacity of the land, their marshes are now so limited in area that they could never regain their former abundance. The continual conversion of land to man's uses makes the birds increasingly dependent upon sanctuaries and refuges where the natural conditions are preserved.

I shall speak from now on in the past tense, even of those birds that remain, because it seems fitting to do so. They still perform their aerial drills above our autumn marshes, a fragment of a once great host, but the big flights are vanished to return no more. There are tens today where once there were tens of thousands. Vast reaches of marsh and prairie are empty and silent where once the sweet voices of these birds made an unending melody from dawn to dusk of each spring day. Skies across which their migrating flocks once drifted like swarms of overgrown bees know them no more. All things taken into account, the past tense seems to suit the shorebirds better than the present!

Natural-born wanderers, strong and swift in flight, they came close to claiming the championship of the feathered world for long-distance travel. Many of them nested on the sun-bright moorlands of the arctic and wintered below the equator. Only the Arctic tern, capable of feeding from the sea itself, made a longer seasonal journey.

The Eskimo curlew, for example, was known in the United States only as a migrant. Its breeding ground was on the Barren Lands of Canada west of Hudson Bay, and its path of migration was a strange one. Quitting in July the remote and lonely land where they had bred and reared their young, the curlews headed eastward across the Canadian arctic, arriving on the coast of Labrador by early August. There they fed and loitered for a brief time, blanketing the hillsides and gorging on the purple-black fruit that came to be known as the curlew berry, until they were stained from bill to toe with its dark juice. By the time they left Labrador they had grown so fat that, tumbling from the sky at the hunter's shot, their breasts often burst open like overripe melons. In that fashion they acquired the name of dough-bird.

From Labrador the migration moved across the Gulf of St. Lawrence to Nova Scotia, on the way to the far-off winter home of the

▼ WILSON'S SNIPE, long-billed recluse of the marshes. One gunner bragged of shooting 366 in a single day. In 20 years this one hunter killed over 69,000

Allan D. Cruickshank from National Audubon Society

⋏ THE LESSER YELLOWLEGS claimed an extensive winter range from the southern United States to the tip of the South American mainland. One hunter killed 106 at one time by firing into a flock on a beach

clan. What happened next depended on wind and weather. If storm or fog hindered the birds, they followed the coast south, and at such times hunters on Cape Cod and other favored places in New England shot curlews by the wagonload.

If weather favored them, however, the doughbirds did not include the New England coast on their south-faring route. When they vanished from Nova Scotia they were not seen again until they made landfall on the coast of South America, 2000 miles away. Strong westerly

gales, overtaking them on the flight, sometimes drove them as far off course as Iceland and the British Isles, but still they survived. Mid-September found them on the pampas of southern Argentina, 8000 miles from the tundra of Canada where they had pastured two months before.

The route of their spring flight was completely different. From the grassy plains of Patagonia, they came up across South America and reached this country in the region of the Texas coast. They then passed directly north to their nesting grounds through the prairie country west of the Mississippi. The Atlantic coast saw them in spring only as stragglers.

The golden plover followed an almost identical flight pattern and, in the old days, shared migration lanes and summer and winter home with the Eskimo curlew. Hunters looked confidently to find the two together.

The black-bellied plover, rated by many gunners as king of all the shorebirds, had a wider range and made a shorter flight. It laid its four spotted eggs in a moss-lined bowl on the tundra along the arctic coast of Alaska and Canada west of Hudson Bay. It migrated all across the continent and was seen everywhere from Cape Cod to Puget Sound, both spring and fall. Its winter home was in southern United States and northern South America.

The yellowlegs, both greater and lesser, known to hunters as the tattler because of its noisy ways, nested on the patches of muskeg that are scattered within the northern coniferous forest zone from Alaska to Newfoundland. On the salt meadows and over the countless small ponds of that lonely but beautiful land, its sweet clear call notes were a common sound through the long bright days of June and July. The greater tattler, lingering longer on its nesting grounds and reaching the United States later, earned the name of winter yellowlegs. The lesser was often called the summer yellowlegs. Both claimed an extensive winter range, from the southern United States all the way down to the very tip of the South American mainland. Many individuals made an annual round trip of 12,000 to 16,000 miles.

Magnificent travelers, the shorebirds, harboring no dread of distance and following migration lanes that led sometimes above marsh and prairie, sometimes over the empty leagues of the sea itself!

All the members of the great host had certain traits in common—qualities that endeared them to gunners and made them exceptionally vulnerable as targets. They traveled, migrated, and fed in flocks, many of them in close-packed bands from which it was no feat to drop a score with a single shot. They were swift of flight, wheeling, turning, dashing above the marsh, providing sporting targets. Yet they were easily whistled up, came readily to decoys. Often they were so unwary that when part of a flock dropped dead or wounded, the survivors came wheeling back time after time, calling plaintively to their fallen comrades, only to fall themselves in turn, until no more than a remnant remained to flee to the uncertain sanctuary of the outer mud flats.

They were conspicuous birds, most of them silvery-white below and dark above, flashing in the sun as they pivoted and drilled over the marsh meadows, sure to catch the gunner's eye and whet his shooting

▼ THE GOLDEN PLOVER. Audubon estimated that 48,000 were shot in a single day in one Louisiana marsh

AMNH photo

lust. And finally, they were fat and well-flavored, succulent table birds. Long years they hung in the market stalls of Boston and New York, Chicago, St. Louis, and other cities by the thousands and tens of thousands. Long years the guns of the market hunters raked them through spring and summer and fall, setting a record of slaughter not by the brace, not by the score, not even by the hundreds, but by the barrelful and the wagonload.

The story of the shorebird killing is an incredible tale. No chapter in the long chronicle of our sorry dealings with America's wildlife is more shameful or reveals more starkly the greed of the lusty days of our country's youth, the total lack of consideration for the generations that were to come after!

There were no limits save those imposed by skill and luck, weather and chance. The hunter shot while the opportunity lasted; and if he apologized, it was not that he had killed too many but because he had not killed more!

None of the clan was immune. Birds smaller than a bluebird and not much more wary than a caged canary were struck from the sky by the hundreds, gathered up, and toted home in brimming baskets While the hunters waited for plover or yellowlegs or curlew—the "big birds" of the shore—to come to the decoys, they whiled away their time with the peeps, as they knew the members of the sandpiper tribe.

The least sandpiper, no bigger than a sparrow, was prized because it flew in dense flocks. The tiny

▼ HUNTERS shot the willet throughout spring, summer, and fall. Nest robbers hounded it for the eggs wherever it bred

spotted sandpiper was a legitimate target, too, but less popular because it was more solitary in habit.

Sanderlings, turnstones, and kill-deers, robin-sized migrants whose smallness alone should have shamed the men who shot them, stood high on the "game" list of the shore-bird hunters. Turnstones hung in the Boston markets at ten cents a dozen. The killdeer, best known of all shorebirds, was shot so heavily both for sport and market that it all but disappeared over large areas of the country.

And while the lesser shorebirds were dwindling, the campaign of destruction was being waged even more savagely against the bigger members of the tribe.

Of them all, Wilson's snipe, long-billed marsh recluse known to gunners as the jacksnipe, supplied

the greatest kill. Authorities say more snipe fell before the guns of hunters than any other game bird in the history of North American field sport.

Just to cite one fragment of evidence in support of that claim, there was a hunter who shot in the marshes of Louisiana, for "sport" and not for market, in the 20 years from 1867 to 1887, and published a complacent record of his kill. In one day, in December of 1877, he shot 366 snipe in 6 hours! He could have done much better, he explained, had he shot with two guns and used a loader. In 7 days of shooting that winter he accounted for 1943 jacksnipe. The winter's kill was 6615; and in 20 years, more than 69,000 snipe died to satisfy the egotism and blood-lust of this self-styled "sportsman."

Commenting on his kill, he unwittingly set down in clear and simple words the creed of his time toward all wildlife, the creed that sealed the death warrant of the great shorebird flights and shorebird shooting. "The snipe being such great migrants, and only in the country for a short time," he wrote, "I had no mercy on them and killed all I could, for a bird once missed might never be seen again."

All across the country, from Canada to the Gulf and from Cape Cod west to the prairies, there were thousands like that, some shooting for sport, some for a livelihood. It is little wonder the jacksnipe is no longer on the open list, little wonder the fall flight of yellowlegs has dwindled to a thin wisp that passes like ghostly smoke over the sea marshes of Monomoy. Little wonder

Hugh M. Halliday from National Audubon Society

⋏ BEST KNOWN of our shore-birds, the killdeer was all but exterminated from large areas of the country

if the Eskimo curlew is gone forever from the curlew-berry patches of Labrador and the mud flats of Nantucket!

It was the misfortune of the sweet-voiced willet to nest within the borders of the United States, along the Atlantic seaboard. Not satisfied with hunting him throughout spring and summer and fall, including the full period of his breeding season, men set a price on his eggs as well, and nest-robbers hounded him wherever he bred.

The dowitcher, the brown-back of the hunters, was among the least wary of all shorebirds, returning to the guns time after time in response to a whistle that mimicked the cry of a wounded bird. Flying and alighting in compact formations, it was not unusual for 20 to 30 of these big snipe to fall at a single shot. Audubon saw 127 killed at once by the discharge of three barrels. The dowitcher went swiftly from abundance to rarity and missed by a hair's breadth joining the passenger pigeon in the Legion of the Vanished.

The story of the godwit was much the same. It was still sufficiently numerous in the '80's on the prairies of Minnesota that if its nesting grounds were invaded, it hung in bands of half a hundred above the traveler's wagon, where its loud notes of protest made a deafening din. Forty years later a man could have crossed all that prairie country and counted himself fortunate if he heard the alarm cries of a single godwit!

What a striking and sorry parallel exists between the story of the luckless godwit and Alaska's caribou, numbering tens today where there were thousands no more than three decades ago!

Next to the jacksnipe, the heaviest

toll to the guns was paid by the yellowlegs, plovers, and curlews. A few scattered episodes serve to document the staggering record.

A shipment of nearly 500 yellow-legs went in one day from the marshes at the mouth of the Merrimac to a single game stall in Boston in 1904. A Rhode Island hunter accounted for 1362 yellowlegs in 8 seasons, and another killed 106 at one time by firing into a close-packed flock on the beach.

The big black-bellied plover, the beetlehead of the gunners, was more wise and wary than most of his kinsmen, but that was not enough to save him. He died by the scores before the beach pits and seaweed blinds, and the markets that retailed turnstones and yellow-legs and curlews rated him one of their best birds.

The golden plover kill is hard to believe. In 1821, Audubon spent a day at Lake St. John, near New Orleans, shooting with a party of French gunners. There were 200 hunters in the marsh, strung out in lines of 20 to 50 at promising places. The shooting was continuous from sunrise until after sunset. One hunter killed 750 plover, and Audubon estimated the average take of the 200 guns at 240 birds apiece, a total of 48,000 that fell in one marsh in a single day. And that was an ordinary day, and in March, too, when the spring flight was moving north to the nesting grounds!

So plentiful was the Eskimo curlew that the hunters were not satisfied with a brimming wagonbox, even when sideboards had been added to double the capacity. It was no rare practice, on days when the shooting was good, to dump an entire load of dead birds and leave them to rot in the spring sun, refilling the wagon with a fresh kill.

And when the great flocks were seen no more, the old tales were told as to why the birds had disappeared, the old alibis offered by the men who had wiped them out. Storms had blown the curlews out to sea, they said. Epidemics had overtaken them in the far north. Their summer food supply had failed, and they had perished of hunger. They had changed migration routes and were going north

▼ BEING SOLITARY in habit, the tiny spotted sandpiper was hard to get, but it too was sought by the gunners

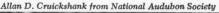

Allan D. Cruickshank from National Audubon Society

and south by new and undiscovered paths.

The same stories were told of the pigeon. They have been told of every bird that has grown alarmingly scarce or disappeared from the earth. The answer to all of them is the same. They are plain and simple lies, invented by men unwilling to admit their own guilt in the sorry business of wildlife genicide.

No evidence of disease was ever found in the Eskimo curlews, and their arctic pasturelands fruited each summer with lavish profusion. They were strong flyers, and their migration was prolonged from July to September, so that no one gale could have overtaken more than a small fraction of the flight. As for new migration routes, that was the thinnest alibi of all. By the time that tale was spun, the gunners were covering, spring and autumn, every mile of salt marsh and beach and prairie across the continent by which a curlew or any other shorebird could pass between its summer and winter home!

The facts were simple, the story clear. The doughbird had vanished for one reason and one alone. It could no longer run the long gauntlet of the guns across two continents, from the pampas of Argentina to its arctic nesting grounds and back. The smoking guns, both of market hunters and "sportsmen" who had no understanding of the meaning of the word, took a greater toll than the gentle bird could endure!

For that same reason the other shorebirds dwindled from a mighty host to a sorry, ragged company!

Their death was needless and without excuse. They were friends, not foes, of agriculture. For the most part they bred in the far north where vast nesting grounds still await their return. They wintered chiefly south of our limits, in countries where the lack of sporting guns would prevent excessive shooting even today.

They would still be here, the beetleheads and tattlers, the golden plovers and doughbirds, were it not for the spendthrift attitude of an earlier generation. We would still be knowing the pleasure of their presence, in that season when the marshes put on their bronze livery and the morning wind smells of fall, had the need for wildlife protection been understood and respected a few decades sooner.

Will the same thing happen in Alaska? Is the last primitive storehouse of wildlife remaining under the American flag being drained in the same headlong fashion that marked the reckless depletion of the shorebird host? All available evidence indicates an affirmative answer. The alarming decline of many of Alaska's game animals is past denial.

The caribou herds of the interior have all but vanished. Competent wildlife authorities say there are not 500 caribou now in areas that formerly harbored half a million or more. The Dall sheep has dwindled so alarmingly that the Alaska Game Commission gave the species the full protection of a closed season in 1949. The Sitkan blacktail deer have been seriously reduced in numbers. The moose population of the Kenai Peninsula is little more than half what it was fifteen years ago. Even the bald eagle, the bird that holds a proud place as the national emblem of America and enjoys complete protection in the continental United States, is being hunted down in Alaska now under a vicious and indefensible bounty law!

Without exception, Alaskan wildlife authorities agree that excessive shooting, both legal and illegal, is the foremost factor behind the rapid shrinking of the Territory's game supply. Other factors, such as increased wolf predation, admittedly enter in, but they are not the key to the situation. The wildlife treasure house is being emptied largely for lack of adequate funds to enforce the game code and keep harvest in balance with supply. Result: the same type of ruthless and unregulated killing that doomed the shorebirds in an earlier day.

Shall we correct this mistaken policy in time? Shall we reverse the trend of reckless slaughter and inadequate protection before it is too late? Before the roof-of-the-world white sheep has joined the doughbird in extinction? Before the giant moose of the Kenai have shrunk down to a remnant comparable with the tattlers? Before the caribou has gone the way of the golden plover?

The answer rests largely with unselfish conservationists outside Alaska. There are competent game officials in Alaska eager to do the job if they are given the money with which to do it, pleading for a chance, begging Congress for the needed funds. And there are enough Americans who love wildlife, if they will lift their voices in effective unison, to secure for the remaining Alaskan game herds the protection they must have to survive and regain their former plentitude.

The shorebirds stand as a sorry but classic example. The result of unregulated killing and inadequate protection was never proved more clearly and forcibly than in their case. It is not yet too late, in Alaska. But it is later than many realize!

▼ MARBLED GODWIT, pausing
to feed on a beach

Allan D. Cruickshank from National Audubon Society

Tiger of the Grass Roots

By Tom McHugh
Photographs by the author

"IT is a ravening beast that biteth deep and poysoneth deadly," wrote one 17th century naturalist. He was not describing some prehistoric monster. He was referring to a very tiny, sharp-nosed creature called a shrew, which at that time was feared as much as a viper.

But those beliefs were soon put in the class of quaint folklore; and when the science of bacteriology was born, it was said that shrews were no more poisonous than a common house mouse—the danger was simply from infection. But this reasoning broke down in 1889.

In that year a Mr. C. J. Maynard was accidentally bitten by a shrew. The skin on his fingers was punctured scarcely enough to draw blood, yet within 30 seconds a burning sensation shot up his arm and the area began to swell rapidly. Shooting pains lasted for a week, and the swelling did not go down for nearly two weeks. Here was something quicker than bacteria!

After hearing what happened to Maynard, Dr. Oliver Pearson got busy on the case. In the salivary gland of the short-tailed shrew he found a unique type of granule. When he injected saliva from this gland into mice he found it to be quite poisonous. It quickly brought on paralysis in the hind legs, labored breathing, and bulging eyes. The mice died in as little as three minutes, in a series of violent convulsions. The effects of this venom show that it is quite similar to the nerve poison of the deadly cobra. The glands of a single shrew have enough doses of it to kill 200 mice!

The shrew knows just how to use it to best advantage: Observers have noted how the short-tailed shrew bites mice through the skull —the very place where a nerve poison could act most rapidly. If the poison does not kill the mouse, it will render it so sluggish that the shrew has the upper hand in any battle.

This midget of the grass roots then turns out to be quite a package of dynamite. It is a beast with a bite like that of a weak cobra, an appetite of as much as twice its own weight in meat each day, and the power to whip an animal three times its size.

At the same time, there is no reason to fear the shrew. You will ordinarily have difficulty in getting close to one, and many scientists

The short-tailed shrew has an appetite for twice its weight daily and carries poison enough to kill 200 mice

have handled dozens of them without being injured in any way. Actually, they are of great benefit, because they can eat their weight in insects each day, and they keep mice in check.

The startling thing about these animals is their small size. The body of the common type is only about two inches long. And I say "common" with reason—they are all around us. You or I never see them because they scurry through small tunnels under logs or leaves. But they are there, nevertheless. In the woods and fields, right up to the very edges of the city, and even in some vacant lots, they abound

wherever there is cover and food.

Food for shrews is usually snails, insects and earthworms, but it may include almost anything that moves. For their size, they are the most bloodthirsty and ferocious creatures alive; they love nothing better than using their sharp teeth on a living victim. One scientist was foolish enough to put three shrews together in the same cage. A few hours later he found only one shrew left—one shrew with a very fat stomach.

A shrew loves to dine on a mouse, even though the victim is twice his size. When he tackles a mouse, a gory drama unfolds, a battle as furious as a grizzly's attack on an elk

▼ THE SHORT-TAILED SHREW (*Blarina brevicauda*) in a defensive pose. So rapid were the animal's movements that the picture had to be taken with speedlight, at about 1/10,000 of a second

reduced to a Tom Thumb scale.

As soon as the shrew gets the scent, he gives quick chase and seizes the mouse's tail in his teeth. The mouse tries to flee and drags the shrew along behind in cave-man style. Then the shrew makes another lunge and grabs the mouse around the belly, rolling over and over with it in a mad melee of biting. By this time the poison is slowly taking effect, and the mouse is becoming more sluggish by the minute. The exhausted prey frees itself only momentarily, for next the shrew has it by the ear and starts to munch on that tender item. Again the mouse tears loose, and again it is seized by its foe, this time in the final death struggle. The shrew's battle is won when he crunches through the skull and begins eating his dessert first—mouse brains. The whole tragedy may take as little as ten minutes.

Whether it be mice or snakes, the fearlessness of a shrew is incredible. One man placed a two-foot water snake and a short-tailed shrew in the same box. The snake was quite lively when placed in the cage in the afternoon and bit at everything within reach. The next morning, streaks on the glass sides of his prison documented his efforts to escape. He was then lying on the floor exhausted, while the shrew was busy tearing out his jaw muscles.

The poison obviously aids the shrew in its never-ending search for food; for above all, this pugnacious assassin is a slave to its stomach. Very seldom does it rest. Perhaps that is why death from old age comes at but 14 months.

▼ SHREWS are the smallest mammals. This common shrew (*Sorex cinereus*) weighed about as much as a five-cent piece

African Jumping Shrew

A frican Jumping Shrews have long heads, necks, and forelegs but comparatively short, naked tails. In their forest habitat, they are among the best jumpers.

Painting by Charles R. Knight

Loggerhead Shrike

George McClellan Bradt photo

L ike other shrikes, the Loggerhead, or White-rumped, shown here, has the habit of sometimes impaling its prey on thorns before tearing it to pieces and swallowing it. Because of this habit, shrikes are nicknamed Butcherbirds. Insects, snakes, lizards, frogs, mice, and other birds are its food. It reaches a length of about nine inches and breeds in various locations from southern Canada through Mexico. (*Lanius ludivicianus*).

Unwinding the Sidewinder

A complete photographic analysis of one of the most extraordinary methods of locomotion in the world of nature

By WALKER VAN RIPER

Denver Museum of Natural History

Photographs by the author

THE Sidewinder, or Horned Rattlesnake (*Crotalus cerastes*), is a denizen of the dunes and is found in desert areas of southwestern United States and northwestern Mexico. As its name implies, this snake is of particular interest because of a unique method of locomotion that enables it to move over the shifting, wind-blown slopes of sand dunes as rapidly and efficiently as other snakes move on solid ground. Few people understand exactly what the sidewinder does. I didn't, and I resolved to find out.

Sidewinding has been variously described as a "side-flowing, looping motion" and "a crawling sidewise, looping the body in the form of an S." It has been said to employ "the device of a caterpillar track" and to be "essentially a rolling movement."

Curiously enough, all of these statements are, to some extent, true. Yet all of them together do not convey a clear idea of what the sidewinder does. Sidewinding is not a complicated movement; it is only

unfamiliar. And any attempt to describe it in words alone is apt to fail, just as does a verbal description of the song of the robin.

Nor do the curious tracks the sidewinder leaves help as much as you might expect. I well remember when I first saw a picture of these slanting, parallel marks. They are nearly straight, and each one extends the full length of the snake, with no marks whatever between them. It would seem that they could only be made by the snake's jumping or flipping from one position to the next and landing fully extended. I experimented with the spring from a screen door and thought I saw just how the thing might be done.

Actually, nothing could have been wider of the mark than my first explanation, as I saw later when I obtained several of the snakes and watched them move in a bed of fine sand. It was then that I undertook to analyze the movement by means of the high-speed electronic flash invented by Dr. H. E. Edgerton of M.I.T., which is a superior instrument for investigations of this sort. Gradually the full truth dawned on me.

If you study the accompanying photographs one by one, I think

▲ THE SIDEWINDER has two horns over its eyes, which may give some protection against windblown sand. In its sandy world, the normal method by which snakes move would be almost useless.

you will understand how the sidewinder travels, without all the trouble I went through.

In the photograph of the tracks, the snake was progressing from left to right. Note that each track begins with the hammer-shaped mark at upper left. This is made by the head and neck. At the end of each track there is a T-shaped mark, which is made by the tail. Note also that there is no pushing up of the sand anywhere along the track as would be the case if traction were obtained in this way, which is

seen in the wriggling movement of other snakes. The prints of the belly scales in the sand also prove that there was no sliding motion in the track. The tracks were made by pressure only from above.

Next, if we turn to the photograph of the snake in the process of making tracks, we can see how the trick is done. Here the subject is again moving from left to right but with its head toward the camera instead of away from it. (Note that sidewinders are not "righthanded" or "lefthanded." They can start off

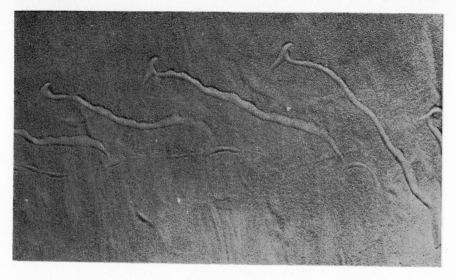

diagonally forward in either direction from a resting position.) Two tracks are always being made at once. The one in the center of the picture is nearly completed, while the one to the right and below has just been started.

Most important: only two parts of the snake are actually touching the sand. The central part of its body, and also its head, neck, and tail, are raised slightly. These parts are moved above the sand, while the two parts that are in the tracks support the whole weight of the snake and are momentarily stationary, just as each foot becomes stationary on the ground when a man is walking. But new parts of the body are constantly touching the ground. The segment that is in contact with the lower track is lifting out at the point nearest the neck and laying down farther along in the direction the snake is moving. At the same time, the hind part of the snake is lifting out of the upper track and flowing into the raised

loop in the center, while the tail is being laid down.

This is illustrated in another way by the triple-exposure picture. This shows the snake in three successive positions in its progress — again, from left to right. The lower track is being completed, the upper has just been started. The picture had to be taken on black velvet instead of sand to get the multiple-expo-

◄ EACH TRACK begins with a hammer-shaped mark (upper left) made by the head and neck. At the end of each track is a T-shaped mark made by the tail. Note that each track is the full length of the snake. Imprints of the belly scales show that there is no dragging or wriggling. There is no connection between the tracks, and each is the full length of the snake. This snake was moving from left to right but looping itself in the opposite direction from the one at right—"left-handedly" it might be called.

sure. The white lines have been drawn in to indicate where the tracks would be. Bear in mind that only those segments under the white lines touch the surface.

Another photograph shows how tracks similar to those of the side-winder can be made by rolling a wire coil or helix, over the sand. For some readers this demonstration may make the movement clearer than the pictures of the snake do. Note how two tracks are made simultaneously and that a completed track measures the full length of the wire. Only the two segments of the helix are in the tracks at any one time. These segments progress with a rolling movement that is not identical with that of the snake but comparable. If you flatten out the central loop so that its motion is a sort of flowing rather than a rolling, you come closer to the sidewinder's movement.

Other snakes, if put on the sand, make only slow and awkward progress and expend great effort

▼ THE SECRET of the sidewinder's motion lies in the fact that only two parts of the body are in contact with the ground at once. The rest of the body is slightly raised above the surface. This snake, moving towards the right, is swinging its head forward while the two portions of its body that are in contact with the sand are laying down new tracks. The tail is about to complete the farther track, and the head will then start a new one.

doing it. I tried a Prairie Rattler, a Bull Snake, and a Blue Racer. They are accustomed to surfaces that will offer friction as they wriggle along. On glass, a wriggling snake can scarcely move at all. The curves travel along its body but the snake stays in one spot, because glass offers no resistance to sidewise motion. But the sidewinder goes along on glass about as handily as on sand. This is because it needs only a surface that is fairly unyielding to pressure applied from above.

Other Winders

Other vipers that have evolved the sidewinding technique are found in the Sahara and Kalahari deserts of Africa and in the arid regions of southern Asia. That side-

winding should have developed in such widely separated parts of the world is a beautiful illustration of the efficiency of the evolutionary process. Where the need has arisen for an efficient way of moving over loose sand, natural selection has favored the snakes that tended to crawl like our Horned Rattlesnake of the Southwestern deserts.

The sidewinder also uses another totally different mode of locomotion called the "rectilinear glide." In this, the snake holds its body fully extended in a straight line, and the movement is much like that of an earthworm. There is a wavelike stretching and shortening of the body, while the belly scales serve to anchor one portion of the snake and then another. This meth-

> ➤ THIS TRIPLE-EXPO-
SURE of a snake progressing from left to right shows the successive positions of the body. The white lines are drawn in to show where the tracks would be made if the surface were sand instead of black velvet. Only the two parts of the snake under the white lines are in contact with the ground. All the rest is raised slightly.

od is slower and probably not so efficient as sidewinding, but rattlesnakes do use it even in sand. Boas and pythons also use the "rectilinear glide."

In its "looping roll," however, the sidewinder has evolved a method that is not only unique but is as close to mechanical perfection as our imaginations can picture. You may see this for yourself someday if you are in the deserts of our Southwest or northwestern Mexico. The sidewinder does not frequent the haunts of man as a rule and is mostly active at night. You are not apt to see it in broad daylight, for hot sunshine will kill it in about ten minutes. The name Horned Rattlesnake comes from the pair of horns it has over its eyes, which

may provide some protection against wind-blown sand. The sidewinder rarely reaches a length of three feet and is stouter than other rattlers. The females, unlike other snakes, are larger than the males. A row of dark blotches runs along the back against a ground color of cream, tan, pink, light brown, or gray, depending largely on the color of the snake's native sand. There are smaller dark spots along the sides.

Though the sidewinder is poisonous, it is generally placid, and one can safely get close enough to watch it in motion. The performance is well worth witnessing. The reader may recall having seen it in Disney's motion picture, "The Living Desert."

▼ A COMPARISON of the tracks made by this helix may help to explain the motion of the sidewinder, though here the loop goes much farther above ground than the snake's.

Talk-Without-Talk

THE INDIAN'S GREATEST INVENTION

By Robert Hofsinde

(Gray-Wolf)

All pictures posed by the author
Photographs by EDWARD WEYER, JR.
unless otherwise credited

THE American Indian's greatest invention was the sign language. By a system of several hundred signs, representing all the parts of speech, the Indians of the Plains conversed together with a flow of motions which equaled the articulatory dignity of spoken speech. Nowhere else in the primitive world was such a system of talk-without-talk even approached.

The old Indians laugh when they tell the story of how an early white man observed Indians using the sign language and thought that they were childlike persons incapable of full, normal speech. Actually the white man was witnessing the most marvelous gesture-development found in any continent, a method of communication comparable to the invention of the Chinese ideographs of the Orient. Further than that, the Indians were using what was to them virtually a universal language—the potential value of which we can easily see in our modern polyglot world.

When the Indians of the Plains hunted the bison over a large area, fifteen or 20 tribes speaking different languages were brought into contact with one another. Unable to converse in any other way, they developed the use of signs, and in time perfected this marvelous language. The American Indian sign language attained a vocabulary and complexity at least 20 times as great, and by some standards 100 times as great, as any other comparable system elsewhere in the primitive world.

All who have studied the sign language of the Indians have marveled at the eloquence and strength with which its few hundred signs can express almost any message that the speaker wishes to convey. The American Indian sign language has given romance to the study of the American Indian. It has also thrown light on the grammar and fundamental concepts of the Indians' spoken word. More than this, the sign language has been one of the features of the American Indian's life well adapted to being taken over into our white civilization, the silent sign serving many purposes in the modern world. The Boy Scout movement has taken up the sign language with eagerness; and its use as an adjunct to the hand-alphabet of the deaf and dumb has scarcely been explored. Probably no other phase of Indian culture has proved so interesting to the American public at large.

At present there are comparatively few Indians left who can talk sign language fluently. Those Indians so fortunate as to have learned the flow of signs from the generation which went before them are now aged survivors; and the time is near when the best speakers will be no more. There is a real need, therefore, to kindle a broader interest in the sign language and to preserve it for the future.

The picturesque clarity of the American Indian's sign language is shown by the gesture-word for "buffalo" *(at left),* the animal which, more than any other force in the life of the Indians, necessitated the development of the universal language of the Plains. The extended thumbs, representing the ears, wiggle; and the forefingers, indicating the horns, may be omitted entirely to symbolize a calf

From a mural in the American Museum by the well-known Indian artist, E. W. Deming

John P. Harrington

Bureau of American Ethnology, Smithsonian Institution

Below are shown a series of signs illustrating how the various parts of speech can be represented in the sign language

PRONOUN: "I" Expressed by the simple gesture of touching the thumb to the chest

ADJECTIVE: "HUNGRY" Motion like sawing body in two with edge of hand

INTERJECTION: "ALAS" Means also surprise or joy with appropriate face

PREP: "AMONG" Weaving motion among fingers

NOUN: "OJIBWAY"

Two signs are needed to express this proper noun. The first shows a soft, puckered moccasin; the second, with a rubbing motion, denotes red skin

Continued

ADVERB: "TIMIDLY"
The raised finger, denoting "man," falls backwards like a coward

VERB: "CAPTURE"
The posture of bondage signifies to capture or be taken prisoner

PUT THEM ALL TOGETHER AND YOU HAVE:

"I was so hungry, alas! that when I found myself among the Ojibway Indians I timidly allowed myself to be captured."

How they Express some Basic Concepts

All photos by Melvin Martinson

FIRE—Snap fingers up from thumb repeatedly, like leaping flames

TRADE—From shoulder position, cross forearms, forefingers extended

QUESTION—Rotate raised hand in a small circle by wrist action

ARROW—Motion to shoulder imitating withdrawal of arrow from quiver

Continued

EQUAL—Forefingers move forward side by side, imitating an even race

LIE—Two spread fingers show "double talk" or man with split tongue

Photos by Melvin Martinson

HOUSE—Like a log house. Cheyenne pointed fingers up like gabled roof

KEEP—Grasp moving left finger in right hand and hold firmly

FRIEND—Fore fingers together, meaning brothers growing up together

WALK—Move hands alternately forward, as if walking on hands

Photos by Melvin Martinson

WHITE MAN—Indicate hat brim by drawing finger across forehead

RAIN—Drop hands straight to waist
SNOW–Same swirling, like a blizzard

Morimura. Arai, and Co.

Silkworm

O rdinarily the silk from these cocoons would be unwound for use in making silk thread, but some of the moths have to be allowed to hatch from their cocoons in order to perpetuate their kind. The cocoons broken open by the emerging adult are unfit for reeling.

A full-grown silkworm, magnified about twice its actual length. It has finished feeding and is searching for something upon which to attach the first outer layers of its cocoon.

Gunze Raw Silk Mfg. Co.

"Scorpion"

of the

Treetops

The terrifying appearance of the Greater Five-lined Skink
has caused southerners to imagine that it is a dangerous
creature

By ROMEO MANSUETI
Biologist, State Dept. of Research and Education
Chesapeake Biological Laboratory

ON a hot summer afternoon in June, after a busy morning of snake collecting, I glimpsed on a tree trunk above me a fiery redhead, flicking a pinkish forked tongue. The animal was about three feet away. Looking harder, I saw that it had four legs and a smooth and shiny brown body not as wide as its head. Magnified 100 times, it reminded me of some hideous primeval monster that would put dinosaurs to shame. It was the most fierce-looking animal for its size I had ever encountered.

That was my first meeting with the "scorpion" of the treetops, the greater five-lined skink. I had heard so many tales about the "sco'pion" during past excursions in southern Maryland that I began to doubt its existence. Now the legend leered down at me with unblinking, bead-like eyes. The animal was about nine inches long and a uniform light brown in color except for its reddish-orange head. The latter instantly reminded me of a venomous copperhead snake's crown.

Throughout its range—in woodlands and swamps from central Texas to southern Illinois, and from southeastern Pennsylvania to Florida—it is commonly regarded as poisonous by the inhabitants. Most southerners consider the striped skinks harmless enough but greatly fear the redheaded variety, not realizing that the striped and redheaded lizards are one and the same species.

The greater five-lined skink may be called the Dr. Jekyll and Mr. Hyde of the saurian world because of the contrast of color and pattern in one species. Males among birds display more colorful hues than females. So it is with skinks. Only the adult female is striped with a bluish tail, while the mature male

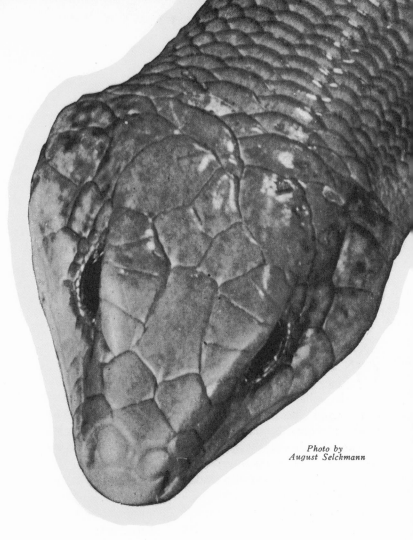

Photo by
August Selckmann

A THE MUMPLIKE JAWS, found only in the male, are blood-red. The color deepens during the mating season. when the eager male, looking as polished as Beau Brummell with scales, goes out to secure the affections of the nonchalant female

parades a blood-red head. Both sexes, nevertheless, begin life looking alike. Juveniles have five yellow stripes—sometimes with an additional poorly defined line beginning behind each forearm and extending backward—and bright blue tails. With the increase of size and age in the female, these characteristic stripes tend to disappear, but vestiges remain. The males, however, lose all traces of their stripes and become brown, while their jaws become reddish and at the same time gradually swell, so that they look as if they had a serious case of mumps. The females exhibit the light stripes throughout life and often have a blue tail when full-grown. They are somewhat smaller and do not sport the swollen jaws.

This curious attire parallels the development of the common five-lined skink and the Floridian five-lined skink, two very closely related but smaller cousins. To add to the general confusion in identifying these members of the skink tribe, all three may be found in similar kinds of country. Both of the smaller relatives reach a little more than half the size of our giant among American skinks and have the same life history—the males resembling miniature redheaded "sco'-pions," while the females retain the stripes.

On hot summer days the greater five-lined skink revels in sunlight, but at high noon it usually remains hidden from excessive heat. It dashes with great alacrity after insects, up and down tree trunks, along fences, in sawmills, and in abandoned houses down south. Here it is sometimes called by such colorful, vernacular names as "adder," "blue-tail," "cow-sucker," and "striped lizard."

A friend once told me about his first experience with a redhead: "I saw a flash go up the tree, then my eyes caught the thing staring directly at me, and then its head seemed to light up like a red neon light." Although the sun's reflections helped considerably to color his yarn, it is generally known that during the mating season the male's head is more lavishly adorned in a deeper red.

In April, looking as polished as a Beau Brummell with scales, glistening males go all out to secure the affections of the nonchalant females. Pugnacious males seem like brass projectiles as they shoot out after rival males trespassing on their territories. They often engage in aerial combat in trees, snapping their wide jaws at one another's neck or limbs. When one secures a good hold on an adversary, he shakes him vigorously, like a bulldog shaking a cat. The fights are short and packed with plenty of tearing and tumbling, the loser generally fleeing from the territory of the jealous suitor. It is not unusual for the ladylove to be totally unperturbed by the whole affair; she seems more interested in catching insects. In captivity, the female of the smaller common five-lined skink is much less inhibited. She has been known to attack a male without provocation in order to initiate courtship proceedings.

Although a tree climber, a pregnant female resorts to living on the ground during the egg-laying season. If you dig into decayed logs, particularly ancient chestnut or fallen oak trees, you may find the mother with her usual quota of six eggs. Sometimes she may be found encircling them, though not actually coiled around them. Since her body does not radiate an appreciable amount of warmth, the brooding instinct is interpreted as a protective measure for the eggs.

After about seven weeks the eggs hatch, and the blue-tailed youngsters immediately scramble off for parts unknown. In a few hours they chase tiny flies with great zeal and chew them energetically. The mother forgets about her children a few minutes after they hatch.

When I carried home my first greater five-lined skink, my small brother's first reaction to the name "skink" was to decline it as "skink, skank, skunk," and since no animal exists under the name "skank," he gave that name to the captured skink. Efforts to tame it proved fruitless, but my brother dangled meal worms over its head and succeeded in having it pluck them from his hand. Placing the lizard in a terrarium containing a heterogeneous assortment of reptiles, he noticed that the population was soon mysteriously depleted. At first he suspected that the lizards were escaping from his "escapeproof" terrarium. In a short time he called me excitedly and pointed to an overfat skink. We became sure of "Skank's" sau-

▼ THIS SPECTACULAR LIZARD, the largest found in eastern United States, is a master of aerial acrobatics, and if you break off its tail, it will simply grow another

Photo by August Selckmann

rophagus habits when we discovered our pet in the act of devouring a common five-lined skink. Later we found that it fed on almost all insects that it could catch, crunching beetles with great relish. It is said to break the shells of small eggs so as to lap up their contents. Whether the greater five-lined skink can be classified as a true cannibal has not yet been ascertained. A large redhead that I received from Georgia disgorged a six-lined race runner when I surprised it swallowing the lizard.

When I grasped my first male greater five-lined skink, it nipped my finger viciously with its teeth and viselike jaws. Actually the skin was broken, and a small amount of blood was visible. Other than this sharply painful pinch, I found this skink perfectly harmless and found that it would never attack or bite unless provoked.

Were it not for its shyness and highly nervous disposition, this spectacular lizard, the largest species found in eastern United States, would be better known. In captivity the shock of handling will often cause it to be highly erratic for many days. Father William H. McClellan, S. J., of Woodstock College, Maryland, has succeeded in keeping them for several years. By erecting a hibernating medium of moistened sawdust or wood pulp with a considerable depth, which closely resembles their natural winter sleeping quarters, he has kept them alive but inanimate all winter in a cold place. In spring they emerged and began to eat normally.

When a greater five-lined skink comes in contact with a black racer,

a pilot black snake, or perhaps a rough green snake, it fights with blind fury, making no noises except hisses. Hawks probably eat many skinks, pouncing on them in daylight from above with terrific impact. Young skinks fall prey to most small snakes, mammals, and birds.

This skink has been the taxonomic football of many scientists for about 150 years. It was first made known to science in 1801, by Johann Gottlob Schneider, a celebrated German scholar and herpetologist. He called it *laticeps*, or "broadhead." In 1838, Dr. John E. Holbrook, the "father of American herpetology," recognized and illustrated the large redheaded skink as different from the smaller common species. but he also made the mistake of considering the redheaded variety different from the striped female. Later, the greater five-lined skink lost its identity through confusion with the common five-lined skink (*Eumeces fasciatus*). Finally, in 1932, Dr. Edward H. Taylor, who had studied this group extensively, yanked it out of obscurity. This caused a certain amount of scientific furor, and some herpetologists refused to recognize a difference between the two creatures. Today the greater five-lined skink, *Eumeces laticeps*, is acknowledged to be a different species from its smaller brethren, the common five-lined skink and the Floridian five-lined skink, *Eumeces inexpectatus*. The latter, it is interesting to note, was discovered as late as 1932, when the area was supposed to be finished so far as new reptiles were concerned.

Plant or

Animal?

The beautiful slime molds, at the border line of the two kingdoms, are everywhere, but few people know them

By CONSTANTINE J. ALEXOPOULOS

With photographs by Philip G. Coleman

HAVE you ever looked at an old log in the forest? Really examined it at close range? On your knees? If you haven't, you may have a surprise coming. Some bright sunny day in the middle of June (earlier if you live in the South), two or three days after a heavy rain, go adventure hunting to the nearest log in the neighboring woods. Even if you have 20/20 vision, take a good 'reading glass along. If you own a hand lens, hang that around your neck, too. What you will find may be very small.

How do you begin? Just walk to the first wet log you see, kneel beside it, and start looking. No luck? Try another log, a fallen tree branch, a moist stick, or some moist dead leaves. And there it is—a naked, slimy, shapeless mass, which in a matter of hours will change into a hundred exquisitely shaped jewels! You will see a beautiful lacy network of bright yellow jelly today, a mass of tiny perfect, shiny balls tomorrow. It is naked as an

animal at one stage, and is clothed in a wall at another, with all the colors of the rainbow playing upon it. It creeps like a snail this afternoon and will be anchored down like a miniature flower by morning. What is this thing, this contradiction of nature? Is it a plant or an animal? Actually, some say it is neither. It's a slime mold.

You are more likely to find the fruiting stage of a slime mold than its creeping, jelly-like stage, because a slime mold comes to the surface to fruit. So let us concentrate on the fruiting bodies to begin with; they represent the plantlike phase of the organism.

Bright red or orange, chalky white or iridescent purple, silvery or golden yellow, brown or even black—their color depends on the species you stumble on. And that is entirely a matter of chance. You may see tiny spheres or ovals with or without a slender stalk; or oval discs on nodding stalks; or pear-shaped bodies, pointed-end-down; or long, branching miniature tubes

▲ IT WAS A STEMONITIS that was exhibited at the Chicago World's Fair in the "Believe It or Not" pavilion as "Hair Growing on Wood." This is *Stemonitis axifera,* which forms beautiful clusters of feathery, cinnamonbrown sporangia supported by slender stalks. The fruiting bodies may be nearly an inch high

forming a network; or tiny doughnut-shaped bodies; or masses of slender, feathery bodies; or minute cups, each supporting a springy mass of delicate threads.

You are likely to find any of these colors and shapes, and many more; and the fruiting bodies will always—well, almost always—be infinitesimally small, so small that the average stroller passes them by and never sees them. He has done this for thousands of years and, consequently, has never named

them. None of these miniature beauties have poetic names like Spring Beauty, Lady's-slipper, or Buttercup. Their only names are the Greek and Latin binomials that the scientist has given them—very descriptive names but strange and hard to pronounce until you become acquainted with them and begin to associate them with the particular species to which they are attached. *Stemonitis, Hemitrichia, Arcyria,* and *Ceratiomyxa* then become as familiar as the common names of wild flowers and just as easy to say.

Now, what about the naked stage —that slimy, jelly-like stage that gives the slime mold its name? This, too, is not difficult to find if you know where to look for it. In the growing stage, a slime mold hides in moist, dark places. You are likely to find it under a log, creeping imperceptibly between the bark and the wood, or inside the wood of a moist, well-rotted log. You may also find the *plasmodium* —for that is what the scientist calls the jelly-like stage of the slime mold—under dead, moist leaves on the floor of the forest, or even in the compost heap in your back yard. This is the animal-like stage, in which the slime mold creeps and feeds like a giant amoeba, taking in solid food like any other animal. Its food consists of bacteria, protozoa, fungus spores, or bits of dead leaves and other organic matter lying in its path. It takes them into its jelly-like body, digests them, and moves on, leaving its wastes behind.

Such a plasmodium is a fascinating thing to watch. Strip a piece of bark from an old wet log and look on the underside. If you see

◄ LARGE CLUSTERS of dark purplish-brown sporangia are formed by *Stemonitis splendens* on decaying wood. They reach a height of one inch

▼ ONE of the most spectacular of the common slime molds is *Arcyria nutans*. The yellow capillitial net from each sporangium expands tremendously and droops over at maturity. The cluster pictured here is one-half inch in diameter

a bright yellow network of delicate, jelly-like threads, break off a piece of the bark bearing a portion of the plasmodium and put it in a Mason jar. When you get home, cut a piece of absorbent paper, such

as paper toweling, to fit the bottom of the jar. Wet it thoroughly and pour off, all the water that has not been absorbed (slime molds are not aquatic). Then put the bark with the plasmodium on the paper and loosely replace the lid on the jar.

Keep the jar away from direct light and observe it from day to day. It is a show worth watching. Feed the plasmodium every few days by sprinkling on it a few grains of rolled oats just as they come from the box. Once in a while add a little water to keep the paper moist. With a little luck (not all plasmodia will grow well in captivity), in a week or so you will have more plasmodium than you know what to do with. If you were lucky enough to collect a good species, the plasmodium will be all over the paper and the sides of the jar within a week, fanning out in all directions.

You may also have much bacterial and fungus growth, and a foul smell that will nauseate you if you open the jar. When such things come to pass, scrape off with a matchstick some of the plasmodium from the sides of the jar and start all over again with a clean jar, a clean piece of paper, and the bit of plasmodium you saved. Put in a grain or two of rolled oats, and you are in business again.

When you tire of growing the plasmodium, don't throw it away. Stop feeding and watering it and bring the jar out into direct light. Some day soon you will go to the jar and find no plasmodium at all. Instead, you will see masses of tiny fruiting bodies. They have formed

▼ PURE WHITE CLUSTERS of fruiting bodies are exhibited on wet logs or sticks by the abundant and widely distributed *Ceratiomyxa fruticulosa*

TRY IT YOURSELF

With only a Mason jar, a piece of absorbent paper, and some rolled oats, you can "capture" these curious organisms in their animal-like stage and watch them grow. Keep the paper moist but not wet and feed the plasmodium every few days. In a week or so, you may have more plasmodium than you know what to do with. Like a giant amoeba, the organism will take solid food into its jelly-like body and creep from place to place.

on the paper, on the sides of the jar, and very probably on the underside of the lid. This transformation from plasmodium to fruiting bodies takes only a few hours and is one of the most remarkable changes you can observe anywhere in nature.

A plasmodium is not a very complicated structure as living things go. It is just about the purest form of protoplasm that one can expect to find, and it appears to be without form or structure. How a relatively simple mass of jelly can organize itself into intricately shaped and sculptured fruiting bodies within a few hours is one of the many wonders of nature.

When the fruiting bodies are completely mature, usually the day after they first appear, rub a few of them between your fingers. You will find that they break very easily and release a powdery purplish or yellow dust, the color depending on the species you have. This dust consists of the microscopic spores

▼ UPHOLDING THE REPUTATION of the slime molds for variety, *Leocarpus fragilis* produces glossy brown sporangia almost an eighth of an inch long. It is rather common in the Northern Hemisphere and easily recognized. It often occurs in wide belts on the bark of fallen or living trees

of the organism which, in nature, are dispersed by the wind and start the life cycle over again.

You have now seen as much of the life cycle of a slime mold as you can possibly observe without a microscope. The jelly-like stage changes into fruiting bodies which bear the spores. The spores germinate, and eventually a plasmodium is formed. What happens in the interval between the germination of the spores and the formation of the plasmodium requires a micro-

scope to explain. Let us follow the life cycle of one of these plant-animals (fungus-animals some scientists call them). The fruiting body is as good a place as any at which to begin.

The fruiting stage of a slime mold may consist of a large number of small bodies (*sporangia*) massed together on a transparent, cellophane-like base. All of them have developed from a single plasmodium. Each body is surrounded by a wall (*peridium*) of one or two layers. The outer layer is often covered with lime. The wall breaks at maturity and reveals the interior of the sporangium, which generally consists of thousands of spores, often intermingled with a network of threads, the *capillitium*. In many species the capillitium is elastic and expands in a springlike fashion, bringing the spores up high above the fruiting body where they can be scattered easily by the wind.

In some species, instead of a group of sporangia, the fruiting stage consists of one massive fruiting body (*aethalium*), which may be several inches in diameter. In still other species the plasmodium, just before fruiting, masses itself around the main veins of its network, covers itself with a wall, and becomes converted into a network of tubes. We call such a fruiting body a *plasmodiocarp*, because it more or less retains the general aspect of a plasmodium. Forms intermediate between these three main types of fruiting bodies also occur.

Each species, of course, forms its own type of fruiting body, by which it can be recognized. The type of capillitium and the size, color, and sculpturing of the spores are other characteristics useful in identifying species.

The spores of the slime molds are microscopic. They vary in color from colorless through yellow, rosy, lilac, and purple to brown. They also vary in the thickness and the ornamentation of their walls. It seems that slime mold spores can live almost indefinitely waiting for temperature and moisture conditions that will induce germination. Spores have been successfully germinated after 54 years of storage in a herbarium—a very dry environment if there ever was one. Once thoroughly wet, however, it does not take long for the spore coat to crack open. The spores of some species will germinate within 20 minutes after they have been placed in water. Spores of most species germinate 24 to 48 hours after soaking, but those of a few species require as long as 7 days, at least under laboratory conditions.

When the wall cracks open, a naked, pear-shaped "swarm cell" creeps out from the germinated spore. Swarm cells at first remain quiet, as though the effort of being born has tired them out; but soon they put out two whiplike hairs (*flagella*) and start swimming. The peculiar rotary movements of a swarm cell are fascinating to watch under the microscope. Quite often the naked cell will sit on its rounded lower end, extend its neck, and begin rotating. (I always think of a trained seal when I watch a swarm cell go through such contortions.) At other times the cell will swim around aimlessly. These movements may last a few minutes or several hours. Sometime during this interval a swarm cell finds a compatible mate and the two unite, fusing completely into a single cell. This double cell (*zygote*) soon loses its flagella and begins its creeping movement. It is now in the first stage of becoming a plasmodium.

The zygote feeds and grows, feeds and grows. If it meets with other zygotes like itself, a merger takes place. Several zygotes may flow together and coalesce. They add their respective volumes together and form a plasmodium. This merging process may continue for some time, a plasmodium taking in other plasmodia or zygotes and adding them to its volume. Since there are no walls, the union of these structures is a relatively sim-

⋏ SMALL CLUSTERS of quarter-inch fruiting bodies, mouse-gray in color, distinguish *Lycogala epidendrum*. The plasmodial stage is a beautiful coral-colored ball

⋎ YOU WILL easily find this one, *Hemitrichia clavata*. Next to *Ceratiomyxa fruticulosa*, it is perhaps the most common slime mold in the temperate zone. You will recognize it by its yellow, cuplike, stalked sporangia. When mature, they break and expose a ball of yellow, springy capillitial threads. The height of the fruiting bodies is one to two millimeters

ple process. But if a plasmodium, or a zygote for that matter, comes in contact with a swarm cell, it engulfs it and uses it as food. As we have already seen, the plasmodium feeds on bacteria, various spores, and even swarm cells of slime molds, including those of its own species. When a plasmodium is formed, it creeps away from the light, seeking a dark, moist environment. It oozes under the bark of a log or even penetrates into the soft, rotting wood. There it lives and grows until it is ready to fruit.

What causes a plasmodium to fruit no one is ready to state with any degree of certainty. We know, for example, that pigmented plasmodia, especially those that are yellow, will not fruit unless exposed to light. Type and amount of food and variation in moisture are also related to fruiting. It is probable that exhaustion of food and the advent of dry conditions throw a plasmodium into a fruiting mood, but much research needs to be done before we can be sure of what happens. At any rate, it is fairly well established that when the plasmodium gets ready to fruit, it crawls to the surface of the log in which it has been hiding, and in a matter of hours changes into the particular type of fruiting body characteristic of the species. Many species will also fruit on dead leaves, on small sticks, on the soil, or on the surface of mosses or other living plants on which the plasmodium crawls.

There you have it. Half animal, half plant, at the border line of the two kingdoms. The slime molds live wherever they find enough moisture and warmth to enable their spores to germinate and their

▼ AMONG the several species of Trichia with bright yellow sporangia supported on very short stalks is *T. favoginea*. Its individual sporangia are only 0.6 millimeters in diameter and about 1.5 millimeters tall

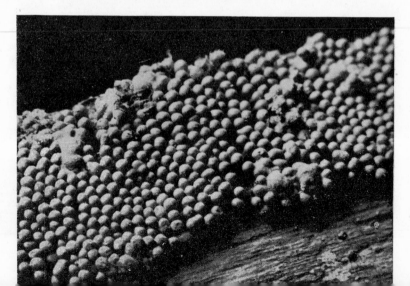

swarm cells to swim. They constitute the best argument for those of us who think that the classification of all living things as plants or animals is an entirely artificial one.

There are over 400 species of slime molds known the world over. A good many of them are cosmopolitan in their distribution, but a few species seem to be confined to the temperate zones or are only rarely found in the tropics, whereas others are more abundant in the tropics, if not strictly confined there. As with other living organisms, however, the known distribution of slime molds often coincides with the geographical distribution of the biologists who hunt them! If you look for them long enough, the chances are good that you will find many of the 400 species, no matter where you happen to be. Slime molds should be abundant during the moist season in any woods in which logs or stumps have remained on the ground long enough for decay to have set in, or in which there is a good covering of leaf mold. Now, suppose you are sufficiently interested in these organisms to go out looking for them. How would you be able to identify them? Because of their smallness, this is a little more difficult than it is with wild flowers. For positive identification of most slime molds you will need a microscope, but there are a number of common species you can learn to recognize with certainty at a glance, even without a lens.

One of the most common slime molds you will find early in the season in almost any forest is *Ceratiomyxa fruticulosa*. This species forms large masses of pure white, many-branched, more or less coral-

▼ TRICHIA PERSIMILIS is another common slime mold. It has tiny yellow sporangia about 0.5 millimeters in diameter. Sporangial clusters, however, may cover an area of several square inches

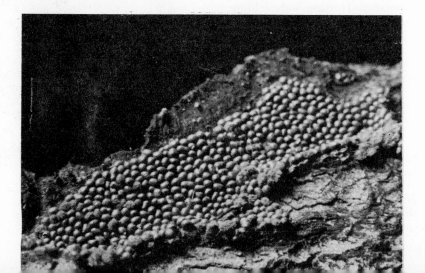

shaped fruiting bodies on wet logs or sticks. They are so conspicuous that once you learn to recognize them you will spot them several feet away.

Another common slime mold is *Stemonitis axifera* or, indeed, any one of three or four other species of Stemonitis, which are just as common. Stemonitis has the appearance of a tuft of cinnamon-brown or dark brown hair growing on wood. In fact, Stemonitis had the distinction of being publicly exhibited in 1933 at the Chicago World's Fair in the "Believe It or Not" pavillion, over the caption: "Hair growing on wood—Believe

▲ PHYSARELLA OBLONGA forms clusters of tiny yellowish-brown sporangia on orange stalks. The sporangia are thimble-shaped. The entire fruiting body seldom exceeds one millimeter in height

➤ PLASMODIUM of *Physarum polycephalum,* growing on agar in the laboratory. This is the animal-like stage, naked and slimy. The plasmodium of this species is bright yellow

It or Not!" Needless to say, slime mold hunters did *not*.

Other very common species that are almost unmistakable are *Arcyria cinerea*, which produces masses of ash-gray sporangia; *Arcyria denudata*, with its groups of red sporangia; *Lycogala epidendrum*, with its coral-colored plasmodia and mouse-gray, cushion-shaped aethalia; and *Fuligo septica*, with its massive, lime-encrusted aethalia.

And now we'll pretend that you cannot sleep another night without starting a collection of the slime molds in your vicinity. How can you collect and preserve them? It is all very simple. You will need a sharp hunting knife or an ordinary pocketknife, and a market basket or something else equally cheap

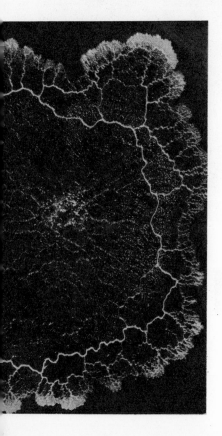

and handy for carrying the specimens. Or, if you are one of those people who must have an "outfit" to start out on a new venture, you can assemble one without too much trouble. If you buy an ordinary metal picnic basket, about 10 x 13 inches and 8 inches deep, and stack 5 plastic silverware trays in it, you'll have the almost perfect slime mold collecting kit. Don't forget a lens and mosquito repellent.

When you find a slime mold, cut the portion of the bark or wood that bears the fruiting bodies and place it in one of the compartments of a plastic tray. After you return home, if you wish to keep these specimens and really start a collection, spread out the trays and let the specimens dry thoroughly. This will take two or three days. After they are thoroughly dry, trim the edges neatly and glue the specimens in small boxes. Pillboxes or matchboxes are excellent for this purpose. Store the mounted specimens in a metal or heavy cardboard box, and sprinkle some moth crystals (paradichlorobenzene) in the box to kill the insects. Insects and mites feed upon the spores of slime molds and can destroy your specimens in a hurry.

You will inevitably ask, "What good are the slime molds?" The scientist is gradually formulating an answer. He is using the plasmodium for chemical analysis to discover what makes up that "physical basis of life," protoplasm; and he is turning more and more to the slime molds for a study of the fundamental life processes. The slime molds may hold the key to the mystery of life, but they will not give it up easily.

Photo by
Hugh S. Davis

the
Upside-Down
Animal

Many have marveled that a creature so slow and stupid could have survived at all

By WILLIAM E. LUNDY

*Photographs by George J. Herring
unless otherwise credited*

TWO weeks in the tropics was far too short a time to prepare my bride for the sight of the first "pet" I brought to her while we were living on the Panama-Costa Rica border. Standing some feet away, she gazed in astonishment at a sloth with long brownish-gray hair, which was hanging upside down from the seat of my railroad scooter.

An area of short, orange-colored hair on its back, encircling a black stripe along the spine—the so-called saddle mark—indicated that it was a male of the Three-toed species, so named because of the three claws on each of its feet.

The sloth's eight- or nine-pound body, with long forelimbs and short hind limbs, was suspended by twelve curved claws, three inches long, which held with a viselike grip. The claws seemed to grow from its ankles, for the soles of its feet were completely covered with long hair.

A mere stub of a tail and almost no semblance of a head made its long neck look longer, while the face appeared as only a splotch near the end. Small dull eyes, utterly devoid of expression, a small nose, and only a slit for a mouth combined to form the most idiotic face to be found on a mammal. Swaying slowly back and forth on the much-too-long neck, the eyes stared vacantly at nothing, while a hissing sound came almost continuously from its mouth.

My wife's look of astonishment turned to revulsion when she saw what appeared to be parasitic flies, disturbed by my handling of the sloth, working their way back into the long, coarse hair. As a seasick look played around her mouth, I realized that the joke had been carried far enough.

With a neighbor's help—for it is more than a one-man job—I pried loose the long claws and placed the sloth on the ground near a tree.

A sloth on the ground is a pitiful sight. Its shoulders appear to be out of joint, for the limbs cannot support the weight of the body when the animal tries to walk as other four-footed mammals do. It is forced to drag itself along, belly scraping the ground.

When it reached the tree, the sloth began to climb slowly. Reaching a limb, the creature advanced along it, body hanging underneath, suspended by the long claws of all four feet. So slowly did it take each step, so deliberately did it place each set of claws over the limb, that one would have thought it was stalking something rather than traveling its natural highway back to the jungle and freedom. There, the contrast was remarkable. Gone was the crippled appearance; though still very slow, the sloth was now master of its movements.

▲ ON THE GROUND, the sloth is a crippled caricature
of himself. "Had I taken a description of him as he lay
sprawling on the floor," wrote C. Waterton, "I would
have misled the world and injured natural history"

So strange is the appearance of these animals and so unique their habit of walking upside down through the treetops that explorers and naturalists have, over a period of four centuries, written reams of fiction about them. Fortunately, a number of scientists also have been interested in these strangely aberrant mammals. Three, George B. Wislocki, Curt P. Richter, and Robert K. Enders spent months on Barro Colorado Island, in the Canal Zone, studying large numbers of sloths, and they have recorded many interesting facts. Yet no description, including my own, can give an adequate picture of the sloths in their native haunts.

Some local residents are unaware that another species, the Two-toed (*Choloepus hoffmanni* Peters), is not uncommon here, though possibly outnumbered five to one by the Three-toed (*Bradypus griseus griseus* Gray). Too many authors have seen specimens of only one species and in writing their impressions have used the general term "sloth." One who knows only

The limbs are of almost equal length.

While sleeping, rolled into balls with their necks tucked in between the forelimbs, sloths look more like inanimate objects than living animals. The Three-toed, squatting in a crotch, looks like a termite- or wasp-nest. The Two-toed, suspended among vines, becomes a half-hidden bird's nest or just a bunch of dried leaves.

During the dry season, when foliage is less dense, I vie with my wife in "spotting" sloths along the old Chiva-Chiva Road, some ten miles from Panama City. Once when she saw one, I contended that it was a termite nest until she announced triumphantly, "There, your termite nest is scratching its side!"

To Margorie Allee, one looked like "a dirty, shaggy doormat." A visitor from the States once asked, "What is that old mophead doing in the crotch of that tree?" I once climbed to investigate a bird's nest —only to have it produce arms and legs and move slowly away through the vines. Yes, many people have seen sloths without knowing it.

Because he and his men had never seen sloths eat anything, Oviedo, the first chronicler of the Indies, wrote in 1535, "I could never perceive but that they live only of air." This idea must have been short-lived, for the sloth is a notorious glutton.

The Three-toed lives almost exclusively on leaves of the Cecropia tree, locally known as *Guaruma*. This is the principal food of the Two-toed also, though in captivity it will eat bananas and various vegetables.

a single species would consider a description of the other grossly inaccurate.

From a distance, you might easily mistake one kind for the other. At close range, however, many differences in looks and actions will be quickly noticed.

In sharp contrast to my wife's "pet," the Two-toed Sloth's face *does* show animation when disturbed, and its normal-sized eyes *will* focus on its enemies. A large bare nose, ending in wide nostrils, covers a mouth that is quite large when opened. It has no tail, no hair on the soles of its feet, and only two claws on its front feet.

▲ To CAPTURE a Three-toed Sloth is only a matter of grasping it in the arm pits and loosening all four feet at one time. This specimen was still wet from a heavy rain

A Three-toed Sloth may be handled with safety by grasping it from behind in the armpits. Its efforts at self-defense, to quote Dr. Beebe, can be circumvented by any creature except another sloth. The lethargy of this species, attributed by many writers to sloths in general, is far from true of the Two-toed. One that I captured recently struck out furiously whenever I came near. Their sharp,

sickle-like claws can inflict serious wounds.

A bit of Spanish humor is shown in the account of the sloth written by Oviedo. He says, "The sloth is one of the slowest beasts in the world, and . . . can scarcely go fifty paces in a whole day." He then tells that they nicknamed it Perico Ligero ("Nimble Peter"), a name still used by many of the natives today. Others call it Perezoso ("Lazy").

Sloths are so slow in their movements when undisturbed that there is no need to exaggerate, yet many writers have done so. Dampier told that before they could come down from one tree and climb another, they were skin and bones, though they were fat when they started, and that it took eight or nine minutes for them to move one leg forward three inches. Dr. Beebe claims that "In action, the second hand of a watch often covers more distance."

When approaching the trunk of a tree, suspended beneath a horizontal limb, a Three-toed Sloth must do a rightabout-face in order to descend, for unlike Dracula, it backs down. Only a movie could adequately describe the process. Holding with the forefeet, the animal unhooks the hind feet; and the rear end, still on a level with the head, describes a half circle very, very slowly. The sloth then proceeds backward down the trunk.

I have never witnessed a fight between sloths in the wild, nor have I heard of such an encounter. It is well known, however, that placing two females in a cage together will often start a fight, which

ACCOUNTS of the creature's lethargy are sometimes exaggerated, but all agree that the creature moves by s-l-o-w motion. The Three-toed Sloth shown here is beginning his unhurried journey back to the jungle and freedom

may end in death if they are not separated. Wounds are inflicted both with teeth and claws.

The Two-toed Sloth that I captured would repeatedly snatch a stick with which it was touched and bite it savagely with the canine teeth. Yet sloths have been classified under the order Edentata—or toothless!—and Oviedo said, "They bite not, nor can they bite, having very little mouths."

An incredible thing about the sloths is their ability to swim. These creatures, which have become so highly specialized for aboreal life that their feet are reduced to mere hooks for grasping, would seem to be the least likely to have this art. That sloths *can* swim has been known for nearly a century, for it was mentioned by Henry Bates in

his *Naturalist on the River Amazons*. Others tell of sloths swimming rivers a mile or more in width.

Dr. Beebe called the sloth a "languidly loving creature," because two courtships he watched in Guiana resulted, as he put it, in nothing more serious than his own amusement. Perhaps the sloths of the Canal Zone take their love-making more seriously, for one love affair witnessed by Dr. Robert Enders lasted "from time to time over a period of two days"—and might have continued for an even longer period but for the accidental death of the "swain." Furthermore, he states that in a group of sloths that he bought, the "females . . . either had babies with them or were pregnant or both."

▲ THE THREE-TOED'S efforts at defense can be avoided, to quote William Beebe, by anything but another sloth

➤ THIS TWO-TOED snatched a stick and bit it savagely

Baby sloths are born singly. These small balls of hair cling to the mother's chest, their tiny claws entwined in her long, coarse hair. In this way they are carried about until they are able to shift for themselves.

The Three-toed Sloth's defense of its young is little more effective than its self-defense—a slow swinging sweep of the forearms. When separated from her baby, the mother Three-toed apparently soon forgets it and goes about her business undisturbed. This is not so with the Two-toed mother, which fights viciously to protect the young. Some claim that she will destroy the baby rather than have it taken from her. Perhaps this does not occur intentionally but as a result of her savage efforts to defend it.

During the rainy season, when the jungle is greenest, multitudes of tiny green algae grow on the hair of the Three-toed Sloth, giving it a green sheen which makes the creature less conspicuous in the trees. Here, then, is a vegetable parasite that is of direct benefit to its animal host. Indeed, we should not call the alga a parasite but a partner.

Small moths are often found in large numbers in the hair of our sloths. It was some of these that my wife mistook for parasitic flies on her "pet." They have been observed to take moisture from the eyes and nostrils of a Two-toed captive. Local entomologists have combed the hair of many moth-infested sloths, searching in vain for the larvae, which have apparently not yet been recognized locally.

Almost unbelievable are some of the stories told of the tenacity with which these lowly mammals cling to life—recovery after suppression of respiration for 30 minutes by ether, recovery after 40 minutes of immersion in water, and survival for 30 hours after decerebration. "Of all animals," wrote Charles Waterton, "not even the toad or tortoise excepted, this poor ill-formed creature is the most tenacious of life. It exists long after it has received wounds which would have destroyed any other animal; and it may be said, on seeing a mortally wounded sloth, that life disputes with death every inch of flesh in its body. . . . I saw the heart of one beat for half an hour after it was taken out of the body." He told, however, that one sloth

↑ THERE IS NO LETHARGY in the Two-toed Sloth's defense. This one lunged at the author with remarkable speed

died in ten minutes, apparently without pain, after having been shot in a leg with an arrow that had been dipped in "Wourali" poison, a concoction made by the Indians of South America.

If records meant anything to a sloth, this strange creature could boast of at least two. Of all mammals, it has the highest number of neck vertebrae, varying from six to nine instead of the usual seven. It also has the lowest and most variable body temperature. From a low of 75 degrees F., it ranges to as high as 91 degrees. Even its "normal" temperature fluctuates between 85 and 91 degrees, according to Dr. Curt P. Richter.

It would have been strange indeed had no myths developed around a creature so weird in appearance and so unique in habits.

The lassitude of the sloth was believed by the early Spaniards to be due to heart trouble, which they thought the animal attempted to cure by scratching over the heart with the claws of the left hand, ". . . and thus the claw is the approved remedy against this evil."

According to one of the Spanish friars, "He who eats of the flesh of the perico ligero dies of it; because it is so phlegmatic." This myth may have influenced the natives of this section, for I have never heard of them eating one of these animals. This belief has probably helped considerably to ensure their survival in fair numbers in the Canal Zone. When the Indians of the Darien region of Panama saw one being prepared for Dr. Thomas Barbour's supper, they told him that the flesh of the sloth was unfit for food. It is well known, however, that many of the Indians of South America consider it a delicacy.

Many who have seen the ungainly Three-toed Sloths in our Canal Zone jungles are surprised that there is such an animal today. Remembering all that they have heard of the constant struggle for existence and the theory of the survival of the fittest, they marvel that a creature so slow, so stupid, and seemingly so unfit to cope with the many predators of a tropical jungle could have survived. Yet survive it has, while the mighty ground sloths which once inhabited this area are known only by fossil remains.

Probably its survival is due to a combination of many factors, foremost of which could well be protective coloration and its habit of feeding mostly at night and remaining motionless during most of the day. Its 23 pairs of ribs, heavy coating of fur and hair, and thick, tough skin all tend to protect the viscera from claws and talons of predators, while its extreme tenacity of life gives Nature time to repair wounds.

To those familiar with sloths in the wild, it is evident that Count de Buffon's observations were limited to animals on the ground. "The inertia of this animal," he wrote, "is not so much due to laziness as to wretchedness . . . Inactivity, stupidity, and even habitual suffering result from its strange and ill-constructed conformation... Its only safety is in flight . . . Everything about it . . . proclaims it to be one of those defective monsters, those imperfect sketches . . . which, having scarcely the faculty of existence, could only continue for a short time . . . They are the last possible term amongst creatures of the flesh and blood, and any further defect would have made their existence impossible."

At the other extreme we have the statement of Major R. W. Hinkston that "No animal is better adapted than the sloth to a life in this virgin forest."

Perhaps their extreme specialization for life in the jungles will eventually work their downfall, for man is fast encroaching on the tropical forests, and to the extent that he does so, the domain of the sloth shrinks.

Unless large tracts of jungle lands are set aside for the preservation of wildlife, as was done on Barro Colorado Island in the Canal Zone, not many more generations of men will see these creatures walking upside down through their habitat, for as Buffon expressed it, "They will be erased from the catalogue of living things."

How Snakes are Born

Not yet broken of their age-old egg-laying habits, those that seem to be progressing toward the mammalian method of bringing forth their young encounter difficulties and sometimes can only be relieved by Caesarean operation

By CARL F. KAUFFELD

Curator of Reptiles,
Staten Island Zoological Society

THE American Museum's seven-foot bushmaster from Trinidad deposited an egg on the night of August 3rd. Being the first bushmaster to lay eggs as a captive in the United States, hopes were high in the Museum that this mother would produce more eggs and that young bushmasters might be hatched out in captivity for the first time. She did indeed lay more eggs, but unfortunately all of them proved infertile. Once more the prospect of raising a brood of this, the most deadly venomous snake of the American tropics, could not be realized.

However, the incident of the bushmaster eggs has attracted popular attention to snake births in general, one of the more fascinating subjects in the evolution of animal reproduction.

Eggs swell

The eggs of birds are familiar to all of us. Even dinosaur eggs are no longer shrouded in mystery. But the eggs of living reptiles, particularly snakes, share the prejudice which exists against the creatures themselves, and many people consequently have been prevented from learning some of the more interesting facts of natural history. It is not generally known, for instance, that snake eggs increase in size during the period of incubation, or that the young snake is provided with a special tooth at the time of hatching which enables it to free itself from its encasement.

The essential difference between snake eggs and bird eggs is the leathery covering as distinct from the hard calcareous shell of the latter. At the time of laying, the flexibility of this membranous shell facilitates their extrusion by the mother. They are forced from the vent in the same manner as a partially inflated balloon can be pressed through the fingers encircling it. The glutinous quality of the shell at the time of laying causes the eggs of some species to adhere to one another in one mass, although they are deposited individually. The eggs of our common hog-nose snake and of the whip snakes are exceptions to this rule. After exposure to air or moisture, the skin-like shell drys and toughens.

Again, unlike bird eggs, the eggs of snakes are capable of absorbing moisture; in fact, this is essential to the development of the embryo. Most snake eggs show a noticeable increase in size from the time of laying to hatching, sometimes as much as one third their original size.

Snake eggs show no great diversity of structure. Unlike bird eggs there is no variation in color—all snake eggs are white or cream colored. They may become discolored from substances coming in contact with them during the period of incubation, but at the time of laying they are immaculate.

Some eggs, such as those of the common blacksnake and related species, and those of the gopher snake, *Drymarchon*, are covered with granular excrescences which give them a decidedly rough surface.

The number as well as the size of eggs deposited varies with the species. Pine snakes lay from four to a dozen, and bull snakes (of the same genus, *Pituophis*) lay as many as 22. Hog-nose snakes, common to most sandy regions of the United States, lay as many as 30. Large pythons have been known to lay more than 100.

Laid in transit

At the Staten Island Zoological Park we were astonished once upon opening a crate containing a 25-foot regal python from Singapore to find that the snake was coiled about a huge mass of eggs.

Photo by Alexander Klots

A MOTHER BLACK SNAKE *(above)* laying her eggs. Two have already appeared; a third, bulging near the tail, is on its way. Their somewhat elastic, leathery covering makes snake eggs less fragile than those of birds and easier to lay since the mother snake can compress the egg like a rubber balloon at the moment of extrusion. Most snake eggs grow (sometimes one-third original size) from the time of laying to hatching. Though roughly 70% of all species are egg-layers, some types are now tending to retain the eggs in the body until the young are ready to be hatched without further brooding.

They had been laid during the long journey and the mother was brooding them in characteristic python manner. She so completely hid the eggs that only a few were visible at the top of her coils. We tried to remove her and the eggs from the crate in such a way that she would not be disturbed, but our efforts were of no avail. She forsook the eggs, which proved to be clinging together in a solid hemispherical mass about two and a half feet in height. The individual eggs were at least three times as large as hen eggs. There were more than 75 in the clutch.

Although the mother could not be induced to resume brooding them, they continued to develop under the artificial conditions provided by us. The time for them to hatch had almost arrived when an attack of fungus, possibly due to excessive moisture, killed the nearly mature embryos which we found occupied each egg.

The eggs of pine snakes are fully as large as hens' eggs, and the snakes that hatch from them average more than 14 inches in length. Regal pythons average at least 24 inches at the time they emerge but are not so large in proportion to the parent as the 14-inch pine snake offspring. On the other hand, the pine snake may lay only one-seventh or one-eighth as many eggs as the python. In a particular species, small mothers do not lay small eggs, they merely lay fewer.

The shape also varies with the species. The eggs of the exceedingly slender tree snakes are extremely elongate—sometimes tapering to sharp points at both ends. But for the most part, snake eggs are capsule shaped, that is, cylindrical and round at both ends, or truly egg-shaped —round at one end, pointed at the other.

Different methods of incubation are employed. Mothers' parental care in most species consists only of choosing a nest-

Photos by Alexander Klots

(Above) THE THIRD EGG is emerging from the captive
specimen. Wild black snakes, like many other species, defy
cameras by laying in an underground "nest." Snake fanciers
cannot cultivate semi-wild pets by proffering the bird lover's
"bribe" of nesting sites. Rarely approaching the domesticity
of birds, most snakes pay no attention to their eggs once they
are laid, abandoning them to mechanical incubation by natural heat and moisture. However, certain species do brood
their eggs, and the famed King Cobra is particularly dangerous when guarding its nest

ing site—a sunny sand bank, or a mass
of decaying wood pulp in a fallen tree
trunk where the heat of decay aids incubation. There is little opportunity for
the snake fancier to induce snakes to
nest near his home in the way that bird
lovers attract birds with houses and other means. Snakes for the most part have
little domestic life, that is, in the way
birds have. When a mother snake has
found a suitable spot, she digs a hole in
the sand or soil and afterwards lays her
eggs at a depth of several inches. Leaving them here to develop with the heat
and moisture received from the sun and
rain, she usually never returns to them
or displays further interest in them in
any way.

Parental attention

However, among our native snakes
the black rat snake, *Elaphe obsoleta,* has

been observed to take a very decided
and prolonged interest in its nest. A pair
was once observed to have nested in a
sawdust pile where not only the female
parent but the male as well brooded the
eggs. When one snake was with the
eggs the other would sun itself on the
surface of the mound and after a time
burrow into the nest and relieve the
mate. It is probable that they hastened
incubation by carrying heat to the eggs
with their sun-warmed bodies in this
way. Our knowledge of the breeding
habits of snakes is sadly incomplete, and
it may be that many more species than
we suspect share this habit of brooding
and aiding the incubation of their eggs.

Parental affection of the kind we
know in birds and mammals is very rare
in snakes. The male parents particularly
are almost unknown to take any sustained interest in either their mates or
offspring. It is highly doubtful whether

(Above) THE FOURTH EGG has been almost completely expelled, and the fifth is bulging toward the vent. The number
of eggs laid varies with the species. Pine snakes lay from
four to a dozen, large pythons, 100 or even more. Eggs will
develop in the laboratory at room temperature if kept in a
slightly moist medium. But too much moisture will result in
rotting or attacks of fungus. In the wild, the hazards are
increased by predators who destroy the eggs of species leaving
unguarded nests. However, predators are often thwarted by
brooding species like the pit-viper who defends its eggs so
tenaciously that it suggests a maternal instinct comparable
to a bird's

males, except in a few species, ever
knowingly encounter any of their pro-
geny. Nevertheless, there are snakes
which take their parental responsibilities seriously. Besides the black rat
snakes just mentioned, there is the bushmaster, the only viperine snake in the
New World that lays eggs, which coils
about them throughout the period of
incubation instead of burying them. The
advantage of having the eggs thus protected against enemies is obvious, although possibly they might suffer more
from desiccation than if they were
buried.

This habit of the parent coiling about
the eggs instead of burying them is by
no means confined to the famous bushmaster. All pythons invariably stay with
their eggs until their development is
completed. Some mothers that have been
studied reveal an increase of body heat
of several degrees over the normally
fluctuating body temperature of reptiles.
But this increase in temperature may not

be essential to the development of the
eggs, since atmospheric temperature is
sufficiently high to hatch the eggs of
other snakes. Mr. Clifford Pope, while
in China, came upon a pit viper, *Tri-
meresurus monticola*, tenaciously guarding her eggs. Her devotion to this mass
of potential young was so pronounced
that it suggested a maternal instinct as
fully developed as that of a brooding
bird.

Cobras with eggs

Some species of cobras are egg layers
and guard their nests, sometimes in pairs.
The king cobra, or hamadryad, is notorious for the fearlessness of its attacks on
intruders, but its belligerency reaches its
height during the mating season and at
the time it is incubating its eggs. So dangerous is this behavior that certain roads
in India have at times been closed to
prevent some unsuspecting traveler from
being attacked by a pair of king cobras

PINE SNAKE EGGS *(above)* have the sticky shell common to
many species at "birth." They can thus form an adherent
cluster although each is delivered singly. Unlike birds',
snake eggs absorb moisture from the damp earth or decaying wood in which they are usually buried. This moisture is
necessary to embryonic development and its lack in cold or
dry climates seems the chief reason why northern snakes
are tending to abandon th egg-laying method

nesting in the neighborhood.

Not all snakes are egg layers. In about
30 percent of the species the mother retains the eggs within her body until they
mature, and gives forth living young.
But these snakes are not live-bearing
creatures in the strict sense of the term
nor have they dispensed with eggs entirely. They merely brood them internally.

The evolutionary tendency among
snakes seems to be toward developing
the live-bearing, or ovoviviparous, method. From my observations among captive snakes, the mortality among both
infants and mothers is higher among the
live bearers, yet it is true that they are
more prolific and seem more successful
as species. We have such classic examples as the garter snake and water
snake, to say nothing of the rattlesnakes
and copperhead. Yet the observer of
living snakes is constantly impressed
with the large number of premature
births and pathological conditions which
cause the death of both mother and
young. The writer has frequently seen
gravid females of the notorious fer-de-
lance which had died in attempting to
give birth to their young because the
oviducts were so clogged with infertile

eggs that neither these nor the normal
embryos could be evacuated. Not only
the fer-de-lance, but even our common
water snakes and garter snakes, as well
as other species, often suffer from this
same condition. Autopsies of these specimens show the embryos in the ducts interspersed with hard masses of yolk.
There seems to be a lack of uniformity
in the process of fertilization with the
resulting infertile masses imprisoning the
normal young with fatal effects on them
and the mother. We have made it a
practice with valuable specimens of captive snakes to remove the contents of
the oviducts by the Caesarean method,
before the period of gestation is complete, where we suspect such a condition
to exist. Mother snakes undergoing this
operaion invariably survive, whereas
they often die if young are retained.

There was a female bull snake, *Pituophis sayi affinis*, which the writer presented to the American Museum's School
Nature Room. It was immature at the
time it was received. Some 3 years later,
having grown to maturity, it developed
infertile eggs. Never having been mated
with a male of the same species no
fertilization could possibly have taken
place. Six of the hard masses of yolk

Photos by Staten Island Zoological Society

VARYING MARKEDLY in size, and sometimes departing from the usual capsule-like shape, snake eggs differ little in color. Above *(left to right)* are the clustered eggs of the hog-nose, king, and pine snakes compared to the hen's egg in foreground. Snakes that issue living young are not strictly live-bearers, rather they brood the eggs internally. Roughly the proportion of live bearers increases with the distance separating their habitat from the equator

were thrown but the remaining ones were retained and threatened to cause the snake's death. However, they were easily removed by making a small incision (which was later sutured) and pressing them through the opening. Nine additional masses were removed!

Captive snakes rarely breed

Snakes rarely breed in captivity. Those that lay eggs or have young in confinement usually have mated while in a natural state previous to their capture. The peculiar case of the bull snake described above may be attributed entirely to the fact that it had always lived as a captive, for ordinarily the egg-laying species dispose of the problem of propagation with an ease which is in strong contrast to that of the live bearers. The eggs are laid without difficulty and usually most of the eggs hatch, giving forth healthy and robust young. In a natural state, it is true, the destruction of the eggs by predators is a constant danger. But although some of the eggs might escape such attacks, the young of a live-bearing snake would all succumb with the mother were she to be killed while carrying them; and since the young are retained at least twice as long as with the egg layers the hazard is twice as

great. A factor which offsets this is the danger of insufficient moisture, or too much moisture, which would cause the eggs of the latter to dry up or rot during the long incubation period if weather conditions were unfavorable.

Hatching eggs in the laboratory

Hatching snake eggs in the laboratory is a simple matter. Placed in a closed container, buried in moist sand, or just covered with a damp cloth, they will develop successfully at room temperature. The only attention necessary is to be certain that the moisture is not so great as to cause rotting. To give them too little moisture is far less detrimental than too much. Mosses of various kinds, especially sphagnum, and wood pulp have long been favorite hatching media, but destructive fungi are very likely to attack eggs thus treated.

We can only speculate as to what caused certain groups to become live bearers. Undoubtedly various factors in the environment selected the live-bearing or eliminated the egg-laying individuals, or brought about a gradual change from one to the other within a species. The transition from one method to the other is well illustrated by the sea snakes. Having evolved from a group

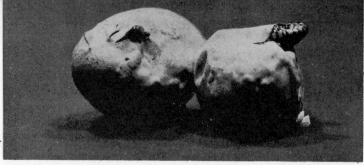

(Above) THE TWO PICTURES show baby bull snakes concentrating on the important task of getting out into the world, a performance that often takes them about two days. An egg tooth on their snouts enables them to rip the shell from the inside, after which the tooth becomes superfluous and is soon lost. The youngster in the first picture has just used the tooth to get his first breath of air. This tooth survives for no earthly purpose among some of the live-bearing snakes; indicating that they are not yet quite "broken" of their egg-laying habits. But further evidence of incomplete

which is principally egg-laying, the cobras and related snakes, this method would have obvious mechanical difficulties as the snakes became more and more confined to a marine environment. Possibly only those that were live bearers before "took to the sea." However, there is living today a genus of sea snakes which is not yet devoid of the power to move on land—a stage between the entirely pelagic sea snakes and the terrestrial cobras. As might be expected, this genus retains the egg-laying habit —evidence arguing the acquisition of the live-bearing habit subsequent to the adoption of the marine life.

The common viper of northern Europe and Asia inhabits such cold climates, for a snake, that if it were an egg layer its eggs probably would never hatch, and the species would never have established itself in the wide area which it is known to cover. In cold climates or at high altitudes there is insufficient heat to incubate the eggs of an egg-laying form.

Thus we see that the live-bearing habit does have survival value. In fact, it could perhaps be demonstrated that as one goes north from the equator the proportion of egg-laying species de-

creases and the live-bearing increases. It is difficult to explain the loss of the egg-laying habit in most forms or to correlate it with the habits of certain groups. Most large groups are predominantly one or the other, but there are always exceptions. The viperine snakes for the most part are live bearers, but there are the African night adders, the burrowing vipers, certain Oriental pit vipers, and in the New World, the bushmaster, all of which lay eggs. The almost cosmopolitan genus *Natrix*, to which our common water snakes belong, consists of live bearers for the most part; but in China, where a number of species occur, there is only one which bears its young alive—all the rest are egg layers!

Period of gestation

The length of time necessary for the development of the young within the eggs varies somewhat, particularly in tropical snakes. The period of gestation in most live-bearing snakes is about four to six months. With the egg layers, gestation is, of course, much shorter, but the total length of time required for the maturing of the young from the time of conception to parturition or

Photos by Staten Island Zoological Society

adjustment lies in the fact that some fatalities occur from obstetrical obstructions which can be relieved (in captivity) only by a Caesarean operation. Add to this the wholesale decimation of unborn young resulting from the death of pregnant mothers, and the cultivation of the live-bearing method seems to this extent ill advised from the snake's viewpoint. Yet in many cases, the dangers of egg-laying appear to outweigh those of living birth. And particularly in northern, marine or mountainous regions, live-bearing has a definite survival value which may be on the increase

hatching, as the case may be, is approximately the same with most of our native snakes. Since the eggs are laid about the second month after mating, the incubation period of the eggs is usually about two to three months.

The young of the egg-laying species are remarkably large and vigorous when the time comes for them to emerge from their leathery encasement. They are always provided with a sharp tooth projecting from the premaxillary bone at the front of the mouth, with which tooth they cut the shell. The tearing of the shell takes place a few days before they leave the egg permanently. Most young snakes remain for a day or so with just the head thrust out of the opening they have made with the egg-tooth and gaze about them before coming out to stay. At this time they are entirely capable of shifting for themselves. One poor youngster, of a brood that once hatched for the writer, was apparently so discouraged by his first glimpse of the world that he drew back into the egg and never came out again! Snakes of all ages display great curiosity—even these babies—but instinctively they draw back out of sight into the shell when they think danger threatens. It is a ludicrous sight to see a clutch of eggs with a head protruding from each and to watch them simultaneously draw back into the shell out of sight, ostrich-like, as a sudden movement frightens them.

Often they deliberately tear the egg shell again and again, sometimes from stem to stern, much more than would seem necessary for their escape. Having served its purpose, the egg-tooth is lost within a week or so after the emergence of the young snake.

Advance of some snakes

Proving the recent acquisition of the live-bearing habit in some species is the presence of this same egg-tooth in newly born specimens for whom it could serve no earthly purpose except as a temporary ornament. There are snakes that have advanced far beyond this stage. They have lost the egg shell and developed placenta-like structures for securing oxygen from the parent's body. Since the yolk of the eggs is not reduced we cannot speak of viviparity here in the sense of mammals. It is nevertheless a step in the direction of mammalian evolution.

Snake Eat Snake

As a former Curator of Reptiles in the Tulsa Zoological Garden, Mr. B. Hathcock, who presents these unusual photographs, has handled more than 10,000 snakes, both afield and in captivity.

Few snakes are habitually cannibalistic, but many spe-

cies will take to the practice occasionally, especially if their normal prey is scarce. The accompanying photographs are a credit to Mr. Hathcock's vigilance as well as to his photographic skill, for the eating of one snake by another cannot be regarded as commonplace.

◀ PACIFIC RATTLER EATING A SMALLER SNAKE OF THE SAME SPECIES. When several snakes of a collection of 57 Pacific Rattlers *(Crotalus viridis oreganus)* received by him refused food, Mr. Hathcock one day was confronted with the rare sight shown above. It is believed to be the only picture ever taken of a cannibalistic rattler

BULL SNAKE VS. SPOTTED KING SNAKE. Three views of a battle in which the King snake was killed and eaten

1. The Bull Snake, in the clutch of the King snake, maneuvers with open mouth for the first bite of a long meal

2. The Bull snake has swallowed the head of its opponent. Note the Bull snake's flatly folded body indicating an empty stomach

3. The victor is apparently enjoying his repast. Snakes' jaws, being unhinged, can spread on occasion to receive creatures much larger than themselves

If shorter than its victim, the Bull snake might have reached a point where it could chew but not swallow; but such was not the case. It ate the King snake entire

Though the King snake was the loser in the fore-going series of photographs, Mr. Hathcock states that he has seen Spotted King snakes devour Black snakes, Pine snakes, Copperheads and even Rattlers, as well as smaller and less offensive species, and only rarely has there been a digestive upset.

In the wild state, he classes the Indigo as one of the most cannibalistic snakes in America:

"I remember a certain Indigo snake *(spilotes corais couperi)* in my zoo collection, which killed every King snake ever put into its quarters. Its favorite delicacy, though, was a Garter snake, and countless numbers of these small, striped serpents passed through its jaws.

"The poisonous snakes of America are not given to feeding upon their relatives to any great extent, with the possible exception of the Cotton-mouth, or Water Moccasin, of the South. This venomous creature has long been known for its habit of eating other water snakes, especially in particularly dry seasons when its natural prey is not readily available. Garter snakes and Ribbon snakes are also often victims of the rarely appeased appetite of the Moccasin.

"I have known of but one case of a Copperhead feeding upon another serpent—a Banded Water snake—though lizards form a portion of the natural diet of this serpent.

"My friend, Mr. Marlin Perkins, Curator of Reptiles at the St. Louis Zoo, once had a King Cobra, which was as temperamental as an operatic prima donna. This snake utterly refused every-thing put into its cage but Blue Racers and I still have Perkins' frantic letter, asking for a large shipment from our zoo collection."

FOR MORE THAN AN HOUR this fight between a Blotched King snake and a Spotted King snake raged. Finally the Blotched King *(Lampropeltis calligaster)* secured a firm hold upon the head of its foe and it was but a few minutes until the beautifully spotted body of *Lampropeltis getulus holbrooki* was disappearing into the mouth of the victor

HOW TO

How you can quite simply preserve replicas of snowflakes in all their infinite variety and beauty: an ingenious method described by its inventor

A.M.N.H. photo by C. H. Coles

FINGERPRINT
A *SNOWSTORM*

By Vincent J. Schaefer
Director of Research, Munitalp Foundation, Inc.
All photographs by the author unless otherwise designated

WHETHER it be a November flurry, a January storm, or a March blizzard, there is always a fascination about falling snow, and its coming touches a responsive chord in young and old alike. Perhaps this feeling harks back to earlier, harder days, when deep snow meant greater struggles with the elements to obtain food, to move about, or to keep warm. Today, snow generally symbolizes sleigh rides, Christmas Holidays, ski runs.

With a goodly portion of the world's population living within its seasonal path, it is not strange that even among the early natural philosophers there were those who pondered upon snowstorms and found much interest in them.

So far as I know, Aristotle, in the fourth century B. C., was the first to comment on the formation of the snow crystal. Many others no doubt made subsequent observations which, without the printing press to record them, have not survived the passage of time.

In 1555, Olaus Magnus, Archbishop of Upsala, Sweden (where they have fine snow—and skiers), depicted for the first time a group of snowflakes, in a book on natural phenomena published at Rome. One hun-

◄ A "FROSTED WINDOW" that is permanent. This flexible replica of "frost flowers" is made by applying the same process to a whole pane of glass

dred and ten years later Robert Hooke, in his *Micrographia,* published a full page of snowflake drawings, showing in accurate detail many of the characteristic forms that may be found (*see illustration*). Commenting on the pleasure he derived from exposing a piece of black cloth or a black hat to the falling snow and observing their infinite variety, he states that it would be impossible to draw the shape of every one of them. His "coarse draughts," as he states apologetically, referring to his drawings, were all that the coldness of the weather and the ill provisions he had for such a purpose would permit him to make. He observed that whenever the flakes had any regular shape "they were always branched out with six principal branches . . . , each of them being inclined to either of the next branches on either side of it, by an angle of 60°."

Captain William Scoresby, the Arctic explorer, in 1820, published a considerable number of excellent drawings of snowflakes. In 1863, an elaborate book with. the title *Cloud Crystals — A Snowflake Album* was published in New York, "edited by a Lady." Replete with scientific papers, prose and poetry, and containing 28 woodcuts depicting some 194 different crystal forms, this book typifies the spirit that led John Tyndall, while carrying on scientific observations in the Alps, to remark, "While I remained at the station a layer of snow an inch thick fell on a blanket used as a screen, the whole layer being composed of these exquisite flowers. ... From the clouds to the earth Nature was busy marshalling her atoms and putting to shame by the beauty of her structures, the comparative barbarities of art.'

In the past 50 years many observations have been made on snow and ice crystals. A score or more of scientific studies, using the electrometer, X-ray, and the microscope, have disclosed many interesting facts about them. The work that did most to popularize their exquisite beauty was performed by Mr. Wilson A. Bentley, of Jericho, Vermont. Over a period of nearly half a century he made thousands of beautiful photomicrographs showing the endless variety one finds when observing winter storms.

Considering that during a single 10-inch fall of snow more than a million flakes may gather on a 2-foot square, and that no two flakes are alike, it is obvious that anyone can easily discover unusual new types of crystals formed in Nature's inexhaustible laboratory of the skies.

Yet with the slightest warmth, the orderly symmetry of the crystals is destroyed and one has only tiny drops of water. Naturally, the evanescent nature of snow crystals has always been a discouraging feature.

The method

During the winter of 1940, while watching some particularly fine crystals melt on my coat sleeve, the thought occurred to me that it might be possible to preserve these forms. If before the crystals had a chance to melt they could be coated with a substance that would harden, the exact design would be retained. As sometimes happens with hunches, the first attempt to perpetuate snowflakes

worked perfectly. Though I have tried many other substances and solutions since that time, none as yet has worked as well.

For making replicas of snowflakes the equipment is quite simple. A complete kit would include the following items:

> two square feet of black velvet
> a card table
> a flash light
> a whisk broom
> a thermometer
> a supply of clean microscope slides
> a pointed glass rod or wire
> a solution of polyvinyl formal resin dissolved in ethylene dichloride.

Your local druggist may be able to help you procure the last-named material; or write to any of the large chemical supply companies.

This equipment should remain outside throughout the collecting period, so that it stays cold and is available at any time. If possible it should be kept in a place where it is sheltered from wind and falling snow.

When the flakes begin to fall, the black velvet, tacked to a broad board, is exposed to the sky. As soon as several good specimens are observed, it is placed on the table. The glass rod is then dipped into the bottle of the resin solution and removed with about half a drop, which is transferred to the glass slide. Without delay the rod is brought into light contact with the selected snowflake, and since a little of the solution remains on the rod, the flake adheres to it. It is then touched to the drop of solution on the slide. The flake leaves the tip of the rod and is quickly engulfed by the solution. If the flake is particularly large, a second small drop may be added.

All of the selected specimens are treated in this manner, and after a group of flakes have been prepared, the slide is put in a protected place until the solvent evaporates. This takes only several minutes. As soon as

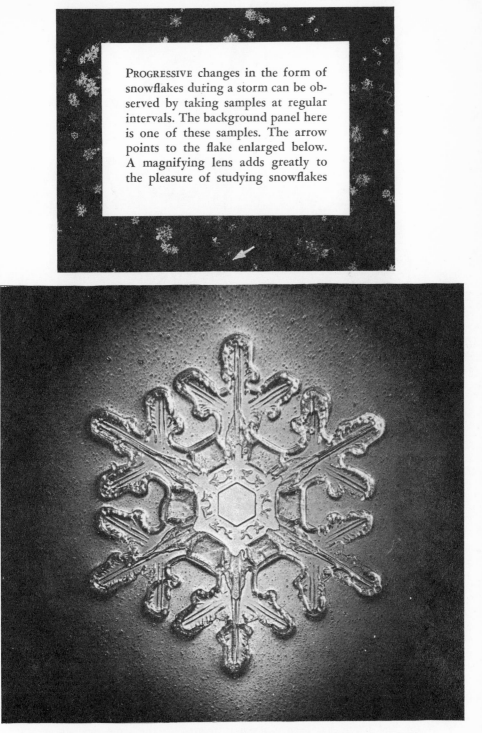

PROGRESSIVE changes in the form of snowflakes during a storm can be observed by taking samples at regular intervals. The background panel here is one of these samples. The arrow points to the flake enlarged below. A magnifying lens adds greatly to the pleasure of studying snowflakes

↑ MAN-MADE REPLICA of a snowflake: illustrating the new method by which anyone can make a permanent collection of frost crystals

▲ ONE OF THE EARLY writings on snowflake designs: from an important book published in 1665 by the famous English physicist, Robert Hooke. Snowflakes have attracted the interest of students of natural science since Aristotle's day, and doubtless much earlier

evaporation is complete, the several specimens can be brought into a warm room, where they can be examined to better advantage with a hand lens or a low power microscope. If they seem to have considerable mass, it is best to allow them to warm slowly. This permits the water to pass through the resin film covering the crystal without distorting it. If this all sounds complicated, perhaps I should say that one of my best pupils has been a seven-year-old girl.

If a 1% solution is used, the thickness of the film covering the flake after the solvent has evaporated is only about 8/100,000 of an inch.

Another process is still easier to carry out than the single flake method. Enough 2% solution is poured onto a sheet of glass to cover it in a thin layer. It is then held out under the sky until a considerable number of flakes land on it. The specimens are then treated in the same manner as just described, a small drop of the solution

HOW YOU CAN DO IT

▼ A pointed glass rod or a wire is dipped into a bottle containing a 1% solution of polyvinyl formal resin dissolved in ethylene dichloride

▼ A half drop of the solution is then placed on a glass slide on which the snowflakes are being preserved. These materials must all be cold

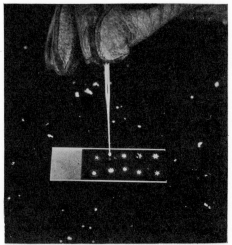

▼ From the black velvet collecting board a snowflake of the desired design is very gently picked up on the tip of the still moist glass rod

▼ The snowflake is touched to the droplet, which engulfs it. When the solution dries, the replica is brought into the warmth and examined

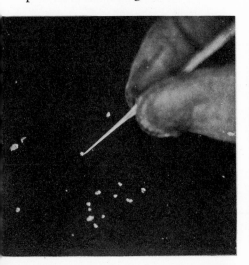

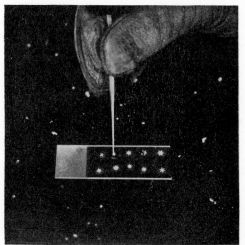

being applied to each crystal if necessary to cover them.

This storm sample method permits the study of changes occurring throughout a storm. By taking specimens at regular intervals you can obtain a permanent record showing a true cross section of that particular storm, as revealed through changing size, type, and abundance of crystals.

In one March snow fall in the Mohawk Valley, for instance, 150 replicas that I was able to gather in a 30-minute period illustrated a rather typical series of transitions. As frequently happens in this section, the large symmetrical crystals fell at the close of the storm, which laid down a total of ten inches in this case. The barometer was falling at 29.70 inches, and a northwest wind was blowing. The thermometer was at 26° F. The big symmetrical crystals, which at first had a considerable amount of frost about them, were gradually replaced by the more common confused, unsymmetrical flakes. These continued for several hours; then the wind changed and the skies cleared.

In regions near the edge of the snow belt the finest specimens often fall at temperatures above freezing. Under such circumstances, melting will prevent the replicas from being satisfactory, unless a freezing chamber is used. In such regions good specimens can often be obtained at night or early in the morning.

Under a starlit sky

Often beautiful crystals can be collected under a starlit sky. One night last February, for example, when I set my collecting board under the light of a full moon, I obtained crystals that were five to ten times smaller than the usual forms but which contained rare types common only to the far north. During this collecting period a very beautiful 44° halo could be seen around the moon. And it may be significant that one of the coldest periods of the winter followed this unusual crystal fall.

Winter sleet, the kind that rattles on the windows and is often mixed with rain, has the general form shown in the upper right-hand illustration on the next page. These icy pellets, unlike snow crystals, form from liquid water which would have fallen as rain except for passing through freezing masses of air. Their usual lack of symmetry is caused probably by the formation of an icy shell around most of the liquid waterdrop. Subsequent freezing of the water inside, accompanied by its expansion, possibly accounts for the protuberance on the upper side of this specimen. I have found identical forms of earthly origin early on a frosty morning where raindrops resting on fallen leaves have frozen.

Soft hail or graupel is common at the beginning and end of winter and is formed in an entirely different manner. It starts originally as a snow crystal formed directly from gaseous water vapor, without passing through the liquid phase at all. The falling crystal passes through warm air with high moisture content and picks up secondary frost deposits on one of its surfaces, probably the under side. Eventually a pyramidal shape is formed, and if it continues to fall, further modifications in form occur and the surface becomes covered with rounded bumps, like miniature snowballs before they are tightly packed. I have storm sample replicas that show all of the formative steps described. Graupel forms a most interesting snow for skiing. If it falls to a depth of several feet (as I once found it at Indian Pass in the High Peaks of the Adirondacks), the skiing is not fast but incredibly smooth.

Speaking of skiing, perhaps the poor-

These flakes were collected under a starlit sky. A number of types common only in the far north were found

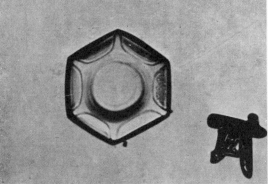

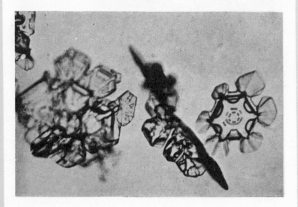

est "dry" snow for skiing is formed by a fall of ice spicules. One might have better sport sliding on coarse sand and gravel. The ones shown opposite are in a cluster. But some of the individual spicules have a six-sided cross section and are apparently twin crystals, in which the growth started in the middle and proceeded with mutual symmetry on either side of the nucleus. In the vicinity of Schenectady this form of snow is very common in the middle of winter and at times comprises the bulk of the fall.

As the reader may have noticed, many snowflakes falling in a storm consist of a considerable number of clumped particles. Often the particles comprising the clumps have lost most of their original crystalline form in passing through layers of relatively warm air. Some, however, retain their sharp symmetry.

After snow has been on the ground for a time and subjected to alternate periods above and below freezing, particularly during the latter part of winter, the original form undergoes a change. The earlier part of this change produces particles with angu-

➤ ICE SPICULES like these make the poorest "dry" snow for skiing. One might as well ski on sand

▼ SOMETIMES a flake loses its delicate crystal detail during descent, as illustrated by this curious example

▼ UNDER DIFFERENT CONDITIONS a whole cluster of fragile flakes will arrive at the collecting board intact

lar outline. Later this shape becomes rounded to exhibit fantastic forms, and these particles make up the "corn snow" that is the delight of late winter skiers.

The most elaborate variations in snow crystals seem to fall from low-hanging clouds in local storms. In the region of Schenectady, snow flurries often sweep down the Mohawk Valley with the prevailing west and northwest winds. The flakes that come with these short storms are often in a badly battered condition, and they are apt to be very asymmetrical, with one of the six arms several times as long as the others. Solid hexagons come in cold periods when there is little moisture in the air.

▼ ALTERNATE melting and drying, particularly in late winter, reduces a snow crystal to a rough, angular mass

▼ ... UNTIL FINALLY all the corners are rounded off and the once beautiful ice jewel assumes a curious shape

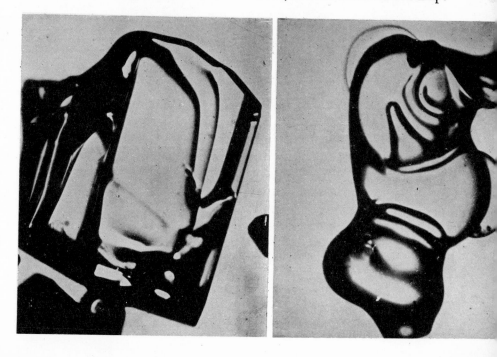

Perhaps the most interesting types of ice crystals are those popularly known as "wheels and axle," or "cuff buttons." These are twin crystals, growing as hexagonal columns from a common origin and terminating in a pyramid, more commonly with an extended capping similar in appearance to the solid hexagonal snow crystal. The illustrations at the bottom of this page represent typical forms

The frost that gathers in fernlike patterns. on the window pane, as well as other terrestrial forms of crystallized water, can be preserved in replica form as readily as snow crystals. The frosted specimen can simply be dipped into a shallow tray containing the resin solution and then exposed to the air to dry; or the solution may be applied with a camel's hair brush or sprayed on. Afterwards the thin film is stripped off in a single sheet; and the beauty and delicacy of the continuous pattern recorded on its

surface has to be seen to be appreciated. Many forms other than those shown will be found. Furthermore, most of them can be grown and treated in the freezing compartment of a home refrigerator at any time of the year.

The preservation and study of crys-

▲THESE TWO FLAKES are typical of the snow flurries that commonly sweep down the Mohawk Valley, in New York State. Many of them have one arm several times as long as the others

FURTHER EXAMPLES showing how frost patterns may be taken from glass by applying the resin solution to the frosted surface. After evaporation, the pattern may be stripped off in a single film. The "snow fern" at far right was made at Lake George by Dr. Irving Langmuir, using the Schaefer method. Frost patterns of this type can be made and treated at any season in a home refrigerator

tals from winter storms, besides having interesting scientific aspects, will repay the observer in many ways. Since the process is so easy, it is induce-

ment enough that the time spent studying snow crystals will help one to realize that Nature is continually producing a never-ending wealth of beauty, ready to be enjoyed by anyone who will search for it close at hand.

▲ LOCALIZED snowstorms with low clouds seem to produce the greatest variety and complexity in flakes

▲ SOLID HEXAGONS of this sturdy type usually fall in cold periods when there is not much moisture in the air

AN ESKIMO GIRL

BUILDS A SNOWHOUSE

An unusual series of photographs

by the Venerable D. B. Marsh,

Archdeacon of Baffin Island

MEN are generally the builders of houses throughout the world, but the accompanying photographs show a girl at Eskimo Point on the west coast of Hudson Bay constructing one of the houses for which the Eskimos between Labrador and western Canada are famous. This is a smaller house than the typical snow hut which serves through the winter as a dwelling among many of the Central Eskimos. But the latter is usually a more ambitious structure than one person can conveniently construct alone. The usual practice is for one man to stand on the inside and lay the blocks, while another cuts them from the snow outside and hands them to him through a hole in the lowest tier of blocks. The house pictured here is a convenient size for overnight shelter on the trail, and as shown, even a girl can build it quickly without any assistance from a second person.

1 CHOOSING AN AREA where the snow is compact, the girl cuts blocks about a foot and a half long and a foot wide. On a trip an Eskimo sometimes carries a special snow knife

2 SHE LAYS the blocks around the hole left in the snow—an easy system for one person. But if the house is to stay warm when the door is open, the floor must be higher

3 NOTICE that the girl has cut the blocks slightly curved. With thinner blocks the house could still be kept good and warm, and there would be less thawing during cooking

4 THE WALL slopes slightly inward, and at one point it tapers down to take the next tier in a continuous spiral. This snow would be called excellent for housebuilding

5 THE BLOCKS are laid around in a rising tier. Most persons do not realize that a snowhouse can be kept much warmer than freezing. The cold outside keeps the snow from melting

6 EACH BLOCK is now leaned against the next in order to keep them from falling in. The colder the weather the warmer you can keep the interior without weakening the roof

9 THE LAST FEW BLOCKS can scarcely be angled up through the narrowing hole and are laid with care

10 A FINAL BLOCK closes the hole in the center and the dome is completed—a masterpiece of ingenuity

8 SHE IS now almost hidden, and the hardest part is about over. The wall is curving inward sharply

7 LAYING THE BLOCKS is warm work, and the architect in snow pulls the hood of her fur jacket back

12 LASTLY, SHE FILLS the chinks with snow. In time, a snowhouse grows so strong you can stand on it

11 REMOVING A BLOCK with her knife, she emerges triumphant. The house is now quite substantial

They Bust AVALANCHES Wide Open

Snow Rangers fight avalanches with artillery,

dynamite, and skis to protect   half

a million people who work and play

in the alpine zones of the West

Seattle Post-Intelligencer photo

⋏ TARGET: MOUNTAINSIDE. Artillery Captain Stanley R. Mathews, Jr., directs gunfire with a battery commander's scope

▲ ALLURING BUT FICKLE MT. BAKER (10,750 feet), in the Cascade Range of northern Washington, was the scene of one of the worst avalanche tragedies. Near its summit on a sunny day in July, a monster snowslide swept over a party of 25 climbers, killing six of them. Four bodies were never found

Bill Parke, USFS photo

By HOWARD E. JACKSON

◄ A BIG GUN ROARS in the battle of the avalanches. An army gunner from Ft. Lewis, Washington, pulls the lanyard of a 155-mm. artillery piece and sends a shell screaming toward a potentially dangerous area. A direct hit in a sensitive spot will bring the avalanche down on man's timetable instead of a mountain's

"WHAT gives?" you wonder as you slow your car to a stop behind the stalled cars on the mountainous, snowlined highway.

You lean forward to set the handbrake.

BOOM!

You bolt upright, keenly alive as you hear the roar of cannon ahead. The eerie scream of a shell speeding through space sets your nerves tingling. There is a dull thud as the projectile hits the mountainside.

"What the heck . . ." you start to say as you roll down your window and anxiously search the snow-covered peaks.

BOOM!

The second blast sounds louder, nearer. The shell goes screaming into the distance. You hear it crrump into the mountain.

Puzzled, you impatiently await a state patrol car moving down the line toward you.

"What's up?" you yell as it draws near.

"Avalanche blasting with artillery," the officer shouts back. "Dangerous snow conditions threatened the highway. Those shells knocked a slide across the road. Snowplows will clear the way in a few minutes."

"Who puts on the show?" you ask.

"Snow Rangers!" the officer answers cryptically as the patrol car passes by.

You might have this unusual experience in the near future. It could happen to you on a main or secondary highway in the high Cascade Mountains of Washington or Oregon, in the rugged Rockies of Colorado or Utah, or in the snow-capped Sierras of California.

At one time the odds against a car and an avalanche arriving simultaneously at the same point were great. The odds have been getting smaller with increasing winter travel. But the Snow Rangers fought and won what amounted to a pitched battle—artillery versus avalanches—at Alta, Utah, during the winter of 1950-51, and, since then, more and more western states have become interested in the possibility of controlling snowslides by gunfire. Colorado has established its own highway avalanche protection service. Washington has built snowsheds to protect

▼ TECHNIQUE No. 2 for busting an avalanche is blasting it with pre-set high explosives. There are no set rules, says a veteran Snow Ranger, except to use plenty of dynamite

Howard E. Jackson photo

⋏ COMMANDER of the artillery blasting detail, Major Tremaine Smith, points out the top of a ski lift where a 75-mm. artillery piece was hauled to blast snow cornices overhanging a skiing area

travelers, is now seriously experimenting with artillery fire for controlling avalanches.

Although the Swiss have lived with the avalanche for centuries, and have long since learned how to release dangerous snowslides by artillery fire, avalanche research is new in this country. It had its feeble beginning in 1937-38 when Forest Ranger C. D. Wadsworth was detailed to Alta in the Wasatch Mountains of Utah as a full-time snow and avalanche observer. But our avalanche control program grew slowly. It grew strong only with the coming of the Snow Rangers.

Snow Rangers may seem like a new occupational group, but in reality they are U. S. Forest Rangers on winter duty. In summer you see them in our National Forests doing administrative work, making timber surveys, riding sheep and cattle ranges, and perhaps fighting forest fires. During the winter you probably remember them the way you saw them last, in an unchanged environment. It

is perhaps surprising to learn that their winter duty is quite different. It is often cold and dangerous, and at times touched with tragedy.

Their chief concern is the safety of skiers using winter sports areas in our National Forests. When an accident happens they feel personally responsible. And accidents do happen . . . like what happened to Keith Jacobsen, only child of Berne Jacobsen, city editor of the Seattle *Post Intelligencer.* Three 17-year-old boys—Keith, Larry Schinke, and Edward Almquist—were on an overnight ski tour to Source Lake. Shortly after noon, five miles north of Snoqualmie Pass, a slide rumbled down the slope and engulfed Keith and Larry. Edward escaped. It was three o'clock by the time he made his way back to the Pass.

Ross Files was the Snow Ranger on duty. He immediately dispatched two rescue parties, but the going was rough and the weather foul. Many volunteers had to turn back. Despite shortages of men and supplies, and then darkness and biting cold, he and the remaining helpers found Larry shortly after 9:30 that night. Larry had recovered consciousness after being hit, to find himself buried under three feet of snow. His arm made a small air pocket which allowed him to breathe. Although trapped for nine hours, he suffered only mildly from exposure.

The search went on until midnight when a storm made further probing and calling impossible.

"It was a rough night," Ross relates. "We had but half a dozen sleeping bags among the score of volunteers. The men grabbed what rest they could by taking turns."

At sunrise the search began again. Keith was found at eight o'clock—dead from a broken neck caused when he struck a rock.

His death was especially tragic because it could have been prevented. The boys were not experienced mountaineers. They violated the rules of good ski-touring technique. They did not inquire about snow conditions from the local Snow Ranger, and they made the fatal mistake of exposing more than one member at a time to a dangerous slide area. No doubt the area looked safe, but any slope of more than 20 degrees can avalanche.

"Skiers forget that they are dealing with a great natural force, comparable to a flood, earthquake or tornado," points out Ross Files. "Of them all the avalanche is the most complex, and the dividing line between danger and safety is the most obscure. It is both powerful and deceptive."

Novices are not the only ones fooled by an innocent-looking slope of snow. Recently (April 1954), no less a veteran than William Degenhardt was caught by an unexpected slide. Degenhardt is president of Seattle's famed Mountaineers, and has been climbing and skiing for more than 30 years. He, his wife, and a Mrs. Loretta Slater were working up a hogback which he thought perfectly safe. The snow had softened to a depth of four

▼ AFTER IT WAS ALL OVER. This distant view shows the terminus of the fatal Mt. Baker avalanche. Rescuers appear as black specks in the center of the picture

➤ CLOSE-UP VIEW shows where a college student's body was found. Of the six persons killed, only two bodies were recovered. Others were believed lost in crevasses

Bill Parke, USFS photos

inches, and the slope was not steep. Despite this, an avalanche ripped loose. Degenhardt managed to stay on top but suffered hip and internal injuries when he struck rocks as he plunged over a 20-foot drop. The women were not in the slide-path. Rescue operations were relatively simple. Degenhardt was embarrassed.

"I felt like a blankety-blank fool for getting myself in a spot like that," he said with a grin from his hospital bed.

Although the avalanche busters' chief concern is for the skier, they also feel responsible for the safety of pleasure-bound mountain climbers, highway maintenance men, telephone and pipe line crews, and loggers who use or work near public land.

Accidents happen to them too. Headlines tell the stories: "Highway Workers Buried in Pickup; One Dead." "Sno-Go Crewman Smothered by Snowslide." "Watchman at West Tunnel Entrance Killed by Avalanche." "Ski Tow Operator Swept to His Doom."

One of the strangest of these accidents happened not in winter but in summer, on a July 22nd. Bill Parke, who directed rescue work, tells the story: "A party of 25 Western Washington College students and faculty were making an annual climb up Mt. Baker. They were on Deming Glacier, about to go over what is known as the Roman Wall,

a steep promontory a few hundred feet from the top, when a snow avalanche started and caught every member of the party."

The climbers suddenly found themselves standing on a moving carpet of snow. "Dig in!" shouted the guides. When the group frantically sank their alpenstocks and ice axes into the firm snow underneath, the force of the slide bent them over like blades of grass and quickly swept the climbers off their feet. After that it was every person for himself as the snowslide tumbled them about. Many of them dropped into deep crevasses.

This out-of-season accident claimed six lives. Only two bodies were recovered.

Today, as more people visit the western mountains, the number of accidents is increasing. During the past two seasons we have had confirmed avalanche fatalities in Utah, Idaho, Colorado, California, and Washington.

The Forest Service inherited the avalanche hazard problem because most of the desirable alpine skiing terrain is on National Forest land. This land includes 90 per cent of the country's slide areas—notorious graveyards for avalanche victims— but ideal areas for recreation development.

The Forest Service is not content with the old-time answer to the avalanche hazard (either stay out of the mountains or take your chances), and in the interest of public safety has launched itself into the business of combatting avalanches.

Home base is Alta, Utah. During the heyday of the Gold Rush, Alta

was destroyed repeatedly—but temporarily—by avalanches which brought death to the miners and destruction to their camps. It was obliterated finally by snowslides in 1874, with a loss of 60 lives. It seems fitting that it should be reborn as a winter ski area and be the site of the first observation and research center in the Western Hemisphere. Other main stations are at Berthoud Pass, near Denver, Colorado, and Stevens Pass in the Cascade Mountains of Washington.

Snow Rangers are stationed at these and other areas in the western states. The "White Death" has played a grimly historic role near all these areas. The greatest ava-

Bill Parke, USFS photos

◄ MONTY ATWATER, No. 1 "Avalanche Buster" and father of the Snow Rangers. He claims his respect for snow-slides is prenatal

⋏ PORTRAIT OF A DEAD AVALANCHE. This innocent-looking pattern, resembling a much-used ski slope, is the trail of a fairly small avalanche. Note the "fracture point" (where it started) at the top of the picture. Ski tracks alongside give size comparison

lanche disaster in our nation's history took place just below the Stevens Pass station. It happened at Wellington, Washington, in March, 1910. Three trains were snowbound on parallel tracks. A single snowslide swept them off the little plateau and into the canyon; 118 people were killed and more than a million dollars' worth of rolling stock was destroyed.

Snow Rangers were the idea of Monty Atwater — America's No. 1 "Avalanche Buster," who claims his interest in avalanches is prenatal. Two years before he was born his father was buried in a slide that killed 50 men in a mining camp at Telluride, Colorado.

"That avalanche was what we call a double-killer," he explains. "It hit the bunkhouse, and when everybody rushed in to help, a second slide struck and did most of the killing."

Monty's father was rescued alive. The man who had been standing next to him was not found for six months.

Monty was born in a mining camp in Oregon. He himself had his first brush with an avalanche before he was one year old. "A snowslide came in the back door and filled up the kitchen while my mother fled with me in her arms to the front of the house."

He became personally interested in avalanches—simply as a matter of self-preservation—after he graduated from Harvard and became a game protector in the Glacier Park country. He saw deer, elk, mountain goats, and other animals caught in slides while foraging on steep open hillsides. He witnessed first-hand how railroads could be crumbled by snowslides. What impressed him most was the experience of a fellow worker. Monty tells the story as gospel truth:

"The man was held fast beneath the slide by his snowshoes for 24 hours. Finally he worked a hand free, got out his knife, opened it, cut the snowshoe bindings and dug his way out. Since he had no snowshoes, he had to swim ten miles down an icy river to get home."

During World War II Monty

♠ JOHN HERBERT (left), a Forest Service official, fastens together sections of aluminum tubing used for probes in avalanche rescue work. Monty Atwater holds a red safety cord used by "trigger man" when skiing down an avalanche

served his country in mountain and winter warfare. Afterward he returned to his old job in Montana, and again became interested in avalanches. When an avalanche guard job opened up at Alta he took it. There he championed the newly organized avalanche program, and in a few years fathered the Snow Rangers.

These bold mountain men are a triple-threat to potential snow slides. Busting an avalanche by means of bombardment is only one

▲ OUT ON SKI TOUR, Atwater (left)
and Herbert check avalanche hazards at a popular winter sports area

Howard E. Jackson photos

ot their three commando-like tricks. Its chief advantage over the other two methods is that an entire area can be shot out easily and quickly from one location—even during a storm.

Firing projectiles into avalanche paths has disadvantages, though. The conventional 75-mm. or 105-mm. artillery piece is cumbersome in snow-covered terrain, and shells cannot be directed at targets close to fixed installations like chair lifts, rope tows and shelters. But the advantages will far outweigh the disadvantages when the lighter, more mobile, recoilless 75-mm. rifles become available.

Fighting avalanches with dynamite is the second technique. It is somewhat more dangerous than supervised shellings, which generally are made with the aid of army or state guard units. With this technique the avalanche is triggered by charges of military demolition, tetrytol, C-3 or TNT blocks. The charges are placed in shot holes or tossed out so that the operator can work from a protected position.

This is a tailor-made operation, since slopes vary and many slide-paths have more than one release point, all of which must be tested. Cornices offer special problems, tricky problems that can cost a life if not worked out correctly. Often the rangers resort to pre-planted charges where cornices collect year after year and are an annual source of hazard.

"There is no set technique," Monty says. "The only hard and fast rule is to use plenty of dynamite!"

"Skiing down" an avalanche is the last of the three stratagems employed by the Snow Rangers. It is by far the most dangerous; takes skill and good judgment, and can be troublesome even for an expert.

Two men work together. They climb, via a safe route, to the top of the slide area. One man keeps watch. The other makes a ski run across the face of the prospective slide, cutting it inches above the fracture point. Beforehand, this "trigger man" generally loosens his ski bindings, removes his ankle straps and unfastens his ski pole slings from his hands. In case he is caught in a slide he can quickly shake off these encumbrances and save himself by "swimming" on top of the snow mass. He also trails a long red parachute cord behind him. His partners — he hopes — will find him by following the cord if he does get buried in the snow slide.

His weight, and the shearing effect of his skis, crack open the snow with a loud snap. As he races for safety the avalanche breaks loose and crashes down the hillside—piling up at the bottom to a depth of 50 to 100 feet.

"Personally I prefer planting explosives to using my hickory staves to create an avalanche," Ralph Wiese frankly admits. "Every time I ski down an avalanche I get the flutters in the pit of my stomach."

Despite the danger, no Snow Ranger has taken a fatal ride in a self-made avalanche. A number have been caught. Some have been buried. Generally they get tripped up when stubborn snow requires a second run. The snow starts sliding just as they enter the area and quickly engulfs them. They can't do much to help themselves then.

"You can't stop an avalanche. You can't outrun it," Monty points out. "In the Alps they've been clocked at more than 100 miles an hour. It would take a lot of wax on any man's skis to beat a mass of snow and ice going that fast!"

Alexander Cushing is one of the few men to win a race with an avalanche. It happened at Aspen, Colorado, in 1948. He, Percy Rideout, and Alexander McFadden were sweeping down a steep slope into a shallow trough. Rideout, first, ended halfway up the opposite slope. McFadden, second, stopped at the bottom. Cushing was halfway down when he heard the awful hissing sound of hundreds of tons of snow let loose behind him. Terrified, he raced ahead of the avalanche and was saved only by gaining some distance up the opposite slope. Even then he barely won . . . since he was caught and partly buried. He was lucky. His friend McFadden never had a chance. He was carried down the

Howard E. Jackson photo

valley by the avalanche and smothered to death.

A person should do what he can
for himself if caught by an avalanche—and it is precious little.

"Riding it out is like being tumbled in the surf," Monty says,
speaking from experience. "You

▲ A PENETROMETER TEST is made
by Snow Ranger Frank Foto.
"Hammer" (rod within a tube)
is dropped to determine resistance in various layers of snow
and consistency of snow pack,
useful information for predict-
ing avalanches

come to the surface, then get sucked under again. You can't tell which end is up. The mass of snow and ice seems alive. When it slows down it closes in on you, and crushes you with a great suffocating weight."

Since there is a wavelike action to avalanches, a heave will sometimes help bring you to the surface. Once Monty did that and the avalanche tossed him out. Another time a heave at the right instant enabled him to stick his head out of the snow. If a man is buried when the slide stops, a big heave at the last moment will give him breathing room. A mask of ice will form around his face soon enough, and cut off his air supply—so this last heave is important. When a person is buried, the Snow Rangers figure they have about two hours

▲ REALISTIC EXERCISES call for simulated avalanche rescue work. "Victim" is located with aluminum probes; evergreen branches are used to mark his position; shovelers dig him out

to get him out alive. After that his chances of surviving dwindle rapidly. Very few persons have been buried in the snow 10 or 12 hours and lived to tell about it. The record is 72 hours, but that bordered on the miraculous.

Avalanche study is never-ending, but as Frank Foto, Snow Ranger at Stevens Pass, Washington, said not long ago, "We have been able to reduce the hazard to manageable levels. We can pinpoint our shots, and cut a potentially aggressive avalanche down to size, piecemeal, the way we want, or we can bust him wide open!"

⋏ "Victim is carried on a stretcher to first aid toboggan...

⌖ . . . and transported down the mountain to a waiting pick-up truck

⋎ At avalanche school, Snow Rangers learn first aid for common slide accidents. Even a little slide can break a leg

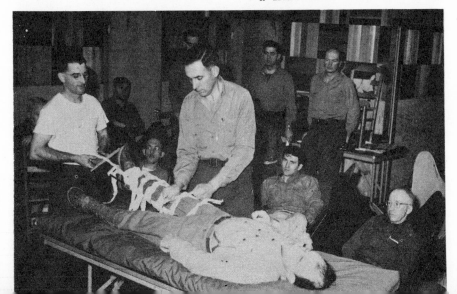

Spanish Moss

Spanish Moss is neither Spanish nor moss; it is an air plant or epiphyte, and strangely enough is related to the pineapple. Its long gray streamers hanging from the branches of trees and telegraph wires are a familiar sight in many parts of our South. Unlike mistletoe, which draws some of its nourishment from the tree supporting it, Spanish Moss seeks only an anchoring place. It derives all its food from the air. It turns greenish in wet weather and has a tiny, greenish three-petaled flower. Various commercial uses have been found for it as a packing and stuffing material.

An Immigrant that Thrived

Once regarded as a curiosity, it spread to appall those who invited it.

The English Sparrow is mentioned in the Bible. It lays five or six grayish-white eggs speckled with brown, and raises several broods each year. Even if there were only one brood each year, a pair of English sparrows could multiply so rapidly that in the twentieth year over *seven billion* sparrows would theoretically be hatched. Obviously, natural checks prevent this unlimited increase. In North America the English Sparrow increased very rapidly, because food was available and there were relatively few natural enemies. The population has now reached the saturation point in the available habitat. In fact, it has sharply decreased in many urban centers. Formerly, the sparrow found a plentiful supply of food in the undigested seeds in horse droppings. The advent of the automobile therefore greatly reduced the number of sparrows in cities—their favorite home.

In 1850—the same year that Jenny Lind made her Metropolitan debut—eight pairs of this bird were brought to New York City. The birds did not thrive, and two years later more were imported. Those that survived the winter in confinement were freed in Greenwood Cemetery. They increased in the ensuing years to millions and spread over the whole country.

Photograph by WALKER VAN RIPER
Denver Museum of Natural History

SPEED

MAN AND THE ANIMALS

Numerals next to dots indicate speed in miles per hour
All nautical miles are converted into statute miles

IN THE AIR

MILES PER HOUR   0   10   20   30

SCISSOR-TAILED FLYCATCHER (A) 10 •
WOODCOCK (A) 13 •
SWAINSON'S HAWK (A) 15 •
CATBIRD (A) 16 •
SNOW BUNTING (F - ¼ hr. - J) 16.7 •
SONG SPARROW (A) 17 •
VESPER SPARROW (A) 17 •
BLUEBIRD (A) 17 •
AMERICAN EGRET (A) 17 •
ARKANSAS KINGBIRD (A) 17 •
SLATE-COLORED JUNCO (A) 18 •
GOLDFINCH (A) 18 •
BLACK SKIMMER (A - 3 mi. - O) 18 •
CHIPPING SPARROW (A) 20 •
PURPLE MARTIN (A) 20 •
BLUE JAY (A) 20 •
FLORIDA CORMORANT (A - O) 20 •
MEADOWLARK (A) 20 •
INDIGO BUNTING (A) 20 •
TURKEY VULTURE (E) 21 •
NIGHTHAWK (A) 22 •
BROWN THRASHER (A) 22 •
RED-TAILED HAWK (A) 22 •
YELLOW-BILLED CUCKOO (A) 22 •
RUFFLED GROUSE (A) 22 •
KINGBIRD (A) 23 •
RUSTY BLACKBIRD (A) 23 •
RAVEN (A) 24 •
BLACK-BELLIED PLOVER (A - Q) 24 •
NORTHERN FLICKER (A) 25 •
SPARROW HAWK (A) 25 •
LAND RAIL (G) 25 •
TREE SWALLOW (A) 25 •
BLACK DUCK (A) 26 •
BALTIMORE ORIOLE (A) 26 •
WILLET (A - O) 27 •
GLAUCOUS-WINGED GULL (A) 28 •
BOAT-TAILED GRACKLE (A) 28 •
GREAT BLUE HERON (A) 28 •
RED-WINGED BLACKBIRD (A) 28 •
COMMON TERN (A) 29 •
BLACK-HEADED GULL (A) 30 •
BRONZED GRACKLE (A) 30 •
BROWN PELICAN (A) 30 •
BANK SWALLOW (A - H) 31 •
GREAT BLACK-BACKED GULL (C) 31.1 •
BULLOCK'S ORIOLE (A) 32
SEMIPALMATED PLOVER (A - P) 32
SEMIPALMATED SANDPIPER (A - Q) 32
RUDDY TURNSTONE (A) 33
SHARP-TAILED GROUSE (A - 1.5 mi.) 33
HUDSONIAN CURLEW (A - 7 mi. - Q) 34
GREEN HERON (I - T - A) 34
EUROPEAN CORMORANT (A - G) 3
HOUSE SPARROW (A) 3
MAGPIE (A - H) 3
RING-BILLED GULL (A) 3
LONG-BILLED CURLEW (A) 3
HERRING GULL (A)
ROBIN (A)
BELTED KINGFISHER (A)
CROSSBILL (C - P) 3

A Speed measured by automobile speedometer	**G** Frightened **N** Ground speed
B Speed measured by airplane	**H** Chased **O** Head wind
C Timed by watch	**I** Without due exertion **P** Tail wind
D Speed measured by theodolite	**J** Migrating **Q** Wind abeam
E Speed measured by train	**K** Average maximum **R** Wind calm
F Speed measured by boat	**L** Top Speed **S** Light wind
	M Air speed **T** No wind

A number of the figures, although they are the best observations
on record, are not necessarily the highest speeds obtainable

Continued ➡

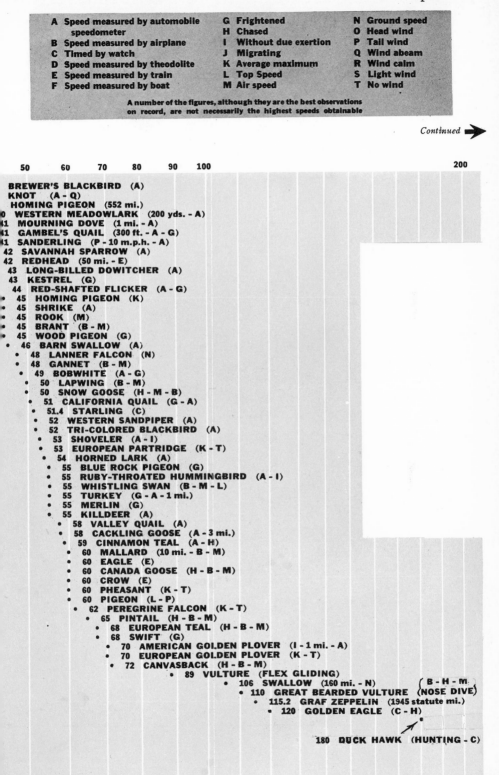

50   60   70   80   90   100   200

BREWER'S BLACKBIRD   (A)
KNOT   (A - Q)
HOMING PIGEON   (552 mi.)
0   WESTERN MEADOWLARK   (200 yds. - A)
41   MOURNING DOVE   (1 mi. - A)
41   GAMBEL'S QUAIL   (300 ft. - A - G)
41   SANDERLING   (P - 10 m.p.h. - A)
42   SAVANNAH SPARROW   (A)
42   REDHEAD   (50 mi. - E)
43   LONG-BILLED DOWITCHER   (A)
43   KESTREL   (G)
44   RED-SHAFTED FLICKER   (A - G)
45   HOMING PIGEON   (K)
45   SHRIKE   (A)
45   ROOK   (M)
45   BRANT   (B - M)
45   WOOD PIGEON   (G)
46   BARN SWALLOW   (A)
48   LANNER FALCON   (N)
48   GANNET   (B - M)
49   BOBWHITE   (A - G)
50   LAPWING   (B - M)
50   SNOW GOOSE   (H - M - B)
51   CALIFORNIA QUAIL   (G - A)
51.4   STARLING   (C)
52   WESTERN SANDPIPER   (A)
52   TRI-COLORED BLACKBIRD   (A)
53   SHOVELER   (A - I)
53   EUROPEAN PARTRIDGE   (K - T)
54   HORNED LARK   (A)
55   BLUE ROCK PIGEON   (G)
55   RUBY-THROATED HUMMINGBIRD   (A - I)
55   WHISTLING SWAN   (B - M - L)
55   TURKEY   (G - A - 1 mi.)
55   MERLIN   (G)
55   KILLDEER   (A)
58   VALLEY QUAIL   (A)
58   CACKLING GOOSE   (A - 3 mi.)
59   CINNAMON TEAL   (A - H)
60   MALLARD   (10 mi. - B - M)
60   EAGLE   (E)
60   CANADA GOOSE   (H - B - M)
60   CROW   (E)
60   PHEASANT   (K - T)
60   PIGEON   (L - P)
62   PEREGRINE FALCON   (K - T)
65   PINTAIL   (H - B - M)
68   EUROPEAN TEAL   (H - B - M)
68   SWIFT   (G)
70   AMERICAN GOLDEN PLOVER   (I - 1 mi. - A)
70   EUROPEAN GOLDEN PLOVER   (K - T)
72   CANVASBACK   (H - B - M)
89   VULTURE   (FLEX GLIDING)
106   SWALLOW   (160 mi. - N)
110   GREAT BEARDED VULTURE   (B - H - M / NOSE DIVE)
115.2   GRAF ZEPPELIN   (1945 statute mi.)
120   GOLDEN EAGLE   (C - H)

180   DUCK HAWK   (HUNTING - C)

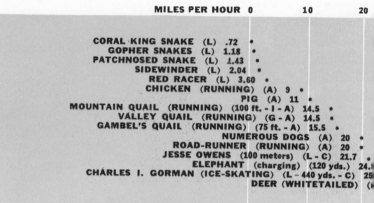

SPEED

MAN AND THE ANIMALS

Numerals next to dots indicate speed in miles per hour
All nautical miles are converted into statute miles

ON LAND

	MILES PER HOUR 0	10	20
CORAL KING SNAKE (L) .72 •			
GOPHER SNAKES (L) 1.18 •			
PATCHNOSED SNAKE (L) 1.43 •			
SIDEWINDER (L) 2.04 •			
RED RACER (L) 3.60 •			
CHICKEN (RUNNING) (A) 9 •			
PIG (A) 11 •			
MOUNTAIN QUAIL (RUNNING) (100 ft. - I - A) 14.5 •			
VALLEY QUAIL (RUNNING) (G - A) 14.5 •			
GAMBEL'S QUAIL (RUNNING) (75 ft. - A) 15.5 •			
NUMEROUS DOGS (A) 20 •			
ROAD-RUNNER (RUNNING) (A) 20 •			
JESSE OWENS (100 meters) (L - C) 21.7 •			
ELEPHANT (charging) (120 yds.) 24.5 •			
CHARLES I. GORMAN (ICE-SKATING) (L - 440 yds. - C) 25			
DEER (WHITETAILED) (3			

IN WATER

CARP .9 •		• 7 SALMON	
TENCH 1.1 •		• 10 PIKE	
PIKE 1.1 •		• 10 SUBMA	
BLEAK 1.3 •			
PERCH 1.3 •			
BREAM 1.5 •			
J. WEISSMULLER (100 yds.) 4.01 •			
SUBMARINE (Cruising Speed, Submerged) 4.6 •			
BARBEL 4.9 •			

A	Speed measured by automobile speedometer	G	Frightened	N	Ground speed
		H	Chased	O	Head wind
B	Speed measured by airplane	I	Without due exertion	P	Tail wind
C	Timed by watch	J	Migrating	Q	Wind abeam
D	Speed measured by theodolite	K	Average maximum	R	Wind calm
E	Speed measured by train	L	Top Speed	S	Light wind
F	Speed measured by boat	M	Air speed	T	No wind

A number of the figures, although they are the best observations on record, are not necessarily the highest speeds obtainable

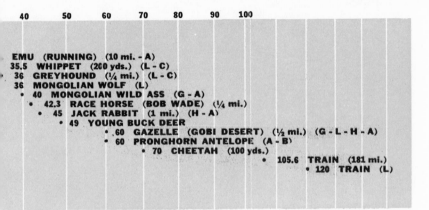

```
   40        50        60       70        80        90       100
```

EMU (RUNNING) (10 mi. - A)
35.5 WHIPPET (200 yds.) (L - C)
• 36 GREYHOUND (¼ mi.) (L - C)
36 MONGOLIAN WOLF (L)
• 40 MONGOLIAN WILD ASS (G - A)
• 42.3 RACE HORSE (BOB WADE) (¼ mi.)
• 45 JACK RABBIT (1 mi.) (H - A)
• 49 YOUNG BUCK DEER
• 60 GAZELLE (GOBI DESERT) (½ mi.) (G - L - H - A)
• 60 PRONGHORN ANTELOPE (A - B)
• 70 CHEETAH (100 yds.)
• 105.6 TRAIN (181 mi.)
• 120 TRAIN (L)

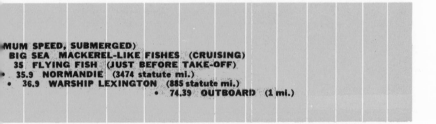

...MUM SPEED, SUBMERGED)
BIG SEA MACKEREL-LIKE FISHES (CRUISING)
35 FLYING FISH (JUST BEFORE TAKE-OFF)
• 35.9 NORMANDIE (3474 statute mi.)
• 36.9 WARSHIP LEXINGTON (885 statute mi.)
• 74.39 OUTBOARD (1 mi.)

Spiders for Profit

By NAN SONGER HOOK

How to feed them, breed them, and wind up their webs for use in scientific instruments

EVERY outdoorsman has had the annoying experience of walking abruptly into a strand of silken spider web stretched across a woodland trail. When the glistening filament strikes the bridge of the nose, one usually gropes for it in irritation, plucks it away with momentary surprise at its strength and elasticity—and then promptly forgets it.

Next time this happens to you, pause a moment and examine the strand. What you have struck is the "dragline" of a spider, quite possibly one of the strongest materials made by a living creature. Because spider web is so fine (sometimes only a millionth of an inch in diameter), it is seldom thought of as strong. Actually, the draglines of certain spiders have greater tensile strength than steel, and are said to be exceeded in this respect only by fused quartz fibers. There is almost nothing of equal fineness and equal strength.

▲ CAREFULLY SE- LECTED spider silk has been used in 100,000 dot reticules for rifle scopes. Special proc- ess makes the dot dry circular instead of diamond-shaped.

◄ THE AUTHOR in her "spidery."

➤ THE BANDED GARDEN SPIDER spins a web with a metallic sheen that makes it useful for illuminated sights.

Walker Van Riper

The dragline is only one of many kinds of silk a spider can produce, but it is the most familiar kind. To a typical web-spinning spider, it is literally her lifeline. She hangs from it, uses it as a bridge, and lays

Don Alexander

⋏ A BLACK WIDOW makes egg-sacs like this, each yielding several hundred young.

Don Alexander

⋏ ARANEA GEMMOIDES' coloration makes her look like a bump on a log.

down the main supports of her snare with it. Throughout her life, she skitters about with a little bit of dragline silk trailing behind her —ready for instant use.

Naturally, such a wondrous material has not been overlooked by man in his endless experimentation. Primitive people in many parts of the world have put spider silk to work. It has been used for fishing lures and nets, for bird snares, and as a fiber for weaving small bags and ornaments. It has even been tried for making clothing, though without much success, because it is so costly to extract.

There is one use, however, well known to hunters, engineers, and scientists, that makes spider web important in modern-day technology. This is its use as cross-hairs in high-powered optical instruments. For the past sixteen years, I have supplied spider web to this highly specialized industry, working mostly from the sun-room of a cottage in Yucaipa, California. My business, conducted on a part-time basis, is the rearing and "silking" of spiders. In recent years, my husband Ray has worked at my side.

My entry into this field was actually an extension of a girlhood interest in insects. As a teenager with a butterfly net, I used to collect specimens for professional entomologists. But my hobby was interrupted for many years by family duties, and only when my children were away at school was I able to resume my experimental work. At first I tried breeding crickets, then branched off into a study of spiders and their webs. In 1939, I learned through a friend that in-

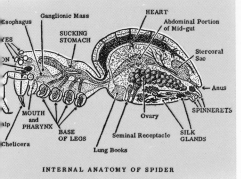

Esophagus — Ganglionic Mass — SUCKING STOMACH — HEART — Abdominal Portion of Mid-gut — Stercoral Sac — Anus — SPINNERETS — SILK GLANDS — Seminal Receptacle — Ovary — Lung Books — BASE OF LEGS — MOUTH and PHARYNX — Chelicera

INTERNAL ANATOMY OF SPIDER

Drawing by George Childs

⋏ VARIOUS groups of glands, each producing a different kind of silk, connect with the spinning tubes at the rear tip of the body.

quiries had been made to the U.S. Bureau of Standards asking *if* and *where* spider web could be obtained in quantity. This interested me, so I wrote to Dr. Willis Gertsch, of the American Museum of Natural History, and asked him whether I might be able to contribute something in this field. He replied that so far as he knew almost no work had been done and that very little was known about the commercial properties of webs.

This was just the sort of thing for me, so I wrote to the Bureau of Standards and volunteered to undertake a "spidery."

The Bureau offered encouragement and supplied me with a list of potential customers, but when I corresponded with the latter I found that they didn't know what sizes or quantities of web they wanted. So the first few years were largely experimental (which means I didn't make any money at it). The companies would furnish the best specifications they could, and I would send them samples of web. All too often, something would be

wrong and I would have to try and try again to satisfy them. Gradually I began to build up a system that greatly reduced the number of failures, and in time I developed a number of steady customers.

So far as we know, Ray and I now operate the only business in the world where spiders are reared and silked of webs of specified size, strength, and elasticity. At certain periods, we may have as many as 10,000 spiders in our home. We extract web from the much-maligned Black Widow (*Latrodectus mactans*), from the beautiful Banded Garden Spider (*Argiope trifasciata*), and from *Aranea gemmoides*, which has no colloquial name but is one of the large, common orb weavers.

We have tested more than 50 of the some 2,500 different species of spiders in North America and have settled upon these three as best for producing web for optical reticules.

Because we have come to appreciate spiders as something more than "ugly, creepy things," we are completely casual about them, and have even acquired three large tarantulas as pets.

Despite its amusing aspects, our work has a very serious purpose. We supply spider web to more than a dozen leading manufacturers and users of optical instruments. Our web finds its way into surveying transits and levels, gun-sights, range-finders, astronomical telescopes, bombsights, microscopes, and medical instruments like those used for obtaining a blood count. Almost every well-known telescopic rifle sight with a "dot reticule" uses our web (see illustration). Probably all surveying transits and levels have spider web cross-hairs. Most microscopes with a reticule and observatory telescopes use it.

It should be pointed out, though, that we did not initiate the use of spider web for reticules. The practice is an old one. It is said that spider web was used for fine instruments in Germany many years before it was used here. About 25 years ago, Dr. John Albright, of Cleveland, was collecting and silking Golden Garden Spiders (*Argiope aurantia*) for this purpose. He would catch them in the fall when they were mature and place them on a piece of canvas. As the spiders crawled and trailed their draglines behind them, he would wind it up and store it away for future use. Also, several manufacturers of optical instruments have long been using silk from spiders' cocoons for reticules. And as much as 30 or 40 years ago Keuffel and Esser in Hoboken took dragline threads from living spiders and even employed a "spider lady" for this role. Experience has shown that the dragline is much better than the filament from spiders' cocoons, for it will stretch fully 20 per cent of its own length.

There are other types of optical reticules made with fine steel or platinum wires, nickel-alloy wires, and nylon. In some instruments, the reticule is etched directly on the glass. But for a combination of fineness, strength, and elasticity, nothing is superior to spider web. When a strand of dragline web is stretched across a metal ring and inserted in a telescope, it will afterwards remain straight and true under almost any conditions of temperature. Other materials of equal fineness either tend to sag after a time or, if they are not elastic, are prone to break in the frigid temperatures of the stratosphere. I think that is one reason why blond human hair is no longer used in bombsights, as it used to be.

Standardized Spiders

Our chief contribution is in meeting requests for web of *specified* size, strength, and elasticity. Actually we don't do it; the spiders do. We have learned through experience that a given species of female spider (we never use the puny males), of a certain age and size, will invariably produce the same size and type of dragline silk.

Thus, with our inventory of different kinds and sizes of spiders, we are able to mail out order sheets on which we list available web varying from extra-fine (1/50,000th of an inch in diameter) to extra-heavy (1/5,000th). Incidentally, even the heaviest web is nowhere near as coarse as human hair, which averages about 1/250th of an inch in diameter. Our prices are subject to some variation, of course, but right now we sell the standard types at $5 for 10 feet and $30 for 100 feet.

Our extra-fine web is extracted from very young Black Widow Spiders and is used for telescopic rifle sights. Another standard size is used where a center dot is needed in the crosshairs. This web is 1/20,000th of an inch across and consists of a strand split from the

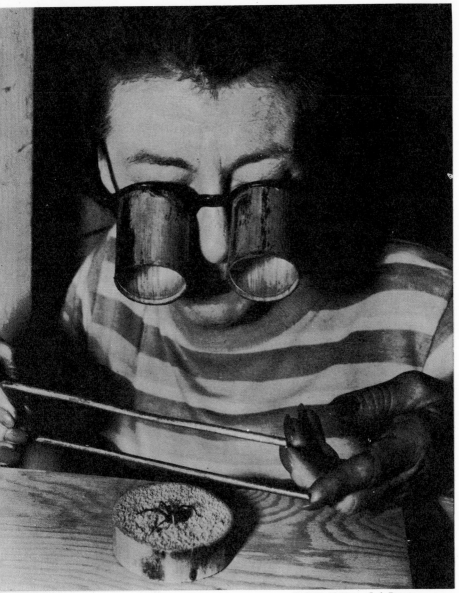

Wide World Photos, L.A. Bureau

⋏ SILKING. The spider is secured with small staples over body and feet. The web is then drawn from the spinneret.

dragline of a half-grown Black Widow.

Notice the word "split." "Whole web" is not smooth enough for many applications, so we have learned to separate the two or three strands in the dragline and extract only one. To understand the silking and splitting processes you have to know a little about the anatomy of a spider and the nature of her silk.

The plump abdomen of a spider is her silk factory. Inside it she has a multitude of tiny silk-producing glands. These are connected to a cluster of openings on tiny fingers at the hind end of her body, called spinnerets. When the silk is inside her, it is liquid, but it hardens almost instantly when drawn from the spinnerets. The spider does not spin it out as you would cast a fishing line—it must be pulled from her. Usually she tacks down the end of the web and then scrambles or drops away, so that the long filament is extracted from her body. Sometimes she draws out a few inches with her rear legs and lets a breeze do the rest. When she has released as much as she wants, she reaches back and cuts the strand with a claw on the tip of her foot.

The various kinds of silk (each produced by a different set of glands) all have a part in the spider's normal activities. If she makes a web, its main supports are of elastic dragline silk that will absorb the impact of a flying insect, as a tennis net does a ball. Other strands in the web are weak and sticky, and will sag; they are for entangling a victim's wings. The silk she uses to "lasso" and wrap a victim is like a white ribbon. Still other kinds are used for constructing the cocoon-like egg sac.

The actual silking process is not too difficult, but it does require experience and patience. We use only the dragline, and basically, there are two methods, depending upon whether "whole web" or "split web" is desired.

To obtain whole web, I remove the spider from her jar and place her upright on a small pedestal of yucca wood. Then I immobilize her by positioning a staple over her narrow waist and pushing the prongs into the soft wood. Next I use a small camel's hair brush to "tickle" her spinnerets until she produces a little of her dragline. I draw this out with the brush and secure it to one end of a U-shaped metal frame, on which it is wound "spiral" fashion. I space the silk at quarter-inch intervals so that each section may later be removed independently. When the frame is filled,

▼ Wound on the U-shaped frame, a single length can be used without disturbing the remainder.

Wide World Photos, L.A. Bureau

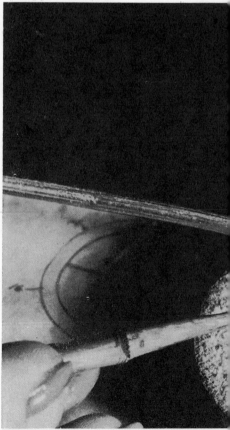

▼ To OBTAIN SPLIT WEB, the spider is placed upside down on the pedestal and immobilized with staples placed over her waist and legs (two legs per staple). The two- or three-strand dragline is drawn out and cemented to the rim of the work light. Then a needle is flipped back and forth across it until a loop appears into which the tip of the needle can be inserted and slid down to the spider's spinneret. At this point, a single strand can be wound onto a frame without extracting unwanted web.

Drawing by George Childs, after Nan Songer Hook

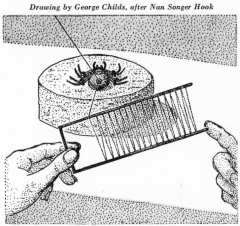

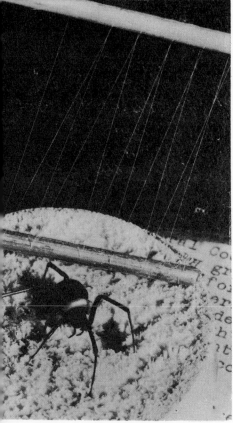

it is placed in a specially designed box for shipment.

Separating The Strands

If split web is to be extracted, I secure the spider on her *back,* since the two or three strands of the dragline seem to separate more easily when she is inverted. Besides snugly stapling her waist, I also secure her feet (two per staple) to keep her from reaching back and cutting the web. Then I pull out a length of whole web and cement the end to the edge of my worklight. To split away a single strand, I pick back and forth across the web with a needle until a snag appears, then insert the needle in the loop and slide it down to the spinneret. The single strand may now be wrapped around a frame in the manner described for whole web.

The unwanted strands do not emerge further.

Splitting the dragline has eliminated many of the objections that were encountered at first. The technique was developed quite early in the work because the Bureau of Standards and several of the private concerns reported that the twisted strands of whole web made it too irregular for high-powered optical instruments. Split web is much smoother under high magnification than whole web—even than whole web of equivalent diameter extracted from a very small spider.

This linear smoothness is an important characteristic. At present there is much demand for a heavy single-stranded split fiber 1/3,000th of an inch in diameter. This approximates the size of heavy cocoon web, but technicians would prefer the more resilient dragline. No spider we have in this country will produce silk so coarse.

When producers of microscopes and gun sights told us they needed a finer split strand than adult spiders could produce, we began experimenting with younger ones. They proved satisfactory for the job, so we began breeding them from the egg sac.

One species that we use, the Banded Garden Spider, produces web that has a metallic sheen which reflects light. I do not know how the reticule is used, but I have seen the lighting apparatus when it was brought to our house by technicians. Tiny electric bulbs, placed at the ends of the cross-hairs, made the web glow like a miniature neon sign.

One of the best-known telescopic rifle sights in this country uses a reticule that I helped perfect. I worked with the manufacturer, Mr. T. K. Lee. The problem was to establish, by a process of elimination, web of a size that would support a tiny, perfectly round dot without obscuring vision. The search was made difficult by the fact that the dot must be liquid when applied. If the cross-hairs were even a microscopic amount too large, the tiny dab of liquid would cling to the corners, forming a diamond shape rather than a circle. After much experimentation, we were successful, and the process is now patented.

I am told that there are now more than 100,000 of these dot reticules in rifle scopes and that they are used on African safaris going for the world's biggest and most dangerous game. Quite an accomplishment for spiders whose normal prey is less than an inch long and who are in mortal danger at the downward swoop of a flycatcher.

Measuring Thickness

You may wonder how optical technicians can determine precise measurements of such fine strands. It is done with a device called a delineascope—which works on the same principle as the old magic lantern. By projecting a highly magnified image of a reticule onto a screen where the ratio of enlargement is known, measurements can be made of the screen-strands and converted arithmetically to actual measurements.

We don't have to use such an

Don Alexander

⋏ THE INDIVIDUAL SPIDER may produce 150 feet of web at a silking and can be silked again a few days later. A mature Aranea holds the record at the Hook spidery, with 1000 feet. In old age, the spider's silk glands grow less productive. Only the females are worth bothering with.

instrument because, with our data gathered over the years, we usually know just what species, age, and size of spider will produce web of a certain size. The size of web never varies if the workers are not stunted and are in good condition. Once a manufacturer selects a size and type he likes, we merely pick out the appropriate spider when he places a repeat order.

We can't substitute one species for another. Even if the spiders themselves are exactly the same size, their webs won't be. For example, the dragline of a one-inch grass spider is not nearly as large or as strong as that of a *baby* Aranea the size of a matchhead.

The reason we always use females is that spiderdom is apparently one province in the animal kingdom where the ladies excel in almost everything. They usually grow much larger, are tougher, and spin better quality silk. Even when you match sizes by pitting a young female against an adult male, the female will be the better performer. Her silk will be stronger and she will produce much more of it.

A female spider may be silked

as many as 25 times, barring injuries, and can easily produce 100 feet or more in a single sitting. The record at our spidery is a thousand feet, and was set by a mature Aranea spider.

We have learned much about how to keep spiders healthy and contented. This may sound absurd, but spiders do respond to good care. Some of the regular producers get as docile as old milk cows, particularly the Black Widows.

When we want to silk a spider, we remove her from her jar as carefully as possible, lest she become excited and injure herself struggling to get free. We are also careful not to destroy her orb, particularly if she is a large adult and too heavy to be agile at weaving. She would tire herself needlessly building a new one.

Fresh spiders are used for each order, and we always allow a few days rest before silking them again. When they become old and are nearing the end of their life span, we must remove them from among the producers, for though they can still make silk they do it feebly and the strands do not have the required strength. Evidently, as with humans, their glands do not function properly in old age.

Most of our spiders live less than a year, so we are continuously replenishing the supply. Some we raise from the egg sac; others we collect; still others are donated About half of our adults are reared in the spidery.

The principal reason for raising spiders is that this is the easiest way to keep on hand a supply of spiderlings for extremely fine webs.

The breeding cycle of the Banded Garden Spider begins when the adult female lays 300 to 400 eggs in the fall, encasing them in round egg sacs. The eggs hatch during the winter and the spiderlings remain within the sacs for some time before emerging. They do not grow perceptibly during this period, although they do feed upon one another. We often force them to emerge prematurely by pulling the egg sacs apart. Then we put them into warm cages and provide abundant food to make them grow faster. In a typical spring, we may have on hand 100 adult spiders and 10,000 young ones just emerging.

The cages for the spiderlings have a wood frame, a glass front, and gauze at the sides and back. A circle is cut out of the bottom of each cage so that it can be placed over a potted plant infested with aphids (plant lice)—the spiderlings first food. After they have grown a little, we move them to larger quarters and introduce a diet of fruit flies. Later, when the spiders have grown too big to escape through wire mesh, we place them in large, screened cages and feed them insects we obtain by sweeping the grounds with a net. When nearing maturity, each spider is placed in its own glass jar and fed home-grown meal worms.

The mortality rate is extremely high. Out of the thousands of spiders that emerge each spring, we are lucky to rear 40 or 50 to adulthood. First, there is cannibalism. If the spiderlings were free, the brood would scatter after a very short time; but, confined, they feed upon each other. Then many are

Wide World Photos, L.A. Bureau

⋏ THE U-SHAPED FRAMES of silk are packed in this type of case for shipment to manufacturers of optical instruments.

lost during the moults. In the hot summer months, well-fed spiders grow rapidly and moult frequently. Some individuals seem to lack the fluid that softens the old skin and die when they are unable to shed it. (Older spiders seem to have more difficulty extricating themselves than young ones.) Others are injured during the moulting process. The legs are very wet and soft at first, and the spiders must hang from their old skins by the tips of their feet until they have completely dried. The larger ones frequently fall too soon, injuring them-

selves, so that their legs dry bent and twisted.

Despite the careful handling we give them, we lose a number of spiders during the silking process. The biggest problem is trying to keep them from pulling off their own legs. Gruesome as this sounds, it is not fatal to spiders; on the contrary, is their means of escaping enemies—up to a point. Most spiders can lose at least two legs without being severely crippled. Nature has provided them with a "weak link" in each of their seven-segmented legs which facilitates "bloodless" amputation. They regenerate smaller but perfectly usable legs at their next moulting. Unfortunately, some spiders struggle so frantically that they cripple themselves beyond rejuvenation.

The old-timers become so "tame" after successive silkings that we have very little trouble with them.

Spiders may not "recognize," but they certainly become accustomed to handling and silking. I do not believe that everyone could put their hands into the jars, remove the Black Widows, and allow them to crawl over the hands and arms without being bitten as I have done for years. This is not necessary to the silking process, but I have persistently done it to prove that they positively will not "attack."

The three species we use differ not only in habits and adaptability but also in disposition. Aranea refuses to make her orb in small quarters. She simply *sits*, looking like a bump on a log, until suitable space is provided. She is the only one bold enough to take an insect from tweezers and can be quite belligerent about it. Sometimes there is an audible click of her fangs against the tweezers as she pounces and bites.

The Banded Garden Spider, unless she is heavy with eggs, will improvise an orb in a very small jar and is always ready to eat anything that is dropped to her, even in the daylight. But at silking time she is harder to manage without injury than the others.

The Black Widow, despite her reputation, is the gentlest of the three. When she is held by the feet with tweezers, she will, of course, try to pull off her legs unless care is used. But she will struggle to the last to free herself, rather than attempt to bite. Neither Ray nor I have ever been bitten.

We are fully aware, however, that Black Widow venom, though small in quantity, is many times more deadly than the venom of a rattlesnake. It affects the nervous system in the manner of cobra venom. Even the tiny drop that the Widow can inject is potent enough to produce severe systemic symptoms and, on very rare occasions, death.

We did not adopt the Black Widows out of an attempt at bravado but only after we learned that the large orb weavers die off in the fall after their eggs have been laid. Orders were coming in, and we were out of spiders. So we tackled the Black Widow as the only large aerial web-spinner that naturally lives through the winter months in the adult stage. Its web proved to be the strongest obtainable of its size (about 1/7000 of an inch). The U. S. Army and Navy, now procuring their own web for repairing their instruments, use Black Widows exclusively.

Living and working with spiders has never produced much in the way of monetary return. The most earned in one month was $300. It has been chiefly rewarding in that it has provided us with an intimate understanding of some of nature's most remarkably specialized creatures and has allowed us to make worthwhile contributions to the knowledge about them.

Black Star

◄ THE BABY SPIDERS are fed with fruit flies blown into their jar through a tube.

Spiders that Eat Birds and Fishes

After Merian

⋏ THIS GIANT SOUTH AMERICAN SPIDER of the genus Mygale has just captured a humming bird and dragged it from its nest in order to feed on it. Its ability to do this has been attested by more than one naturalist.

⋎ A FEMALE of *Dolomedes sexpunctatus* capturing and killing a catfish under water, as witnessed by O. Lloyd Meehan of the U. S. Bureau of Fisheries. This spider is common east of the Rockies.

Drawing by Hope Haupt

The Bath Sponge

An Intimate but Humble Friend of Man

AN ENLARGED MODEL showing about ⅛ inch of bath sponge, reproduced in wax and glass. The righthand part shows the skeleton alone, the left the skeleton combined with the living tissue. (From an exhibit in the American Museum of Natural History.)

AMNH photo

By GEORGE H. CHILDS

Department of Invertebrates
The American Museum of Natural History

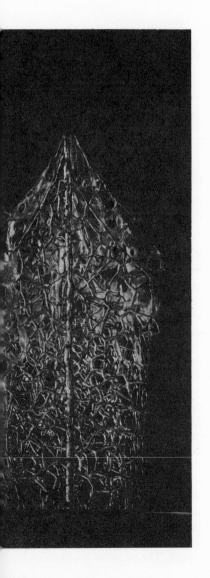

L IKE many fossil animals that are far more impressive, the humble bath sponge is known to most of us solely by its skeleton. The sponge as we see it can scarcely prepare us for the shock we would receive on meeting its living owner.

The living sponge is a creature as far removed from our conception of physical cleanliness as anything could be. If you immersed an ordinary skeletonized sponge in rancid oil and then lightly rubbed it with some sooting material, the resulting object would give an approximate idea of the living animal. On the sea floor, the sponge is an amorphous mass similar in general outline to its skeleton but overlarded and impregnated with slimy gelatinous tissue ranging in color from jet black to dirty brown.

But let us renounce our repugnance and show the bath sponge the respect due it as a fellow living animal. It gets its food by straining microscopic plants and animals from enormous quantities of sea water, constantly flowing through its tissues. On close examination its whole slimy surface is seen to be dotted with small, conelike elevations (conuli) at about ⅛ of an inch intervals. These serve merely as fleshy coverings to the free endings of the principal elements of the skeleton, which project slightly beyond the level of the surface. Interspersed among the conuli and occurring at about the same frequency are comparatively large pores of variable size, which function as escape vents for the water in the sponge and are, therefore, known as exhalent pores. Upon still closer examination we find that the areas between the conuli and the exhalent pores are perforated by innumerable, very minute inhalent pores, through which the sea water passes into the interior of the sponge. This is one of the instances wherein the sponge stands unique in the animal kingdom, for of all creatures that have their exits and their entrances, only in the sponges are the former more conspicuous than the latter.

Having explored the surface of the living bath sponge, let us see what the interior has to offer us. First we dis-

▼ THE ARROWS show the movement of the sea water from which the sponge takes its nourishment in the form of microscopic plants and animals. Important parts of the sponge shown in the model are named here

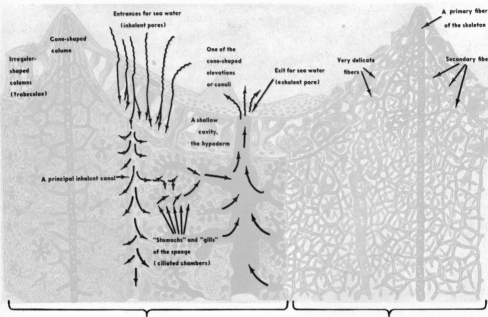

Entrances for sea water (inhalent pores)

A primary fiber of the skeleton

Cone-shaped column

Irregular-shaped columns (trabeculae)

One of the cone-shaped elevations or conuli

Very delicate fibers

Secondary fiber

Exit for sea water (exhalent pore)

A shallow cavity, the hypoderm

A principal inhalent canal

"Stomachs" and "gills" of the sponge (ciliated chambers)

LIVING TISSUE AND SKELETON

SKELETON

cover that the surface itself is just a thin skin roofing over a shallow cavity (the hypoderm) and penetrated by the tiny inhalent pores. From the floor to the roof of the hypoderm stretch three kinds of columns. The largest are conical and contain the ends of the principal skeletal elements as central axes. A second type are cylindrical and contain the tubes through which the sea water leaves the sponge. The third kind of columns, called trabeculæ, are by far the most numerous and are irregular in shape. These serve only as supporting pillars for the roof.

On the floor of the shallow cavity we find a second set of inhalent pores, larger and less numerous than the ones that penetrate the roof. These lead directly into the principal inhalent canals, which like the principal exhalent canals extend downward through the sponge mass and form many coalescences with their fellows as they approach the base of the sponge. Thus the principal inhalents, smaller and more numerous than the exhalents, cannot be reached by the inflowing water until the shallow cavity has been traversed.

From both sets of canals many greatly branching tributaries are given off; but never will we find the terminal branches of the two systems directly coalescing, for between them is a vast number of elliptical chambers of uniform size, through which the sea water must pass to go from one to the other. These organs are the stomachs as well as the gills of the sponge. The peculiar cuplike cells which line them not only digest food matter from the water but also possess vibratile hairlike processes, or cilia, the collective movement of which keeps a constant current circulating through the sponge. Thus the digestive and respiratory activities of the animal depend entirely on these cilia, and the structures in which they occur are consequently known as ciliated chambers.

Finally, let us turn to the skeleton, which is the bath sponge's badge of admission to the bath tub or wash basin, places to which the creature's many more attractive but prickly relatives have no entree. This skeleton is made up of a very tough but yielding substance known as spongin, which is chemically related to the keratin of

our hair and nails, and consists of three kinds of fibers. The principal fibers are the large ones already mentioned in connection with the cone-shaped elevations, and these follow a course parallel to the principal inhalent and exhalent canals. Branching off from the principal ones are a network of finer fibers, interconnecting them. Finally bundles of very delicate fibers occur in the roof of the hypoderm and its supporting columns and invest all the principal canals of the inhalent and exhalent systems. In the process of bleaching, these finest fibers are so completely torn away that in the average bath sponge skeleton nothing remains to indicate the roof of the hypoderm, the trabeculæ, or the actual outlines of the canals.

▼ THE COMMON BATH SPONGE: only its skeleton   *AMNH photo*

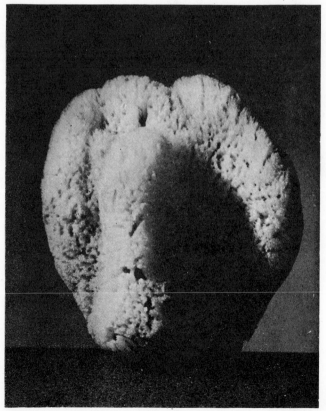

Some of the strangest dramas of the deep are enacted by the squids—rebel relatives of the sluggish snails—which have become faster than the swiftest fishes in the sea

By N. J. BERRILL

McGill University

"**THIS** is the squidiest year I ever twined in" said the Maine fisherman. Off Bailey's Island north of Casco Bay the mackerel seiners had caught 16,000 bushels of squids in their nets in one night. That is an awful lot of squids, and though you can sell some for bait and some for college biology classes, there is little use for squids by the ton. They make a squashed dead weight that breaks nets, and they ooze slime and ink and make a nasty mess generally. The Japanese and certain Mediterranean people eat them, but perhaps the Chinese make the best use of them, drying them for food or piling them up in large vats to wait for the ink to run from the ink sacs. Within the squid there is a translucent shell that is like an old-fashioned pen; ink and pen together are a good reason for the squid's being known as the clerk of the seas.

The miracle of the squid is not so much the way it shoots through the water like a living arrow. Rather, it is that squids are mollusks — relatives of the sluggish, heavy-shelled, crawling snails of the sea floor—and yet mollusks that behave in a most unmolluscan manner.

Squids do not swim continuously as fishes sometimes do; but in general they compete with fishes on the fishes' own level. Of the two, size for size, the squids are by far the faster swimmers, and salvage divers swear they are the more in-

Submarine Rockets

telligent. At the other extreme of their phylum, or tribe, are the equally molluscan oysters, without a head, without power to shift their position a fraction of an inch, forever straining the water that lies within reach for the particles of food it may hold. Both are mollusks, each with a shell, a molluscan heart and gills, muscles and nerves on the molluscan plan, and a system of intake and output of water.

An oyster sits permanently on the spot where it first landed. It has no need to see where it is, for it's going nowhere, and it goes in for thicker and harder shells, wherein lies its safety. In the life of its relative the squid, everything is different. The squid never rests on the sea floor and has lost the lime in its shell in order to lighten the load. It has the streamlined shape of a rocket, for speed is its specialty. And it has a head with all the equipment needed for oceanic navigation and the hunting of prey.

It can do everything a fish can do, but it does it in its own way, with its own unique equipment. It is streamlined for speeding backward, not forward like a fish, and is reminiscent of that mythical backward-flying bird that doesn't care where it's going but would like to see where it has been. It can also swim slowly forward by undulating a pair of fins. But where the fish sculls with a driving thrust of muscle and blade against water, the squid draws water quickly in through the wide mantle opening and then sends it like the jet of a rocket out through the funnel. Some fishes use the water from their gills to aid them in swimming, but the squid is Nature's rocket par excellence.

Its motion is true jet-propulsion. Water is the agency; the bands of muscles encircling the body and the water chamber within supply the power. And none of it was originally designed for travel, for the whole mechanism is, in its basic make-up, the respiratory gill system that all mollusks have. The gills

are still there in the squid, lying like feathers in the watery mantle chamber. And because the animal is a high-speed, energy-consuming living rocket, it needs more oxygen than the oyster, not less. So the gills that collect the oxygen, the blood that carries it, and the heart that pumps the blood are even more efficient. The fish manages to work with one heart to pump its blood through gills and body. The squid does better—one heart for the body and one for each gill, so that the gills run on a supercharge. Rocket-shaped, jet-propelled, with special fuel pumps—it's no wonder speed has been developed.

Yet speed has little value by itself and by itself permits an animal neither to capture nor to escape capture. So we come to that amazing organ, the head of a squid (or an octopus, for they amount to much the same thing). The head is a head-and-hand rolled into one. Think for a moment about where

squids have to operate. Most of the time they prey upon fishes, often far from shore and usually a long way above the floor of the sea. To stay within proper physical bounds it is necessary for them to detect whether they are moving toward the surface or toward the sea bottom. So eyes, of a kind, and gravity organs are both necessary and present. Their gravity organs are simple—little more than sacs with weights in them. Squids, like most animals, have a pair of them buried within the squid brain itself.

Apart from these organs of sight and balance, and the brain within, the head of the squid is a circle of a few long whiplike tentacles, each with its double row of vacuum-suckers to hold with, and a formidable beak at the center where the mouth lies.

Few people have ever seen squids either mating or depositing their egg masses, and I doubt if there has been anyone who has seen both

THE SQUID has a tubular body and ten arms that trail behind when it rockets its way through the water

activities. It is a rather complicated business, not so much because the sexes are separate and are not combined in the same individual as in many snails, and only partly because the eggs must be fertilized before they get all wrapped up in jelly. These are factors, of course, but it is the combination of these with the free-swimming life of the animals in the open ocean that makes things rather difficult. Most of the whole pointed end of a female squid is set aside for the production and ripening of eggs. The jelly is added to them as they are passed out of the oviduct into the gill chamber, just before they are deposited. And to develop they must be fertilized on the way. That means sperm must be there in the right place at the right moment. So we come to the male animal.

Squids of both sexes have ten arms. Eight of them are moderately long and correspond to the eight arms or tentacles of an octopus. The other two are much longer and are used more like hands in the actual capturing of animals for food, as distinct from holding them. Now, it would do no good for sperm to be shed freely in the water. It has to be ready for use in the mantle or gill chamber of the female when her eggs are ready. Even if the water carried sperm into the chamber, the chances would be remote for the eggs to be fertilized. What happens is this. The microscopic sperm cells are made up into small pencil-shaped packages called spermatophores, each about a half inch long, in a special gland possessed by the male. As these packages accumulate, the male inserts one of his two long arms down into his own gill chamber, grabs a handful of sperm packets, swims alongside a female, and shoves the collection into her mantle chamber. Or he may deposit them in a special pit beneath the mouth in a membrane that surrounds the mouth. Later, perhaps very much later, when the eggs are ready to be laid, each packet explodes inside the female, to liberate a cloud of sperm cells, which fertilize the emerging eggs. By this time, of course, the independent male may be several hundred miles away chasing a fish or a crab.

I doubt if there is anything more entrancing and more beautiful than a newly-hatched squid. This sounds hard to believe, but everyone who has seen one has had the same feeling. It is tiny, dartingly active, almost all eyes, but above all it is covered with innumerable small patches of color—red, yellow, green, black—not in a set pattern but each flashing, large and small, to make the creature a scintillating jewel of tiny life.

The Giant Sunflower Star

In the hands, this creature is like a wet newspaper, but on the bottom of the ocean it is an "engine of destruction"

By WOODY WILLIAMS

Photographs by the author

THIS Sunflower Star, or Twenty-rayed Star, *Pycnopodia helianthoides,* is for bulk and size the largest starfish recorded by marine biologists. The North Pacific species attains a diameter of from two to four feet and can weigh in the neighborhood of ten pounds. It is one of the most spectacular of a long array of starfish in which the North Pacific is particularly rich. At least nine other species may attain a diameter of two feet, but they lack the bulk of Pycnopodia.

This unusually active echinoderm ranges into Southern California, but it is not common south of Monterey Bay. In Puget Sound, British Columbia, and Alaska, the creature attains its greatest abundance and size. It is often found at low tide, also as an unwanted invader of crab pots or as a surprise package on the bait of some fishing line.

Pycnopodia is an audacious predator that will tackle seemingly impossible foods, such as a giant long-spined sea urchin, *Strongylocentrotus franciscanus.* It can swallow this huge spiny creature whole; and then a day later it will eject the shell cleaned within and the spines disarticulated. On sandy bottoms it will attack the great

Moon Snail, *Polinces lewisii,* which is itself a famous devourer of clams.

The Sunflower Star commences life with perhaps only six arms. Additional arms bud in pairs, one from each side of a primary arm. The process of budding continues between the same primary arms, until the adult may boast as many as 24 arms.

On the underside of the arms is an army of tube feet that propel the creature along and aid it in capturing food. Each foot is a hollow tube with a sucker tip that is connected with a centralized plumbing system called a water vascular system. Water enters this system on the top surface at an intake called a "sieve plate." It is then pumped through the system to the tube feet and their suction discs. One Pycnopodia may boast 15,000 such legs.

Pycnopodia, like many other marine giants, is unexpectedly flabby

THOUSANDS OF TUBE FEET are seen on the bottom of the Sunflower Star (*Pycnopodia helianthoides*), considered the largest living starfish. It reaches a diameter of two feet or more in the North Pacific. At left: a small specimen being examined by two California teachers

when you remove it from the sea. Mr. Fred Ziesenhenne, Curator of Echinoderms at the Allan Hancock Foundation of the University of Southern California, says it is like picking up a soaked copy of a Sunday newspaper. The creature is apt to shed its arms when roughly handled or thrown into preservative.

Yet in its own environment, Pycnopodia has been characterized as an "engine of destruction." Watch this yellow, orange, red, purple or gray disc, as it cruises rapidly over the rocks searching out its prey, and you will see one of the least helpless of the many creatures that have never acquired a backbone.

A Fish that Gives you a Shock

Occasionally dredged up from the sandy Chesapeake bottom is a sluggish, bizarre-looking fish with a startling secret weapon

By ALICE JANE MANSUETI

All photographs by the author

SHOCKING discoveries of one sort or another usually leave an indelible impression on one's mind. My most electrifying experience left me weak, shuddering, and slightly indignant.

One evening about dusk in mid-Chesapeake Bay area, a friend and I slowly poled our small skiff, dipping for crabs in the shallow coves of the Patuxent River estuary near the Chesapeake Biological Laboratory at Solomons, Maryland. As we languidly moved about, I noticed a peculiar, club-shaped fish about a foot long with an English bulldog snout. It was moving sluggishly along the bottom but was nearly imperceptible because its murky-brown color blended with the sand.

"Oh, that's only an old toadfish," said my companion. "We see them all the time."

But I was still curious, and I dipped the fish up with my net and drew it into the boat. When I grabbed it with one hand, I screamed loudly and nearly fell out of the boat as I hurled the fish to the deck.

I had received an electric shock!

The creature on the floor danced a mad staccato beat. It gasped spasmodically with strangely-fringed lips and stared up with a seemingly soulful, accusing gaze.

Never before had I seen such a bizarre excuse for a fish. Its head was wide and completely flat on top. Especially prominent were the eyes, set like jewels flat on a muddy mass of flesh. Its gaze seemed to be directed permanently skyward.

"Afraid of a poor little toadfish like that!" my companion remarked. But his scorn vanished when he reached down and grasped the fish himself.

"Ouch!" he yelled, releasing the fish immediately. Unfortunately, this time the fish flopped out of the boat and dove for the bottom, raising a cloud of sand as it hit. Hoping to glimpse it again, we waited until the sand settled, but the fish had disappeared.

Curious about the little fish's ability to give an electric shock, we searched in various ichthyological tomes, trying to identify it. After flipping pages here and there, we were pleasantly surprised to find that the fish was dubbed, appropriately enough, the "stargazer." Fish scientists knew, of course, that it could deliver an electric shock when grasped on the head close

➤ NOT AN ANCIENT MEXICAN CARVING, but an actual fish. The fierce-looking mouth is created by sand-filtering fringes on the lips

to the eyes. My friend and I both had taken hold of our stargazer by that part of its anatomy, trying to keep its wide mouth clamped shut.

Amateurs though we are, we had always been proud of our knowledge of marine life, so our ignorance about the stargazer had taken us down a few notches. Our chagrin, however, was relieved by a musty old news clipping we found. In 1937, *The Baltimore Sun* ran a headline, "Dr. Beebe unable to identify strange fish caught in Bay." The article began with, "William Beebe, B. S., Sc.D., LL.D., author of *Half a Mile Down,* co-author of *Field Book of the Shore Fishes of Bermuda,* et al., explorer of the ocean depths in his bathysphere, took one look at an eight-inch fish [from Chesapeake Bay] and shook his head." Later, of course, he identified the fish as a stargazer. It is not actually an extremely rare fish, but it is uncommon enough so that Dr. Beebe had not come in contact with it previously.

The fish delivers its shock from two smooth, naked, rectangular areas just behind the eyes and along each side of a bony Y-shaped structure on top of its head. This structure looks as if someone had taken a Y-shaped piece of rubber an inch long and glued it between the fish's eyes.

The electric personality that the stargazer cherishes is not unique among fishes. Most people at one time or another have heard also of the electric ray, or torpedo, the electric eel, and the electric catfish. Dr. C. Ladd Prosser, Professor of Physiology at the University of Illinois, who has conducted a great deal of research on electricity in fishes, states that certain muscles change when the fish is very young into a series of numerous electric plates. These are called "electroplaxes." The flat upper surface of each plate receives nerves which activate it, and the bottom surface has many tiny fingers, known as papillae, which receive the nourishing blood vessels. In the stargazer, two eye muscles have been converted into groups of these electric plates; consequently, the electric organs are immediately behind the eyes. When a stargazer has been stimulated, either

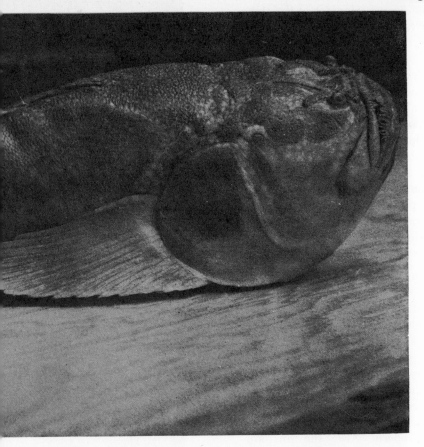

⋏ Rarely exceeding 10 inches in length, the stargazer has a club-shaped body and a bulldog snout. Eyes are fixed skyward

by human hands or perhaps by an enemy, or food in the water, each group of plates fires repeatedly.

How much of a shock can a stargazer produce? Looking at it objectively, I have to admit that an electric eel would be worse, for it is much larger and its electric tissues occupy a greater proportion of its body. An electric eel has been known to drown a horse. But even a six-inch stargazer can give a perceptible shock, and a freshly-charged 12-inch specimen like the one I grabbed will always get a

wide berth so far as I'm concerned.

From our boat, we observed that the stargazer was a bottom-dweller, either living quite close to or actually burying itself in the sandy floor of the bay. It moved slowly, as do most other fishes with electric organs. They are more likely to catch their prey by shocking it than by scurrying around after it. In fact, if we had been crab-dipping earlier in the day, we would have missed the stargazer, as they habitually spend their days buried in the sand.

The disappearing act of the stargazer faintly resembles the mambo dance. The fish buries itself with a side-to-side, squirming motion, usually leaving only the top of the head and tip of the tailfin visible. Not only does it bury itself to wait for food, but also to escape approaching foes. There is a flurry as the fish digs into the sand, and a cloud hides its escape. In emergencies, the stargazer is able to go as deep as 12 inches, making it difficult for the most persistent enemy to dislodge it.

The stargazer possesses several amazing adaptations, which Dr. Ulric Dahlgren, a well-known physiologist, has described in detail. For example, the upper surface of the head is flat clear to the tip of the snout, causing the eyes to lie flat on the top of the head. This permits the fish to submerge and conceal itself almost completely, yet allows its eyes and mouth to function properly. Also, the fins are well developed and placed in a position to facilitate digging. The "shoulder" fins are about as low as they could be, and are widely spread, almost like a pair of shovels fanning out from the fish on both sides. When small fishes, isopods, and other small invertebrates swim within grasp, the stargazer quickly emerges, opens its upturned mouth, and engulfs its supper.

Stargazers are primarily ocean fish, liking warm, salty waters, but they will migrate into places like Chesapeake Bay, at least during the summer months.

At spawning season, they apparently swim to deeper ocean waters. The baby stargazers do not

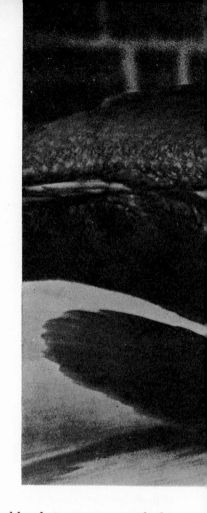

resemble their parents until they are about one inch long. When hatched, they resemble the more conventional fishes in shape, with eyes on the sides of the head and mouth horizontally placed. Later the eyes move to the top of the head. The adults rarely grow over a foot long; most of those in the United States vary from six to twelve inches.

Few creatures have scientific and popular names that are more nearly identical. The generic name of the stargazer is *Astroscopus*, from *astra*, meaning "star," and *scopus* meaning "to look." The specimen

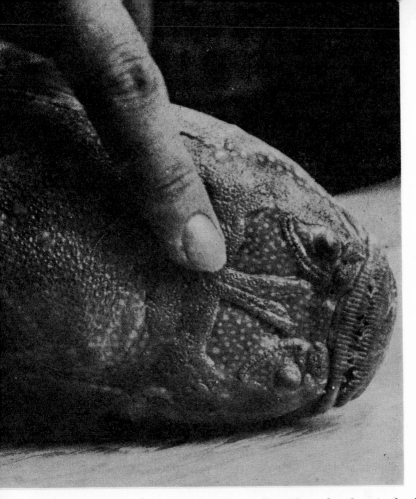

▲ Smooth areas, suggesting "eyebrows," produce the electric shock that startles fishermen. Strength of the jolt grows with the fish

that caused so much commotion in our boat belonged to the more northern species, named *Astroscopus guttatus,* meaning the stargazer that is "spotted like rain drops," for it has pale brown spots on the darker brown back.

A friend once asked, "What good is this crazy-looking fish?" For a moment, I was stymied. Certain fishermen in Chesapeake Bay are known to have eaten them, and its relatives reach better eating size in the Mediterranean Sea and in waters around Japan, New Zealand,

and the East Indies. But I searched my mind to justify the poor creature's existence. My final reply was that scientists studying the electrical organs of fishes contribute to the better understanding of the muscular-neural processes, which may benefit medical science. Such a goal sounds rather distant, yet astounding discoveries have been made through study of the physiology of such unusual animals. In any case, I concluded that the stargazer would remain the most unforgettable character in my life.

A Desert

Walking Stick

Now you see it, now you don't—as
Nature's living twig defies the sharpest eye

By Lewis Wayne Walker

WE were in Lower California's Viscaino Desert when we saw this insect, looking for all the world like a common tree twig walking across the dark sands beneath the car. While in motion, we could see that it was alive; but in repose, it could have been a bit of straw dropped by the desert winds. As we watched, the horizontal matchlike body crouched low to the oil-stained surface, then lifted itself about an inch above the ground and, with stately, measured tread, walked away. Upon the oily ground, this desert walking stick was a conspicuous white on black, but the moment it reached normal sand, it simply melted away. It became so nearly invisible that we could hardly follow its course to a silvery-gray smoke tree.

As this living twig cruised about the angular thorns and branches, it became with each motionless stop just another bit of the plant swaying with the breeze. It was a perfect example of protective coloration and form, from its angular legs, replaceable if damaged, to its thicker body, which matched the heavier limbs. A single tap on a twig—our imitation of a bird alighting—brought about a complete and instant rigidity, which made the walking stick and the smoke tree one and the same thing.

Photo by Lewis Wayne Walker

➤ WHERE DOES the twig end and the walking stick begin? The creature is so well camouflaged that in nature you may look squarely at it without seeing it

The Stork

The saga of a much talked about bird—sacred to some and
cherished by nearly all peoples

By Ruth Elwonger

THE STORK FAMILY—
male, female, and two
young ones—poses for a
picture.

WE are used to seeing him race with screaming ambulances and police escorts. He is the motif of countless baby showers. He is the glamour bird of advertising, and his picture appears on billboards, in streetcars, in newspapers and magazines. Consequently, almost everyone is familiar with the snowy plumage, the bright red bill and legs, and the characteristic one-legged stance of the White Stork.

In spite of this flourishing life in the public eye, few people in this country have ever actually seen him. In Europe you may see him raising a family on the rooftop, and he winters in South Africa. But in the United States, the shy Wood Ibis of our southern coast, a distant relative, is the only member of the stork family. The stork has close relatives in other parts of the world, although some of these would hardly be recognized as such. For instance, there is the Marabou Stork of tropical Africa, a gaunt gray bird with a dangling neck pouch and a bald head and neck, who functions as the scavenger and street cleaner of native villages.

The most unusual thing about the White Stork is the degree to which —unwisely it would seem—he has thrown in his lot with man. For ages longer than recorded history he has built his nest on a roof, in an unused chimney, or on a cart wheel placed on a pole for his convenience. Sometimes he builds in trees but seldom far from human habitation. Many peoples have held him sacred. By nearly all he has been unmolested and petted. In folklore he is the bringer of good luck to the household on whose roof he settles. The story that he is also the bringer of babies is of uncertain though recent origin, as legends go. Most probably, as someone has suggested, this idea was simply the inspiration of some harassed parent.

The stork's high qualities as a family bird have endeared him to man. From the moment of his arrival in the spring until the day his young are ready to leave the nest the stork concerns himself with the repair and upkeep of the nest. His love for his home seems to be in direct proportion to its size, for he continues to add to it even after it has become enormous. One nest on a huge wagon wheel in Holland measured 12 feet across the top when it was finally blown down in a windstorm after 52 years of continuous use.

When the birds return to the north in March or April, the pair at once begins to toil on the nest. Brushwood is brought for the exterior; dry stalks and twigs for the interior; and moss, straw, soft grass —impartially even a clump of horse dung—for upholstering. One bird works up the material that the other drags home. But so great is the stork's attachment to his nest that early in the season even the mate returning to the nest after a brief absence is apt to be greeted with defensive postures and behavior. By the time the first egg is laid, however, these momentary lapses of memory no longer occur.

Courtship consists chiefly of the two birds facing each other with heads far back and noisily clapping together their long red bills. The stork is without voice or song, but this clappering, variable only in intensity and tempo, apparently serves adequately to express inner feelings, for eventually three to five white eggs appear in the nest.

It has been the belief of many people that storks mate for life. Actually, the perils of the long migratory journey are so great that often one of the pair fails to return to the nesting area. In such a case, the survivor must, of course, take a new mate.

Both birds share equally the arduous task of incubating the eggs continuously for a month. When one of them arrives to take over, the relieved partner does not fly away immediately to his frog-rich marsh or swamp to feed, but remains for a time beside the nest, clappering and preening. At night the female sits on the nest, and the male sleeps near by in the familiar stiltlike posture. Neither bird ever goes far from the nest. When danger threatens, the absent mate appears as if from nowhere. A complication of this idyllic homelife is the presence of "bachelor birds" who roam the countryside. These unmated or immature birds of both sexes, occasionally attempt to drive the owners away from their nest. Spectacular stork battles ensue, which may last all night, or even all week. The reason is by no means clear, for this is known to occur where there is no shortage of nests.

When the young finally hatch, the parents enter upon three months of unceasing labor. Feeding goes on without let-up from earliest dawn to dark. Until the young are several weeks old, only one parent leaves the nest at a time to search near-by meadows and stream borders for frogs, mice, insects, reptiles, small fish, crabs, and worms. These are carried in the crop to the nest and regurgitated in the center of the circle of voracious young ones. No matter how hard the parents work, there is seldom enough food to completely satisfy all appetites. Occasionally the last-hatched young is unable to compete successfully with his older brothers and sisters and eventually dies. There may possibly be some connection between this not infrequent occurrence and the last part of an old belief that storks leave rent in payment for a nest site—a feather the first year, an egg the second, and a young bird the third.

Natural ups and downs in the stork population might, if viewed too narrowly, give an unnecessarily pessimistic impression of the bird's future. Actually the stork was more abundant in certain sections of Northern Germany around 1935-

STRAINED AND AWKWARD poses such as this are characteristic of the storks' mating ceremony.

Photo by Morean

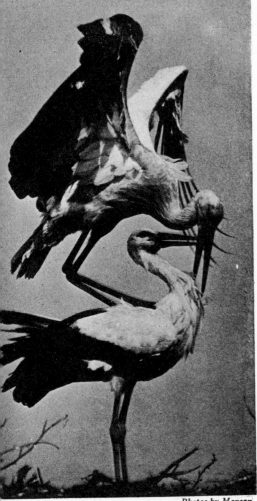

Photos by Morean

COURTSHIP OVERTURES without vocal accompaniment. Though voiceless, storks express themselves loudly to each other by clapping their bills.

1937 than in any other period in history. And it has spread greatly in Russia during the past 50 years. In other sections, for example Switzerland, the storks have not recovered from the low of the cycle that occurred about 1905-1925.

The parent on guard during these first few days not only keeps an eye out for danger but protects the young from too much heat by standing on the sunny side of the eyrie with wings spread. The inadequately garbed chicks accurately fit themselves into the shadow thus thrown across the nest.

Not until they are a month old do the young birds master the art of balance. Up until that time they awkwardly hitch themselves about the nest on their "heels." Facility in standing seems to develop in connection with the young birds' habit from the first of repairing to the edge of the nest to answer the call of nature, where, face to the wind, they teeter precariously. This habit, incidentally, keeps the nest clean, but the same cannot be said of the roof below.

More and more time is spent in wing exercises, but it is not until the third month that the wing feathers are sufficiently developed to permit real progress toward flight. Then the young birds soon gain enough skill to leave the nest for neighboring marshes and meadows. For several weeks more, however, they continue to return to the old homestead to spend the night and beg food from their parents.

By the end of August—when flocks of small migrating birds have already begun to dot the telegraph wires—the nest is finally deserted for the year. Soon after, the storks from all round the area begin to gather in a brown stubble-field. These annual reunions, at which each new arrival is greeted with much clappering, constitute the celebrated "Councils of the Storks." Here, according to legend, the date and hour of departure is set, and those unfit to travel are killed!

The itinerary of the storks of Central and Eastern Europe has been well plotted through the recovery of banded birds. The flock flies southeast over the Balkans, growing larger as small groups from other areas join it. It crosses the Bosporus into Asia Minor and skirts the eastern Mediterranean, finally crossing into Egypt by way of the Isthmus of Suez. The birds follow the Nile to its headwaters and pass Lake Victoria and Lake Tanganyika. By December they have reached their destination, the southeastern tip of Africa,—a 6000-mile journey. Their rate of flight is about 125 miles a day. Wherever there is plenty of food—a mouse plague in the valley of the Danube or a locust infestation along the Nile—the flock rests and feeds for a day or two.

Storks from western Europe and North Africa doubtless cross the Sahara on their way south. A few White Storks are believed to winter in Nigeria and Cameroun, but the vast majority go south of the equator. Numbers of them reach the Union of South Africa.

In South Africa the European White Stork is called the Greater Locust Bird. Here, free from the responsibilities of family life, he wanders about in small groups and fattens on locusts and caterpillars. But his vacation soon comes to an end, and by February he sets out again for the long return trip, unless he is one of the few stragglers who choose to remain in the South. Northward flight is even more rapid than that of autumn. It is as if the storks were in haste to reach

MAJESTIC PINIONS carry a female stork off the nest in the never-ending search for food. The spread is about six feet from tip to tip.

their northern home and raise a family.

Two thousand years ago people fell on their knees at the return of this wanderer, who meant to them the end of winter's cold and hardship. As late as the eighteenth century, watchmen on the town walls announced the arrival of the first stork of the year with a blast of the trumpet.

How man overcame some of nature's most frustrating obstacles

to gain a vital element for industry and agriculture

O. Winston Link photograph, Freeport Sulphur Co.

⋀ SPRAYING THE MELTED SULPHUR into a storage vat. Layer
by layer the sulphur builds up, solidifying when it cools

Sulphur—

For Our Way of Life

By Jennie E. Harris

A VISITOR from another planet might well exclaim, "Your civilization depends upon sulphur, yet no one I talk to knows anything about it. How can people be so ignorant of a substance of which about 75 pounds are used each year for every man, woman, and child in your land?"

This most versatile of all chemicals, and one of the cheapest—about a cent a pound at the mines—is also one of the oldest. The ancients called it "burn stone," the stone that burns. For centuries its blue flames were believed to kindle the furnaces of Hell.

"Flee for your lives," angels warned Lot. "Take your wife and your two daughters and escape, for we will destroy this place." As soon as Lot fled, brimstone and fire rained terror and destruction upon the two wicked cities, Sodom and Gomorrah. Thus even in Biblical times sulphur seems to have been known.

Sulphur bleached the linens for priests' robes and mummy cerements in long-ago Egypt; it entered the brilliant paints and pigments that decorated temples when

Menes was king. Sulphur was also a purifier. Homer had Odysseus burn sulphur after slaying his wife's suitors. "Burn sulphur, burn sulphur," screamed primitive man, stooping over yellow rock in a cave and igniting a blue flame to chase away evil spirits. "Let me burn enough sulphur," Cagliostro boasted to Marie Antoinette, "and I'll turn any base metal you bring me into gold."

About 100 trillion tons of sulphur exist in our oceans. Sulphides, nature's combination of sulphur with the metals and semimetals, abide deep within the earth. Meteorites from outer space bring evidence of their own sulphur in nodules of triolite, an iron sulphide. Volcanoes spew out sulphurous gases; mineral springs gush forth hydrogen sulphide gas and sulphates. Vegetation requires sulphur, which means that sulphur is in our coal and petroleum deposits, too; and in our food, both vegetable and animal; in our tissues and fluids.

But sulphur-mining in the United States developed comparatively recently. Mines exist mainly in Louisiana and Texas, in strange geologic formations.

Far down below the coastal plain of the Gulf of Mexico stand pillars or plugs of rock salt. Some pillars are more than a thousand feet below the surface, others but a few hundred feet. All hold up, as it were, a thick roof of gumbo, sand, and clay.

Sea water evaporating millions of years ago left salt—a vast mother bed of salt lying perhaps 20,000 feet below sea level. Upward and downward pressures, through geo-logic eras, combined, men believe, to force some of the salt upward into pillar-shapes. These stand straight, smooth, sheer—as though guarding the entrance to some giant underground coliseum.

Covering the tops of the plugs of halite (rock salt) are several layers of cap rock composed of anhydrite, gypsum, and limestone. It is chiefly in the pore spaces or in solution cavities in the limestone that the yellow crystals of sulphur occur. These cap rocks have most likely been torn loose and brought up from below by the forces that produced the salt plugs and were thus carried upward on top of the disrupted salt formation. Again, there seem to be some extensive sulphur deposits that are in the form of a bed about 100 feet thick under 300 or 400 feet of sediment-ary rocks and not related to the salt domes mentioned above.

Men drilling for oil in the Cal-casieu Parish, Louisiana, in 1867, came upon the yellow evidence of sulphur. "Look! Pure sulphur!"

They found it in a dry ridge rising about eight feet above a cypress marsh, where not many years before, a physician digging a well near by had found a petroleum seep. Now the Petroleum and Coal Oil Company drilled down, down, pierced cap rock, found crystals of sulphur, gypsum, more gypsum, but no oil.

Puzzled, they consulted Professor Hilgard of the University of Mississippi and were surprised at his excitement. "Not much future in petroleum here," he exclaimed. "But think of the future in sulphur!"

Our industrial sulphur had all

Leon Trice photograph, Freeport Sulphur Co.

⋏ THE HARD, BRIGHT YELLOW SOLID is brought up molten from deep wells
All the sulphur wells of the Freeport Sulphur Company in the region
shown here are drilled from floating rigs. These rigs cost a quarter of a
million dollars each. The rigs are kept busy, because each well can remove
the sulphur from only about half an acre

been coming from Sicily. On that mountainous little island, sulphur existed near the surface and could be mined as a solid. Sulphur in Louisiana! How it could boost industries—paper, pulp, petroleum!

"But how are we going to bring it up? It's down ,there under hundreds of feet of quicksand!"

Ordinary mining methods failed. A French company shipped a huge caisson from France in sections, then tugged it and rolled it to the island—and abandoned it when hydrogen sulphide fumes suffocated five of the miners.

Other companies — Austrian, American — formed and failed. Quicksand and clay swallowed up every effort the way they also swallowed up hundreds of thousands of dollars in the ventures. Probably a thick, rich bed of sulphur existed down there, definitely needed in the economy of the United States, but how to get it out of those ogre depths?

While these companies labored, a brilliant oil scientist on vacation from the Standard Oil Company in Cleveland, Ohio, was quietly drilling only a mile and a half away. He was Dr. Herman Frasch, who had already discovered a way to desulphurize petroleum. He had a simple suggestion. "Why not heat water above the melting point of sulphur, pour it down on the crystals, and pump up sulphur as a liquid?"

Simple; but the soft sands would move in, plug up pipes. How could you penetrate to any depth?

Dr. Frasch and the Union Sulphur Company, who now possessed the mine title, worked against terrific odds. New problems in physics and geology arose to confront them. Just getting enough hot water to the well and down it, still hot, was like cleaning out an Augean stable.

But in 1894 came the first flow of sulphur from the Calcasieu deposit. Gold-brown, transparent. The warm liquid heaved a little—and settled. Dr. Frasch stroked his beard. He had done it! He had brought up sulphur from 1100 feet, through all those treacherous deposits of quicksand and clay.

Eight years of discouragement, heartache, heartbreak followed before the Frasch process became established. Dr. Frasch died in Europe in 1914, but not until after he had been acclaimed Father of the American Sulphur Industry. All in all, he was granted 64 patents. Through petroleum, other chemicals, and sulphur, he increased our national wealth by millions of dollars.

Today, most of our elemental sulphur is mined in the Frasch way. Men steam for sulphur. They drill a well straight down through maybe a thousand feet of sedimentary rocks, till they touch the bottom layer of cap rock. They run a six-inch pipe down to this depth. Then inside this a three-inch pipe reaches almost to the bottom of the sulphur-bearing stratum; and inside *it*, a one-inch pipe reaches almost to the second pipe's depth.

Water heated above the melting point of sulphur (which is about 240 degrees F.) is pumped down between the two larger pipes. It flows through perforations into the surrounding sulphur crystals and melts them. The melted sulphur,

Freeport Sulphur Company photo

↟ A FLOATING MINING PLANT in a sulphur operation that is wholly marine. At left are two tanker barges that carry out the sulphur in molten form to storage 75 miles away. There is no stable land here at the Freeport Sulphur Company's Bay Ste. Elaine operation, located on the coast of the Gulf of Mexico

heavier than water, sinks and forms a pool in the bottom of the well. Water pressure forces it up several hundred feet in the middle pipe; then compressed air released in the inmost pipe raises it the rest of the way.

It enters steam-heated sumps, is measured and pumped into storage vats. Layer by layer, more sulphur enters the vats, to cool and solidify till each vat is full. The sulphur becomes a solid yellow block, which must be blasted for shipment.

In Texas and Louisiana, hills of solid sulphur line railroad tracks, each vat with its own track. Vat walls may be made of sheet metal, built up and broken down in rotation; or the walls are solid sulphur, strong, waterproof, enduring—1300 feet long, 160 feet wide, hills of pure yellow rising 50 feet against the blue sky. Each vat holds a half million tons of solid sulphur.

Each day the flow of sulphur into a vat is spread evenly over the whole surface to insure uniform cooling. Too much sulphur flowing too fast into one spot could cause pockets of liquid encased in the solid. For shipment, a vertical block 12 to 20 feet thick is removed at a time and broken into desired sizes for transportation by rail or water.

Millions of dollars in investment go into a sulphur well in the form of power plants, reservoirs, generators, compressors, derricks, and drills. There must be new pipe lines often, for each well can take in only the sulphur around it, about a half acre. New wells must be sunk, new pipes laid, before the old wells are abandoned.

A map of the wells drilled into the Calcasieu deposit looks like a whirligig of pin points. By 1924, that deposit was abandoned, but not before it had yielded 9,400,000 tons of pure sulphur. The original mines of the four great mining companies have all been abandoned — Texas Gulf Sulphur Company, Freeport Sulphur Company, Duval Texas Sulphur Company, and Jefferson Lake Sulphur Company.

Swampish surroundings and cave-ins add to the expense of mining. Some wells last only a few weeks, others a year or more. The longer men work a well, the weaker its supporting rock, though some subsiding helps. "Bleed" wells carry off surplus water; mud wells force mud into gaps.

"We're shoving off to another well. This one's giving out." Replacement wells are sought constantly, then drilled. But much equipment stays permanent, such as reservoirs that hold millions of gallons of water (two to eight million gallons pumped into a sulphur deposit a day). There are permanent power plants, thousands of feet of pipes between plant and mine field, steel derricks, laboratories, storage and loading facilities.

Permanent, too, are the sulphur towns, homes of workers and their families. New Gulf (Texas Gulf

Sulphur Company) has 300 residences, a community house, an atheletic field, a golf course, churches, high-ranking schools, a large public library, a modern hospital.

Port Sulphur (Freeport Sulphur Company) boasts of comfortable homes, playgrounds, a community house, swimming pool, schools, stores, churches, all well equipped. Employees ride to work in streamlined Diesel launches.

Jobs last all year, require steady watchful work. The sulphur must never have a chance to cool and freeze in the pipes. Dredges must keep pumping in mud to avoid underground cavities. Water, heat, pressure require minute by minute adjusting. Laboratories control the entire process.

Magnetometers, gravity meters, seismographs help locate the hidden domes over those strange pillars of salt. "There's a salt dome, for sure." Men drill it in hope of oil—and in a few cases have come upon sulphur. Of 200 or more domes thus far discovered in Texas, Louisiana, and Mississippi, only 12 have been found commercially practicable. Of

▼ A STEAM-JACKETED PIPE carrying molten sulphur

from the sump, or collecting station, to the vat areas

Texas Gulf Sulphur Co., Henry Southerland photo

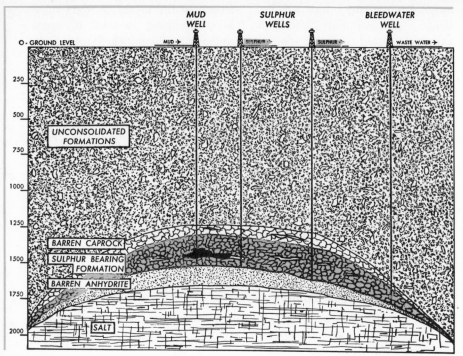

O - GROUND LEVEL   MUD →   SULPHUR →   SULPHUR →   WASTE WATER →

250
500
750
1000
1250
1500
1750
2000

MUD WELL   SULPHUR WELLS   BLEEDWATER WELL

UNCONSOLIDATED FORMATIONS

BARREN CAPROCK
SULPHUR BEARING FORMATION
BARREN ANHYDRITE
SALT

Courtesy Freeport Sulphur Co.

these, five have already been exhausted.

Even when men learn where sulphur is, they must drill into it time and again before they can feel sure of the amount present. There is always a vast risk. The Freeport Sulphur Company sank $4,000,000 into Grande Ecaille mine before receiving any degree of proof that its sulphur would justify further effort.

Time was when the Grande Ecaille was nothing but marsh. The salt dome, about 35 miles below New Orleans, lay below salt grasses matted to a thick fiber. Here red-winged blackbirds migrated by the tens of thousands. Here herons stood motionless on stiltlike legs, and mosquitoes swarmed like fogs.

Drilling penetrated 1250 feet of sediment to cap rock and its inner layer of treasure. But how could they build a plant in this forbidding place? No fresh water for miles around. No highway or railroad near. Tides and hurricanes threatened. Mosquitoes menaced like mad. The two million gallons of water to be heated every day to melt the sulphur would have to come from the Mississippi River through a ten-mile canal. And men must excavate for a reservoir to hold 50 million gallons.

They built the plant directly over the salt dome, where any dropped tool was lost forever. "Whoops! She's a goner!" The marsh was so sucking-soft that foundation-piling 75 feet long sank half its depth without aid of a pile driver. The only way to hold up piling was to drive it so deep that friction did the trick. The plant had to be

◄ MUCH OF OUR SULPHUR in the Gulf Coast region lies in dome-shaped layers above deposits of rock salt, 1000 feet or more below the earth's surface. The difficulty of removing it long kept us dependent upon Sicilian sulphur

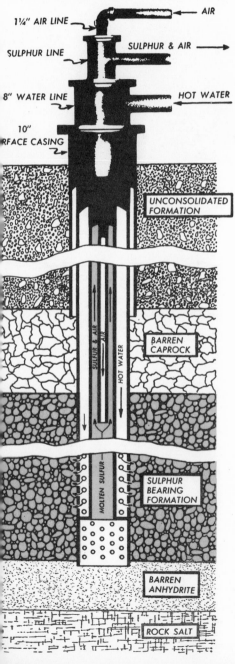

1¼" AIR LINE

AIR

SULPHUR LINE

SULPHUR & AIR ➤

8" WATER LINE

HOT WATER

10" RFACE CASING

UNCONSOLIDATED FORMATION

SULFUR & AIR / AIR / HOT WATER

BARREN CAPROCK

MOLTEN SULFUR

SULPHUR BEARING FORMATION

BARREN ANHYDRITE

ROCK SALT

anchored in concrete to withstand hurricane force. Then land that made way for the reservoir built the town, Port Sulphur.

Facts About Sulphur, by the Texas Gulf Sulphur Company, gives an impressive list of industries and products requiring sulphur. You can scarcely name an industry not included. There is the whole alphabetical list from acids and alcohols, through food preservatives, fumigants, glue, glycerin, pharmaceuticals, and plate glass, to water purification. Acids and chemical industries use greatest amounts. Next in order come superphosphate, ammonium phosphate, pulp and paper, rayon, rubber and agriculture.

We'd be in a sorry state without sulphur. It is back of our crops, our newspapers, magazines, books; back of every car on the highway, back of its steel, upholstery, the oil and gas that run it, its safety glass, its antiknock—30 pounds of sulphur for every automobile.

Sulphur helps make our enamel kitchenware, our tin cans for food, our plastic cloths and drapes, canister sets, refrigerator dishes. It enters the making of camera film and ·film for motion pictures and X-rays.

◄ DR. HERMAN FRASCH turned men from sulphur mining to sulphur "pumping" by discovering the hot water method of removal. In this diagram, hot water under pressure at 320 degrees F. is pumped down the largest pipe to where the sulphur is. The hot water melts the sulphur and forces it up inside the middle-sized pipe, three inches in diameter. Several hundred feet higher in the well, compressed air released in the innermost pipe raises the sulphur the rest of the way

Texas Gulf Sulphur Co.

⋀ HUGE BLOCKS OF SULPHUR are built up between railroad tracks that give access for shipment

It helps make dyes, fats, oils, soaps —tens of thousands of products. Wipe these from our civilization, and where are we? Sulphur is in the recovery of bromine from sea water—the bromine needed in medicine, photography, and the whole petroleum industry. Sulfa drugs, rushed to battle victims, have saved thousands who would have died in earlier wars.

These enormous, spectacular uses of sulphur have spurred scientists to try to extract it elsewhere. Germany found a main source in coke oven gas before World War II. Norway got it from pyrites by smelting — United States, Britain, Canada, the Far East gain amounts from natural gas and petroleum refinery gases. Oil refineries have their own sulphur recovery plants, regenerate their used sulphuric acid, break up hydrogen sulphides ob-

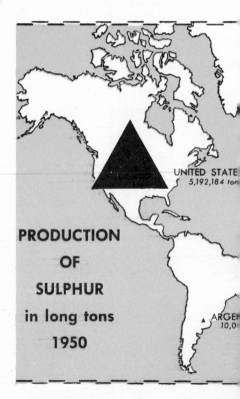

PRODUCTION

OF

SULPHUR

in long tons

1950

UNITED STATE
5,192,184 ton

ARGEI
10,0

tained by distilling crude oil—cool and solidify the hot sulphur in vats.

Still, sulphur from buried deposits stays cheapest, simplest, and best. Gulf Sulphur is King in U.S. and world markets.

About 80 per cent of our elemental sulphur goes into sulphuric acid. Sulphur has no odor; but sulphuric acid—you can smell it a thousand feet away! Sulphur is a mild laxative. But sulphuric acid would eat out your insides; it even eats metals. Men burn sulphur to get sulphur dioxide and convert this into the acid. It is heavy, oily, fumy, and burns painfully. Men who work with it take many precautions.

Yet a third of all the sulphuric acid made feeds the earth. About 100 years ago, farmers realized that the ground-up bones that make good fertilizer are even more useful to plants if mixed with sulphuric acid. The acid makes the phosphorus of bones available to the

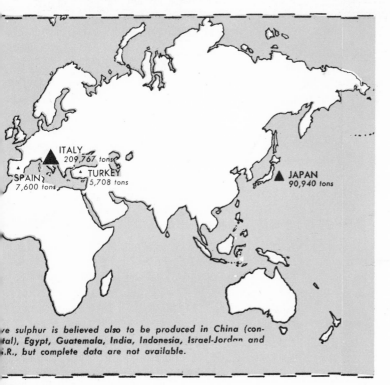

ITALY
209,767 tons

SPAIN
7,600 tons

TURKEY
5,708 tons

JAPAN
90,940 tons

ve sulphur is believed also to be produced in China (con-
tal), Egypt, Guatemala, India, Indonesia, Israel-Jordan and
.R., but complete data are not available.

tiny mouths of roots. Acidulating bones became big business in England. Old-time cemeteries were ransacked for bones. Mummies from Egyptian tombs arrived by shiploads in England. "Are those mummies for museums?" "No—for you, eventually." The mummies were ground up for fertilizer.

When men discovered phosphate rock in South Carolina in 1868, and in Florida in 1885, the fertilizer business in America gained impetus. Crushing rock was better than shouting "Old bones!" in streets. In time, acid-treated phosphate became "super-phosphate." Plants could assimilate it easily. The fed soils feed vegetables and fruits, which in turn feed us.

For paper alone, the United States and Canada together require 700,000 tons of sulphur a year. The magazine containing this article required sulphur for paper and ink. Sulphur dissolves out resins, gums, and other impurities in the wood pulp—250 pounds of sulphur to 1 ton of sulphite pulp, basis of our paper industries, newspapers, writing paper, wrapping paper. Basis also for rayon and all fabrics metamorphosed from coal, oil, and water.

Count Hilaire de Chardonnet, pupil of Pasteur in France, is credited with starting rayon. He was helping Pasteur overcome a disease that threatened silkworms and asked, "Why can't we make a spinneret machine on the order of the silkworm's spinnerets? Force collodion through the holes and get a silky thread?" So he devised a spinneret.

In 1893, three English chemists, Cross, Bevan, and Beedle, treated cellulose with caustic soda and carbon bisulphide. "Look at that fine silky film!" In 1908, a French chemist built the first practical machine for producing this transparent film. That is how cellophane began.

Sulphur prepares and dissolves the wood pulp for rayon. Its acid bath fixes rayon threads; the dyes it helps make give rayon its soft pure colors. Rayon has been spun in finer and finer filaments and given added strength by simple stretching. Now it enters high tenacity cords for bomber tires, packs pump rods and plungers, insulates telephone and radio wires.

In 1839, you could have found Charles Goodyear cooking sulphur with white lead on his kitchen stove. He knew how people detested rubber—those suddenly popular rubber shoes and mackintoshes that hardened and cracked in winter, turned sticky in summer, and smelled to high heaven. "No more of that rubbery stuff!"

Goodyear experimented till he hardened rubber. Literally, from his kitchen stove sprang the whole rubber industry—tires, inner tubes, rubber heels, water bottles, raincoats, jar rings, floors, gloves, bathing caps—a multimillion-dollar business.

Apart from sulphur's use in superphosphate, ammonium sulphate, potassium sulphate, sulphur itself is a fertilizer. It stimulates root growth, encourages seed formation, makes for plant vigor. Those sickly stunted plants that seem to have yellow fever or measles sometimes need sulphur. Sulphur controls insects, too, as every farmer knows.

We cannot drink sulphur from the soil, as plants do; but it nurtures us all the same. Amino acids containing sulphur build our body tissue, make up part of our skin and hair, strengthen our physiological functions.

War makes huge demands upon stores of sulphur—because of explosives, increased crop goals, refined oils for aviation. Blasting gelatin and TNT have sulphur in their making. But peacetime uses require at least five million tons of sulphur a year, for the makings of our civilization.

Spain's sulphur comes from pyrites. Chile's is in the Andes, up 18,000 feet, where miners dig in terrific cold, almost freezing their hands. The bulk of our sulphur is Gulf Coast, from Frasch-processed mines. Here the yellow rhombic crystals, like cool jewels embedded in limestone above pillars of rock salt, are melted and brought to the surface.

The birth of every new industry means another role for sulphur. A new method may temporarily decrease the need for sulphur, then all of a sudden sulphur leaps into a formerly unknown role. Recently a new sulphur dome was discovered in the Gulf. To what unfamiliar uses will some of its sulphur be put tomorrow? No one dares predict.

Texas Gulf Sulphur Co., Elwood M. Payne photo

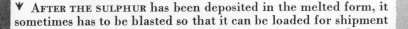

▼ AFTER THE SULPHUR has been deposited in the melted form, it sometimes has to be blasted so that it can be loaded for shipment

Tails · Some strange caudal appendages adapted by nature to meet special requirements

By CHARLES E. BURT

Formerly with the Department of Herpetology
The American Museum of Natural History

LET us trace, in a general way, the development or formation of the tail in the animal kingdom. One of the simplest and most generalized animals known, the minute, one-celled *Amœba proteus*, is without constant body form. Therefore, there is no tail, just as there can be no head, no mouth, no eyes, no ears, and no legs—the mass of living substance or protoplasm constituting the species serving as all of these and more. In many other simple one-celled forms, however, the body is constant in outline and, in addition, in many of them one part of the body is always behind and another is always in front as the organism moves about. Here we find *longitudinal orientation* of the protoplasmic mass which constitutes the body and hence, as regards the tail, the foreshadowing of future developments.

The free-living, fresh-water flatworm *Planaria*, a larger, more advanced, many-celled animal, offers a very perplexing problem when we attempt to divide it into general sections or parts according to the popular method. This

Photograph by Herbert Lang

Monkeys of the New World belonging to the family Cebidæ nearly all have prehensile tails, wheras those cf the Old World do not. Above is a picture of an African monkey; the one shown below is Central American

Photograph by Frank M. Chapman

curious organism is always cross-eyed, if its tiny "eye-spots" are really to be regarded as eyes, and its mouth is situated near the middle of the body. Now, if we consider the fore part of the animal as the head, including the mouth as usual, we find that most of the planarian is head, but if we regard the portion back from the "ears" or sensory lobes as tail, much of this head really proves to be something else. Thus, at this point we are still unable to positively separate head, body, and tail.

This same indefinite condition or status of the tail holds to a greater or lesser degree throughout the lower or invertebrate series of animal groups, although it is true that certan of these show caudal developments which are worthy of note. The crayfish has a series of five terminal plates which the animal often uses in swimming rapidly backward through the water. Numerous insects, such as the cricket, have conspicuous posterior hairs or filaments which some may regard as a tail. Bees have developed a strong sting behind. Scorpions, which also sting with

Photograph by Arthur Fisher
THE PEACOCK'S FAN
The animal kingdom holds no more elaborate tail than that of the peacock. The fan is spread
only during courtship

an apparatus at the terminal part of the abdomen, likewise show no real tail—and so on.

In the back-boned animals or vertebrates the tail appears as a definite structure. Here, in the fish, amphibians, reptiles, birds, and mammals, there is prob-

Photograph by Mary C. Dickerson
WOODPECKERS REST ON THEIR TAILS
The downy woodpecker hangs to the tree with his
claws and props himself with the stiffened spike-
like quills of the tail feathers

ably no part of the physiognomy that has been subjected to a more interesting series of variations and uses than this appendage.

Take for instance, among the reptiles, a fossil form, the ancient *Ichthyosaurus* or "fish-lizard," was obviously specialized for pelagic life like the porpoise and the whale, but the most primitive modern species, the tuatara of New Zealand (*Sphenodon punctatum*) shows none of this. Its tail is merely strongly compressed along its length, as are those of many other reptiles which live in marshy or semi-aquatic habitats—such as the crocodiles and their allies, or certain large South American lizards of the family Teiidæ (*Dracaena guianensis* and *Crocodilurus lacertinus*). Such tails are long and strong, being obviously adapted to aid in swimming movements and in defense. A similar type of modification is found in the marine snakes which occur so commonly in the vicinity of the islands of the Pacific and Indian oceans. These creatures usually have the elongate body and other general characters of the serpents, but their tails, instead of being rounded as in the terrestrial species, are often much compressed, so as to form a helpful rudder which may be waved from side to side while the animal swims about.

The tails of the turtles, like those of the horned lizards (*Phrynosoma* and *Moloch*), are almost too small and insignificant, as reptile tails go, to warrant discussion here, being reduced to but a relatively small fraction of the total length—usually less than thirty per cent.

Many reptiles vibrate their tails when disturbed, but none are better equipped by nature to capitalize this tendency than the venomous rattlers, which, unlike most other poisonous snakes, usually warn their would-be victims before attempting to molest them. The snakes of the genus *Coluber*, known generally as the racers, are unusually nervous and will frequently vibrate the tail when disturbed. Exhibiting this same tendency,

Photograph by Mary C. Dickerson

MOLLY COTTONTAIL

This rabbit carries a tuft of snow-white fur on the underside of its tail. The pursuing hunter can trail the rabbit by this white spot until the rabbit squats and hides its tail

a small lizard, the common spiny-swift of central Kansas (*Sceloporus undulatus*

Photograph by N. Y. Zoological Society

THE THIRD LEG OF THE TRIPOD

Kangaroos habitually sit on their powerful tails. So supported they can even strike an adversary with their hind legs

Photograph by A. J. Ortenburger

A GILA MONSTER

Our only poisonous lizard, *Heloderma suspectum*, uses its tail as a food reservoir. The tail is rich in fatty tissue and this is absorbed in times of fast

The tails of many lizards, including those of various geckos, skinks, and "glass-snakes," are very delicate and consequently fragile and easily broken. This feature often spares the life of these animals, for an enemy in pursuit, having succeeded in grasping the tail alone, usually gets a section of just that, and nothing more. If the tail of a skink is injured in any way, so that it starts to come off, the section back of the injury is very apt to be shed whether it is firmly held or not. I have personally observed this phenomenon in the field in the case of an adult Sonoran skink (*Eumeces obsoletus*), which severed its long tail by a series of quick muscular contractions after a slight cut had been made accidentally near the base. After the tail has been broken, the wound heals readily and new or regenerated tissue grows. The part that develops in this

thayerii), reminds one of a pleased dog as it quivers its little tail in anticipation of food.

The Old World chameleons have a prehensile or clinging type of tail somewhat similar to that of the opossum. This is a rather unique development among the reptiles, although it is said also to have taken place in a rare iguanid lizard of the West Indies which is known to scientists as *Xiphocercus valencienni*.

Inhabiting the southwestern United States and the Mexican mainland are the poisonous gila monsters, which have large, rounded tails. These are covered with beadlike scales and are said to act as reservoirs for food, fat being stored in them during times of prosperity and used from them during the periods of inactivity known as hibernation and æstivation.

THE RATTLE TAIL

At each molt, rattlesnakes fail to shed the tips of their tails, which remain attached to the earlier tips. These tips form the rattle. Rattlesnakes are so deaf they do not hear their own rattle, but its warning sound serves to ward off enemies that might tread on one of these serpents

Photograph by Raymond L. Ditmars

THE ALLIGATOR'S TAIL!

Big alligators have powerful armour-plated tails that are used in swimming and defense. A blow from such a tail could break a man's leg

Photograph by Julian A. Dimoc.

manner, although not as long as the section lost, often becomes fully as long as or even longer than the remaining stub of the original tail. In many regions various adult skinks and, in fact, certain other lizards, too, nearly all have regenerated or incomplete tails, and middle-sized or even young examples frequently show this state as well. Regeneration often produces freaks, as many scientists have shown, and extra tails are sometimes added after an injury. Two tails are found rather frequently in lizards, but three-tailed examples, although occasionally seen, are decidedly rare.

Amphibians have been divided into three main groups, the tailed and the tailless sections, and the section comprised of the little-known, wormlike cæcilians which we need not consider. The tailed amphibians do not undergo a complete change in outline between th young and adult stages, but are much th same in general appearance throughou their existence, whereas the tailless am phibians, named with reference to th adult anatomy, have a primary or tadpol stage in which the tail is present as in th other group and a secondary or adul stage in which the tail is lost. All degree of transition between these two extreme may be seen in a carefully selecte developmental series of our common frog and toads. It seems appropriate at thi point to call attention to the fact that i certain salamanders, particularly in som plethodontids, the bas of the tail is constricte for loss at times of dan ger, thus serving the sam protective purpose as th tails of the lizards men tioned above.

Fishes are specialize for aquatic life and pos

THE TURTLE'S TAIL

Tails are of little use to slow moving creatures and mos turtles have them reduced t mere stubs. The box turtl endeavors to protect its tai by turning it sideways unde its shell

Photograph by Raymond L. Ditmars

Photograph by M. C. Dickerson

THE BULLFROG TADPOLE
In its first stage of metamorphosis into a frog the tadpole possesses a long tail with a finlike border

the bird of paradise, and the peacock. On the other hand, woodpeckers and chimney-swifts have developed the more practical habit of clinging to vertical surfaces and bracing themselves by means of their tail feathers, which in turn have become stiffened and thereby definitely modified for the purpose.

The wide variations shown by the tails of mammals are thoroughly interesting. For instance monkeys of the New World, belonging to the family *Cebidæ*, nearly all have prehensile or grasping tails, but monkeys of the Old World, curiously enough, have only ordinary, non-prehensile ones, which may, perhaps, be considered decorative, but which perform no useful arboreal or gymnastic duties.

Then, there is the very short tail of the "cottontail" rabbit, which is covered by thick, soft, white, downy fur, as the common name implies, and is conse-

ess flattened, rudder-like tails that aid in swimming as do similar tails in other groups. The fish-tail, although essentially constant in function and compression, is subjected to numerous variations in detail and outline. Therefore, the structure and appearance of the tail has been deemed of great importance in the classification of the group.

In the birds, the tail is formed internally by a short bony support, the pygostyle, and by the surrounding muscles, and externally by dermal elements, particularly feathers. It is in the feathers that the most obvious and interesting avian variation exists.

Perhaps in no group of animals have the tails become more specialized for purposes of ornamentation or display than in the birds, particularly in the males. In this regard, it is only necessary to mention such striking examples as the lyre bird,

PREPARING FOR THE LAND
In the second stage, the finlike border on the tail is absorbed and the legs assume more important functions

Photograph by M. C. Dickerson

Photograph by M. C. Dickerson

FURTHER METAMORPHOSIS
The bullfrog has now grown serviceable legs and comes out on land. His tail, however, is not yet fully absorbed

quently incapable of any monkey-like uses, but for all that it is still useful enough. Since the back and sides are brownish and much darker in color, this fluffy little ball is very conspicuous when the rabbit is running. Therefore, an enemy in pursuit of "bunny," be it man or beast, usually finds his attention fixed upon the "cottontail" rather than upon the prospective victim as a whole. This frequently results in the rabbit's escape, for when it suddenly ceases its zigzag run and as suddenly squats to hide the tail from view, the pursuer frequently finds himself completely baffled, for with the disappearance of the "white spot" the whole animal seems to disappear.

In contrast to the rabbit's type, the tail of the jumping mouse is sparsely haired and of an inconspicuous color. Moreover, instead of being short, and rounded, it is very elongate, measuring about twice the length of the body.

The flying squirrel has a large, flattened hairy tail, which serves as a balancer in his soaring jumps from branch to branch and tree to tree, but the opossum has a long hairless, prehensile tail that could not possibly aid its owner in the same manner. Instead, the opossum often grasps objects by winding its tail about them. This trait appears early in life, for each baby opossum thus clings tightly to "mamma's" opossum's tail as she swings it over her back and goes for a quiet evening stroll, while later, in the adult, the entire weight of the body may be easily supported from some convenient limb by this remarkable appendage alone.

There is an old saying that "if you pick up a guinea pig by the tail, its eyes will drop out." Since the caudal appendage is so short,

Photograph by Herbert Lang

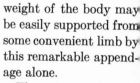

THE SALT MARSH FROG
The adult frog carries no external tail, but backwards from his hump is a true tail bone lying under the skin

being a mere vestige, guinea pig eyes seem perfectly safe. How fortunate it is, however, that the guinea pig does not feel called upon to show its feelings in the same way as does the dog, for it would have to wag the whole end of its body energetically to express a happy emotional state.

The muskrat and the beaver have much in common, for both of these rodents live in the vicinity of water, both are very fond of vegetable food, and both build more or less elaborate houses or dens for themselves, but when it comes to tails—the resemblances seemingly end. The muskrat's tail is flattened vertically along its length, and while it may serve as a rudder in swimming, it is too weak to be used as a beaver uses his. The beaver's tail, which is flattened crosswise into a broad, paddle-like appendage, has developed an unusually strong set of muscles, so that it may be maneuvered both easily and effectually. This tool is used particularly in swimming and in personal broadcasting when danger threatens. Loud danger signals are often sent out to fellow beavers by a vigorous slap of the alert one's

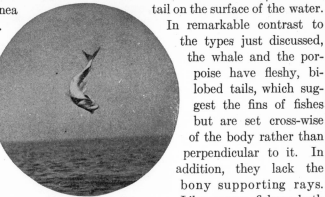

Photograph by Julian A. Dimock

THE TARPON JUMPS WITH ITS TAIL

Tails are the chief organs of propulsion in fishes. The tarpon could not leave the water without the aid of the tremendous force exerted by the sculling of its tail

Photograph by J. H. Batty

OPOSSUMS' TAILS ARE SCALY

Even when the opossum feigns sleep, it will usually curl its tail about one's finger if picked up by that appendage. More commonly it serves as a cable by which to hang when gathering persimmons

tail on the surface of the water. In remarkable contrast to the types just discussed, the whale and the porpoise have fleshy, bilobed tails, which suggest the fins of fishes but are set cross-wise of the body rather than perpendicular to it. In addition, they lack the bony supporting rays. Like many fishes, both the whale and the porpoise are specialized for life in the open seas.

Again, Nature has been especially generous with the kangaroo, in so far as his tail is concerned, whereas it has decidedly slighted the world's champion heavy-weights, the elephant, the rhinoceros, and the hippopotamus. So strong is the kangaroo's large tail that in times of danger it may support the entire weight of the body while the animal kicks viciously with its hind feet. At other times it is regularly used as a prop in sitting or as a spring or propelling force in locomotion. Exactly contrary to this condition, the elephant's most useful appendage was placed in front of the body instead of behind, while the unlucky hippopotamus was cheated at both ends.

The Lady of

Corina, the tapir, confronted her human friends with

many a delicate situation   when she insisted upon

becoming The First Lady of Barro Colorado

CORINA as an infant, in company with a coati. The overfriendly tapir had not lost her youthful markings or begun to act like the dowager of the island at this age.

the Lake

By KEN STOTT, JR.

Formerly General Curator,
Zoological Gardens of San Diego

Paul Hermle photo

MY wife and I had been assigned a bungalow just north of the laboratory at the biological station on Barro Colorado Island. The cottage was hemmed in by jungle on two sides, but below stretched a wonderful view of Gatun Lake, which is a part of the Panama Canal waterway. And beyond lay the sprawling, lushly forested hills of the Republic of Panama. As soon as we had unpacked, I stepped into the bathroom for a shower, leaving Peggy standing by the window staring slightly awe-stricken into the distance.

It was only a few minutes later (I had just come out of the shower) when I heard a clattering on the porch and a terrific thump against the side of the house. Immediately afterward, Peggy's voice drifted in through the closed door between the bath and the living room. My wife sounded disgruntled.

"Go away!" she ordered. "Get your big wet feet off the door and go back into the forest where you belong."

More thudding sounds, this time accompanied by a shrill bleat.

"No! You can't come in . . . and for heaven's sake, get your dirty nose off the window."

Towel-draped and dripping, I ran into the room to discover that the nose in question was not only dirty but excessively large, and it was pressed against the pane in the door like that of a child against a candy store window. Had it not been for the dimensions of the nose and the grotesque, ungainly creature to which it belonged, the scene might have taken on a wistful quality, but under the circumstances, nothing could have been further from the truth.

The dirty nose belonged to a half-grown Baird's Tapir; a lady Baird's Tapir it was and a very dirty one all over. She was standing on the front porch with her hind feet firmly implanted on the floor and her front feet propped against the closed door. Alternately, she worked at the doorknob with her nose and mouth, and upon failing to turn it, peered in agonized frustration through the window, squealing lustily while her piggy little eyes watered in a manner that was both profuse and unattractive. Her ears, great round things with cream-colored edges, turned back and drooped.

"She has mange," Peggy observed tactlessly.

As a matter of fact, she didn't. With the exception of the hairy tapir of northwestern South America, all tapirs are notoriously short-haired. Often the growth of hair is so sparse that the black, shiny skin beneath shows through, and this was true of the brown-coated Baird's Tapir that now stood before us. But while I could defend the condition of her coat, I could not deny the existence of myriads of ticks about her neck and ears and the resulting sores.

The tapir's visit was obviously a matter of social obligation, but it was equally obvious that Peggy did not feel up to receiving our guest.

"Don't be rude," I admonished. "Ask her in."

Peggy glared at me coldly and turned to face the tapir again. "Call again some other time . . . after we're settled."

The tapir, sensing defeat, heaved a horrible sigh and moved back from the door. Then, mincing as only tapirs can mince, she stepped slowly and daintily down the porch steps. At the bottom, she paused

➤ AT THIS AGE, Corina had scarcely begun to show the long snout so characteristic of the adult

Paul Hermle photo

to look back over her shoulder; and her eyes, still watering, seemed to indicate the hurt she had suffered. She sighed again, very deeply and very sadly, and trundled obediently off into the woods.

Over lunch a few minutes later, Dr. James Zetek howled over Peggy's account of the visitation. Dr. Zetek was the Director of the Canal Zone Biological Area (as Barro Colorado is officially designated), and from him we learned the truth about the tapir.

Her name, we were told, was Corina, and she had been captured by natives near the village of Maje on the Rio Chepo o Bayana in eastern Panama. She had been just a baby at the time and still had the white spotting and striping characteristic of all infant tapirs. When her capture had come to Dr. Zetek's attention, he had spared no effort to acquire her for his island sanctuary. At about the same time, he had obtained an eleven-month-old fawn, Chevita by name, and the two had been set

loose in the clearing around the laboratory. They had become fast friends, Chevita and Corina, and were often to be seen in each other's company as they wandered through the forest. Wild tapirs and deer lived naturally on Barro Colorado but were extremely shy, partly nocturnal, and rarely encountered. "But," Dr. Zetek explained with evident satisfaction, "Corina and Chevita have changed all that."

During the ensuing weeks, we came to know the two strange companions well, particularly Corina, whose friendship was more easily won. Chevita never came to trust us thoroughly, and I am certain that she came around us only to be near Corina, not because she enjoyed our company. Any sudden movement or loud noise would send the rust-colored fawn bounding off into the forest; and after such a departure, we seldom saw her again for the remainder of the day. But Corina found us thoroughly acceptable at all times, and we in turn came to accept her, though not so completely. I must confess that our chief aim in cultivating her friendship was not one motivated by the heart but rather by the mind. Corina gave us the opportunity to study at close hand a member of one of the most remarkable animal families on the face of the globe.

The tapir clan is a distinguished one, not so much for what it is today but for what it has been in the past and because of its relationships with other groups of animals. Actually, the clan is currently at a low ebb. There are only four existing species, and these are restricted chiefly to tropical climes.

Three are native to the New World and one, the saddle-backed tapir, is found in the swampy jungles of southeastern Asia. At one time, thousands of years ago, tapirs were an important part of the animal kingdom. Not only were they well represented numerically, but there was considerable variety and the family enjoyed wide distribution. Within the United States their fossil remains have been unearthed from California to Florida, and formerly they occurred in Europe as well. Now, of course, they are much more limited geographically, and nowhere within their present range are they to be considered plentiful.

Although the term is apt to grow tiresome owing to overuse, tapirs can best be described as "living fossils," for the surviving species show little change from those that existed in the Pliocene, years ago. Tapirs now as then are characterized by their somewhat rhinoceros-proportioned bodies and their moderate dimensions (about those of a blue-ribbon sow or a Shetland pony). Their legs are short and stocky, and their broad-crowned teeth are designed chiefly for grinding vegetable matter. Whether or not the ancestral tapirs possessed the long prehensile snouts so typical of their descendants is a point for conjecture, since fossil skulls can only begin to indicate the contours assumed by the flesh that once covered them.

Tapirs belong to the group of animals known as the Perissodactyla, or "odd-toed" hoofed mammals. This "odd-toed" business refers to the number of toes, not the nature of them, and serves to distinguish the animals to which it is applied from the cloven-hoofed or "even-toed" creatures like deer, cattle, giraffes, and camels. The order Perissodactyla now includes the tapir family and two others: the rhinos, whose relationship to the tapirs is fairly apparent, and the horses, whose relationship is not. The horse, with only one functional toe (having lost all of the others during evolution) is the most specialized and highly developed of all; the three-toed rhino comes next; and the tapir with four toes still on each front foot and three on each hind foot stands as the most primitive, the least modified of the lot.

Here again is confirmative support for the contention that the tapir is a living fossil. Temperamentally, however, Corina was tireless in her efforts to enter the modern world of man.

Totally uninhibited, she felt compelled to express any impulse she might have, and no amount of discouragement seemed to faze her. Although she appeared quite aware of a negative response from one of her human friends and was even more sensitive to a scolding, her dim little mind seemed incapable of controlling the compulsions of her great brown body. All the while, it was easy to imagine that her mournful eyes were saying: "I'm not really like this; I just can't help myself."

Often as we sat on the laboratory porch, watching some creature in the treetops or bringing our notes up to date, she would slip quietly up behind us and surprise us with a playful nip on the ankle, or place her wet rubbery nose against the neck. The unbounded affection she felt was never mutual; and as we came to know her better, we loved her less.

A persistent, petulant, and over-zealous female she was, and when she felt in the mood for attention, she never gave up until she got it. If we pretended to ignore her, her playful nips would become increasingly less playful until eventually we were forced to forget about the birds and the beasts for the moment and concentrate on Corina.

She doted on being petted, and when we scratched behind her ears, she became ecstatic with joy. Her eyes rolled upward, and she closed the eyelids until only slits remained. If we continued—and we had little choice in the matter—her knees began to tremble and her whole body wavered alarmingly. Then all at once she would drop to the ground like a collapsed balloon and roll over on her back with her legs flailing in all directions.

When we became weary of Corina's whims and ceased our caressing, she would lie quietly for a few moments. Then she would begin to kick violently with all four legs—an impatient, insistent gesture which made it clear that she expected further petting. Sometimes we acquiesced, but when we failed to do so, there was the devil to pay.

Corina would struggle to her feet—a process which, considering her size, build, and unparalleled lack of grace, was no mean feat. Then, tossing her head this way and that and whinnying at the top of her lungs, she would gallop wildly about, paying little heed to anything that lay in her path— shrubs, chairs, or us. And the more she ran, the less rational she became. Her hysterical cavortings, which had been aimless at first, gradually took on purpose, and the hostile resentment she felt toward our indifference grew overpowering. Then she would charge.

If we had time, we would run into the lab, but often we could only scramble up on our chairs and attempt to keep our legs and feet out of reach. She would roll toward us with mouth agape and saliva dripping from each side, and when she failed to make contact, she would run in a circle before repeating the charge. It was during such a lull that we always made

our escape into the laboratory, and there we would wait for Corina to regain her composure.

The length of time required for recovery varied, but on each occasion it involved a stage of violent frustration, during which she would bite or butt anything within reach. Then came a period of pathetic squealing at the door; and finally, complete (but only temporary) resignation. Dejected and drooping, she would amble slowly away, leaving us to wonder why and how this particular living fossil had managed to survive.

But Corina was not always so objectionable. There were times, as when we explored the dense rain forests of Barro Colorado, that we found her company quite comforting. The jungle, whether filled with squawks and squeakings as it always was in the cooler parts of the day, or silent as death during the warmer hours, was a strange and awesome place; and the presence of a familiar being (even Corina) who knew and understood its depths, contributed somehow to our peace of mind, even though the tapir was no more at ease there than we were.

Regardless of her size and forest origin, Corina was constantly nervous and on the alert. Her cream-rimmed ears trembled at each soft noise, and she paused frequently, standing stock-still in the trail, when any sound or sight disturbed her. Often as she stood there, she would lift one front leg, bringing to mind some nightmarish sort of bird dog.

When she became thoroughly frightened, she would whirl in her tracks and come barreling back down the trail toward us, whistling like a runaway steam engine. Generally we had no choice but to dive into the vegetation on one side or the other and give her the right of way. She would pass us without a glance and keep on running full tilt until she reached the clearing.

Prior to our excursions with Corina into the hilltop forests of Barro Colorado, I had thought of tapirs primarily as creatures of the water, for they are unquestionably best adapted for such an environment. They are excellent swimmers, and they can move their great, thick-skinned bodies through the water with only the tip of the long flexible nose showing above the surface. A large part of their diet is provided by plant life growing along lakes or rivers, and I have been told that they feed also on vegetation that grows beneath the surface of the water.

But Corina could traverse the treacherous up-and-down trails of the jungle rapidly and quietly, and her feet were as well suited for use on muddy trails as they were in swamplands. When exposed to the pressure exerted by the weight of her body after each step, the burdened foot would spread and sink into the mud; but when the pressure was removed, it would decrease in girth and she could extricate it quickly and easily, despite the sucking action of the moist soil. Usually her pace was slow, but when the occasion demanded, she could move like the wind (a rather large wind, at that!).

Dr. Zetek told us that the wild tapirs on the island spent the greater part of the day either in the water or in the vegetation along the lake margin but that at night they were often encountered on the hilltops and far from the water. It was only at times such as these that tapirs proved dangerous, and even then the menace they provided was entirely unintentional. In their fright they sometimes ran toward an intruder rather than away; and being run down by a tapir is an unpleasant experience, regardless of the animal's intent.

The Baird's or Central American Tapir is not the only one that temporarily forsakes the lowland marshes. The Common or Amazon Tapir frequently makes inland and upland trips of short duration, and the little-known Hairy Tapir exists only high in the Andes Mountains of Colombia, Ecuador, and perhaps Peru. It has been recorded at altitudes above 13,000 feet. So, despite any erroneous preconception I may have had, tapirs are far from confined to lowland waterways or their immediate vicinity.

But Corina remains the only tapir I ever heard of who made herself a sort of official hostess to a bunch of scientists at a jungle laboratory.

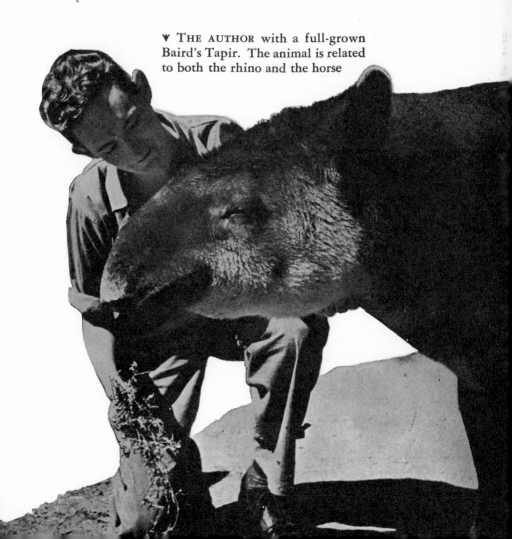

▼ THE AUTHOR with a full-grown Baird's Tapir. The animal is related to both the rhino and the horse

The Termite Problem

The social organization of these insects pits man against an ancient and spectacular legion of military engineers

By ALFRED E. EMERSON

Professor of Zoology, University of Chicago

As the pulse of spring beats more rapidly with the northern advance of the warm rays of the sun, mysterious forces are generated within the bodies of living organisms. The swelling buds of the trees, the appearance of flowers on the floor of the woods, the rhythmic song of the birds —these are the more obvious indications that life is awakening from winter dormancy.

The influence of spring is felt in secretive places not usually penetrated by the inquisitive eyes of man, however. As the frost leaves the ground, myriads of tiny organisms penetrate to the surface from their winter quarters well removed from the freezing temperatures of the first foot or so of soil. Along with the earthworms which become so readily transformed into the evening song of the robin, one notices the excavated soil of the omnipresent ant. If a log on the forest floor is rolled over, one may find tunnels leading from the soil depths into galleries in the wood which have been eaten by termites.

The termites, thus invading the wood in contact with the soil, have spent the winter in subterranean chambers. The rise in temperature seems to influence growth forces which produce the winged reproductive caste. At a period of high humidity, often following a spring rain, these winged progenitors fly forth from exit holes prepared by the wingless sterile workers. At the beginning of the flight, the winged termites fly slowly away in every direction, only showing brief orientation to the source of the most intense light. In a few minutes, however, the response to light seems to be lost and they settle to the earth.

The founding of a colony

As seeds scattered by the wind may lodge in unfavorable situations, the winged termites may end

COMPARE THE RIGHT-HAND PHOTOGRAPH of an apparently solid timber removed from a New York building with the lower photograph of its underside revealing that it has been almost completely destroyed by termites

Science Service Photos. Courtesy Fordham University

their flight on the surface of a lake or in the web of a spider. Providence is kind to the favored few, however, that may alight more or less by chance near a decaying log. The female quickly drops her four transparent wings by bending them back and breaking them off along a crack or suture at their base adapted to this function. She then lifts her abdomen into the air and emits an attractive odor which entices a male. As soon as the male has found her, the female, followed in tandem by the male, seeks a sheltered niche in or under the log, and together the king and queen seal off the first excavated chamber from the encroachment of their numerous enemies. If all goes well, the bridal couple may become the parents of a small number of white nymphs within a few weeks. These are fed with droplets of

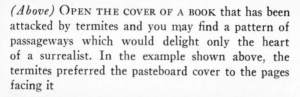

(Above) OPEN THE COVER OF A BOOK that has been attacked by termites and you may find a pattern of passageways which would delight only the heart of a surrealist. In the example shown above, the termites preferred the pasteboard cover to the pages facing it

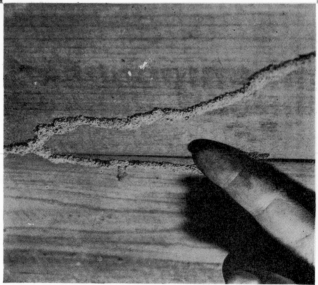

Publishers Photo Service

(Above) TERMITE TUNNELS: Protection from enemies and from the drying effect of the air is afforded by these tube-like passageways built by certain termites

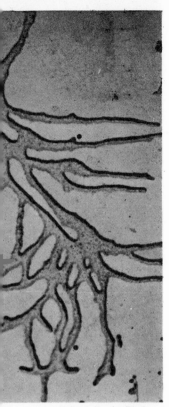

food ejected from the mouth by the young king and queen until the nymphs are large enough to forage for themselves and their parents.

The flight of the colonizing termites occurs as early as February in the deep south and is not noticed in the northern states until late April or May. If the termite colony has invaded the wooden foundations of a human dwelling designed to maintain a tropical internal climate in the most severe winter, one may expect to find the flying termites emerging earlier in the season than their relatives in the neighboring woods. They are unable to distinguish the wood of a house from that on the forest floor and they do not react differently to the temperature produced by a furnace than they do to the warm temperature of the southland.

Mistaken for flying ants

The householder who has been unconsciously harboring a colony of termites is astonished at the sudden appearance of the flying forms. He is likely to call them ants unless he has heard that ants have wasp-like waists as compared to the thick waists of the termites. He may also know that termites shed their wings by quickly breaking them along the basal suture, while the winged ants have greater difficulty in shedding their wings which are often broken off along irregular jagged lines.

Whatever the state of his knowledge, the householder is not likely to ignore the appearance of the flying termites, and before long his friends have increased his worries by tales of collapsing buildings and furniture. Newspaper reporters may even call upon him for a "local-interest" story and, with adequate expansion through the use of vivid imagination and a glance at a handy encyclopedia, the reporter is able to fill a few inches of space in his local paper,

(Left) PLANKING, BOOKS, AND EVEN AN ALARM-CLOCK with a cardboard dial are vulnerable to :ermite invasion

Our commonest termites must have connection with moist soil; hence an adequate precaution is to keep all untreated wood free from contact with the ground

Certain termites in the South, however, need no connection with the ground, and against them furniture and building wood sometimes have to be treated with penetrating chemicals to the consequent profit of termite-exterminator companies.

Professor W. M. Wheeler once wrote a delightful satire on human society. in the form of a letter from the king of an African termite colony discussing the problems of termite and human society. One would gather from this letter that termites have a delicious sense of humor and that termite chuckles could be heard at the furor they cause above their quiet underground sanctuary. Be that as it may, the observer of human nature may find much to amuse him and at the same time to distress him when he sees humanity reacting to the fears engendered by ignorance. A very large section of our populace derives its means of economic support through the conscious or unconscious exploitation of such fears.

Instead of looking at termite society from the point of view of the householder dominated by his financial worries, let us penetrate into the life of the termite from the viewpoint of the scientist whose curiosity is aroused by a social organization strikingly parallel to our own. Many of the marvels of existence may be found in the activity of insects, provided one can concentrate on other attributes than their feel and their taste.

At some time during the Age of Reptiles, termites slowly evolved from roach-like ancestors, if we correctly interpret the circumstantial evidence of strikingly similar structure and the scraps of connecting links preserved by fossil impressions. Certain characteristics of termites were already developed in the roaches. A few roaches eat wood in which they excavate their nesting chambers. Wood, composed largely of comparatively undigestible lignin and cellulose would seem to be a poor source of nourishment, but these insects have interesting aids to their digestion. Their intestines harbor millions of protozoans (microscopic single-celled animals) that help to change cellulose into easily absorbed sugar. At least some kinds of termites also have similar protozoan friends that are distributed to all members of the colony by the termite habit of eating portions of each other's excrement as well as wood. The net result is that the termites, by gnawing

AN EAST-WEST EXPOSURE is invariably achieved by the millions of tiny insects that build this type of nest. The effect of the sun on the temperature of these curiously designed nests is suggested as a practical explanation.

(Left) NATURE'S UMBRELLA: This mushroom-shaped nest of *Cubitermes sankurensis* illustrates an architectural plan which preserves the termite "city state" from dissolution on the edge of the rain-forest of the Congo basin. Sometimes several of these umbrella-like caps are built one above another   *(Photo by Herbert Lang)*

wood, obtain both food for themselves and a snug dwelling for the colony where it may be relatively secure from natural enemies.

The need for adequate defense against predatory enemies, particularly against the true ants, was met through the development of a soldier caste which evolved strong biting jaws and a correlated behavior well fitted to ward off invasions from without. Efficient specialization of the soldier for defense involved the relinquishment of other functions found in solitary insects. Wings became degenerate and functionless, the reproductive organs, both male and female, became sterile, and the jaws were no longer of use in chewing wood.

Chemical warfare

The soldier caste, once established, further evolved special defensive apparatus such as a head gland for the emission of a volatile liquid which evaporated readily to form a poisonous gas. The soldiers of other termite species adapted the head gland for the production of a sticky secretion which could be shot out of a nozzle-like projection of the head at an ant a half-inch away. In a few cases different types and sizes of soldiers were produced within the same colony with the consequent added efficiency of the army for defense.

The reproductive castes retained the essential characteristics of the roach-like ancestors. They kept the functional wings, eyes and reproductive organs, although the latter became highly specialized for great fecundity in the more advanced termites. Captive queens of tropical termites have been observed to lay over seven thousand eggs a day and in some cases this number is probably exceeded. Egg-laying is a continuous activity in these tropical queens without cessation during the daily or seasonal cycles. After the establishment of the first chamber and the production of the first nymphs, the abdomen of the female gradually enlarges with the growth of the ovaries until it may reach a size several hundred times the volume of the abdomen of

THE QUEEN'S CHAMBER IN A TERMITE NEST:
The base of operations for one of the most destructive creatures of the animal kingdom. Especially in the tropics, termites cause enormous damage through their wood-eating habits. Here the Queen, a veritable egg-laying machine, is shown surrounded by a few of her myriad offspring. Notice the nozzle-like projections on the heads of the soldier caste, from which they squirt a sticky secretion at their enemies, the ants. The King, who is constantly near the Queen, is seen at the lower left. Near the head of the Queen, at the right, is a termite guest, or termitophilous beetle *(Photo of model by permission of Buffalo Society of Natural Sciences)*

the winged female. The enlargement of the abdomen often results in relative immobility and the queen may be confined to a royal cell in the nest from which she could not escape even though she had the impulse. The king remains much the same size he had attained when he possessed wings, and lives constantly with the queen in or near the royal cell. The average life-span of the kings and queens of tropical colonies is probably between ten and fifty years.

In our northern climates the colonizing reproductive pair is often replaced by supplementary royalty. Among even the most primitive termites, supplementary kings and queens may be derived from fairly mature nymphs which do not undergo further development into winged forms. There is reason to suppose that an inhibiting substance is produced by the queen which prevents the development of the supplementary queens. If the population grows to the point where the inhibiting substance does not reach some of the nymphs in effective concentration, or if the queen is removed from the colony, supplementary queens develop in a few months. Likewise the king seems to secrete a substance which tends to suppress the development of supplementary kings. Extracts of the inhibiting substance of either the king or queen, fed by placing it upon filter paper, tends to delay the production of the respective supplementary reproductive forms. Such chemical agents may also serve to regulate the production of the sterile castes. Thus we have evidence of a sort of social hormone which influences the coordination of the parts of the society much as the true hormones of our bodies are known to produce a balance of functional relationships through their inhibiting or accelerating effect.

FOSSIL TERMITE WING from Tertiary rocks. Sometime during the Age of Reptiles the termites are believed to have slowly evolved from roach-like ancestors. Their development involved, among other things, a highly specialized caste system with division of labor, and the ability of the winged reproductive caste to shed its wings after the colonizing flight.

Down through the geologic ages the termites persisted and prospered, ultimately to the exasperation of man

(Right) PROTECTION AGAINST TORRENTIAL RAINS: A striking example of the architectural proficiency of termites in tropical South America. In dry weather the workers of this species *(Amitermes excellens)* build a tube vertically up the side of a tree. From this they construct side tunnels extending downward in a chevron pattern, which effectively shed the rains that later descend. Later the nest is constructed as seen on the middle trunk

Primitive termites had thus progressed beyond their roach-like ancestors in attaining a division of labor between the individuals composing the society which was an outgrowth of a family organization. The basic caste differentiation involved specialization of the functions of defense, reproduction and nutrition. Nutrition, however, was still the function of the young nymphs of the soldier and reproductive castes. The more advanced termites split off a third adult caste through the specialization of soldier nymphs before the soldier characteristics had taken form. This new worker caste did not differ markedly in structure from the soldier nymphs, but growth ceased. This worker caste thus resembled the soldiers in lacking wings, eyes and functional reproductive organs, but retained the jaws adapted to chewing wood which were possessed by the soldier nymphs but had been modified into defensive weapons by the adult soldiers. Nutrition became the first concern of the workers. In an important group of Old World termites, the workers even prepare beds for the growth of nutritive fungi which they harvest. Secondarily the excavating and building habits underwent a remarkable evolution which ultimately resulted in an astonishing complex nest architecture in a large number of tropical species.

(Photo by Herbert Lang)

Long before man appeared on the American continent, various species of termites were busily engaged in aerating the soil and transforming dead vegetation into plant food. These activities made them an important link in the cyclic chains of organic energy and life. Their rôle was even greater in the tropics where the continuous warm climate was more favorable to their development. Two of the genera now found within the borders of the

(Right) THE NEST PROPER of *Amitermes excellens,* is also able to withstand the rains, being equipped with overlapping eaves and finger-like projections which easily drip off the excess water

United States *(Zootermopsis and Reticulitermes)*, however, are practically confined to temperate regions, and fossils from the Oligocene of Europe and the Miocene of Colorado indicate that these genera have been in temperate climates for at least forty million years. The tropical origin of our termite fauna is therefore very remote.

There is no indication whatever that we need fear the introduction of tropical species of termites into temperate regions. Native species, however, have been taken in every state in the United States and are also known from southern Ontario and Vancouver Island, British Columbia. Only a few species are to be found in the northern United States. Thirty-nine species out of the known fifty-seven species in the United States are recorded only from the states bordering Mexico and the Gulf.

When man upsets the balance of nature by cutting the forests and utilizing wood in the construction of his buildings, it is to be expected that termites will be found damaging wood and wood products. The damage caused by termites in the United States every year is probably in excess of $40,000,000. The largest proportion of the damage occurs in the southern states, but the states bordering Canada should also take some precautions against the cellulose appetite of these remarkable insects.

Our commonest termites, species of the genus *Reticulitermes,* must have connection with moist soil for their existence, and the simple expedient of keeping all untreated wood free from ground connections is a sufficient precaution for most construction work. However, certain more primitive termites in the South (species of the family Kalotermitidae) are able to live without ground contact in the dry wood of furniture and the superstructures of buildings. Special precautions through treatment of wood with penetrating chemicals is sometimes necessary to prevent their attack. A few species of the genus *Amitermes* in the southwest are eaters of grass. There is little important destruction by these grass-eaters in our country, though harvesting termites in South Africa and elsewhere are often a serious economic problem.

Detailed studies of the intimate life of these insects are necessary for the development of proper control measures against their destructive activities. And beyond the practical value of further study, the social life and evolution of these insects have much to contribute to the solution of numerous profound biological problems.

(Photo by A. Emerson)

Clouds, Lightning, and Rain

An explanation of the forces that produce the familiar summer thunderstorm

By HAROLD E. VOKES

Department of Geology,
Tulane University

THERE are summer days when the interior of the home seems stuffy and oppressive. The breezes that rustle through the trees are particularly enticing, and in many minds the thought occurs that it is just the day for a picnic. But the very warmth of the air that makes a picnic day also serves to make it a day for possible sudden showers.

As the bright rays of the sun are reflected from the surface of the earth, they warm the air immediately above that surface much more than they warmed the higher air through which they descended to reach it. The air being warmed expands and thus becomes lighter in weight. As it becomes lighter, it rises and is displaced by heavier, cooler air. And as the warmed air rises it carries with it water vapor that it has obtained through evaporation from the surface of streams, lakes, and other bodies of water, through transpiration from the leaves of trees and grass as well as from the breath of all living animals, and through capillary attraction and evaporation from the surface of the ground itself.

While this warmed air rises higher and higher into the sky it is subjected to less and less atmospheric pressure, so that it is gradually permitted to expand more and more as it goes up. This expansion results in an equally gradual loss of its heat, and the air, therefore, cools as it ascends. When the temperature of the air falls far enough it reaches a stage known as the "dew point," where the water can no longer be retained as invisible vapor. It then condenses out as the very fine, suspended, water particles, which are the substance of clouds.

On a warm summer day the clouds formed from the water vapor in an ascending mass of humid air will assume the beautiful, cotton-wool, billowy shape which the scientists call "cumulous" clouds. The picnicker, unconcerned with their name, loves to watch and read from their ever-changing form imaginative pictures of great

A WEATHER WIZARD trying to make it rain in 1880. The device consisted of a balloon that would lift explosives into the sky, where they could be set off electrically through the mooring wire. Meteorologists today doubt the practicality of any such methods

The Bettmann Archive

Photograph by W. A. Bentley

The rounded summits of this cumulus cloud show distinct thunder heads

variety. It is a beautiful picnic day.

All the while the warm air is rising, its place is being taken by somewhat cooler air which, in its turn, may be warmed and rise to form more clouds. If the influx of this cooler air is just sufficient to balance the amount of warm air being displaced, the picnicker may return home tired, dusty, and grumbling about the ants—having had a most successful day. However, if the current of cooler air becomes so strong and deep that its effect is eventually felt upon the cloud masses themselves, a storm is very likely to mar the picnic.

The new mass of cooler air is denser than the air in the cloud, and the latter begins to rise again. But the outer surface of the cloud is being made cooler than the inner part, so this inner part rises with a strong, chimney-like up-draft while the cooler, outer surface is swept in at the base to take its place. As a result the cloud piles up to a height that may reach as much as five miles, and the entire mass is churning in great convection currents, upward in the center and inward on the bottom. You and I generally know these high, somewhat anvil-shaped masses of clouds as "thunderheads," but to the meteorologist they are "cumulo-nimbus" clouds.

As condensation continues within the cloud, the drops of water grow larger until they become too big to remain suspended in the air and start to fall. Often they are swept inward at the base of the cloud, are caught in the strong up-drafts of its center, and are blown upward with great force, generally being blown to bits. Some of the drops will not be caught in the vortex of the great up-draft, however, and will churn around and round until they reach a size where their weight is sufficient to overcome the force of the upwelling currents. These will then fall free of the cloud and reach the earth. This is the reason why so many of our summer rainstorms are marked by the large size of the first drops of rain. These early raindrops aid in cooling (and thus in condensing) the air through which they fall and also cool the surface of the earth itself. This reduces the strength of the upward movement of warmed air from below the cloud and, together with the cooling of the cloud itself, gradually reduces the strength of the up-draft within the cloud chimney. Then the smaller drops of rain will finally succeed in falling clear of the cloud, and our picnickers have to run for shelter as a general rain sets in.

What in all this is responsible for the brilliant flashes of lightning and the rumbling thunder that nearly always accompany these summer storms? It used to be held that these were a result of the friction developed within the cloud by the churning of the convection currents. But more recent studies explain the matter very differently. An English meteorologist, George C. Simpson, discovered that the rupturing of drops of distilled water (and rainwater is distilled water) by blasts of air resulted in the development of a strong positive electrical charge in the broken particles of the drops, while the air around them, together with the finer particles of spray, had a negative charge. Applying the facts of this discovery to the conditions we know to exist within a cumulo-nimbus cloud, it would seem that when the falling drops of water are carried into the area of the central up-draft in the cloud and are broken up, the finer spray particles will be carried up with the air while the larger remnants will remain at a lower level. Thus the negatively charged material will accumulate in the upper part of the cloud, while the positively charged elements will remain at a lower level.

Now in electrical charges, as in many other things, the rule is that opposites attract each other and, as the opposite electrical charges accumulate in the cloud, they tend to build up to the point where the power of their attraction to each other is sufficient to overcome the resistance of atmospheric agents separating them. When this occurs there is an almost instantaneous rush of the whole charge along a sinuous and often many-branched route from one point to another, generally from a higher to a lower point within the cloud or from within the cloud to the earth. This electrical discharge ruptures the air through which it passes, roughly forcing aside all of the atoms in its path and partially breaking from them their electrons which have made them normally neutral in electrical charge. In effect, the passage of the discharge forms a long vacuum tube whose walls are formed of free electrons and positively charged atoms. This condition cannot long remain, and there is an instantaneous rushing together into the vacuum of electrons and atoms. The reaction, designed both to fill the vacuum and to re-establish the neutral nature of the air mass, is a most violent one, and a portion of the energy generated by the collision is given off in a flash of light. This flash is our lightning. It is not caused by the actual passage of the electrical charge but is a result of the automatic repair of the damage done by that passage.

And the thunder which always accompanies the lightning? That is the result of the atoms being violently hurled aside by the charge as it darts through space. The effect of this is the same as that of a violent explosion, and the sound produced has exactly the same origin.

This is, in brief, the story of the events that occur before and during a summer shower and thunderstorm. As picnickers we may see in them only a conspiracy of the gods to spoil our pleasant day; as scientists we recognize in them the inevitable results of the workings of natural laws set in motion by the warm weather.

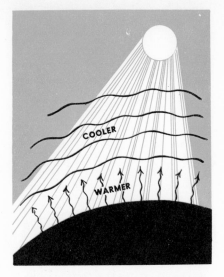

▲ ON A TYPICAL PICNIC DAY the sun's hot rays make the air directly above the land hotter than that higher up

▲ THE HOT AIR rising from the earth picks up moisture from streams, lakes, leaf surfaces, the breath of animals, and the damp soil

Drawings by Museum's Illustrators' Corps

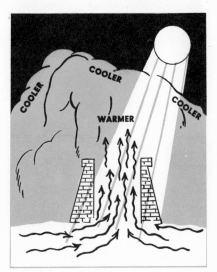

▲ AS THE MOISTURE-LADEN AIR rises, it expands and grows cooler. This causes the moisture in it to become visible as clouds

▲ THE OUTSIDE of the cloud becomes cooler than the inside when a mass of cool air comes in contact with it. Therefore, the inner part rises with a strong, chimney-like draft

▲THUNDERHEADS are formed—clouds known to the meteorologist as cumulo-nimbus. These are enormous churning masses of moisture-laden air

▲ DROPS OF WATER form within the cloud. Some are swept upward by rising air until they become heavy enough to fall as the first large drops

▲ WHEN DROPS are broken by a blast of air, a strong positive charge of electricity is developed in them, while the air and the finer particles are negative

▲ IF THE NEGATIVELY charged material accumulates in the upper part of the cloud while the positively charged elements remain at a lower level, a thunderbolt is in the making. Opposite electrical charges attract each other. When these overcome the resistance of atmospheric agents separating them, there is a flash of lightning

TICKS_

a menace to animal life

Many are harmless, but dog owners, cattle raisers, and others are becoming increasingly aware of them as carriers of certain diseases. The simple preventive measures outlined in this article will prove valuable

By C. H. CURRAN

Curator, Department of Insects and Spiders, The American Museum of Natural History

TICKS, those little things that get on you when you walk in the fields or woods, are repulsive creatures, and few people can suppress a shudder when they find one on their person. These animals are encountered over most parts of the world, and in some places they are greatly feared by natives. The famed Doctor Livingstone found during his travels in Africa that the natives of the Congo region lived in deadly fear of certain kinds of ticks, claiming that their bites resulted in death. This was in 1857. Scores of years passed before it became known, in 1904, that certain kinds of ticks in that region were capable of carrying the often fatal relapsing fever. This is but one of a number of diseases carried by ticks and there was a time when ticks threatened to destroy the great cattle industry of Texas and adjacent states.

To understand why ticks can be such a menace and why they are, on the whole, increasing in America, it is necessary to know something about how they live and grow. There are many kinds of ticks and there is a great deal of variation in the way they live and develop. Some ticks, including those causing relapsing fever, lay only a few hundred eggs, but other kinds may lay as many as 40,000. Fortunately, those that are the greatest menace lay not more than 3000 or 4000, and of these only a small percentage can be expected to reach maturity. When an animal lays as many as 40,000 eggs, the chances are that only something like one in 15,000 will grow to maturity, since Nature provides a natural balance. No kind of animal is likely to show any permanent increase in numbers unless the normal conditions under which it lives have been changed. An increase in the number of animals upon which ticks feed will cause an increase.

In general, ticks have been increasing in the United States and Canada in recent decades. However, certain

From Insects in Your Life, *by permission of Sheridan House.*

kinds have been reduced, owing to studies made by the Department of Agriculture and the application of specific control measures.

Most ticks require two or three different kinds of hosts upon which to feed, and these hosts are usually of different sizes. Notable exceptions to this rule are the brown dog tick, the winter tick, the fowl tick, and the Texas fever tick. These can all de-velop to maturity on a single animal, and two of them (the fever tick and the winter tick) never leave the host once they become attached to it. They are therefore known as one-host ticks. Ticks that become attached to animals only twice are known as two-host ticks. The brown dog tick drops off the host after feeding, so it is either a three- or four-host tick, even though it can develop to maturity on a single dog. Other ticks, such as the

THE TICK AND THE ANIMAL

By no means all of the many kinds of ticks are carriers of disease. But one of them that is and has received much study in this country is the Texas cattle fever tick (*Boophilus annulatus*). Around the turn of the century, herds driven northward to new pastures were spreading the disease each year over a larger area of the middle Southern States when remedial measures were undertaken. Control of this tick depends upon a complete understanding of the tick's life cycle, outlined in these pictures.

The only way that cattle become infected with Texas cattle fever is by having a tick whose salivary glands carry the protozoan parasite attach itself to the animal.

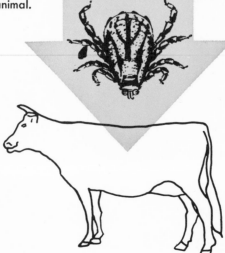

Rocky Mountain spotted fever tick and the Eastern dog tick, require animals of different sizes in order to reach maturity and are usually three- or four-host ticks.

When the young of these latter ticks hatch they are smaller than the head of a pin and are known as "seed ticks." Although ticks are not insects, they have at this stage three pairs of legs, like insects. Since the eggs are laid in masses of a thousand or more, the young seed ticks scatter as much as possible over the soil and among the blades of grass and leaves of low plants. They crawl up on the foliage and await the coming of some small animal, usually a mouse or ground squirrel. If such an animal comes within reach of their clutching legs, they grasp it and quickly work their way through the fur to the skin. Once there, they immediately begin to bore through the skin with their specially adapted mouth parts. It may take them two to six days to obtain a full meal of blood, but when fully satiated they withdraw their mouth parts with apparent deliberation and satisfaction, and seek a place of quiet where the meal can be digested.

When the tick drops from its host it is several times larger than when it began to feed, and assimilation by the digestive system may take from a week to two or three months. Steady growth occurs as the meal is digested, and the "stomach" decreases in size while other parts of the body increase. Since the skeleton of a tick is on the outside, there must be some relief, and to relieve the pressure, a new skeleton, quite expandable, is formed within the old one. When the original skeleton becomes exceedingly tight, it splits open and the emancipated tick crawls laboriously out. There is much pulling and tugging, because it is not easy to withdraw the new and larger legs and body from the confines of a skeleton that has a very definite limit of expansion.

There is one marked difference between the seed tick and the creature that emerges from it. The seed tick had only three pairs of legs. The "new" creature has four pairs (like spiders), and is flattened and leathery instead of being full-bodied and fairly soft. It also has aspirations. It will no longer be satisfied with a blood meal from a small animal. If it can find nothing else, it may feed upon one, but this is rare. Almost always it will die of starvation after a few weeks or months if it cannot find a larger animal, depending upon the kind of tick.

The tick has now become a nymph, and it is no longer satisfied with its former outlook on life. It now seeks low herbs or long grass. Here it sits upon the top of its world, waiting for a rabbit or coyote, or some other animal neither too big nor too small. If a suitable victim comes along within a month or two, the nymph attaches itself and gets another meal. If no suitable host should come along, the tick dies of starvation, and this is what happens to 99 ticks out of 100.

Ticks shed their skins and become mature after varying intervals, depending upon the kind of tick and the availability of food. Some kinds become mature in less than two months, after shedding their skins only twice. Others require two or three years and may shed their skins five or six times. Among those that seek larger hosts after each moult, it is only the mature ones that attack man and large animals. Few kinds of ticks complete their life cycle on a single host, but a large proportion of those that do are a menace to animal welfare.

Back in the days when the West was in its infancy and great herds of cattle were raised on the lush grasslands that still supported innumerable bison, the cattle fever of Texas was well known. Large herds driven north from Texas in search of fresh pastures were known to carry the disease, and northern cattle that came in contact with them often contracted it. Each year the disease was carried northward with the migrating cattle, and each year the infected area spread over a larger part of the middle southern States. ·

In 1889 it was discovered that Texas cattle fever was carried by the cattle tick (*Boophilus annulatus*). Shortly after, the Bureau of Animal Industry began investigations to control the cattle tick. In 1906 this Bureau and the states concerned instituted a co-operative plan for tick control. After more than ten years of study it was found that ticks could be controlled by either of two methods: (1) by use of cattle dips, which would destroy the ticks, and (2) by a rotation of pasture lands. This latter method proved practicable because the seed ticks die in a little more than two months if they cannot find large animals, such as cattle, deer, sheep, or horses upon which to live. By employing five fields and moving the herd from one to another on certain dates it was found possible to clear all the fields of ticks in from two to eight months. Although this method alone would bring the desired results, most ranchers also drove their cattle and other domestic stock through specially prepared dipping yards at regular intervals.

In order that the program might prove completely successful, it was necessary to remove all deer from the areas undergoing treatment and to prevent further entry of deer. After the areas were freed of ticks, tick-free deer were again liberated in them.

Everyone co-operated — if not wholeheartedly, at least with good grace—and the success of the program is evidenced by the fact that to-

The tick that causes Texas cattle fever lays on the average 2,000 to 4,000 eggs. Some of the seed ticks that hatch from these in about 30 days, "inherit" the disease organism from their parent. How they do this is shown at right.

day cattle ticks have been eliminated from the United States.

Unfortunately, not all ticks are so easily destroyed. Up to the present, attempts to eliminate other kinds of ticks have met with little success, because their life cycles do not offer a vulnerable spot. The winter elk or horse tick (*Dermacentor albipictus*) could easily be controlled if it confined its attentions to domestic animals. But in addition to horses and cattle it attacks moose, elk, and deer. Its life cycle differs from that of most other ticks, because it develops during the winter months. Like other ticks, it lays its eggs in the spring and they hatch in about six weeks. Then, instead of going in search of an animal upon which to feed, the seed ticks bunch themselves closely together— 1000 to 3000 of them in a mass—and wait until the first frosty days of autumn before they are ready to attack an unwary host that may come along. Once they find a suitable victim and attach themselves to it, they remain there until they are mature and find a

THE TICK AND THE PROTOZOAN

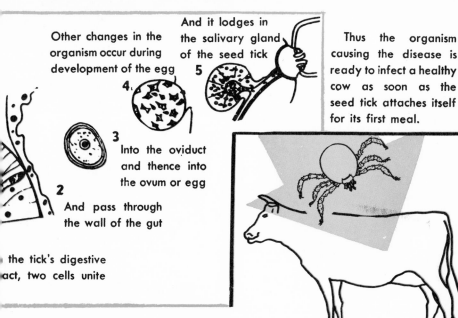

Other changes in the organism occur during development of the egg

And it lodges in the salivary gland of the seed tick

5

4.

3

Into the oviduct and thence into the ovum or egg

2

And pass through the wall of the gut

the tick's digestive act, two cells unite

Thus the organism causing the disease is ready to infect a healthy cow as soon as the seed tick attaches itself for its first meal.

suitable mate. Then the fertile females drop to the ground and find a protected place, such as a clump of grass or dried leaves, in which to pass the winter and begin the cycle all over again in the spring. The ticks remain on the animal for only six or seven weeks, so the poor victim has something to be thankful for by the time Christmas rolls around. But it may have provided meal tickets to several thousand of the bloodthirsty parasites.

The winter tick often occurs in such great numbers that it causes the death of animals. At least 20 per cent of the moose population of Nova Scotia was killed by it a few years ago. Animals attacked become weak˙ and sickly, resulting in a condition that is known as "tick poverty." Domestic animals can be freed of the ticks by dipping them and then keeping them warm until they have become thoroughly dried, but there is no practical way to treat the wild animals that roam our northern woods and those of Canada. It would be of indirect help,

however, to dip the domestic animals annually before stabling them for winter. The winter tick also carries a disease known as tick spirochaetosis, from one animal to another, and spread of this disease may cause further reduction in our game animals.

The poultry tick (*Argas persicus*) is a serious pest in many parts of the world. It attacks its victims from June to September and passes the winter as a fertile adult. When abundant it causes tick poverty among poultry, and in the case of heavy infestation, the loss of blood may cause death. Turkeys are especially subject to its attack. In other parts of the world this tick transmits avian spirochaetosis, but not in America.

To control this pest, all roosts in the poultry house must be thoroughly soaked with kerosene, including every crack and crevice, every three or four weeks during the tick season. The birds themselves may be treated with an ointment made of kerosene, lard, and sulfur to prevent attack.

The spinose ear tick (*Ornithodoros megnini*) occurs in subtropical parts of the United States. It very com-monly enters the ears of domestic animals and man, and causes deafness, serious illness, and even death, par-ticularly when young animals are attacked. To destroy this tick, a mix-

▼ As SUMMER APPROACHES, entire pastur-age is found to contain ticks dangerous to cattle. Section 1 is therefore fenced off with double fencing 12 feet apart

▼ ON JUNE 1, the herd is moved to Field (2). Developing ticks are pres-ent in Fields (1) and (2) and attach themselves to cattle

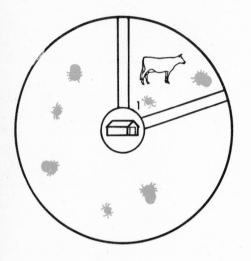 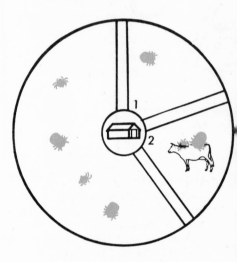

▼ ON SEPTEMBER 20, the cattle have been in Field (3) 20 days and are moved to Field (4), where ticks have died for lack of a host. Ticks on cattle drop off to lay eggs

▼ ON OCTOBER 10, the herd is moved into Field (5), which is free of ticks. Cattle are left there 20 days until remaining ticks have dropped off to lay eggs

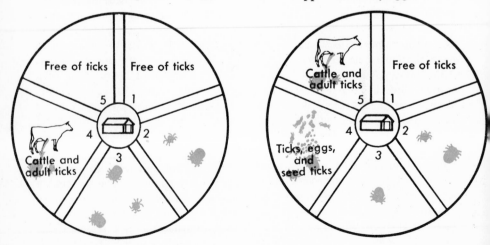

ture of one part of cottonseed oil and two parts of pine tar oil is injected into the ear, at a temperature slightly above that of the victim.

Although the ticks described below

▼ ON SEPTEMBER 1, the herd is moved to Field (3). In Fields (4) and (5), most of the ticks have died for lack of a host, without laying eggs

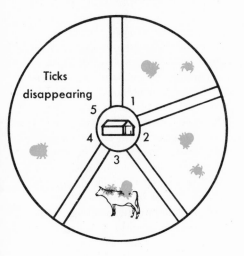

may affect our economy most seriously, dog ticks are the ones that come most commonly to our attention. There are two kinds, the eastern dog tick (*Dermacentor variabilis*), which occurs east of the Rocky Mountains, and the brown dog tick (*Rhipicephalus sanguineus*), which is known from the Atlantic coast regions and the eastern southern States, and has now become established in numerous northern cities. Both are common in the regions where they occur, and their numbers seem to be increasing each year.

The eastern dog tick is the one usually found on dogs that are allowed to run through long grass, weeds, and shrubbery. In its early stages it is found on mice, squirrels, rabbits, and other rodents. The adults attack a great many kinds of animals, from the size of dogs to deer and moose.

The brown dog tick was probably introduced from the Old World on dogs or cattle, and until a few years ago it was known only from tropical and subtropical regions in America. It is now extremely common in the New

▼ ON NOVEMBER 1, the cattle are free of ticks and can safely be moved back into Field (1). Field (2) will be free by July 1 the following year, and others in rotation. Tick's life cycle varies with climate, and this diagram is somewhat generalized; but with minor adjustments the procedure is successful

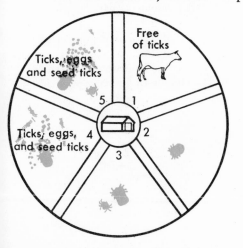

York region and is the cause of almost all the complaints in the Metropolitan area and Long Island. Since this tick is able to develop from seed tick to adult upon dogs alone, it is the one commonly found in dog kennels. When heavily infested, the dog becomes lethargic, and its coat loses its gloss. Dogs removed from infested kennels usually carry hundreds of seed ticks with them. When these drop off after completing their meal, they may cause considerable alarm, but very few of them reach maturity. They disappear into cracks and crevices in order to digest their meal and moult, and only a small percentage are able to locate the dog again. Those that do, usually attach themselves around the ears and between the toes. The adults will also attack man, and they are capable of carrying Rocky Mountain spotted fever. In removing ticks, tweezers should be used, rather than the bare fingers.

Elimination of ticks in kennels and homes is not difficult if a proper routine is followed. Since the seed ticks and nymphs remain attached to the animal for five or more days, it is possible to eliminate the ticks by employing a dipping schedule for all pets every two weeks. Ordinarily an infestation can be cleaned up in less than two months. It is good practice to dip all dogs before they leave the kennel. Similarly, when a kennel has been cleaned up, all dogs brought to it for any reason should be dipped. The dip is allowed to dry on the dogs, and it prevents re-infestation for a week or ten days.

When a large number of dogs must be treated, a vat large enough to hold sufficient material to completely cover the largest dog may be used. In the home, a boiler or tub may be employed.

The following formula and procedure has proved effective in the New York area in keeping dogs free from ticks and fleas.

Sodium bicarbonate .... 2¼ pounds
Arsenic trioxide
  (white arsenic) ..... 6 ounces
Pine tar oil .... ½ pint
Water .... 50 gallons

Dissolve the Sodium bicarbonate in one gallon of water and mix in the white arsenic. Add the pine tar oil and agitate until thoroughly mixed.

This concentrate may now be placed in quart jars to be used as needed. One quart of it will make 12 or 13 gallons of dip. This dip will retain its strength and may be used several times if the container is covered and if sufficient water is added each time to make up for evaporation.

It requires only a minute or two to completely soak a dog. Care must be taken to see that the head becomes thoroughly wet by pushing it under the liquid two or three times. At the dilution recommended there is no danger to dogs, cats, rabbits, or other pets. However, the arsenical used is a dangerous poison, and the concentrate is highly poisonous. It should be so marked and placed in an absolutely safe place out of reach of children.

In using this dip or any of the commercial tick dips, it must be remembered that the solution must be allowed to dry on the animal, and the treatment must be continued until all trace of infestation disappears. During the warm months if a dog is allowed to run in the open, it is excellent practice to dip it every two weeks. When pets are bathed or allowed to swim, the protection provided by the dip is lost.

The presence of one or two ticks on a dog or cat is no cause for alarm. But large numbers may be present without any indication, because the ticks do not cause irritation while feeding. Dog owners may therefore be comforted to know that they can be quickly eliminated by these methods.

Siberian Tiger

Tigers are the largest of the Asiatic cats. There are none in Africa. The example shown here, mounted for a museum habitat group, is the Siberian Tiger, one of the most impressive animals on earth. It is a powerful and aggressive hunter but quite difficult to track down without setting traps or guns in the runways that it makes in the snow during the winter.

A.M.N.H. photo

A toad is

By
ROY L. ABBOTT
Iowa State Teachers College

Strange things happen when

the little defenseless tadpole

forsakes its slimy pond for a

life on land as a complex and

effective organism

IN the dampness and dense shade of the great rhubarb leaf, the toad sat half-buried, her brown, warty skin blending imperceptibly with the crumbly soil. Now and then some big black ants hurried across her broad back, but except when one chanced to pass an inch or so in front of her head, she gave them no attention, for the sun was yet high, and although she couldn't resist snapping up any small fry that came within range of her quick tongue, she would not set out on any active hunting until sundown.

Not that the toad wasn't hungry. Except when hibernating, she was always hungry, and now particularly so, for she had just returned from a two-weeks' pilgrimage to a near-by pond where she had deposited her first eggs —some five or six thousand jelly-covered, shot-sized things left there to hatch and shift for themselves as best they might.

The toad had spent nearly all of her four years in this garden, and, save for the long journey just completed, had never once left it. The egg-laying trip was a new experience, a response to new urges, such as the high, shrill voices of male toads calling from the pond, and the quiet but equally insistent pressure of the many eggs in her body—the voices, as it were, of potential toads clamoring to be born.

The toad herself had begun life in this same pond. But now, squat, pop-eyed, four-legged, and nearly as large as a man's fist, she looked little like the chuckleheaded fishy mite who, along with several thousand others, had wriggled free from the gelatinous, rosary-like egg-strings left there by her mother.

In fact, at that early age, the toad was really a fish, for she breathed air from the water through delicate, feathery gills on each side of her head, and propelled herself by means of a broad tailfin. But, strangely enough, she was a fish who couldn't eat, for her mouth had not yet broken through into her intestine, and until that necessary thing occurred some six days later, there was little for her to do except to cling to some water weeds by means of a pair of head suckers, or to make short, wriggling journeys from one plant to another. But when her broad-lipped mouth with its two rows of teeth above and three below finally appeared, she and the rest set out with ravenous appetites to make up for lost time, scraping the tiny green plants from their supports, biting off fragile, tasty bits from the ends of larger ones, and even sucking in minute animals from the ooze at the bottom or the slime at the top. If a dead fish or a worm was found, she joined the hungry crowd about it, shouldering the rest aside and holding her place at the feast by sheer muscular power until sated.

As a result of all this food-taking she had grown mightily. By the end

ike *THIS*

Photos by
HENRY B. KANE

1 IN THE MIDDLE OF A HOP: a toad leaping. Note that the fast camera caught the animal with its eyes shut

of six weeks she was an inch-long tad-pole, black in color with a fine stippling of gold, and breathing now by internal gills instead of the external ones, which had disappeared.

And at this juncture, strange things began to happen to her. Upon each side where her tail joined the body, rounded buds of flesh protruded themselves and grew steadily backwards— the beginnings of her hind legs. Soon joints appeared in these stumps, then toes and feet, and she then began using her newly formed legs along with her tail in swimming. Meanwhile,

internal changes were also occurring. Her long intestine, coiled like a watch spring, began to shorten. And from the front end of her food tube two saclike growths appeared and pushed backward. These were lungs. They were to fit her for land life, and since her internal gills had already begun to fail, she was even then using these new organs, gulping them full of air at every trip to the surface.

Seemingly, she was to have no front legs. But two weeks after the formation of the hind ones, the front pair appeared suddenly. Quite ready for use, they broke through the gill coverings which had concealed their development, and now for the first time, the embryonic toad really looked like a toad. For even before her front legs appeared, her head had changed greatly. Her tiny mouth had been replaced by a huge one, its wide opening extending far back under her eyes, which in turn had become large and elevated and covered with lids, and which appeared bright and beautiful as a toad's eyes should.

But for all these transformations she was still a rather strange creature —a toad well enough, but a toad with a long fishlike tail. Nature soon disposed of this incongruity, however, by allowing her to resorb the tail and use its materials for other purposes. So, freed at last from all semblance of a fish, she was now a complete toad in all respects except warts; they were to come later.

With the loss of her tail, the toad left her pond, with her several thousand brothers and sisters. That is, with those who had come to real toadhood. For although the sticky, jelly covering had protected the eggs well enough for most of them to hatch, the tadpoles had been less fortunate. Once outside the protective jelly, a host of predators had assailed them. Hundreds perished in the masked jaws of ferocious dragonfly larvae, other hundreds were sucked dry of blood by the grooved fangs of the water tigers; and the piercing beaks of the pearl-colored backswimmers had taken a great toll. To say nothing of those gobbled up by the bullheads and the snapping turtles and by the wide beaks of ducks, shoveling the mud of the shallows.

But in spite of all this, when the toad left the water, a whole army went with her, a host of fleshy, cricket-sized mites, hopping hopefully into the wet grass, each in search of a corner in which to live. Many never found that corner, for outside the water there were hungry grackles and hens, and minks, and frogs, and—one of the worst of all the toad's many enemies—the garter snake.

Yet day after day, still managing to escape the fate of her fellows, the toad hopped farther and farther from the water, until she came at last to a place where there was soft earth, and cutworms, and leaf hoppers, and lettuce and radishes, and wide, shady leaves of rhubarb. Here she settled down to live.

Thus the toad came to her garden in the spring.

The garden was the toad's universe. It was a tiny one, but as she prowled it of evenings or early mornings, she became increasingly aware of its texture and problems. It was a universe comprehended in part through her skin, which told her of variations in temperature and moisture, of things rough or smooth, and of those pleasant or painful to touch. As a tadpole, food had often meant a thing of odors; now these played little part in her life. When she did show discrimination, in either taste or smell, it was usually only to reject— sometimes when half-swallowed—certain noxious or foul-smelling bugs. Likewise, her ears told her that sounds played a part in the world. The singing of a cricket brought her a certain emotional and muscular awareness manifested by the quick cocking of her head or a slower rate of respiration.

But most of all, the toad's world was one of objects, of things seen. Her great golden, black-centered eyes gave her sharp images of the medley of forms around her—the plants, the gardener, the dog, garter snakes, other toads, and a whole assemblage of crawling things, the earthworms, the

2   NOTHING MOVING. NOTHING EATEN.
The toad strikes only at a moving object

snails and slugs, and the insects. The toad's daily life was chiefly a complex of responses to these and to things felt through her skin.

Each evening, when the sun had dropped below the western rim and its glare had gone from the earth, the toad emerged from whatever leaf or cranny had concealed her during the daylight hours, and set forth upon a round of the garden. Hunger was the impelling motive of these nightly quests, but she always started off slowly, as if she knew that game was plentiful and that she had plenty of time. After a succession of short hops she would stop dead still and peer keenly about. When prey was sighted, she moved quickly toward it, her gait often changing to an awkward crawl as she drew near. If at the instant she was ready to strike a caterpillar, it suddenly decided as a defensive measure to curl up and play dead, the toad waited patiently until it again showed signs of life. Sometimes, indeed, she gave it up entirely as a dead thing and moved in search of something alive and active. For no matter how hungry she might be, she never struck at a non-moving object. The creatures upon which she fed, of course, didn't know of this strange "nothing moving, nothing eaten" peculiarity of the toad. Hence, when one moved, ever so little, within two inches of her head, her mouth would open, and her marvelous tongue—fastened at the front and free at the rear—would flash forth with the speed of a striking snake, its sticky surface winding about the victim and drawing it swiftly into her wide mouth.

The toad had no teeth, hence everything entered her stomach in the same form it entered her mouth. The swallowing process, unbelievably enough, was greatly aided by her eyes, which invariably rolled deeply inward and backward during the act, thus forcing the struggling creature into her broad gullet. The number of animals captured of a night depended, of course, upon their size. She could swallow 50 ants or more without discomfort, whereas three or four average-size earthworms or several June beetles would temporarily gorge her to repletion. But her strong digestive juices worked rapidly, and if food was plentiful, she often ate enough to fill her stomach completely four times in 24 hours.

The toad's days were much alike. In her life there was probably little joy and little pain, but now and then came something to interrupt her quiet round of living: the gardener or his dog, for example. The gardener often dragged her bodily from her shady retreat to watch her sleepy eyes blink in the blinding sun. Sometimes, too, he carried her to the screen door and laughed as he held her in his hand, watching the house flies disappear like magic to the Lilliputian whipcracker reports of her flashing tongue. Sometimes he teased her by tickling her nose, chuckling gleefully as she low-

ered her head and butted clumsily at the offending straw.

The gardener's dog, also, now and then diverted himself with the toad by fishing her from the soil and barking and poking at her gingerly with tentative paws.

Often she inflated herself hugely as he mauled her, behaving as she did when a small garter snake attacked her. Sometimes, when overturned by his quick paw, she would play possum, lying belly up and quiet as if dead, even her breathing seemingly suspended. Once, when the dog had hurt her with his teeth, she had shown him one way a toad protects herself by giving off into his mouth a whitish fluid from the big glands on the back of her neck, and the memory of its

3 THEN THE AMAZING TONGUE, attached in front and free behind, flashes forth

awful taste had taught him never to take her in his mouth again.

The extreme heat and dryness of summer also affected the toad. She never drank in the manner of other animals; all the water her body required had to come to her through her food or directly by absorption through her skin, this last chiefly from wet plants or the damp soil. Also, since she was cold-blooded, her body warmed or cooled with the rise and fall of the temperature of the earth and air about her. Hence, hot, dry air

and dry soil took water rapidly from her skin and made her miserable, so on such days she burrowed deeply to come to the earth's dampness, and remained hidden until the sun was well down and the dew had fallen.

Four times yearly there came another interregnum. This manifested itself to the toad's awareness by a sort of general tightening and pulling and constriction all over her body, as if her outer skin had become dry and shrunken. This told her that the moulting period had come; so to rid

4 THE TONGUE'S STICKY SURFACE captures the prey, and . . .

herself of her old skin, she would sit with her back strongly arched, head bent downward, and feet drawn under her body. Her outer skin, already loosened beneath, would then split along the midline of head and back and belly, next from side to side at her rear, and lastly from arm to arm across her breast.

After the skin had split along these lines, she freed her hind legs from their covering by bringing them forward and then rubbing them forcibly backward against her belly, all the while opening her mouth widely and expanding her body in a kind of shrugging motion. The whole effect was to drag the loosened skin forward to the corners of her mouth where it was still attached and gradually sucked in. Next she would drag her

front legs free, and then after a few prodigious gulpings she would swallow the skin all in one piece as the final act of the moult. Then as her discomfort passed and her new skin dried and darkened, she would sit erect once more, open her eyes widely, and go on about her living as if nothing unusual had happened.

Each year, usually in October, the toad found herself heavier and slower and sleepier, with less desire to eat, and pervaded by a vague uneasiness. Unknown to her, the fat of her body, a product of her many nightly feastings, had piled itself into two huge orange-colored masses near her kidneys, and sugar from the same source gorged her liver. The fat and sugar were her food reserve. Some of it would be built into the eggs she would

5 THE TIP of it returns to the back of the mouth, and with it the caterpillar

lay in the spring, some would be slowly burned to warm her as she slept. For the time had now come to hibernate.

So, just as in summer she had burrowed backwards into the soil to avoid the heat and dryness, she now backed even deeper into an old burrow or, mayhap, even into a new one, to avoid the frost, boring deeply backwards and downwards until the earth dropped in and covered her head and half-filled the entrance, this later to be plugged yet further with leaves and snow.

Here she slept. As the days grew colder, she grew colder until she was stiff and insensible to her surroundings but never quite frozen. Her heart slowed until her blood barely moved through the vessels; the fires of her life burned low but never quite went out. She was sleeping against time— against the coming of April. Then, when the red-shouldered blackbirds were singing in the swamps, when the cowslips yellowed the meadow, the ferns were unrolling, and the new red leaves of the pond lilies were struggling upwards, she would awaken from her trance, come forth from her cell, cock her head, and listen once more to the shrill voices of male toads calling from the pond.

Then, too, possibly because of these voices and the pressure of the many eggs within her, she would journey again to the pond, place her eggs there in the water, and without once thinking of their further welfare, return again to her home in the garden. This is the way of the toad.

Useful Drugs from Toads?

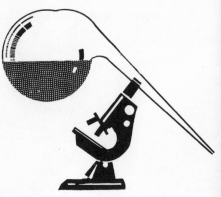

By CHARLES M. BOGERT

Chairman and Curator,
Department of Amphibians and Reptiles,
The American Museum of Natural History

EARLY one morning as I worked along the edge of a river on the west coast of Mexico, I noticed a small boy following me. He watched with obvious interest while I occasionally extracted a huge toad from beneath a boulder. As I dropped a specimen into a sack, he stared with amazement and then commented, *"Echan leche* (They throw milk)."

I realized that it was a pertinent observation. As a small boy, I too had pinched the large glands behind the heads of toads and watched the droplets of whitish liquid ooze out. In fact, I'd gotten some of the liquid on my lips and had found that it was extremely bitter and unpleasant to taste. It was fortunate that a drop of the liquid had not landed in my eye. This can be a painful experience and may even cause temporary blindness, for the thick, milky fluid is a potent poison.

Presumably it is the warty skin of the toad that has given rise to the myth that "toads give warts." Actually the protuberances on the

The creature unjustly accused of causing warts now finds a place in the sun as a possible teammate in the fight against circulatory ailments

skin of the toad are poison glands. They are the toad's solution to the problem of keeping from being devoured. The leaping ability of most frogs and many other tailless amphibians protects them from enemies. During his long evolution, the relatively slow-moving toad has

◄ THE GIANT TOAD being milked of its venom in the interests of medical science

With photographs by
R. E. Atkinson

come to depend less upon his muscles and more upon being distasteful. As many a would-be predator has learned to his sorrow, a toad in the mouth can be downright dangerous.

If left alone, few animals are

less obnoxious—or more beneficial to the garden—than the toad. But if the animal is seized or mistreated, for example by a dog, its poison is brought into play. It pours out on the surface of the skin, particularly from the larger glands (called the parotoid glands) behind the head. After an encounter with a toad, a dog or other animal may froth at the mouth or even vomit. In extreme cases, death may ensue, particularly when one of the larger species of toads is involved.

From the earliest times, toads have been regarded as venomous. In the Talmud, the toad is distinguished from the frog and classified with animals whose touch contaminates. Shakespeare speaks of the toad as "ugly and venomous," and the name *calamita* (from the same root as our word "calamity") was applied to a European toad in 1768. A Brazilian in 1878 observed that in his country there existed a toad, "a veritable giant — whose venom would be worth while to study. It is very probable that this is the species from which the aborigines of the Amazon derive the poison with which they smear the points of their arrows, in place of a sort of curare that certain other tribes use."

Experiments carried out by pharmacologists three decades later confirmed the Brazilian's belief. In 1912, two men working at Johns Hopkins University, John J. Abel and David I. Macht, concluded that the poison of the Giant Toad would indeed be a very deadly one when used as an arrow poison. However, their primary interest in the animal's excretions lay in their search for useful drugs. Since prehistoric times, people have realized that poisons may have medicinal value. The Chinese have long used a preparation derived from toad skins as a remedy for various diseases. As early as 1672, "powdered toad" was recommended by pharmacologists in Europe as a cure for dropsy, nosebleed, and other ailments.

Encouraged by their knowledge of these ancient usages, Abel and Macht undertook an analysis of the excretions from the enormous glands of the large American toad. They found that they could isolate two principles. One was an amino alcohol, with properties similar to drugs formerly used to stop bleeding as well as in the treatment of shock. The other one they called "bufagin," noting that it had many tonic and diuretic properties similar to those of digitalis, a drug long in medicinal use. They concluded that the chemical purity, keeping qualities, and other properties of bufagin warranted trial usages of the substance for medicinal purposes.

More recently research workers with the National Heart Institute have renewed the search for useful elements in the Giant Toad's venom. With more refined techniques than those available 40 years ago, they have discovered a substance in the venom of the Giant Toad that is identical with one called serotonin, found only a few years ago to be present in the blood of human beings. Prior to their finding serotonin in toad venom, it had only been possible to isolate relatively small quantities from hundreds of tons of beef blood. In human beings it is held captive in the colorless discs in the blood called platelets, but when injury ruptures the plate-

▲ WHEN the large parotoid gland is squeezed, the poison spurts out.
It serves to protect the toad against enemies; substances
derived from it may protect man against disease

lets, serotonin is released in minute quantities, causing the walls of the blood vessels to contract. Seemingly it is involved in the normal mechanism that stops bleeding.

Thus serotonin, available in large quantities in the venom of the Giant Toad, may be put to use in the treatment of human ailments. It is a potent substance, and research is now being carried on with radioactive "tags" attached to one of the carbon atoms in serotonin in an effort to discover whether it is involved in the chemical processes of the body that are upset when diseased conditions occur.

Doubtless much work remains to be done, but once again the "ugly toad" may contribute to man's wellbeing. The venom that protects the toad from its enemies may provide a substance that will protect man from his worst enemy—disease.

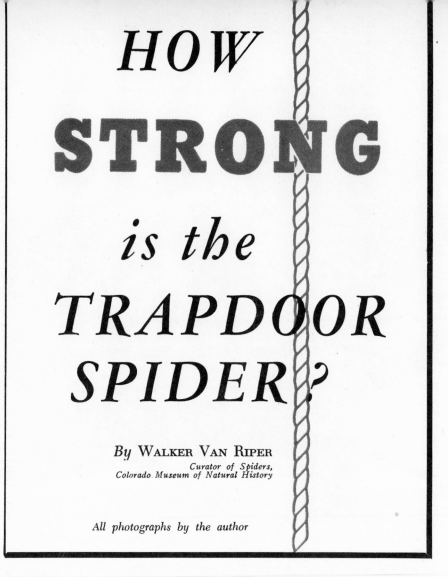

HOW STRONG

is the

TRAPDOOR SPIDER?

By WALKER VAN RIPER

Curator of Spiders,
Colorado Museum of Natural History

All photographs by the author

ONE of the accounts of the common trapdoor spider of southern California (*Bothriocyrtum californicum*) states that it can hold its door closed against a pull as great as ten pounds. This estimate had always seemed excessive to me, and as one of the spiders I had under observation was a vigorous "holder-downer," I decided to try measuring and recording the force.

The high speed photographic flash developed by Professor H. E. Edgerton of Massachusetts Institute of Technology is a remarkable instrument for taking extremely rapid pictures of small creatures at close range. It was with this sort of apparatus that I was able to take the photographs reproduced here. They show not only the measurement of the spider's strength but also its actions in emerging from its trap door, seizing a beetle, and disappearing with it underground. Exposures as short as 1/30,000 second are pos-

▼ A BEETLE has been placed near the door built by the trapdoor spider. When the spider opens the door, contact will be made with the wires visible at upper right and the super-speed flash will be set off, taking the picture. The actual width of the door is 1¼ inches

▼ THE SPIDER within its lair is just opening the trap door

▲Here the super-speed camera catches the spider in the act of seizing the beetle

▲ If the trap door is lifted with a sliver of wood, the spider comes up to pull it down

sible with the high speed flash. The light has high actinic value, so that, when used close to the subject, the lens may be stopped down to f:22 or f:32, thus giving the greatest possible depth of focus.

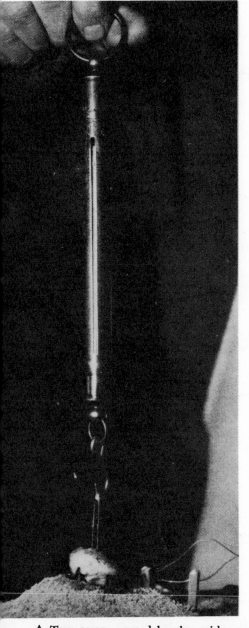

Two wires that can be seen in the first picture were arranged to make a contact and set off the light the instant the spider opened the trap door the right amount. Since the spider is mainly nocturnal in habit, the problem was simple. The shutter of the camera could remain open any reasonable length of time without spoiling the film, and the flash could be regulated to occur at any desired instant. The spider, a female, really took her own portrait.

The next to the last photograph shows her pulling the door shut against the resistance offered by a sliver of wood. It can be seen that she grasps the door around its circumference with the tarsal claws, evidently wedging her body and cephalothorax across the passageway to furnish anchorage. To measure her strength, I drilled two holes in the door and threaded through them a loop of string. The fine wires making the switch were fixed so that the camera and flash would be set off when the door was lifted about an eighth of an inch, this being just before the moment at which experience indicated the spider would let go. Then the door was lifted with the spring scales and the pull recorded.

A force of fourteen ounces was indicated,—nothing like the reputed ten pounds, but a good strong pull, just the same. As the spider weighs about one-tenth of an ounce, the force is 140 times the spider's own weight. For a 150-pound man, the equivalent would be 21,000 pounds, or over 10 tons!

ᴧ THE PULL·exerted by the spider measures 14 ounces, the equivalent of a 150-pound man pulling 10 tons

RAREST TREE

PORT ORFORD CEDAR

WEEPING SPRUCE

REDWOOD

MONTEREY PI

MONTEREY CYPRESS

BIGTREE

BRISTLECONE FIR

TORREY PINE

BIGCONE SPRUCE

Draw by LAURENCE BLAIR

THESE rare trees were chosen through consultation with
ten leading experts. There are other rare trees in the
United States, but they either extend over a larger range to
the south of us or do not differ strikingly from commoner
species. The trees selected do not grow in any other country
in the world.

Justifiable pride is shown in rare trees wherever they grow,
and many travelers journey far to see them. It is hoped that
through this presentation, persons who otherwise might not
become acquainted with them, may notice and enjoy these
living forms, whose seeds contain 200 million years of evolutionary history, though their range is now limited, in some
cases to a few hundred acres.

In the struggle to survive and develop, they have had to
contend with many enemies. Climatic changes have frequently dictated death or decimation. Other forms of life, all
striving to wrest a living from the available land, have forced
them back. Man himself is probably their greatest enemy.
Many trees have been eliminated in this age-old struggle. If
these are exterminated, they will never return, for evolution
does not reverse itself.

CORKWOOD

FLORIDA YEW

FRANKLINIA

STINKING CEDAR

J. Horace McFarland photo

Fred Hess & Son photo

THE "LOST"

FRANKLINIA

Photos courtesy of Elizabeth C. White,
Joseph J. White, Inc.,
Whitesbog, N. J.

THIS TREE (*Franklinia alatamaha* Marshall) has not been found growing in the wild anywhere since 1790. One day in the autumn of 1765, John Bartram, a friend of Benjamin Franklin's, was exploring in the woods of southeastern Georgia. Somewhere along the Altamaha River in the vicinity of Fort Barrington, he found a beautiful tree, whose gorgeous blossoms, over three inches in diameter, resembled those of the camellia. Recognizing its extraordinary beauty and value, the plant explorer made other visits to the spot and introduced the tree into his own famous garden in Philadelphia, naming it after his celebrated friend.

In 1790 the original grove of Franklinia trees was visited for the last time; for from that day to this, though many expeditions have searched, no one has seen this tree growing in the wild. All the known descendants, growing in cultivation, have come down to us from the specimens brought to Philadelphia over a century and a half ago in an overloaded saddlebag.

The smooth, dark gray bark, covering a slender trunk and graceful, sinewy branches has been likened to a greyhound's satin skin. The tree starts blooming when no more than three or four feet high and attains a height of 15 or 20 feet, even 30 feet in extreme cases. From about the middle of September there is a constant succession of blossoms until hard frost. Frequently even after the foliage has turned an autumn crimson the tree remains abundantly starred with white flowers.

The fact that Franklinia prefers an acid soil was discovered by the late Dr. Frederick V. Colville, Chief Botanist of the U. S. Department of Agriculture, working in collaboration with Miss Elizabeth C. White. The Franklinia prefers full sun and has proved entirely hardy about New York and in favorable locations about Boston. It is regarded as a desirable tree for small gardens and thrives when planted by pools and streams.

FLORIDA YEW

THIS TREE *(Taxus floridana* Chapman) grows in the same section of Florida as the Stinking Cedar, but is even rarer. It sometimes attains a height of 25 feet, with numerous stout, spreading branches above a short trunk, which is occa-sionally a foot in diameter. But it is characteristically shrubby in growth and more often reaches a height of twelve to fifteen feet, frequently spread-ing out on the ground.

Its flowers appear in March, and the fruit ripens in October. The wood is heavy, dark, and very close-grained, with nearly white sapwood.

Devereux Butcher photo

Drawing by Annie E. Hoyle, Courtesy of U. S. Forest Service

THE LIGHTEST WOOD IN THE UNITED STATES

NOT FAR from the original home of the Franklinia tree in Georgia can be seen the rare Corkwood tree *(Leitneria floridana* Chapman), which also grows in a few isolated groves elsewhere as shown on the map introducing this article. Rarely described in popular books on trees, this 20-foot shrub or small tree has a slender, straight trunk four to five inches in diameter, branching into a loose, open head. Its bark, about $\frac{1}{16}$ inch thick, is dark gray and faintly tinged with brown, and is divided by shallow fis-sures into narrow, rounded ridges. Annual growth rings are hardly distinguishable in the pale yellow wood. Exceedingly light and close-grained, it is occasionally used for the floats of fishing nets. The leaves are four to six inches long, and the flowers open at the end of February or early in March.

Drawing by Annie E. Hoyle, Courtesy of U. S. Forest Service

STINKING CEDAR

Photos by Florida Forest and Park Service

THE RARE Florida Torreya *(Tumion taxifolium* [Arnott] Greene) is a worthy member of the aristocracy of rare trees because it is confined at the most to a comparatively small number of trees scattered over a 20-mile range. The fact that its sap, crushed needles, and the juice from the seed

BIGCONE SPRUCE

Photo by U. S. Forest Service

cone give off an odor resembling that of green tomatoes, has led to its common name, Stinking Cedar.

In about 1834 a young planter and amateur botanist by the name of Hardy Croom, while traveling to a plantation that he owned in Jackson County, was obliged to wait for a ferry to cross the Apalachicola River. Viewing the nearby landscape that was then an almost roadless wilderness, his attention was drawn to a wooded slope on which grew a grove of evergreen trees that differed from any he had previously observed.

On his return trip, he collected specimens for study. Unable to identify them in his books, he sent samples to Dr. John Torrey, of Columbia College, the outstanding botanist of the day. Torrey reported that the tree was a totally new genus never before recorded.

Fortunately the Florida Torreya, unlike the Franklinia tree, has survived to the present, though its range along the east bank of the Apalachicola River and in the vicinity of Dog Pond, Jackson County, is extremely limited.

The tree seldom attains a diameter of ten inches or a height of more than 50 feet. The branches and twigs are lined with flat, stiff needles about an inch and a half long. The wood is yellow and hard, and is prized by the natives for fence posts, for which it is all too commonly cut. The protection of this unique tree should be ensured by stricter laws than are now in force. The existence of the Torreya State Park in Liberty County gives the only prospect for its preservation.

Hardy Croom, the discoverer of the tree, is said to have planted the specimen shown in the accompanying photograph on the State Capitol grounds at Tallahassee.

(*Information by courtesy of William F. Jacobs and the* Journal of the Florida Education Association)

Drawing by
Mary Robeson Sargent

THIS WORTHY RARITY *(Pseudotsuga macrocarpa* [Torrey] Mayr) occupies steep rocky mountain slopes at elevations of between 3000 and 5000 feet in limited sections of southern California. It is valuable for its adaptability to situations too dry for most other trees, rather than as firewood, for which it is unfortunately largely used. The trunk of the Bigcone Spruce is also utilized by California woodpeckers, who drill into it extensively for the storing of acorns.

The Bigcone Spruce is usually 40 to 50 feet tall, rarely 90 feet, with a trunk three to four feet in diameter. Its wood is heavy but not durable, and is consequently not desirable as lumber. The tree is most serviceable as a protective cover in semiarid mountainous regions at lower elevations, mostly on the sides of canyons.

AMERICA'S RAREST PINE

A STRIP OF TERRITORY eight miles long and less than two miles wide along the mouth of the Soledad River in southern California is the only continental range of the Torrey Pine *(Pinus torreyana* Carrière), though it grows on the island of Santa Rosa and is now planted in the parks of San Diego and in New Zealand.

While it is usually a small tree 20 to 40 feet high, it sometimes attains a height of 60 feet, and under cultivation it promises even greater size than on its native cliffs. Its large, edible seeds are gathered in quantities and eaten raw or roasted. The wood is light, coarse-grained, and not strong; and there is little demand for it, except now and then as fuel.

Drawing by Mary Robeson Sargent

THE WORLD'S TALLEST TREE

THE ORNAMENTAL
BRISTLECONE FIR

Drawing by
Mary Robeson Sargent

From Unsere Freiland-Nadelhölzer,
by Count Silva Tarouca and C. Schneider

THIS TREE *(Abies venusta* [Douglas] K. Koch), with handsome, dark green foliage, is restricted to the outer rim of the Santa Lucia Mountains in Monterey County, California, usually at elevations of about 3000 feet. Trees 30 to 100 feet high are normal, but a height of 150 feet is possible, and the trunk may reach a diameter of three feet. The Bristlecone Fir is occasionally and successfully grown as an ornamental tree in the milder parts of Great Britain and in northern Italy, but it is not hardy in the eastern United States. The wood, light brown tinged with yellow, is heavy, coarse-grained, and not hard.

A SEED scarcely larger than a pinhead is the beginning of the world's tallest tree, the majestic Redwood *(Sequoia sempervirens* [Lambert] Endlicher), which sometimes grows to a height of over 350 feet. The trunk may be as much as 28 feet in diameter and is usually free of branches for 75 to 100 feet. Redwood bark is from six inches to a foot thick.

The Redwood is native to the fog belt along the coast ranges from the southwestern corner of Oregon to Monterey County, California, from ten to 30 miles inland. It is rarely found over 3000 feet above sea level. Specimens about 3000 years old are known.

The wood of the Redwood, from whose color the tree gets its name, takes a fine finish and is of great commercial importance. Durable in contact with the soil, it is light, soft, and close-grained.

Though not strong, it is easily split and worked. Its satiny luster makes it a favorite for fancy furniture and bric-a-brac, while good shingles, fence posts, and railway ties can also be made of it. A concerted effort has fortunately been made, however, to conserve the Redwood, and lumber companies are to be commended for the farsighted policies they have adopted for the preservation of this unequalled giant among trees.

The Redwood grows rapidly and is often cultivated as an ornamental tree in the temperate countries of Europe and occasionally in the southeastern United States.

THE WORLD'S
LARGEST TREE

EXCEEDING THE REDWOOD IN GIRTH, though a trifle under it in stature, the Bigtree of California *(Sequoia washingtoniana* [Winslow] Sudworth) is probably the mightiest living work of Nature. This species is a living descendant from the Age of Dinosaurs and once thrived in great forests in central and northern Europe and in mid-continental America, even to the Arctic Circle. But its range has not spread since the Glacial period, and it is now limited to a number of groves totalling an area of only about 50 square miles, scattered along a 250-mile strip on the seaward slopes of the Sierra Nevadas in central California.

The first white men to see a California Bigtree were most likely the members of Captain Joseph R. Walker's party in 1833. The first report was scoffed at as a wild tale from the Golden West. Color was lent to it by the statement that because there were no seedlings nor young trees, these must be the last specimens of a vanishing race.

The name was taken from a wise Cherokee Indian, Sequoyah, who in 1821 invented the Cherokee alphabet of 85 characters, by means of which the *New Testament* and a newspaper were published for his people.

The giant Sequoias are usually about 275 feet high at maturity, but have been known to reach 320 feet. The trunk ranges from 20 to 35 feet in diameter, and in an old tree is often naked for half the total height. The bark itself may be as much as two feet thick. The gigantic bulk of a single Bigtree is sufficient to produce enough lumber to build a village of 150 five-room houses, yet it all grows from a seed $\frac{1}{8}$ to $\frac{1}{4}$ inch long. The root system of a mature Sequoia spreads over an area of between two and three acres.

So long is the life of the Sequoias that trees which sprang from the soil before Greece and Rome rose to greatness and even before Tutankhamen reigned in Egypt may still be growing. The average age of the big Sequoias is probably about 2500 years, but stumps now standing show 4000 annual rings, and competent authorities have estimated the age limit to be above 5000 years. Measurement of the growth rings, which vary in width according to the amount of rainfall and other climatic factors, has yielded important information about climatic changes through the ages.

Almost every mature Bigtree has been struck by lightning, but no ordinary bolt seriously injures one of these giants. Fire may repeatedly attack it, charring away a large proportion of the bark or eating out as much as 200 feet of its vitals, yet it still lives on. The wood is very light, coarse-grained, and brittle. Even though days may be spent in preparing a soft bed on which it may fall, one of these Goliaths weighing hundreds of tons is usually shattered into unmerchantable lengths when felled. Wood of the Bigtree has been used for shingles, fencing, and in general construction.

A grove of Bigtrees is surely a place where the Romans would have placed their inscription: *Numen inest*—"God is in this place."

Drawings by
Mary Robeson
Sargent

AMERICA'
RARES'
SPRUC

Drawing by
Mary Robeson Sargent

Photo by U. S. Forest Service

DROOPING BRANCHLETS four to eight feet long hanging from the parent branch give the Weeping Spruce *(Picea breweriana* S. Watson) its name and distinctive form. The small section to which it is restricted in northwestern California and southwestern Oregon is not much more than 100 miles from north to south and even narrower from east to west. Perhaps more interesting still is the fact that the range is restricted vertically as well as horizontally: the tree grows only between the altitudes of 4000 and 8000 feet.

A pioneer California scientist, William H. Brewer, was attracted to this then unknown tree, whose drooping branches add charm to so many vistas of lakes and mountains where it grows. In 1863 he collected the first specimen, but since the cones were missing, the Weeping Spruce was not permanently brought to light until 1884, by Thomas Howell.

The tree seldom attains a greater height than 100 feet, though specimens 125 feet tall have been mentioned. The trunk is about two or three feet in diameter above the enlarged base, and in the open is crowded with branches to the ground. The wood is heavy, soft, and close-grained. It is of no commercial importance.

Recent inclusion of the home of the Weeping Spruce in a Primitive Area of the U. S. Forest Service should give this rare tree the protection from future danger that it deserves.

C. Edward Graves photo

MONTEREY PINE

THIS RARE TREE *(Pinus radiata* D. Don), whose distribution on the mainland is restricted to a narrow strip a few miles wide on the California coast from Pescadero to the vicinity of Cambria, is an exception to the other trees in this collection in that it is found in one place outside the territory of United States, on the island of Guadaloupe off Lower California. It is also found on the California islands of Santa Rosa and Santa Cruz.

It is a large tree, reaching a height of 100 feet or more, with a trunk possibly five or six feet in diameter. Planted successfully in parks and gardens, its quick growth destines it for popularity with landscape gardeners wherever the climate is mild enough in winter. Its wood is soft, close-grained, and weak, and is sometimes used as fuel. It has proved valuable for forestry purposes, particularly in Australia.

Drawing by
Mary Robeson Sargent

Photo by
U. S. Forest Service

MONTEREY CYPRESS

Harry E. Rieseberg photo

PORT ORFORD CEDAR

ONE OF THE MOST BEAUTIFUL of the larger cone-bearing trees is the Port Orford Cedar *(Chamaecyparis lawsoniana* [A. Murray] Parlatore). Limited to the coast mountains of Oregon and California, it occupies a strip no more than about 200 miles long and extending rarely more than 40 miles inland.

This unique cedar is a spire-like forest tree growing to a height of 200 feet, with a trunk sometimes as much as twelve feet in diameter.

The 20-mile belt of Port Orford Cedars near the mouth of the Coquille River in Oregon presents a sight that has thrilled many visitors. The feathery, almost lacy, appearance of this "handsomest of the conifers" and its sharply slanting limbs give it so distinctive an appearance that its identification is easy.

The wood is hard and light, and has a pleasant aromatic odor. Very durable under exposure of any kind, it has extremely high commercial value, being used in house-finishing, flooring, boat-building, railway ties, and fence posts. Port Orford Cedar is also prized for the manufacture of battery cases and is extensively exported for making venetian blinds. It is ironic that the wood of this rare tree has been used extensively in the manufacture of matches, a symbol of so much forest destruction.

Drawing by Mary Robeson Sargent

Photo by U. S. Forest Service

THE LAST STAND of this twisted tree *(Cupressus macrocarpa* Gordon) in its native state is limited to an area of about two miles long and 200 yards wide south of the Bay of Monterey, California, with a small grove on Point Lobos nearby. The crumbling bluffs of the shore are gradually being undermined by the waves, and though the gnarled roots of these trees range wide for a foothold, the trees in the front rank seem destined to go down one by one. It is possible that the last of these trees in their native soil will eventually be swept out of existence.

However, the Monterey Cypress has been cultivated for hedges, windbreaks, and as park trees, and is fairly widely grown along the Pacific coast, though it has lately been attacked by a fungus disease. It is occasionally planted in the southeastern states and is common in western and southern Europe, temperate South America, and in Australia and New Zealand.

The Monterey Cypress attains a height of from 40 to 75 feet and in old age becomes picturesquely gnarled and flat-topped.

What is a TRILOBITE?

By JOHN H. GERARD
Photographs by the author

You may find one in rocks that were laid down beneath the sea 195 million years or more ago. Here are a few facts about their life and times

◄ A FINE SPECIMEN, with most of its parts intact. This *Flexicalymene* is an average-sized trilobite. But *Terataspis* reached a length of 27 inches.

eton, rather than the whole animal; the underside is usually embedded in rock, with only the back surface protruding.

Over 1200 species of trilobites have been named, and there is great variation among them. Some had spines and bizarre ornamentation, others were smooth. All have been extinct for about 195 million years.

Because of their abundance, trilobites are useful to geologists in indexing rock layers, and there is a large technical literature on them.

IF YOU have had anything to do with fossils, there is a good chance you have seen a trilobite. They were quite abundant in some of the early periods of earth history, at a time when there were no animals with backbones and few large ones of any kind. Most of the trilobites were only a few inches long, but some measured as much as 27 inches. Their legs were delicate and have rarely been preserved.

Many areas of the United States were once covered by seas in which the trilobites lived. For millions of years they roamed these waters nearly unmolested. Then the fishes evolved, and though many of the trilobites are thought to have been able to roll up in their shells like a ball, they were no doubt eaten by fish. Their skeletons were on the outside of their bodies, and they shed them periodically. So what we find is usually the fossilized exoskel-

A nearly perfect trilobite (*Phillipsia portlocki*), from the Crawfordsville, Indiana, crinoid beds

▼ FINDING TRILOBITES. Geologists determine age of rocks by trilobites and other small fossils as much as by the more dramatic large ones.

The eyesight of trilobites varied. In some, the eyes were constructed of hexagonal sections, while in others they were on stalks, somewhat as in modern crabs. Some apparently had no eyes, while others had eyes with 15,000 facets.

Trilobites are thought to have laid eggs, and objects that may be fossilized trilobite eggs have been found. The first immature stage after hatching was free-swimming and probably looked like the nauplius stage of modern primitive crustaceans. As growth progressed, the outgrown exoskeleton was repeatedly cast off. Trilobites seem to have been creatures of the salt water. Neither fresh-water nor land forms have been found. Modern crabs, lobsters, and crayfish may have descended from the same common ancestor as the trilobites.

Trilobites are thought to have fed on other invertebrates and plants, and some were probably scavengers. Some tunneled through muddy bottoms. In any case, it has been a long time since any of them lived. But there were so many of them and they fossilized so well that you may easily find one if you look in the proper location. Some amateurs, in fact, have made large collections.

LIMESTONE BLUFFS along the Mississippi and its branches have yielded many trilobites. This site is near Alton, Ill. At left: Four *Flexicalymenes* from which excess rock has been expertly chipped.

Pets from Tropical Waters

An introduction to some of the beautiful and interesting fishes that are popular among those who keep home aquaria

By CHRISTOPHER W. COATES

The New York Aquarium

THE keeping of small tropical fish had its inception in Europe in 1869, when a traveler, attracted by the remarkable nesting habits of little fish of the rice fields of China, sent a few to France as novelties. Thereafter, a few fishes from time to time captured the fancies of other trave ers, until now there are scores of mer versed in fish lore, scouring the tropics waters of the world for fishes which ar suitable inhabitants of a container c several gallons capacity. An industr which is rapidly assuming major propo tions is founded on the efforts of thes collectors—the manufacture of aquaria

thermometers, fish food, nets, and specially constructed electrical lighting and heating equipment. This is employing more and more factories, and the distribution of these articles as well as of the fishes is the support of a small army of people. With almost every fast passenger ship from Europe carrying at least a few cans of fish, the importation of these little animals is great, but the

Photographs by S. C. DUNTON, *courtesy the New York Aquarium*

A PAIR OF SMALL
SPOTTED BARBS

◄ STATELY SCALARES swim among sprigs of water sprite, *Vallisneria,* and *Cryptocoryne* in a small aquarium

THE SAIL-FIN, *MOLLIENISIA VELIFERA*
One of the live-bearing tooth-carps, wherein the males are frequently more ornamented than the females, in this species with an enlarged backfin

importers are facing considerable competition from the breeders of the fishes, for many of the fish breed freely in the small aquaria to which they are consigned and there are many establishments wholly devoted to the breeding and wholesale sale of tropical fish in this country.

To the person who is at all inclined toward natural history, these fishes appeal in the *nth* degree, for their form, color, habits and the ease with which they are studied are arresting, and frequently startling. It is not so easy to account for the popularity of the fishes where the amateur aquarist has no leaning to natural history. Perhaps it is because the fishes come from places with romantic names, and the devotees experience a vicarious thrill of travel by transplanting some of the fauna of Siam or the Cameroons into their drawing rooms; or perhaps the aquar-

ist is pleased with his rôle of sole arbiter of the lives and deaths of his finny pets!

The fishes themselves are really remarkable creatures. Of a vast diversity of shape, they are of every color in the spectrum, and while many of them are related, there are scarcely any that duplicate the habits of their cousins. Some of them are fierce, unapproachable beasts, in spite of their small size, while others are as peaceful as a flock of sheep. The main difference between them, however, is in their courting and nesting habits, which range all the way from a casual mating, lasting but a few seconds, to an association lasting for weeks, and sometimes months, during which period the infant fishes receive a maximum of parental solicitude.

It is a curious, and perhaps a significant fact that while the fishes under considera-

A PAIR OF SIAMESE FIGHTING FISHES
It is said that in Siam males of this fish are pitted against one another like game cocks

tion were named and classified primarily on taxonomic characters, these rather artificial and arbitrary divisions are followed through by what, for want of a better name, we shall call the mental lives of the animals. For instance, we do not know of any species of carp which exhibits the slightest interest in its own eggs or young, except as a possible meal, while all the cichlids of which we have any knowledge, devote a considerable amount of their time and energy to the raising of one family after another, tending them against all sorts of possible and impossible enemies. These fishes, for instance, will attack the hand of a man which approaches their nest too closely until the young fish are half as large as the parents. In fact, to such an extent has the care of the eggs and young of this family proceeded, that there are many species of African cichlids that carry the fertilized eggs about in their mouths until they hatch—a matter of about three weeks, during which time the parent takes no food at all. The buccal sanctuary is not closed against the fry after they are hatched, for the parent will allow them to swim about her until danger threatens, then will open her mouth again for the youngsters to enter and remain until in the judgment of the parent, there is no further danger to them. Such parental solicitude is not confined to one sex. Sometimes it is the male which carries the eggs about and sometimes the female, and each is perfectly content, as far as any indications show, with what the other is doing.

The American cichlids—this family occurs mainly in South America and Africa although there are one or two representatives in southern Asia—do not carry their eggs about, but deposit them

A BARB (*Barbus*) FROM SOUTHERN ASIA
This is one of many species of similar fishes found in water tanks and such places in India and adjacent regions. Their small size, attractive coloring, and activity make them well suited to the aquarium

in a nest guarded by both parents until the babies hatch. Then the whole family, sometimes numbering several hundred, is carefully escorted about their

THE VICIOUS PIRANHA
One of the so-called cannibal fishes of South American rivers. Their rather small mouths are set with very powerful teeth

aquarium, each straggler being immediately returned to the school. This goes on for weeks and woe to any fish of even twice the size of the parents that approaches the small cloud of young fish. The parent fishes will turn and rend the intruder with the utmost ferocity.

What social or racial consciousness prompts such self-sacrifice on the part of these fishes is hard to imagine, for there are many other fishes, just as successful biologically, which scatter their eggs about haphazardly, and with no knowledge or consciousness of parental care.

The species which are kept in aquaria, quite free of the obvious dangers to which the youngsters may be exposed, continue in their elaborate precautions against the onslaught of other fishes, although the parent fishes must know that there are no other fishes in the aquarium. The habits seem, therefore, to be blind and unthinking.

From another family that does not ordinarily pay much attention to its eggs or young, comes a fish with another example of care of the spawn, although we do not know that this species devotes any time to the preservation of the young after the eggs have hatched. This is *Copeina arnoldi*, a characinid. For a reason not at all clear to our philosophy, the fish deposits its eggs above the water-line, on a convenient leaf or stone, the pair leaping up together for the actual spawning. Sometimes two or more deposits of eggs are made during the same spawning, after which the female goes about her affairs as though there were no such thing as an egg in the world. Not so the male. He spends the next two days or so splashing water up' on to the eggs every few minutes, hiding a short space away during the intervals when he is not watering the eggs. The next splashing after the eggs hatch washes the baby fish

THE GLASS-FISH
A native of Southern Asia. These fishes are so translucent that their internal structure is plainly visible

into their rightful element, and the male fish then pays them no further attention. Again this remarkable habit is carried over from the wild into the aquarium,

THE SCALARE
An ornamental fish from Brazil belonging to the cichlid family. American cichlids guard their eggs and young

although we do not know why. It may be that the eggs require a certain amount of desiccation, but if so we would be put to it somewhat to explain how it is that the fish discovered this unusual requirement!

These various habits are not, of course, confined to the little fishes which inhabit our drawing-room aquaria. They are to be found, in one fashion or another, wherever fishes are studied, but the fact that the aquarium fish will live, court, and die, without any major adjustments, in our small glass tanks, has added an invaluable tool to science, and an amazingly popular introduction to natural history to the layman, who, until he purchases his first pair of guppies, is completely, and perhaps happily, unaware of such occurences. After he has established his first guppy, he is usually on the way to establishing an aquarium limited only by the space available, or the size of his purse, for what is more natural than that he should, after watching his female fish deliver twenty or thirty living babies

and then eat them immediately, acquire another aquarium to use as a nursery. Then he exchanges tales of his fish with other people equally interested, and they recommend the addition of this or that fish, for its interesting habits or its color or some other peculiarity, and then the process is repeated. He has often to find room for another tank or two.

It may be news to many people that there are fishes which have living babies. There is one whole family of such fishes, all of which occur in the Americas or the adjacent islands, and there are many other fishes, not exactly aquarium specimens, which have the same interesting habit. Some of the sharks are viviparous, as well as a few skates, but our concern is with the small fishes which may be easily kept in the facilities available in every home.

The "live-bearers," so-called because they have families of little fishes instead of depositing eggs about the tank to hatch at a later period, are all small fellows,

THE BLACK-BANDED POECILID, *LIMIA NIGROFASCIATA*
One of the so-called "live-bearers," which have families of little fishes instead of depositing eggs

A GYMNOTID EEL FROM SOUTH AMERICA
There are a number of species of these strange eels, related to the larger electric eel which is capable of giving a powerful electric shock

some of which are very beautifully colored. They are considerably tolerant of the abuse they frequently receive, and they reproduce with amazing rapidity. Most of them are mature at six months or less, when they start delivering broods of youngsters every month or so with little or no effort on the part of the fish fancier. The little fellows, hardy and adaptable, grow rapidly, but they seem to disappear with equal rapidity, for the fanciers, in spite of the number of young ones they raise in their own tanks, tax the tanks of the professional fish breeders to their utmost. At least, there is a continual demand for even the commonest of these little fishes. It is true, no doubt, that many of the young are used to feed other rarer fishes which refuse to eat prepared foods, preferring to catch their own meals on the fin, so to speak, but the keepers of such carnivores are a very small minority of the total of fish fanciers, so we still cannot account for the disappearance of so many little fishes. It is hard to find an aquarist who will admit that he loses fishes

for any reason, unless his tanks are in danger of decimation from some cause he cannot understand. Then he calls for assistance, of course.

This is not always easily given, in spite of the best will in the world, for there are so many causes for death of any animal, and it is so difficult to trace the original cause to its source, that only the most general advice may be repeated, with general hints as to the best maintenance of the tank as a unit.

While these various types of care of the young were developing in the western world, another remarkable nesting habit was developing in the East. This is the very curious nest of the labyrinth fishes, a floating raft of air bubbles manufactured by the fish into which the eggs are thrust as they are liberated. The eggs are not deposited in the nest, but deliberately placed there by the male parent. The female will do this if she is allowed by the male, but he is usually so much larger and fiercer than she is, and so jealous of his prerogatives, that she is invariably driven

THE PIKE–LIKE *BELONESOX*
One of the live-bearing tooth-carps from Central America with the shape and predacious habits of a pike

the price of the latter has dropped from about thirty dollars a pair to three dollars or so in the past few years. A good specimen is a truly spectacular fellow. The body may be deep blue, or red, green, or fleshy pink, and the fins, of an even more intense color than the

away from the vicinity of the nest, and returns at considerable peril. If, for any reason, she can get a few eggs, she will do so, and will watch that they do not fall out of the small nest she will build, much as will the male, but her efforts are not as constant as those of the male.

The curious part of the whole affair is that the baby fish hatch just as well without attention as they do under the constant ministrations of their father, and the little creatures, when they are hatched, are just as likely as not to make a meal for the parent fish.

There are several species of this family suitable for keeping in home aquaria. The paradise fish which was sent from China to France during the last century, the forerunner of all pet tropical fish, is one example. The widely known Siamese fighting fish is another. These fishes breed freely in small domestic tanks, so freely, in fact, that

body, are flowing banners, bigger than the fish itself. Such gorgeous creatures as these are the product of the aquarium. The wild fish are not nearly as large; they do not have the large fins, and while a suggestion of great color is apparent, the fish is usually a dark, nondescript color not at all pleasing to the eye.

What brought this fish into notice was not the color, but the amazing pugnacity of the beast. Stories are current that in Siam two males of this species are thrown into the same tank and left to fight it out between them, wagers being laid on the result. However, the fancy aquarium-bred fishes are not nearly so

THE CLIMBING PERCH
It is said that this inhabitant of southern Asia comes out of water after a shower of rain and invades gardens in search of earthworms

ZEBRA FISH, *BRACHYDANIO RERIO*
From India. An attractive, active member of the carp-minnow family, long a favorite in aquaria

vicious. They do fight between themselves on occasion, but the fighting is more or less confined to snipping bits of each others' fins. While this is not dangerous to the life of the animal, it spoils his looks, for the fins regenerate showing scar tissue which ruins the clear sweep of the rays of the fins. It is only the males which show the large fins, although the females have the same brilliant coloring, perhaps in slightly less degree than a male of comparable heritage.

The most usual way of keeping these small tropical fishes is in communities of as many species as the aquarist can procure as long as the fish will live amiably together, but both the paradise fish and the fighting fish are too large and bad tempered for the community aquarium, although one and sometimes two specimens may be kept with other fish if the tank is fairly large—say ten or twelve gallons capacity. There are, however, a few gouramies, fishes of the same family, with the same general nesting habits, which will live in perfect peace with many other fishes. These will, quite frequently, build their nests in the tank, successfully defending them against any fish which approaches, but when the babies are hatched and start wriggling about the aquarium they will be eagerly snapped up by any other fish that may happen upon them. The best way of securing a few youngsters is to place a pair of the fish in a tank of several gallons capacity, and after the spawning, remove the female. This leaves the male free to keep his mind on the eggs, which fall out of the nest in sufficient numbers to fully occupy him, retrieving and replacing them, until the youngsters hatch and are freely swimming about the tank. Then he, too, should be removed, for the temptation to feast on myriad living fishes may overcome his parental feelings, and

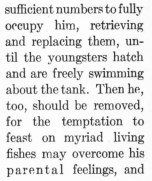

THE MUD SPRINGER
A fish which spends much of its time hopping actively about on mud flats or even relatively dry ground in pursuit of insects or the like

THE PARADISE FISH

A native of China. One of the labyrinth fishes which place their eggs in a floating raft of bubbles constructed by one or both parents, usually by the male

there will be no babies left in a very short while.

While the greatest interest of the aquarist is, perhaps naturally, in the breeding behavior of his pets, very many people are solely concerned with their decorative value. In a properly arranged aquarium, this is very great, and many men have gone to great pains to bring out all the lovely colors and shapes of the varied fishes. Aquaria have been built into walls, with elaborate picture molding affixed to the opening, the total effect being of a living "pond-scape," for the variety of greens and shapes of the different aquatic plants combined with the vast assortment of vivid and pastel colors of the fishes make a really beautiful display. Such arrangements call for considerable ingenuity in the lighting of the aquarium, for a large amount of light will encourage the growth of microscopic plants, valuable in themselves,

but of no æsthetic beauty, and too little light will inhibit the growth of the major plants, a thing to be deplored. However, the right balance is not hard to achieve and the finished work well repays the lover of beauty.

There are one or two fishes whose claim to a small popularity is based on their rather extraordinary feeding habits. These, in the majority of fishes, are not particularly interesting; a small portion of food of one sort or another is dropped into the tank, and the fishes eat it, but some fishes will not eat any food unless it is alive and moving, and is of a fairly large size. *Belonesox*, one of the viviparous top minnows from parts of Central America, refuses to eat anything but small fishes. These, unconscious of their fate, swim about until the pike-like larger fish, opening his mouth, seems to slide right over them. The leaf-fish *Monocirrhus polyacanthus*, of the Amazon, likewise refuses any but living fishes. His approach, however, is considerably more subtle. Shaped and colored like a dead leaf, with the fins which give him motive power quite transparent, he drifts about until he is within striking distance of his victim, when the tremendous mouth opens, the pectoral fins fan a terrific, irresistible stream of water through the mouth and out the gills, and the unfortunate small fish is literally sucked into the yawning cavern.

Of still more spectacular feeding habits are those fishes which depend on the flies they can catch. One of these, the archer fish, *Toxotes jaculator*, a somewhat rare fish from the East Indies, actually shoots his prey,—small flying insects, with a drop of water ejected with considerable force and deadly accuracy. Mr. Chute, director of the Shedd Memorial Aquarium in Chicago, finds that small specimens of this species can project a drop of water about eleven feet, although the limits of accurate firing are about three feet. The fly, suddenly struck with a drop of water, falls to the surface, where the fish immediately seizes it. Another fly-catching fish with a much wider habitat is the mudspringer, *Periophthalmus*. This fish is found from western Africa to the eastern coasts of Australia, along tropical coastal mud flats. It has developed its pectoral and ventral fins into something remotely resembling paddles or flippers, on which it sits and hops about entirely out of the water, returning only to bathe itself and fill the water reservoir at intervals of perhaps thirty minutes. While it is on land it leaps about with the greatest agility, catching and devouring prodigious quantities of mosquitoes.

However, while such fishes are obtainable, they are comparatively rare, and are not to be found in the ordinary domestic aquarium, although they will live there if any are secured. Most amateur aquarists are satisfied not to have these fish-eating and jumping fishes about their homes, for the first are not content without a few guppies every day, and the latter may jump out of an aquarium and never be able to jump back again, faults which make them undesirable as pets.

SWORDTAIL (female above and male below). One of the most popular of the small, tropical, fresh-water fishes kept as pets throughout the world

A SIMPLIFIED PICTORIAL CLASSIFICATION

ORDER OSTARIOPHYSI
Characins, Carps and Catfishes

ORDER CYPRINODONTES
Killifishes, Top-minnows, etc.

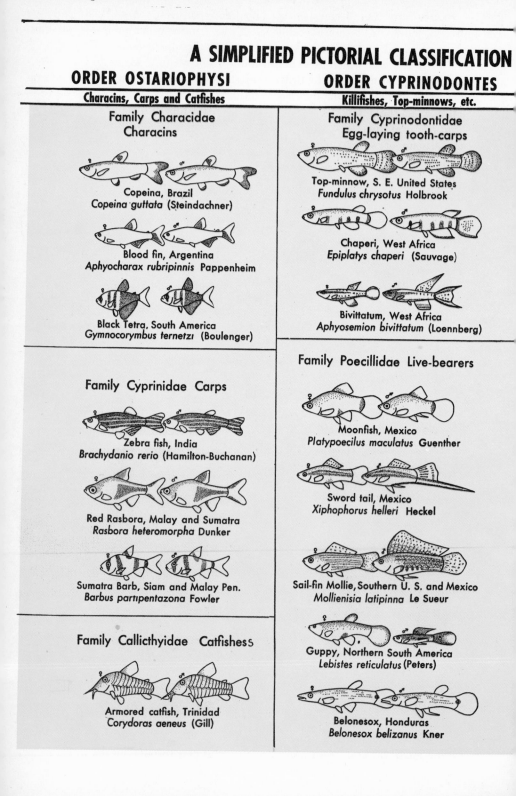

Family Characidae
Characins

Copeina, Brazil
Copeina guttata (Steindachner)

Blood fin, Argentina
Aphyocharax rubripinnis Pappenheim

Black Tetra, South America
Gymnocorymbus ternetzi (Boulenger)

Family Cyprinidae Carps

Zebra fish, India
Brachydanio rerio (Hamilton-Buchanan)

Red Rasbora, Malay and Sumatra
Rasbora heteromorpha Dunker

Sumatra Barb, Siam and Malay Pen.
Barbus partipentazona Fowler

Family Callicthyidae Catfishes

Armored catfish, Trinidad
Corydoras aeneus (Gill)

Family Cyprinodontidae
Egg-laying tooth-carps

Top-minnow, S. E. United States
Fundulus chrysotus Holbrook

Chaperi, West Africa
Epiplatys chaperi (Sauvage)

Bivittatum, West Africa
Aphyosemion bivittatum (Loennberg)

Family Poecillidae Live-bearers

Moonfish, Mexico
Platypoecilus maculatus Guenther

Sword tail, Mexico
Xiphophorus helleri Heckel

Sail-fin Mollie, Southern U. S. and Mexico
Mollienisia latipinna Le Sueur

Guppy, Northern South America
Lebistes reticulatus (Peters)

Belonesox, Honduras
Belonesox belizanus Kner

OF THE MORE COMMON AQUARIUM FISHES
ORDER PERCOMORPHI   ORDER LABYRINTHICI

Cichlids, Nandids, etc.   **Anabantids, etc.**

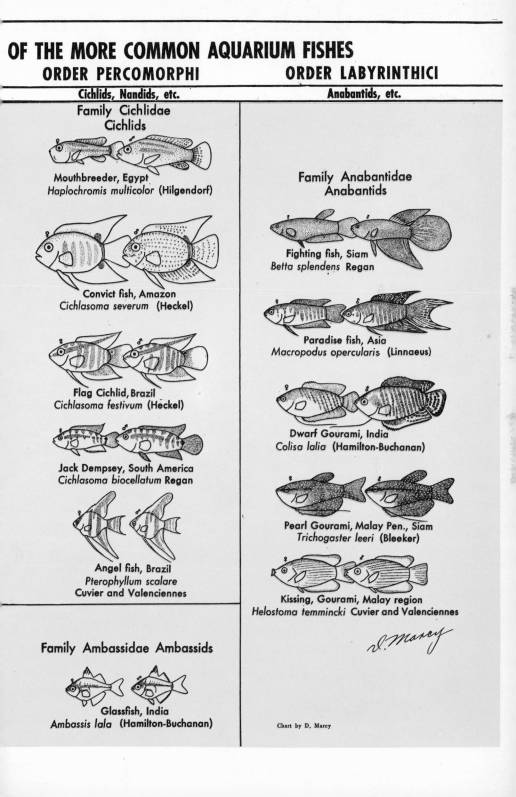

Family Cichlidae
Cichlids

Mouthbreeder, Egypt
Haplochromis multicolor (Hilgendorf)

Convict fish, Amazon
Cichlasoma severum (Heckel)

Flag Cichlid, Brazil
Cichlasoma festivum (Heckel)

Jack Dempsey, South America
Cichlasoma biocellatum Regan

Angel fish, Brazil
Pterophyllum scalare
Cuvier and Valenciennes

Family Ambassidae Ambassids

Glassfish, India
Ambassis lala (Hamilton-Buchanan)

Family Anabantidae
Anabantids

Fighting fish, Siam
Betta splendens Regan

Paradise fish, Asia
Macropodus opercularis (Linnaeus)

Dwarf Gourami, India
Colisa lalia (Hamilton-Buchanan)

Pearl Gourami, Malay Pen., Siam
Trichogaster leeri (Bleeker)

Kissing, Gourami, Malay region
Helostoma temmincki Cuvier and Valenciennes

Chart by D. Marcy

The Trunkfish Swims in Armor

Its motto 50 million years ago was "A Good Defense is the Best Offense," and today in a fish-world geared for speed and a quick get-away it still follows it

By MYRON GORDON

FISHES had elaborate styles of personal armor before ancient man learned to use a simple shield in self-defense.

In the days before the age of dinosaurs, the most popular of all styles in apparel for fishes was a stiff suit of bony scales, movable only along the scale's beveled edges. Then with the arrival of the huge newly evolved plesiosaurs and other fish-swallowing, bone-crushing monsters in the age of reptiles, the former advantages of protective armor were practically nil. The fishes in the Mesozoic seas faced a changing tempo. The "speed-up" movement arrived.

Predatory sharks and larger fishes swam faster after their prey. Speed, not armament, was necessary for survival. Small fishes with fast, flexible bodies, streamlined for speed and powered for a quick getaway, met the challenge of the new mode of life. They fled from the triple threat of reptiles, sharks and larger fishes. Their kind flourished and multiplied.

Out-moded

Nearly all modern fishes have long since discarded the last vestiges of the ancient suits of bony armor. But the modern trunkfishes have re-adopted, with modifications, the old-fashioned, prehistoric style of armor suiting. Like up-to-date dress designers, the trunkfishes have copied merely the spirit of the old style; they have evolved entirely new methods of covering their bodies.

The scales in the trunkfish's body constitute a solid series of hard hexagonal plates, firmly joined together to form a single, inflexible bony case. A tortoise in its shell can move its head in and out and twist it, if it wishes, from side to side; but the only independent movement of the head that a trunkfish can execute, is to ogle its eyes and to pucker its lips. The head is joined immovably to the trunk.

Confined permanently within these strait-jackets of their own making, it is a mystery how trunkfishes get along. Certainly few would have predicted success for fishes outfitted with this ungainly body style of a past age in this modern world with its ferocious marauders, like barracudas and morays, and the ancient predatory sharks that continue to snatch their living from all creatures weaker than themselves.

Evolution of styles

The return of armored styles to modern fishes has its human parallel. Old-fashioned costumes of past centuries reappear with modern flares to clothe the fashionable ladies of today. And personal armor of King Arthur's day has returned in part in the bullet-proof vest and the steel helmet of the modern infantryman.

The story of evolution of armor among men is more complete than the story of evolution of armor in fishes. The human record is infinitely shorter, the number of styles invented by man are fewer, and the materials used are simpler in composition. But the development of both piscine and human armor have had their period of crude beginnings, their period of rapid development, their period of florescence, and finally their period of decline almost to the point of extinction. Trunkfish and men in bullet-proof vests are modern representatives of different ancestral stocks, but their costumes have a common purpose.

The porcupine fish's scales are modified and form a globular series of sharply pointed spines. These jagged needles form an effective coat of mail and oppose the enemy from all points of the compass. The South American armored catfish, on the other hand, is literally sandwiched in between two solid plates of bone. The unfishlike sea horses, that swim so slowly and gracefully through the water by imperceptible movement of their semi-transparent fins, are encased within a series of bony rings.

COMPLETELY ENCASED IN ARMOR, the awkward little trunkfish is like an armored knight of old, seemingly out of place in this modern world that is geared
for speed and a quick getaway. For fifty million years
this fish has followed the motto that a good defense
is the best offense. While most fishes have discarded
their ancient heavy suits of armor the trunkfish has
readopted the old style

Fishes' style center

The trunkfish and their allies live in the coral community of tropical American waters. The seas about the coral archipelago of the Florida Keys is a Paris style-center in the fishes' world. Man lacks the imagination to design the diversity of outlandish styles displayed by the fishes in this marine style-center. A menagerie of fish types pass constantly in review. There are sea horses, of course; then there are pork fish, goat fish and mutton fish; then there are squirrel fish, rabbit fish and lion fish; there are scorpion fish, louse fish and butterfly fish; parrot fish and snipe fish; frog fish, snake fish and lizard fish; and there are monk fish and angel fish! And, to return to the category of trunkfish, there are cowfish.

No contest was ever proposed, no prizes were ever offered for the best choice of a name to suit the personality of the cowfish, a trunkfish which scientists call *Lactophrys tricornis*. If there had been a contest, perhaps someone might have thought of a more dignified name. And yet these curious twelve-inch fishes of the coral reefs do resemble, in a most superficial manner to be sure, a staid milch cow. They have the same wide-eyed, vacuous expression, although on rare occasions they seem to express a mood of deep sadness. When disturbed they appear to be bewildered and amazed.

William Swainson, the English naturalist, writing in 1839, must have had an amusing time in choosing the cowfish's technical name of *Lactophrys*. The horn-like protuberances must have reminded him of a cow. That would account for the "lacto" portion of *Lactophrys*, for "lactoria" means milch cow in Latin. Then there was something appealing about the sad eyes of the cowfish, something about their overhanging, brooding, eyebrow-like eye-sockets that attracted Swainson's sensitive attention, so that he added "ophrys," which means eyebrow in Greek. Could Swainson have meant, then, that this mournful fish looked like a cow with prominent eyebrows? *Tricornis*, the cowfish's specific name, refers to three horns. Actually the cowfish, like its bovine namesake, has but two horns on its head; but in addition, in the rear pointing backward, there are three horns on each side of the shell. You might think that the ichthyologist is bothered by such names as *Lacto-*

(Right) THE SMALL JAWS of the trunkfish are capable of limited movement only, but they have a strong set of teeth designed to break down hard coral hiding-places of worms, shrimps and other tiny sea creatures upon which the fish feeds. The trunkfish's head is joined immovably to the trunk and it can only ogle its eyes, pucker its lips and move its whisk-broom tail and fins. It may not be graceful, but no other fish can display more dazzling colors. It is one of the most beautifully colored fishes of our tropical waters and it can change from one color scheme to another

phrys tricornis for the cowfish and *Lactophrys trigonus* for the common trunkfish, but as a matter of fact the fish scientist is happy about it. Years ago, in 1738, toward the end of the dark ages of biology, the educated fish man had to remember this name for the cowfish: *Ostracion triangulatus duobus aculeis in fronte et totidem in imo ventre subcaudalesque binis*. The author of this prayer-like appellation was Pedrus Artedi, a native of Sweden.

Fish hunting in taverns

Artedi had traveled widely in his lifetime. When in England he made the rounds of the taverns in and about London. He specifically mentions "The Nagg's Head," "The White Bear" and the "Green Dragon in Stepney." These visits were strictly on business for it was in these and other inns that various natural history curiosities from the new world of America were exhibited. The trunkfishes as a group became well known to European naturalists because of the heavy demand for, and the extensive traffic in, the dried shells of these fishes. So thorough were the catches of trunkfish hunters in American seas that every species now recognized as distinct had been described some two hundred years ago from curio specimens.

It was at the height of this trunkfish curio fad period that Artedi described several of them. In London Artedi visited Sir Hans Sloane and saw his collection of natural-history specimens from the West Indies, a collection which was

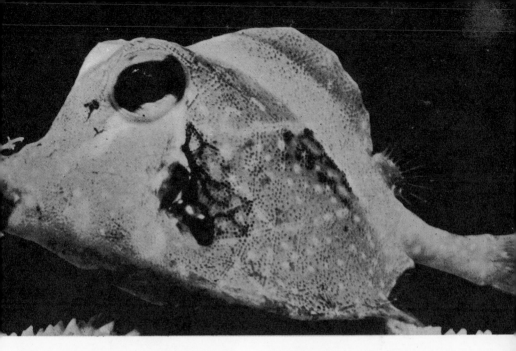

destined to be the beginning of the British Museum of Natural History. There Artedi spotted a rare cowfish. He was convinced that this particular cowfish had never before been recognized or described to the scientific world. Forthwith he supplied the necessary baptismal papers. The words he used were in Latin, the language in vogue at the time for scientific treatises. From that baptismal record, the name *Ostracion triangulatus duobus,* etc. of the cowfish was derived.

But the records show that Pedrus Artedi was fifty years too late in his naming of the cowfish. He was beaten by Dr. Martin Lister, who is not to be confused with Lord Lister of antiseptic fame. Dr. Martin Lister, the original cowfish man, had his own ideas about names for the cowfish. His 1686 name is: *Piscis triangularis capite cornutus cui e media cauda cutacea aculeus longue erigitus.* Lister's and Artedi's names for the cowfish stood on the fish catalogues until 1758, when von Linné gave naturalists the world over a new deal by systematically cutting down the long names of all living things to two words. All naturalists cheered. This practice is still in vogue today. When the modern naturalist thinks back to the days of Lister and Artedi and recalls the long quotations these gentlemen used as names for their specimens, he feels that remembering and saying *Lactophyrys*

tricornis is almost as easy as saying Jack Robinson.

But the honor of having discovered the very first American trunkfish must go, not to Dr. Martin Lister or Pedrus Artedi, but to an unknown member of Columbus' crew. On their first voyage to America in 1492, while at anchor on the coast of Cuba, this unknown sailor-fisherman caught a fish which "was like a swine, all covered with a very hard skin, no part whereof was soft but the tail."

Can change color

Other fishes may have shapes that please the human eye better than the angular conformations of the trunkfish, but no fish can claim more dazzling colors, a more intriguing color pattern, and a greater repertoire of color changes than they.

England's fish expert, J. R. Norman, keeper of fishes at the British Museum, votes the trunkfish of the Great Barrier Reef of Australia the most colorful of all fishes. They have all the colors of the rainbow and can change at will from one color scheme to another. The Florida trunkfishes are brilliant, too, and their remarkable ability to change color is manifest when at one moment they are vivid green, at the next a nut-brown, and a moment later as white as the bleached coral sand. And in the intervals

WHEN DISTURBED the cowfish appears bewildered and amazed. The cowfish was first identified in 1686. But to an unknown member of Columbus' crew must go the credit for discovering the first American trunkfish, which he described as being "like a swine, all covered with a very hard skin, no part whereof was soft but the tail"

between these definite color phases, intermediate transitional stages are flashed in a continuous series of complex combinations.

There certainly is no correlation at all between their beautiful colors and beauty of body lines for they are grotesque and unbelievable. Detached from their normal surroundings they appear clownishly out of place. But swimming slowly among the living coral heads they are dignified and even stately. Their bodies can never relax from their stiff-necked posture, for they are of one piece. When forced to rapid movement they are ludicrous. They have penguin-on-land actions in getting about.

When removed from the water their behavior is pathetic, for they are absolutely helpless, being unable to move their solid bodies. When placed upon a stone, out of water, trunkfishes foam at the mouth in their distress. Some say that they make small grunting noises; others say that they growl like dogs. Large trunkfishes will live two to three hours out of water, all the time, Goode comments, "solemnly fanning their fins". When restored to their native element they cannot immediately sink to the bottom for they have absorbed much air in their sojourn above the water line; but after a short time they seem none the worse for their emersion.

Viewed head-on the chinless face of a trunkfish presents a grotesque appearance, with its lips perpetually pursed as if forever ready to kiss the world. From their funnel-shaped head small jaws protrude which are capable of limited movement only. They have a strong set of teeth, designed to break down hard coral structures which are inhabited by worms, shrimps and other small animals on which they feed. With these powerful teeth they can defend themselves from smaller fishes at close quarters, but in the confinement of an aquarium

belly of the swordfish is well rounded like the bottom of a trim, speedy canoe; the belly region of a trunkfish is as level as the underside of a flat-bottomed rowboat. This flat nether surface enables the trunkfish to execute a safe, upright landing on the bottom of the sea; and here it spends much time resting quietly.

Locomotion

Living their lives encased permanently in bony armor these small, individual, aquatic tanks, being unable to execute body undulations, move slowly through the water, relying upon their fins alone to project them forward. From the rigid case, and joined to it by thin folds of skin, project small, flabby fins; one on each side of the body, one on top, and one on the bottom. From the rear a thin, naked tailpiece with its ridiculously small flap of tail fin sticks out like a stiff whiskbroom tail on a hobby horse. This fin, so important in other fishes' swimming strokes, merely serves the trunkfish as

COWFISH, a type of trunkfish. Perhaps this denizen of the coral reefs has earned its name because of its wide-eyed, vacuous expression and superficial resemblance to a staid milch cow. Here the cowfish displays what appears to human eyes to be a mood of distinct sadness. So great was the demand for dried trunkfish shells by curio collectors that every species now recognized had been described some 200 years ago

the trunkfish is at a distinct disadvantage. Its fins are constantly being ripped to pieces by fishes that are in the habit of biting at anything that moves and then darting away. Trunkfish have lived for long periods in an aquarium, but their cell-mates have been chosen with great care.

Trunkfishes have regained a degree of protection within their rigid bony shell but only at the expense of speed. They do not have the smooth contours and perfect tear-drop streamline form displayed by fast-swimming fishes like mackerel and swordfish. Rather their body styles follow motifs of sharp angles, pointed projections and grotesque elevations, all moulded into a single bony frame. Cleave a swordfish in two behind the head and the outline of the cut is an oval. Split a trunkfish similarly and the outline is a triangle. The back of the swordfish is nicely curved; the back of the trunkfish is a pyramid. The

a rudder. Only when the trunkfish is pressed for utmost haste does its tail revert to the time-honored task of active locomotion. When forced, it will lash its tail from side to side in the best fish manner. In doing this the motion of its tail may be likened to the sculling action of the gondolier's single oar at the stern of his boat.

The burden of locomotion falls upon the small upper and lower fins. These have a half rotary sculling action resembling, but, of course, never effecting, the movement of a screw propeller. Oftentimes the movement of these transparent fins is hardly perceptible and the chunky trunkfish seems to glide through the water without effort and with great dignity.

The fins on the port and starboard side of a trunkfish have a special duty. They not only keep the fish upright but they prevent it from being projected forward like a rocket by the powerful

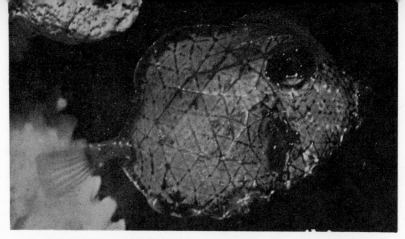

(Above) THE FIRST PUBLISHED PHOTOGRAPH of a baby
trunkfish. In the watery paths among the living coral heads
and encrusted turtle grass, the trunkfish is fairly safe, but
if it strays into the highway of the Gulf Stream it is swept
into a region patrolled by sharks, barracudas and other sea
marauders that are always ready to pounce upon it

force of the water ejected backward
from the small gill openings. When the
fish is at rest the pectoral fins wave
vigorously at the rate of one hundred
and eighty times a minute.

Trunkfish have put their trust in the
principle that a strong defense is the
best offense. They have been practicing
this policy successfully for the past fifty
million years. This may seem a long
time for humans, but the modern age
for fishes started millions of years before the form of man was conceived.

There is no question, as far as trunkfishes are concerned, that the exchange
of speed for security was profitable.
They are not likely to be attacked by
fishes of their own size, with which they
have to compete most of the time. The
trunkfish live among the living coral
heads in tropic seas, among which the
watery paths are often narrow and tortuous. A coral reef community is a city
of narrow streets and crooked alleys.
The denizens of the coral city rarely
stray into the boulevards and highways
of open water. If they do, they are soon

taken out of their native course: the
Gulf Stream will carry them to northern
waters that are colder and uncongenial.
They cannot live a normal life outside
their coral community. Sharks, barracudas, and other predators of the sea
patrol the outskirts and await their
chance to pounce, unhindered by the
many pillars and posts within the coral
city, upon those that stray outside.

Shark stomachs tell stories that cannot
be denied. Sharks have swallowed trunk-

(Right) A SOLID SERIES OF HARD PLATES forms the trunkfish's armor. Out of water it is pathetically helpless, but in
its native element, it is dignified and stately as it swims
slowly. When forced to swim rapidly, its rudder-like tail
fin goes into action and looks like a man frantically sculling a flat bottomed row-boat

fish. Unless trunkfish are swallowed whole they are not likely to be attacked at all. What, after all, has the trunkfish to tempt its smaller pursuers? Its fins are thin and small. Its tailpiece is a little insignificant morsel of flesh hardly worth the effort of a fight. And the trunkfish has a strong set of teeth with which it can defend itself at close quarters. But it cannot defend itself as it passes down the gullet of a shark. Gudger, American Museum fish expert, found an empty and perfectly polished shell of a trunkfish inside the stomach of a shark at Dry Tortugas, Florida. The six-sided, fused plates of the unfortunate trunkfish's bony jacket were worn down so smooth that they revealed their beautiful mosaic construction. The fine striations and scrolls upon each piece appeared as clear as the grain in a slab of well-rubbed curly maple. Sharks have an efficient digestive mill to handle these tough but tempting morsels. When a shark is through with a trunkfish it discards a shell that is as completely freed of soft parts as a skeleton that has been picked clean by the combined efforts of buzzards, ants and dermestids, experts in this funereal job.

Sharks discovered that trunkfishes were good eating long before man did —long before man existed. Even now sharks are beating man in trunkfish hunting—they are nearer the source of supply. Trunkfish are a treat for the epicure, according to America's expert in fisheries, G. Brown Goode. Serious cases of poisoning have resulted from eating the spoiled meat of the trunkfish, but these cases occurred in tropical countries where, if care is not taken, the flesh decomposes rapidly. There is little danger of poisoning if the fish are fresh. Seafood connoisseur Goode says that the flesh of these fishes is delicate in texture and exceptionally pleasant in taste. Goode likes his fishes prepared by first boiling them whole, like lobsters, in salt water, then scooping out the meat; the meat is then mixed with cracker crumbs, eggs, butter and red pepper, and this promising combination is stuffed back into the original trunkfish shell and roasted until nicely browned. Those who have eaten this fish agree with Goode that it is a rare delicacy. Trunkfish eating has not reached commercial proportions as yet. Some enterprising composer of sea food menus could scoop the shore dinner trade by glorifying them as the treasure-chests of the sea.

So enthusiastic was the French fish scientist and fish gourmet, Lacepédè, of the delicacy of the flesh of the trunkfish that he wrote at great length, in 1798, of a method by which the trunkfish of the American tropical seas might be induced to live in the temperate fresh waters of France. "The exquisite flavor and exceedingly wholesome nature of the flesh of the 'triangulaire' should encourage us to make persevering and well considered experiments in this direction." His plan was to acclimatize the fish by gradual, insensible changes in temperature and salinity of the sea water until the cool, fresh water level was reached. There was one serious difficulty to this plan: the trunkfish refused stubbornly to cooperate.

European waters do not provide the coral homesteads necessary for the trunkfishes, and none are found along European coasts of the Atlantic. But tropical shores of the American Atlantic provide suitable places for them, and here they flourish. They are abundant in the vicinity of the laboratories of the Marine Biological Station of the Carnegie Institute at Loggerhead Key of the Dry Tortugas, the last of the Keys of Florida.

One day in the shallow seas surrounding Bush Key, just opposite Garden Key or Fort Jefferson, we hauled a fine-meshed seine at low tide along the outskirts of a fine stand of living coral heads. The net enclosed a milling mob of fishes, crabs, shrimps, sea urchins and other creatures, along with fantastic varieties of seaweed. While getting rid of the seaweed, I noticed a number of green globules of jelly-like stuff that I took to be some kind of algae. As I reached down to remove these bits, they moved a trifle faster than my hand; it was a moment before I realized that they were some form of animal life. They were baby trunkfish.

Overcoming my surprise, I examined one. Its body was already hardened with bone and its small mosaic green shell was beautifully sculptured in an intricate design that followed a hexagonal pattern. Its tiny, transparent fins were hardly visible in my hand; they were entirely invisible in the water. It was these translucent fins that had enabled the little trunkfish to move away in an unfishlike manner from my hand. When I replaced it in the water, the little green fishy ball made off with the smoothness of a toy balloon in a quiet breeze.

Make Mine Vanilla

The story of America's most popular flavoring agent links the golden era of exploration with the modern age of chemical marvels

Bernard L. Lewis, Inc.

↟ THE VANILLA PLANT is an orchid. On most plantations, the flowers are pollinated by hand.

Virginia S. Eifert

By Jennie E. Harris

WHEN the beautiful Mexican girl Marina became interpreter for her beloved Cortez, she told him about the wealth of Montezuma, King of the Aztecs, and about his city, Tenochtitlán, which Cortez was soon to behold. Cortez was interested in gold and silver, and he scarcely imagined that he was going to find something far more valuable. Little did he suppose that the gold and silver goblets that held Montezuma's favorite drink represented a wealth far less important in the long run than the drink itself, *xoco-latl* (chocolate), and its extra flavor, *tlilxochitl* (vanilla).

Soon chocolate and vanilla were to win sensational acclaim in Spain, then in all Europe.

Francisco Hernández, in Mexico

Hernan Cortez was the first white man to taste vanilla, in Mexico, in 1520.

A mural at McCormick and Company Little Theatre

at Philip II's request (1571-77), drew pictures of the garlanding vanilla vine and named it "*Araco Aromatico.*" Apothecaries in tiny shops in Europe sold the dark, cured, vanilla beans along with chocolate beans, to be used together. Because of the scabbard-like appearance of the pod, the Spaniards called it *vainilla* ("little sheath").

In 1602, Hugh Morgan, apothecary to Queen Elizabeth in England, sent some vanilla fruit to a man called Clusius, and he was the first to mention it in botanical literature. He seems also to have started vanilla off on its own as a flavor. "Chocolate needs vanilla," he said, "but does vanilla need chocolate?"

"Why should such a valuable plant grow only in Mexico?" people asked. It seemed to them that it should thrive in other tropical regions and make millions for those who grew it. Not grown from seed, perhaps; seeds were too tiny and stubborn. But why not from cuttings?

When Indians watched men take trial snips of the vine in Mexico, they hooted and jeered; "White man no make grow."

White man did make grow—after a fashion. Planters thrust vine-snips into warm earth under leaves, near saplings or stakes to climb on, and under tall trees for shade. They watched the cuttings root, grow, and thrust out tiny feelers, much as ivy does. Up they went: 15, 20 feet, even 80 feet if allowed; but only the hanging portions produced buds, so the men bent the vines downward, draping them over branches.

The buds burst into satiny beauty at early morning—true orchids, greenish yellow with six floral segments, one petal oddly lip-shaped. But by mid-afternoon of the day it bloomed, each flower was gone. And not a bean formed.

This was strange. Here were healthy vines with sturdy soil roots, sturdy aerial roots, and soft full flowers, but apparently these weren't enough.

In hothouses in England and in Europe, botanists watched the pale petals open, without perfume but most lovely. Then before three o'clock of the same day, the orchids would fade, and no beans would form. For 300 years after Cortez tasted vanilla, not a single vine grown elsewhere came to fruitage.

The trouble was that the short-lived flowers needed to be pollinated by stingless bees or other natural agents that did not exist where the plant was introduced. In 1836, Charles Morren of Liége got an inkling of this and experimented. He took pollen from under a protective part of the flower, and pressed it on the stigma of the same flower. His hunch proved correct; beans began to form, and before long they grew to string-bean length. There lay the answer to three centuries of failure. The frail blooms could not fertilize themselves; they needed special help.

With this knowledge of artificial pollination, France began cultivating vanilla on islands in the East and West Indies, and on Madagascar.

A few years after Morren's discovery, a one-time slave, Edmond Albius, working on a vanilla plantation on the island of Reunion in the Indian Ocean, devised a better

Bernard L. Lewis, Inc.

GATHERING THE CROP in Madagascar, where 63% of our vanilla is grown. Four to 20 beans hang in a group. The plants need saplings or stakes to climb on.

pollinating method. Even Mexico adopted this new method, and to-day vanilla no longer must wait for visits of a tiny undependable bee.

Vanilla planifolia is the vanilla most cultivated. The vines are grown along narrow aisles and hold clusters of buds, 15 or 20 to a shoot. Assumé it is not yet eleven o'clock in the morning on a typical plantation. A quietness is upon the land; no wind stirs; but a few buds stir within themselves as they swell and push with growth. Gradually they thrust apart their crinkle-edged petals. Now they lie fully open. They would fertilize them-selves if they could, but a sort of tongue formation keeps the pollen from contacting the waiting stigma. And since we are in a plantation far from the home of the vanilla plant, "midwives" must help. Down the aisles come women and chil-dren. Each pauses before the soft beauty of an opened flower and with a tiny bamboo toothpick lifts pollen from a golden mass and places it on the stigma of the same flower. Thumb and forefinger press for a moment to make sure the con-tact lasts. Then on to the next fresh flower.

Every morning for many weeks, hands gently hold the few more orchids that have opened, and the little wooden toothpicks go to work. If blooms depended upon nature for pollination, only a few beans might form, even where the vanilla is native. The vines flower twice a year, for about two months at a stretch, but no flower lasts a full day. Each must be pollinated by hand and at the hour when it is fresh and receptive. Only the larg-est orchids are treated, to assure quality vanilla and avoid overwork-ing the vines.

Beans from autumn's pollinating hang mature in March, four to twenty in a group, six to ten inches long, pale green, then slowly browning. Workers move among them each day, gathering those exactly right, not too green, not so ripe as to be splitting. They pluck the stem with the bean, for beans must not be damaged in any way.

If you could taste a fresh vanilla bean you would discover it has scarcely any flavor. If left on the vine till sun-baked, it would smell like vanilla but make inferior ex-tract. Only careful curing brings out the mellow aroma that means vanilla to every candymaker or cake baker.

Papantla is the curing center for the Mexican state of Vera Cruz. Here the planter takes his crop, offers it to this curer and that, sell-ing only a portion to a single buyer because he wants the highest prices possible. The buyer would know which beans are healthier and best even if he were blind. Touch tells him as well as sight, and he has vanilla, you might say, in his veins.

For curing, the beans are sun-dried on large overlapping mats—fast enough to prevent mold yet not so fast as to sweat out the precious oils. (In Madagascar, they may first be immersed in boiling water.) *Camilleros* bring the beans out on stretchers on which they have lain indoors overnight. *Tentedores* place them evenly in rows on mats, one by one, quickly lest the sun grow hot. *Maestros* walk the narrow lanes, leaning over and testing each bean for dryness. Beans seldom dry alike. Young bell-ringers, *Cam-*

Bernard L. Lewis, Inc.

∧ SORTING THE BEANS.
They now contain
their full potentiality
of flavor but have
practically no taste.

paneros, ring for the helpers to
come and collect the beans that
have dried enough.

At midday, the beans are so hot
they almost burn the fingers, and
men fold blankets over them to
make them sweat the rest of the
day. At night, all the beans are carried indoors again and placed in
blanket-lined, air-tight containers.

Every day for two weeks, this
tedious placing and collecting must
go on, with no bean touching
another in drying for fear of spotting. Then, after the sweating process, two months of straight drying.
Then 3½ months of drying in shelter,
till the pods are dark brown or almost black, dry, and shriveled.

When fresh, they were as fat as
your forefinger; now they are pen-
cil-thin and have lost about four-
fifths of their weight. But they are
pliable enough for smoothing and
massaging, for every bean must be
straightened before bundling.

Bundling is an art. All the stem-
ends must point in, all the flower-

Bernard L. Lewis, Inc.

➤ CARRYING the green va-
nilla beans to market.

ends point out. Eighty to a hundred beans are placed in a bundle, and the outside beans are laid on carefully. Then the bundles are pressed, tapped on a table to straighten the ends, tied in the middle, boxed, and cased for shipment.

In France, and in our own food-specialty shops, people buy vanilla beans in glass tubes and grate them in their kitchens as our grandmothers did nutmeg. A recipe for floating-meringue custard may call for the grating of a "1-inch piece of vanilla bean." Dark specks in a dessert attest to the presence of pure vanilla. Most of the time, however, we buy vanilla extract, which is vanilla dissolved in alcohol, the solvent our government specifies.

Making vanilla extract

When the sweet-smelling boxes reach our shores, manufacturers further age the pods in tins in vaults under controlled temperature and humidity. Knives slice the pods to fineness (no grinding, for grinding would crush them, lessening their flavor).

Agitation over heat in alcohol and water follows — maceration (about the way we steep tea), or percolation (about the way we brew coffee). Filtering comes next. Then the extract enters a glass-lined tank for final aging. At last, color, aroma, and flavor are pronounced perfect, and the fluid is poured into sterilized bottles, to be labeled "Pure Vanilla Extract."

Here then is the source of pure vanilla: orchids pollinated by hand, the flower itself an ephemeral thing, with frail beauty; then the careful gathering of beans at the exact stage of ripeness; the painstaking curing and processing.

Strange that vanilla is not more expensive, for in only two places in the world is it grown commercially to any extent: Madagascar and Mexico. And in Mexico, production is limited to a small region in the foothills and lower levels of the Sierra Madre Mountains in the states of Vera Cruz and Puebla. The country that was once the only place in the world where vanilla was known now exports almost its entire crop—mostly to the United States.

The U. S. imports 50 per cent of the world's production. A few beans come from British and French West Indies islands like Guadaloupe and Dominica, also from Indonesia and Tahiti. Some vanilla is grown in Hawaii. But by far the largest part of our import comes from Madagascar—the large island off the east coast of Africa that was known to the Arabs for a thousand years, the place that Richelieu described to Louis XIII as not belonging to anyone. Its soil ranks among the richest on earth. Madagascar produced 63 per cent of all our vanilla imports in 1952 (the last complete year for which the Department of Commerce has issued figures); Mexico produced 21 per cent, all other countries 16 per cent. Our total imports in 1952 were 1,400,069 pounds; in 1954 they were probably about 1,700,-000 pounds.

The beans differ in quality so much that 21 different grades are recognized. Consequently, the price of the finished extract varies. You can buy pure vanilla made from Tahiti beans for about $1.25 a pound, whereas high quality ex-

▼ A GROWER may sell some of his beans to one
curer, some to another, in order to get the best prices.

Bernard L. Lewis, Inc.

McCormick and Company photo

▲ AT THE BEGINNING of the curing process in
Madagascar, the beans are dipped in hot water.

tract from Mexican or Bourbon (Madagascar) beans would bring $7 to $10 a pound.

Vanilla remains the prime favorite among flavors and outsells all others—chocolate, orange, lemon, maple, cinnamon, coconut, clove, almond, banana, and cherry, to name a few. The supply fluctuates considerably: storms and disease take their toll of vanilla crops. Some vines produce continually for fifteen years, others only nine or ten. The land must rest 20 years before being replanted in vanilla.

The basic flavor in vanilla is vanillin (accent on first syllable). It reveals its presence on the outside of the pod in tiny needle-like crystals. Men call this white crystal efflorescence *givre* (French for "hoarfrost") and consider it a criterion of quality. The best pods have it. Actually, vanillin originates inside the bean. It is secreted by tiny hairs lining the inner crevices. Oil around the black seeds diffuses vanillin through the pod. Curing causes extrusion till fine white crystals of it coat the pod. About one-three-hundredth of the weight of the vanilla bean is vanillin.

Synthetic vanillin

When vanillin was discovered in oil of cloves in the last century, the Givaudin-Delawanna Corporation in Europe pioneered in the manufacture of a substitute for vanilla. The discovery was made chain-fashion: oil of cloves yields eugenol, which when treated becomes iso-eugenol (used for synthetic carnation perfume); isoeugenol, further treated, becomes vanillin.

In the vanilla pod, other substances contribute to the full vanil-la flavor. The numerous black seeds contain aromatic oils and a sticky flavorful juice. In tiny cells throughout the pod, volatile oils, sugars, gums, and many unknowns enter vanilla's flavor. Curing enhances these. The full mellowness of pure vanilla is, you might say, a rounded flavor, of which vanillin is only a part. To date, none of the other substances have been imitated.

Vanilla from orchids, vanillin from cloves, and lately vanillin from laboratories.

For years, the Monsanto Chemical Company made vanillin from Zanzibar cloves, then sought to create it chemically so as to have a source untouched by crop failure and price change. A substance called guaiacol, originally obtained from wood-tar creosote and sometimes used for treating chest and throat disorders, was to lead the way. Chemists had known how to synthesize guaiacol since about 1875, and in 1929, Monsanto began producing guaiacol vanillin. In 1931, the same company intro-

TOO RAPID CURING will encourage mold, too slow will sweat out the precious oils. After weeks of careful drying, the beans are bundled for shipment, as at right.

Photo by David Parlet, from McCormick and Company.

duced an ethyl vanillin, trademarked Ethavan, which, though not identical to vanillin, is used as an imitation vanilla flavor. It is more potent than vanillin, and when properly used in commercial applications can be distinguished from vanilla or vanillin flavoring only by experts.

Guaiacol vanillin was in time succeeded by lignin vanillin, synthesized from the spent sulphite liquors from wood pulp mills. It was first developed in 1937 but has been manufactured by Monsanto only since 1953.

Some imitation vanillas contain only vanillin for characteristic flavor. Others contain pure vanilla as well. Each must be labeled "Imitation Vanilla," by mandate of our Pure Food and Drug Administration, unless the contents include 50 per cent pure vanilla, in which case "Vanilla-Vanillin Flavor" is allowed.

Imitation vanilla competes with pure vanilla because it is cheaper. Even in 1940, if you included all the commercial uses, the imitations outstripped pure vanilla five-fold, and the ratio may be 10 to 1 now. But the pure product retains its adherents. As one housewife put it, "All those extra, delicate, natural flavors in the bean make pure vanilla a veritable bouquet."

Women's magazines term vanilla "food perfume"—both a flavor in itself and an enhancer of other flavors. They advise that it be treated like a perfume, kept in a dark bottle, tightly stoppered, in a cool place. This is because air and light alter its precious aroma.

Four squares of chocolate, a teaspoon of vanilla — remember? Fudge, hot chocolate, cake icing, sauce for your vanilla ice cream. Thank Montezuma and his people for both the chocolate and the vanilla.

Bernard L. Lewis, Inc.

VITAL
vegetable
oils

By **HAROLD N. MOLDENKE**
Director of Trailside Museum,
Watchung Reservation, New Jersey

VEGETABLE oils perform many unsuspected functions in numerous chemical processes and in the lubricating and protecting of surfaces, and the average person may not realize what serious results can be caused by sudden shortage. We learned this during World War II, when much of the normal supply was cut off.

On a basis of their physical condition, widely different kinds of substances are called oils, and they are derived, of course, from animal, vegetable, and mineral sources. The animal oils were probably the first to be used by man; even today the Eskimos depend upon seal oil for heat and light. Mineral oils, fairly recent in man's economy, have strongly influ-

Botanical explorers and industrial chemists have joined forces to discover many valuable oils rarely heard of by the average person

enced the pattern of modern civilization. But vegetable oils, even though we do not so often encounter them in recognizable form, make possible a great many things that have come to be regarded as essential in modern life.

We should remember the difference between fatty (or fixed) oils and essential (or volatile) oils. All the commercially interesting fatty oils of vegetable origin are obtained from seeds, with the exception of olive and palm oils. The terms "fats" and "fatty oils" apply to those that consist almost entirely of mixtures of glycerides, which are chemical combinations of various fatty acids with glycerine.

The essential oils, depending on the kind, are found in the roots, stems, leaves, buds, blossoms, seeds, and some fruits. They are, with few exceptions, complex mixtures, which may include alcohols and their esters, aldehydes, ketones, hydrocarbons, and other substances.

Many new products are made from fatty vegetable oils, including detergent (cleansing agents), wetting and emulsification agents, protective coatings, and lubricating mixtures.

The demand for what are called *drying oils* increased enormously as a result of World War II. Not only were many of our regular sources cut off, but war production required much larger supplies. Our industrial use of drying oils in the United States expanded from 640 million pounds in 1940 to 900 million pounds in 1941. The principal oils used in the United States for drying purposes in 1941 were, in millions of pounds: linseed, 670; tung, 49; castor (dehydrated), 44; soybean, 42; fish, 41; oiticica, 40; and perilla, 5.

Probably the most important of all the drying oils is tung oil. In 1940 about 95 per cent of the tung oil used in the United States went into paint and varnish industries. Its drying speed and water resistance are second to none. In addition to being employed in paints for battleships and many other war purposes, tung oil has strategic uses in the production of certain insulating compounds for electric generators, cables, and wires. It is an important ingredient in many types of brake linings and on gaskets for steam pipes, pumps, and engines. It is used in the manufacture of linoleum and oilcloth and for waterproofing fabrics.

The most important source of tung oil is the "China wood-oil tree" (*Aleurites fordii*), native to central and western China. A closely related source is *A. montana* of southeastern China, whose oil is so nearly identical that no distinction is made commercially. Oil differing from true tung in certain important qualities comes from the "Japanese wood-oil tree" (*A. cordata*), cultivated in southern Japan and Formosa, and from *A. moluccana* and *A. trisperma* in the Philippines.

Prior to World War II, China was the only large tung producing and exporting country. Farsightedly the United States Department of Agriculture in 1905 began experimenting with tung cultivation in America. By 1940 there were over 12,500,000 tung trees in the Gulf Coast States, Georgia, and South Carolina. Argentina, Brazil, Paraguay, and Uruguay are also producing tung oil in commercial quantities. Experiments in its production have been undertaken widely in the

CLUSTER OF TUNG FRUIT. About two or three inches wide and shaped like a
tomato, the dark olive-green fruit of the tung tree yields the most important
of all the drying oils. In 1941 the United States used about 49 million pounds
of tung oil.

Caribbean area but without much promise. A distinctly cool winter is beneficial for tung trees, which do best if dormant for three or four months each year.

The tung tree (*A. fordii*) attains a height of about 40 feet or more and an age of about 35 years. Because of its handsome appearance, it is often planted for ornamental purposes. Numerous clusters of snow-white or pinkish flowers are produced in spring and are followed by broad, dark-green leaves. The flower cluster is made up of one or more female flowers surrounded by a large number of male flowers. The tree normally begins to bear fruit at about the third year and should be in full production by the sixth or seventh. The dark-olive green fruit is two to three inches wide and shaped like a small tomato; it turns to dark brown at maturity. The outer husk encloses some three to seven seeds or nuts resembling a castor-bean in shape and color. Ripe fruits fall to the ground and are then gathered and air-dried to remove most of the moisture. In milling, the hard shell is removed, and the white, oily kernel is ground to meal. Then it is heated and put through an expeller to press out the oil. About 320 pounds of oil are extracted from a ton of air-dried whole fruit, but the yield varies.

There is an invaluable substitute for tung oil that is not even mentioned in most dictionaries—oiticica oil. It can be used for almost all military purposes where tung oil was formerly used, especially as a corrosion resisting coating for airplanes, guns, and ships. It is also used for electrical insulations, brake linings, clutch facings, food-container coatings, chemical resistant finishes, waterproof adhesive binders, and in the manufacture of resins. In peace time it serves as a component of pressed fiber boards, fiber bags, and linoleum.

The oiticica oil industry is a Brazilian monopoly. In ten years oiticica has risen to become Brazil's eleventh most important export commodity. Earlier efforts, dating from more than a century ago, failed to develop it commercially, and the first successful production was not achieved until 1930.

The oiticica tree is related to our cherries, plums, and peaches and is the only large native tree in the grasslands bordering the rivers and brooks in northeastern Brazil. It is a long-lived evergreen tree, which may grow to 100 feet or more in height. It is characteristically well-grown and round-headed, and it often grows in large stands, rather than singly. The outer branches frequently hang almost to the ground, where they may take root and form natural arches. The fruit is harvested from January to April, the single seed containing from 45 to 50 per cent oil. The seed is easily removed from the enveloping husk, and the oil is expelled by pressure with or without the action of solvents. The oil possesses a very unpleasant odor and is semisolid at ordinary temperatures. These properties greatly restricted its use until means were found for refining it and keeping it liquid.

A Brazilian writer says: "One who has traveled through northeastern Brazil in the year of a drought will never forget the sweet, cool, friendly shade of the leafy oiticica, which nature seems to have created to thrive just when all other inland vegetation is scorched and dried by the hot winds from the parched *catingas*. For many years the oiticica was used merely as a shade tree. The picturesque troop trains of the Northeast always rested in its ample shade. Under its evergreen leaves, countless travelers forgot for a time, while enjoying a pleasant rest, the inclemencies and annoyances of a hostile Nature and an exhausting climate. The oiticica was then used for no other purpose; even its wood was not exploited, and yet thousands of oiticacas dotted the monotonous landscape, amid the vast and desolate ash-colored fields."

Oiticica oil is used not only as a substitute in many cases for tung oil but also for some other drying oils. The production in Brazil increased 20 times in the three years ending 1938. This great increase has been due to more extensive gathering of seeds from wild trees. But experiments are also being conducted to produce high-yielding strains. Oiticica trees do not mature nearly as fast as do tung trees. However, seedlings budded from high-yielding trees begin to bear several years earlier than those not budded.

An oil that can serve similar purposes comes from another tree of the same genus, *Licania arborea,* native to southern Mexico and Central America. This tree is called the cacahuananche in Mexico, the alcornogue in Costa Rica, the encina in Honduras and Guatemala. Elsewhere it is known as the cana dulce and guirindal. Like the oiticica, it is found growing in open situations and not in regions covered with dense forests. The fruits and the kernels (decorticated seed) are about half the size of those of the oiticica tree. The kernels contain about 68 per cent of oil. The strong drying properties of this oil and its similarity to oiticica were only recently discovered in the United States. Both of these oils are semisolid at ordinary temperatures, but heating them to 210-225° C. for 20 or 30 minutes renders them permanently liquid so long as they are kept stored in well filled, tightly closed containers.

Another tree of Mexico and Central America whose nut appears to have properties as a drying oil is *Loncho-*

carpus roseus. Its oil is burned by the natives as a source of light, and from it is extracted a fatty acid useful in making candies. Preliminary reports indicate that a total of 1200 tons a year could be obtained in the state of Guerrero alone as a substitute for tung or oiticica.

Rapeseed yields a thick, nondrying or semidrying oil and is produced in large quantities in Asia as well as in various parts of Europe. This plant (*Brassica napus*) is well-known as the source of an aphrodisiac bird food, and it is grown as a forage crop for sheep and hogs. The oil is used in the United States in considerable quantities in sacramental lamps and, after blowing, in the preparation of certain lubricants for machinery. In the Western

NUMEROUS CLUSTERS of snow-white or pinkish blossoms appear in the spring. They are followed by broad dark-green leaves. The flower-clusters are made up of one or more female flowers surrounded by a large number of male flowers.

A FOUR- OR FIVE-YEAR-OLD TUNG TREE (*Aleurites fordii*). Tung trees grow to a height of 40 feet or more and live for about 35 years. They normally begin to bear fruit at about the third year and should be in full production by the sixth or seventh.

U. S. Department of Agriculture photos

Hemisphere, Argentina has been the largest producer. Steps are being taken in Mexico to increase rapeseed production materially.

High in the ranks of important vegetable oils is castor oil. Younger readers will probably be surprised that the familiar household use to which it is put accounts for only about one-tenth of the total quantity produced annually. No substitute has yet taken its place as a hydraulic fluid such as is used in retractable landing gear. It is used in the manufacture of sulfonated oil, large quantities of which are employed by the textile and leather industries. It also has a place in the production of certain "perfume aromatics," of sebacic acid (required for

THE RIPE FRUITS of the tung, now dark brown in color, fall to the ground and are gathered and air-dried to remove most of the moisture. About 320 pounds of oil can be extracted from a ton of dried whole fruit, but the yield varies.

making nylon, from which parachutes are made), certain soaps, typewriter inks, sticky fly papers, cellulose baking enamels, and imitation leathers. After being blown with air it is used in making lacquer paste colors and for purposes where a plasticizing oil is required.

Castor oil has no drying powers, and that accounts for its usefulness as a lubricant. Only after conversion into hydrated castor oil, sold under various trade names, is it useful as a drying oil. For certain purposes, the dehydrated oil serves more or less as a substitute for the notably stronger drying tung oil. Unlike the stronger drying tung oils, it has been found particularly satisfactory for use in making white enamel for various hospital and home equipment, including refrigerators. Since 1937, increasing quantities have been used for this purpose, as well as for making protective coatings and overprint and lithographic varnishes for the printing industries.

THE OUTER HUSK of the tung fruit encloses some three to seven seeds or nuts. In milling, the hard shell is removed and the white oily kernel is ground to meal. It is then heated and put through an expeller to press out the oil.

Another possible source of a very strong drying oil which recently has been investigated is that found in the seeds of the tree *Garcia nutans*, a member of the Euphorbia family. The tree grows wild in some parts of Mexico, Central America, Colombia, and Venezuela. In Mexico it is called pinonchillo, and in other countries it is known as the pascualito, avellano, and pepita del indio. The so-called nuts, obtained from Mexico, which look like small brown mottled marbles, consisted of 80.5 per cent of oil and 19.5 per cent shell. The expressed oil not only resembles tung oil in appearance but is found to be of similar composition and to possess the same valuable properties. Experiments indicate that it is even faster drying than tung oil.

In Ecuador collection of the nuts of a palm known locally as "palma real" or "wine palm" (*Ynesia colenda*) was greatly stimulated by conditions produced by the war. The tree grows wild in the forests, and the kernels yield an oil similar to that from other palm kernels, including coconut oil, and can be used for the same purposes. About 1500 tons of the nuts were gathered in 1941—probably twice that amount in 1942.

On rich lands in Mexico and Nicaragua, sesame (*Sesamum indicum*) is now being cultivated for its vegetable oil. Formerly it was imported almost exclusively from India and China; now it is an important export

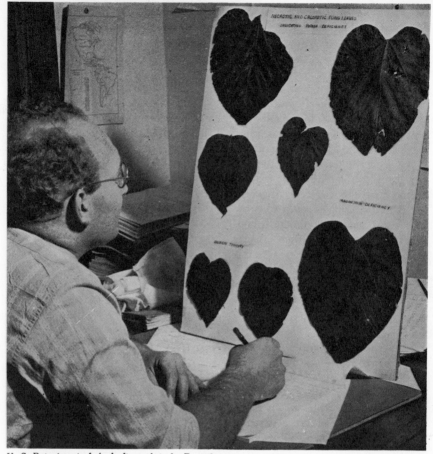

U. S. Department of Agriculture photo by Forsythe

BECAUSE TUNG OIL'S drying speed and water resistance are second to none, the U. S. Department of Agriculture in 1905 began experimenting with tung cultivation. By 1940, there were more than 12½ million tung trees in the United States. Above, Dr. F. S. Lagasse is studying abnormal foliage conditions of the tung with the purpose of determining nutrient deficiencies and requirements.

crop in the above-named Latin American countries, and further studies of its possibilities are planned.

Still another important vegetable oil is chia oil, derived chiefly from *Salvia hispanica*. It is employed in the manufacture of varnishes. In quality it is quite comparable to perilla oil and can be substituted for it. Varnishes made with it are given unusual luster. Its natural range extends from western Texas southward through the high tablelands of Mexico to northern South America. Attempts to grow it in several of our southern states failed. Yields on commercial plantations run up to 1115 pounds per acre, but the average is about 440 pounds. It is possible that chia oil from Mexico may find acceptance as a supplement for linseed and other drying oils essential in the economy of the United States and other industrial nations.

U. S. Department of Agriculture photo by Smith

THE CULTURE NEEDS of these foreign tung trees are studied to aid in the commercial plantings in this country. In a greenhouse at Beltsville, Maryland, the trees are grown in sand culture to determine their nutritional requirements and symptoms of malnutrition.

THE SEEDS OF CHIA, a desert-loving mint, are nutritious and delightfully flavored. In pure stands they could be harvested by machinery

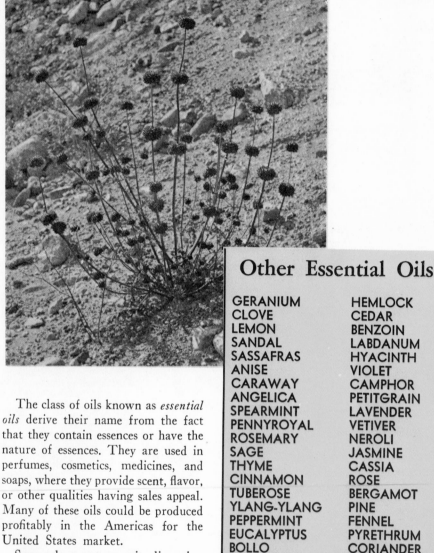

The class of oils known as *essential oils* derive their name from the fact that they contain essences or have the nature of essences. They are used in perfumes, cosmetics, medicines, and soaps, where they provide scent, flavor, or other qualities having sales appeal. Many of these oils could be produced profitably in the Americas for the United States market.

Space does not permit discussing them here in full. Lemon-grass oil (from *Cymbopogon flexuosus*), was formerly imported from India and is important for perfuming inexpensive soaps and as a source of citral in perfumery and flavoring. Half a million pounds were imported annually before the war. Citronella oil comes from a fragrant grass native to Ceylon

Other Essential Oils

GERANIUM	HEMLOCK
CLOVE	CEDAR
LEMON	BENZOIN
SANDAL	LABDANUM
SASSAFRAS	HYACINTH
ANISE	VIOLET
CARAWAY	CAMPHOR
ANGELICA	PETITGRAIN
SPEARMINT	LAVENDER
PENNYROYAL	VETIVER
ROSEMARY	NEROLI
SAGE	JASMINE
THYME	CASSIA
CINNAMON	ROSE
TUBEROSE	BERGAMOT
YLANG-YLANG	PINE
PEPPERMINT	FENNEL
EUCALYPTUS	PYRETHRUM
BOLLO	CORIANDER
FENUGREEK	BORAGE
WHITE MUSTARD	SAFFRON
POPPY SEED	MARJORAM
GOAT'S RUE	RATANY ROOT
SAGE	LEMON-GRASS
SOAB BARK	COPAIBA
ALLSPICE	LINALOE
BALSAM-OF-PERU	GUAYACO
TOLU	CAYENNE
FIR	LINALOE OIL

LAUREL OR BAY TREE
OF WEST INDIES

U. S. Department of Agriculture photo by Forsythe

FLAKED MATERIAL obtained by flaking tung kernals is being weighed at the Gainesville, Florida, station of the Bureau of Plant Industry. Tung oil is used in paint and brake linings, and in waterproofing.

and Java (*Cymbopogon nardus*) and is widely used in soaps and insect repellents. It is extremely important for the chemicals isolated from it, including geraniol, citronellal, and menthol, the first two being used in perfumery and the latter in medicine. Japan used to be our chief source of natural menthol, but for some years mint oil, the source of menthol, has been distilled from Japanese mint grown in one or more of our northwestern states; and

we have begun using menthol from citronella oil produced in Puerto Rico and Haiti.

Other essential oils are listed in the accompanying table.

Thus we see that natural oils, obtained from lowly wild and cultivated plants, are not only of tremendous value on the home-front in the perfumes of milady's toilette, the flavorings on dinner-tables, the ingredients of soaps and medicines, the shoes and raincoats we wear, and the linoleum on our floors, but often are also of strategic importance in the nylon of an aviator's parachute and the paint on a cannon or battleship, in the brake-linings of jeeps and the landing-gear of bombers.

Braconids

THE braconids are a large assemblage of insects, some of which are parasitic on aphids, others on caterpillars or other insect larvae. One of the latter type is shown here, with a caterpillar it has infested.

John H. Gerard photos from Monkmeyer Press

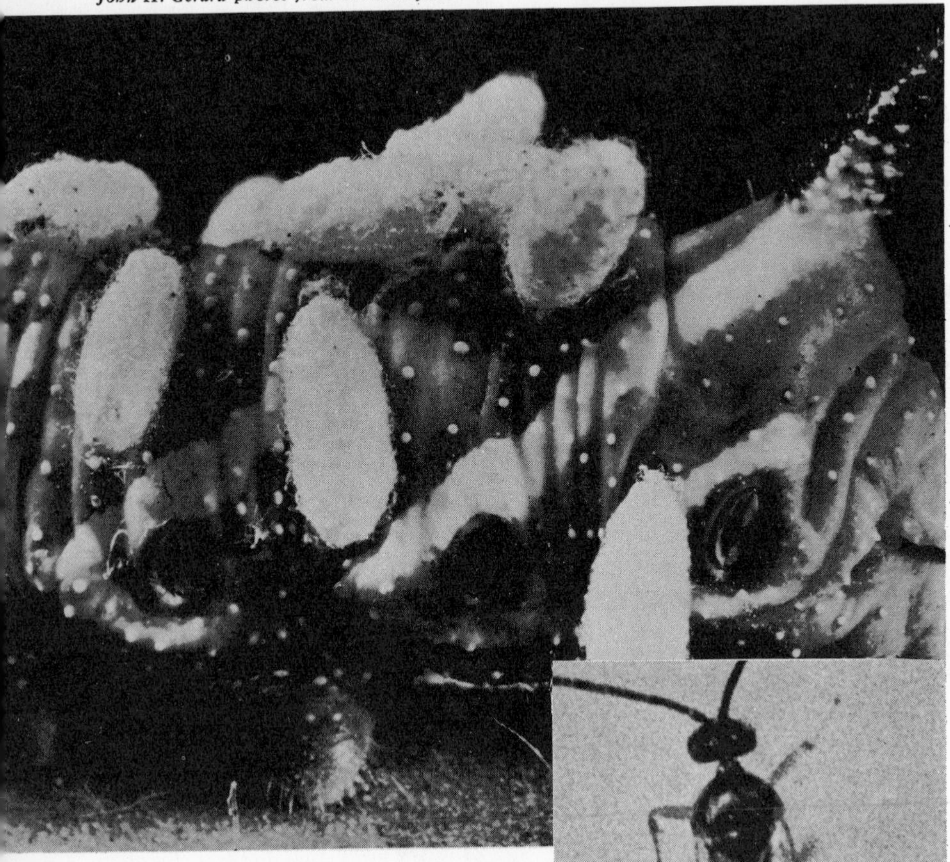

↟ ONE OF the braconid wasps has spun a number of its cocoons on this Hawk Moth caterpillar. The cocoons are about 3/16 inch long. The braconid larvae will eat much of the caterpillar's insides out during their sojourn.

➤ THIS IS THE BRACONID wasp that emerges. It is only 1/8 inch long, but it can cause the caterpillar a lot of trouble.

Paper-making Wasp

USING JAWS hinged at the sides of its head, the common paper-making wasp, *Polistes pallipes,* gouges out bits of wood to chew into pulp for nest making. It produced wood-pulp paper millions of years before man. In eighteenth century Europe, an experimental book was once printed on wasp-produced paper

Edwin Way Teale photo

Courtesy of the Ministerio de Fomento, Venezuela

(Left) TWENTY TIMES as high as Niagara and fully 1000 feet higher than its nearest competitor: Angel Falls, named after the venturesome aviator and prospector whose fearless forays into one of the least known areas of the world led to the scientific exploration of the "Lost World" of Auyan-tepui. Here the falls are shown at the end of the dry season, when their volume is smallest

The Highest Waterfall on Earth

The discovery of Angel Falls and the exploration of the "Lost World" in which it originates is as exciting a story of adventure as modern exploration can tell

By E. Thomas Gilliard

Associate Curator, Department of Birds, The American Museum of Natural History

WHEN Jimmy Angel, American soldier of fortune, aviator, and prospector, flew out of the jungles of Venezuela on a March evening in 1937, he divulged to his associates a series of tales unparalleled in the annals of twentieth century exploration. He told of a vast new range of mountains far to the south in the unknown Guiana Highlands, of a population of aboriginal natives, of rivers rich in

gold, of a plateau in the sky like a huge walled fortress "about 9000 feet high and from a quarter to half a thousand square miles in extent." Most amazing of all, while planing along the cliffs of this Lost World fortress, he had seen a huge waterfall "one mile high."

The mountain he described was not known to geographers. The region was a blank on the maps. Angel said that the jungle reached southward only about 100 miles beyond the Orinoco before it became broken by "hundreds of miles of fine upland grazing country, with savannas as flat as Newark Airport."

This and two other cliff-girt mountains previously discovered in Venezuela came to be called Lost Worlds in reference to the novel by Conan Doyle, *The Lost World,* in which an isolated tableland was found to be inhabited by prehistoric creatures.

On an early flight, Angel had actually landed a prospector named Bob Williamson on the summit. Stories circulated about fabulous gold deposits, and the "island in the sky" where Angel Falls tumbled over a mile-high cliff became the most glamorous land on earth.

Later in 1937, a well-known oil geologist named "Shorty" Martin flew in with Angel. He corroborated the existence of the gigantic waterfall and of Indians whose only association with the white man had been with Angel.

For another assault on the summit, Angel then enlisted the aid of Gustavo Heny, an expert woodsman, and Captain Felix Cardona one of South America's most colorful characters and perhaps the only white man in Venezuela who could outwalk an Indian.

After surveying Mt. Auyan-tepui from the ground and the air, Cardona discerned a narrow chimney crack in the sheer cliffs, through which he thought he might possibly attain the top. He and Heny attempted the climb. They wrestled for days with precipitous rocks and tortuous ledges. Finally they pulled themselves over the last barrier and stood on the summit—the first humans ever to scale this mighty monarch of the Guiana Highlands.

The hope of finding gold had been a strong spur, but three wall-like cliffs barred progress to the section of the mountain where Jimmy Angel thought the wealth might lie. Cardona and Heny managed to pass the first two barriers. However, the third great canyon, into which in all its towering majesty tumbled the giant waterfall, stopped them short.

Beyond it they sighted what looked like a possible landing field. This was the extent of their explorations on top of Auyan-tepui. Later, at the foot of the mountain, they discussed with Jimmy Angel the possibility of landing, and he decided to try it. The attempt was ill-fated. After what looked like a fine three-point landing, a bump

(Below) ARECUNA women carrying babies and loads. The tribe finally agreed to accompany the explorers up the mountain when their chief was offered his first ride in the great silver "thunderbird"

Dillon photo

of rock caught the plane's undercarriage. The tail tilted up, then flopped down into a bog, and gasoline began to drip from a wrenched seam. The party was able to descend after fourteen days.

In October of the same year, at the instigation and with the support of William H. Phelps, an eminent American businessman and scientist residing in Caracas, an American Museum expedition sailed from New York—destination Auyan-tepui. It had as its leader the experienced George H. H. Tate, just returned from a two-year trip with the Archbold Expedition in the interior of New Guinea, William F. Coultas, former leader of the Whitney South Sea Expedition, James A. Dillon, mammalogist, William H. Phelps and his son William H., Jr., and the writer as ornithologist. Captain Felix Cardona was engaged as trail finder and radioman. By the first of December we were in Ciudad Bolívar and ready to fly.

(Below) **Natural landing fields in a region supposed by many to be impenetrable jungle enabled planes to fly to a region that had never been reached on foot**

Heny photo

JIMMY ANGEL in a hut on his wilderness airfield below the lofty mountain.

Simpson photo

Weather permitting, four trips were to be made. Tate, Coultas, Cardona, and four peons would go on the first; Dillion and Billy Phelps on the second; myself on the third; and Mr. Phelps on the last.

I was sitting on the shaded porch ot the Gulf Oil headquarters sipping an iced drink, the last touch of civilization I was to have for almost four months, when the big Lockheed roared back from its second trip. Soon another cabin-load of equipment was in the plane, and, astride it, I was flying over Venezuela. About an hour later, after crossing the Orinoco and flying along the wild Caroni River basin, we passed under a snowy ceiling of clouds. Just before gliding down through a hole, I saw far off to the south a black island, Mt. Auyan-tepui protruding ominously through the mist.

Under a cloud blanket our plane followed a strange and dangerous course. The ceiling lay at about 900 feet; below was an endless green maze of tropical jungle, intermittently broken with a corkscrew river which wandered aimlessly over the country. This river, the Caroni, would offer our only escape from the region in case of accident. Sight of it recalled the ill-fated Eugène André expedition which was wrecked in the middle of the dangerous Arichi Rapids of the nearby Caura River while collecting for the Tring Museum, England. There had been fourteen men in the party, and all they could salvage was food calculated to last eight days and a small boat which held only eight men. Twenty-six days later, much nearer dead than alive, André and seven men emerged at La Prisión; the other six had died.

At length I began to see many stone pinnacles jutting up into the clouds like giant supporting columns. We flew for about an hour in an extremely bumpy layer, passing from room to room in this amazing series of giant caverns, until at last we approached a great forested wall. Our pilot skirted this, and after flying into what appeared to be a huge box canyon, he banked the plane and cut the motor.

Below I observed that there were a number of large, yellowish fields. The seemingly endless forest had ceased except for scattered clumps. Directly ahead were four little white flags pointing the way to our airfield, and to the right stood a palm-thatched hut and a group of strange looking individuals. Our plane nosed down toward the lowest landing field on the side of Auyan-tepui—the Lost World.

Heny photo

VERTICAL CLIFFS like these retarded Gustavo Heny and Captain Cardona in their ascent of Auyan-tepui.

A wilderness Woolworth's

In short order I became acquainted with the Arecuna Indians who clustered about the plane. In the thatched house I viewed the amazing barter shop which Bill Phelps had already set up. All manner of Woolworth's articles were dangling from a long clothesline, on which the poor Indians cast many a wishful look.

It seemed that with all of the potential labor standing about we might easily start at once for our proposed base camp. However, we discovered to our dismay that Alejo, their chief, who was on his way, would have to pass on any such venture. Furthermore, the Indians could never be made to climb the mountain, for it was in some manner regarded as a god. A *kanaima,* or evil one, would inflict injury upon any Arecuna who ventured to scale the lofty plateau.

Lopez Henriquez was tinkering with his plane when a tall, handsome, middle-aged Indian in ragged trousers emerged from the jungle, swinging a glittering machete—the chief. He stepped regally across the clearing, trailed by a score of men and women. The almost naked braves each clutched a bow and arrow or a blowgun. At each woman's neck was a squealing brown baby.

The chief's retinue approached in single file and stood stock-still. Cardona advanced to greet him. With a commanding gesture, majestic despite his tattered trousers, Alejo summoned his three advisers and followed the Captain to the tent where Tate, Billy Phelps, and Bill Coultas awaited the conference.

The silver bird wins the chief

Our best bartering would have failed, I believe, had not the old chief shown an insatiable desire to fly in the big bird. For he had several times trekked out to civilization and was prepared to insist that we pay in silver for everything. But in the end the stern chief strolled out to the silver bird, stroked its sides, and without a backward glance at his many wives, jumped into the cabin.

Lopez, the pilot, didn't like the idea. He grimly pocketed a monkey wrench as he clambered into the plane. The chief, establishing personal contact with a thunderbird for the first time, froze rigidly in his seat, staring straight ahead. He remained as immo-

Hundreds of feet of rope were carried on the first ascent, to be used on stretches like that shown below. Evil spirits believed to inhabit the mountain were not encountered, unless one took possession of the peon Genaro when later he ran screaming into the brush. But difficult rock work they met aplenty

Dillon photo

bile as a cigar-store Indian, while his tribesmen peered in the window. The plane lifted off the ground and flew out of sight.

Alejo left in command his eldest son, Jesús (pronounced Hay-soos), who began shouting orders to his tribesmen. The Indians shuffled up to shoulder their loads, totaling almost two tons. Cardona led the way up the mountain. Behind him trailed the 40 Arecunas, presenting a dramatic picture silhouetted against the sky.

When we reached the 3600-foot camp, from which we would attempt the assault on the summit, Tate was already putting its long palm-thatched shed in order, and Cardona was busy in the radio tent trying to recommission the short-wave set. This station, known as "YVGAH in the Guiana Highlands, calling Valery, Ciudad, Bolívar," had not been touched since Captain Cardona had contacted the outside world with it at the time of Angel's disaster.

Scientific work at once began at this level, and we found two nicely distinguished types of plant and animal life. To the north, about 100 yards from camp, a high, thick bank of tropical rain forest, growing in places to a height of 150 feet, contained many strange birds and mammals—deer, peccaries, giant anteaters, howling monkeys, tapirs, etc., and about 250 different kinds of birds. A number of these had never before been seen by man, and 26 species had not previously been known to live in Venezuela. Bellbirds, Cock of the Rock, toucans, parrots, macaws, and a host of small ground birds were found. To the south, beyond the Angel airfield, a stony slope with spaced-out trees and small patches of savanna proved to be the ideal habitation for all sorts of birds adapted to semiarid conditions. It was watered by a little stream from higher on the slopes of the giant mountain, and was scarred with tapir trails.

For several days an intensive collecting program went on unabated, but always we wondered when our leader would decide to attack the mountain. All went well, and amazingly enough Doctor Tate even pursuaded several of the Indians to carry loads up to the plateau. But a sad accident in far-off Caracas was destined to complicate matters seriously.

Felix Cardona, after tedious days of tinkering, had finally fixed the radio—the little magic machine that stood as a gateway to our safety, an avenue through which the staples of life, if necessary the marvels of surgery, could be summoned. The Captain got a rousing cheer when he walked out of the

radio tent, sweat dripping from his face, to announce that he had contacted Ciudad Bolívar. But he didn't smile. The first news he received was of a fatal accident to his son.

Cardona planned to leave us the following morning. He was the only man in our company who knew the difficult trail to the summit.

In the face of this turn of events there was no alternative but for Tate to undertake the ascent, unassisted. It was, therefore, decided that he should leave as scheduled with six natives. If he succeeded in finding an entrance through the Sanjón, the great chimney canyon through which Cardona and Heny had struggled to the top, he would establish a little camp near the rim, sending four men back with a letter of instructions. If, however, no Indians appeared, Mr. Phelps was to use his own judgment. Early the following morning Tate departed with his six men, carrying food and hundreds of feet of rope.

Cardona, however, ran into difficulties. No airplane could be found to take him out. With Tate gone, and with Cardona either in the sanctitude of his tent or glued to the earphones, the rest of us settled down to cutting hunting trails, to collecting and to watching the steep mountain slopes for signals, both day and night.

No signal

For four days we waited for Tate's Indians to return. Frequently during the day one of us watched through binoculars, but never so much as a flash of light or a wisp of smoke was seen. As the interval lengthened, Mr. Phelps became increasingly worried and decided that Captain Cardona should lead a supporting party. Cardona and four Indians undertook the climb and, much to my pleasure, I received orders to go along.

I set out early the following morning, little dreaming that with the exception of a small dish of rice, I wouldn't eat again for two and a half days. I had whipped together all the little things I thought I would need: gun, 100 rounds of the smallest, lightest bird shells, binoculars, a yellow flag for sending

Gilliard photo

(*Left*) SOUTH POINT, from just below the top wall, looking toward the base camp, which could be seen through binoculars on the plain far below. Flags were relied on (though not at this point) for signaling

Cardona photo

ANOTHER CASCADE, Iacha Falls, passes under the plane in the neighborhood of Mt. Auyan-tepui.

code from the drab rock background, Voigtlander and Leica cameras with as much film as I dared carry, an extra woolen shirt, scalpels, arsenic, cotton, two blankets, a roll of gauze and a bottle of iodine. The gun and cameras had shoulder straps, the rest was lumped into the pack I carried.

Cardona, my new leader, plodded

ahead; I followed the four heavily-laden Indians. My first leader had been Tate, my second Mr. Phelps, and now I was under the command of a man who could not understand a word of my native tongue, nor I his.

The heavy mist was replaced by rain before we were half over the jungle trail toward the edge of the 3600-foot shelf. The rich forest through which we passed continued for about three miles. Shortly after the first signs of the steep talus were reached, Tate's trail led us onto a vast, burned incline. Gaunt, denuded forests of seared trunks attested to the severity of a fire which had ravaged this area ten or fifteen years before, and the going was exceedingly difficult. After four hours of continuous climbing, partly with the aid of ropes rigged by Tate, we reached the crest of the 4900-foot terrace. Soon after, we met and passed the four mud-spattered Indians who had accompanied Tate. This meant that he had gained the summit and was encamped there.

Mud and orchids

After an unpalatable rice stew we turned in, anticipating the thrills that were to follow. It was pouring in torrents when I awoke at dawn. Much to my disgust Cardona gave orders that we start immediately without breakfast. For the first hour we climbed step after step in the bed of a gushing stream and then, leaving this, we headed into the burned remnants of a type of forest new to me. At times the mass of charred limbs through which we crawled, resembled a giant rhododendron entanglement. Elsewhere the peaty soil supported numerous bushes and beautiful ground orchids, both red and yellow, as well as spiny bromeliads about two feet in height resembling tall, slender cabbages open at the top. They were filled with rain water and, following Cardona's example, I drank from them. The process was rather disturbing until I learned to sift out the drowned insects with my teeth. The great cliffs were clad in mist, even the giant

Composite photo by Tate

(Above) THE LOST WORLD of Auyan-tepui, in Venezuela, a wonderland from whose 8000-foot rim plunges the recently discovered waterfall that dwarfs all others in height. The expedition sent by the American Museum, under the scientific leadership of Dr. G. H. H. Tate, sought to study the unusual plant and animal life that might be expected to survive on such an isolated tableland

(Left) MISHAP befell the party on top, which included Mrs. Angel, when their plane in landing settled into soft earth and gasoline began to drip from a sprung seam. Separated from the foot of the mountain by two weeks of difficult trail-breaking, their survival can be attributed to rare skill and persistence. The plane is still on top

(Lower Left) The Angel party on the way out. This is one of numerous rivers on top of the mountain whose waters probably combine to make the great plunge over Angel Falls

Heny photo, right

Simpson photo

SOON AFTER THE ESCAPE of Angel's party from the plane marooned atop Auyan-tepui, the American Museum expedition flew to the base of the mountain, prepared to scale it. Seated in the dining hut at left are shown William H. Phelps, of Caracas, who supported the expedition, Dr. G. H. H. Tate, its scientific director, William H. Phelps, Jr., and James A. Dillon, mammalogist

Gilliard photo

Sanjón crack through which we must pass.

About midafternoon we reached the first wall at an altitude of 6500 feet, a sheer cliff which towered straight up for about one and a half times the height of the Empire State Building. Following to the left, we entered a foggy cleft, walled on both sides. The trail through this narrow, steep canyon is unforgettable. It was so copiously littered with all of the boulders which in the last eon or so had toppled into it, that I felt like a chipmunk in the bottom of a stone quarry. To top this off there were literally hundreds of waterfalls pouring into the abyss. At many points Tate had laboriously rigged ladders and ropes. My clothes were saturated with water and my boots oozing; even the cigarettes and matches under my "Duck Back" hat had been drenched by a cascade of water.

The crew of Indians with their heavy burdens were having a desperate time. Cardona and I were forced to wait for them time and again. Once, pointing skywards, I made Cardona understand that I wanted to know how many hours it would be before we reached Tate. His answer was that we would be with Tate «en una hora.»

Tate photo

At the end of an hour we were still deep in the canyon, and shortly thereafter the fog thickened and we lost the trail completely. Dusk set in just as we found it, but the Indians had no intention of continuing.

Going back I found the four boys, drenched and freezing under a small overhang. Cardona was nowhere in sight. Breaking open my pack, I found some dry matches, and miraculously we started a small sputtering fire at the entrance of the cave. All of our blankets were soaked, and we were so famished and cold that sleep was impossible. All of that night we lay on the rocks in a human tangle.

When dawn broke, Captain Cardona, returning from wherever he had slept, directed in no uncertain terms that we begin still another day without so much as a mouthful of rice. The sun came out brightly and we obeyed, assuming naturally that Tate's camp was near at hand. Somehow we gained an altitude of 8000 feet and by way of a spectacular cat's path leading along the face of the cliff, suddenly found ourselves overlooking a vast, barren tableland. It was so frightfully cut by canyons that it appeared absolutely impossible to negotiate. At sight of this the Indians suddenly threw

(*Below*) Base camp adjacent to the improvised landing field under the very brow of the mountain. Radio communication was maintained here with civilization

down their loads, flatly refusing to budge without food.

To use a familiar axiom, "I didn't know what the score was," but I knew that somewhere out in the god-forsaken stretch of land a nice fire was burning and victuals were cooking. I loaded the old shotgun and headed defiantly past the group. For two hours I picked my way over a barely discernible trail. Finally at 10 a.m. I reached the top of a large loma. Down below, about two miles distant, I spied a little green tent hemmed in among the rocks. I fired one shell and, watching through my binoculars, saw a figure run out of the tent. It was Tate. With the Morse flag attached to the barrel of my gun, I sent him two words: "Mutiny"—"Starved." The poor man probably thought that the base camp had been ambushed and eaten, but at any rate I got results.

Perhaps an hour later in one of those incredible places, where the trail tunneled along anywhere from five to 20 feet above the ground in the upper limbs of an ancient pygmy forest, Tate and I practically bumped heads. Tate's eyes flashed as he listened to my tale, but before undertaking to find Cardona and the Indians he shouldered my pack and led me to food and bed.

The Indians were eating rice when Tate found them with Cardona. After the meal they left for the base camp with a written note from Tate to Phelps. At last we were on the summit of the Lost World. The whole area looked like "the land which God gave to Cain." The canyons, fissures, walls, and entanglements of foliage greatly impeded progress anywhere.

During the next five weeks 32 species of subtropical birds, a great many mammals, and many plants were collected. Most of the boggy humus area was overgrown with a forest of a *Bonnetia roraimae* averaging about fifteen feet in height. This tree, related to the tea group, had previously been known only at the plateau of Mt. Roraima. Here and there throughout this forest were little swamps in which pitcher plants, xyrids, and pipeworts were found.

Now, it had been our fond hope that, once on top of the mountain, we could find Angel's disabled plane. We knew that it probably contained supplies, and that its roomy cabin was waterproof. There I visualized myself skinning birds comfortably amidst the fascinating instruments. But search as we would, we could not find it. Time after time we ran across parts of the trail Gustavo Heny had used in his escape from the wrecked airplane, and our esteem for his woodsmanship grew; but still we could not find our way to the plane.

One morning while collecting in the vicinity of the highest part of Auyan-tepui, I followed a flock of paroquets *(Nannopsittaca panychlora)*

(Right) FIELD LABORATORY: Dillon, Bill Phelps, and Tate at the table where Auyan-tepui's interesting and specialized animal life was examined and prepared for shipment to the American Museum

with my eight-power glasses until they disappeared over the plateau beyond the third wall. This had happened before, and it occurred to me that the vegetation of that area must be much more abundant. Then, as I looked at the far-off plateau, some seven miles distant, a tiny point of light suddenly caught my eye. Through the glasses I made out the lines of a silvery body. We had found the plane.

Tate was incredulous when I told him. Going back with him I pridefully pointed out the general spot and then threw my glasses into range. The airplane was gone! I scrutinized the far-off plateau for some time and finally thought I could make out the field in

which I had seen it. The morning sun had changed position just enough to divert the reflection, and had I not looked just when I did, I should never have seen it.

The plane was much closer than we expected, and its discovery gave us all new enthusiasm. In a day or two we had packed up summit camp No. 1, all but the tent, an emergency supply of food, and a primus stove, and had proceeded north to establish the summit camp No. 2.

Food was a pressing problem, and it was not until the third batch of it had arrived that we began to have faith in the possibility of ever reaching the great plateau beyond. Mr. Phelps

AN abandoned camp of the Angel party *(at right)* spurred the search for the plane, whose cabin might serve as a dry field laboratory. Ultimately the glint of its silver wings was spied some seven miles away. But intervening canyons like the one shown below prevented the expedition from ever reaching it. Against serious difficulties the scientific work was pushed forward, and during five weeks a great number of plant and animal specimens were collected to enrich the Museum's fund of rare types

Gilliard photos

at the base camp had succeeded in bribing four stout Indians to make two trips up the mountain. The two peons who had arrived with Tate grumbled at the "horrible" cold and rain and almost incessant mist, and one day packed up and left. A few days after arriving on top, Cardona started the long trek back to civilization on foot, with five peons.

We weren't doing so well. We were only at the beginning of a very tough job. But the sixth peon, Genaro, a big strapping Venezuelan with a constant smile, was with us, and he, Tate, Bill and myself transported the food, shelter, and housing.

The giant boulders, crevasses, canyons and the no-man's-land of thickets, which during the next 25 days succeeded in blocking our frantic efforts to find a pass over the colossal third wall, proved to be the habitat of many new and fascinating birds. We had been in this camp four days when Genaro suddenly broke out in a fit. He screamed incoherently and ran off to the river. We did our best to console him, because we liked the fellow and we were in desperate need of his assistance. Nothing did any good, however, and some time later he wandered away.

Food shortage

Things looked very bad. All of the Indians below except Jesús, the chief's son, refused to climb the mountain. None of the peons remained, and we were in the middle of the plateau, our goal practically at hand and as yet untapped. When I made the gross error of cooking an anteater and a few pancakes, the boss installed me as cook and manager of the commissary. Taking stock, I figured that we had enough food to last five days. Instead of five days, I starved the boys for 22 days.

The Indian, Jesús, was a blessing.

About every six days his lonely call would drift into camp, announcing that once again the boy who had promised the chief to assist us, was approaching with a five-gallon tin of food and equipment. Bill Phelps took on a huge load of bird and mammal skins and departed with Jesús. Coultas, staggering under a heavy load, returned with him, stayed a short while, and then started the three-day trek out with more of the invaluable zoological specimens. Mr. Phelps and Dillon were the next to undertake gallantly the backbreaking job of carrying sustenance to us and of hauling the priceless scientific booty back to the base camp.

As the days flew by we gradually gave up the idea of reaching the plateau beyond. This was a bitter pill to swallow for we were within two miles of the airplane and the greatest waterfall on earth spouted about a mile and a half away. Gold, waterfall, a luxuriant plateau of unimaginable treasure, the wrecked airplane—all were lost to us beyond that walled horizon.

Seven days without sugar, two days without meat, no vegetables for ten days, no cigarettes for a week, and no more to come. The men looked to me to produce another cache of sugar or meat, but the inevitable had come.

We packed our birds, mammals, plants, insects and photographs. Carrying these and the most valuable equipment, such as guns and cameras, we departed with hardly a backward glance at the fine tents left standing in a scene of unimaginable desolation. I wondered if man would ever see them again.

General Eleazar Lopez-Contreras, President of Venezuela, who had taken a keen interest in our expedition and who had granted many invaluable facilities, was immensely enthusiastic over the results. Not long after our return he commissioned a group of geologists, archaeologists, and engineers to make a survey of the areas surrounding Mt. Auyan-tepui. Dr. George Gaylord Simpson of the American Museum of Natural History, a prominent paleontologist, accompanied the party. Angel, who had obtained another plane, was again engaged as pilot.

In December, 1939, a large volume entitled *Revista de Fomento* was issued by the Venezuelan Government. This work contains the findings of this party and is packed with information, photographs and maps regarding their explorations and surveys. Appearing therein is the full-page illustration of *Salto Angel* (Angel Falls), showing them from top to bottom. This was taken from Angel's plane by the geologists and topographers who, to quote Doctor Simpson "could hardly believe their eyes."

These conservative scientists have recorded in the geological report that Angel Falls are in excess of 3300 feet. Doctor Simpson suggests that even this figure may be too conservative. He saw the falls on March 8th, 1939, at the end of the dry season in their lowest ebb and he tells me that "the altimeter in Jimmy's plane showed the canyon to be about 6500 feet deep and the falls jumped most of that distance." He believes that they may be 5000 feet high—nearly one mile!

The appropriate honor bestowed in naming the falls after Jimmy Angel makes them a monument to the courage and persistence of this explorer-aviator and soldier of fortune.

The full story of this exploration leaves in all of us a profound sense of the high adventure that yet remains in a world that is often thought to hold nothing new.

(Below) **For subsequent visitors: a cairn built by G. H. H. Tate and William H. Phelps, Jr., just prior to abandoning the mountaintop. Few have ever reached this remote plateau of the world's highest waterfall. Beyond it are visible many other wholly unexplored tablelands**

Gilliard photo

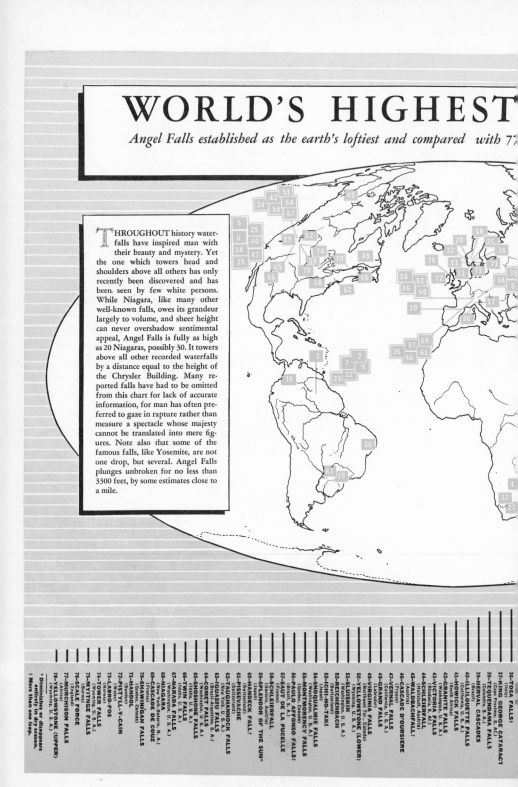

WORLD'S HIGHEST

Angel Falls established as the earth's loftiest and compared with 77

THROUGHOUT history waterfalls have inspired man with their beauty and mystery. Yet the one which towers head and shoulders above all others has only recently been discovered and has been seen by few white persons. While Niagara, like many other well-known falls, owes its grandeur largely to volume, and sheer height can never overshadow sentimental appeal, Angel Falls is fully as high as 20 Niagaras, possibly 30. It towers above all other recorded waterfalls by a distance equal to the height of the Chrysler Building. Many reported falls have had to be omitted from this chart for lack of accurate information, for man has often preferred to gaze in rapture rather than measure a spectacle whose majesty cannot be translated into mere figures. Note also that some of the famous falls, like Yosemite, are not one drop, but several. Angel Falls plunges unbroken for no less than 3300 feet, by some estimates close to a mile.

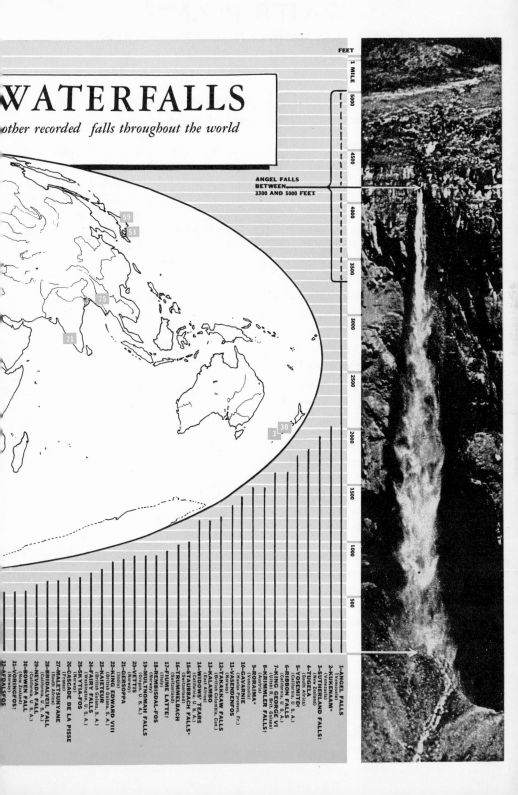

WATERFALLS

other recorded falls throughout the world

FEET

1 MILE

5000

4500

ANGEL FALLS
BETWEEN
3300 AND 5000 FEET

4000

3500

3000

2500

2000

1500

1000

500

1-ANGEL FALLS
(Venezuela)
2-KUKENAM*
(Venezuela)
3-SUTHERLAND FALLS†
(New Zealand)
4-TUGELA
(South Africa)
5-YOSEMITE*
(California, U. S. A.)
6-RIBBON FALLS
(California, U. S. A.)
7-KING GEORGE VI
(British Br. Guiana)
8-KAIEMMLER FALLS†
(Australia)
9-RORAIMA*
(Venezuela)
10-GAVARNIE
(Pyrenees, Fr.)
11-VASENDENFOS
(Norway)
12-TAKAKKAW FALLS
(British Columbia, Can.)
13-KALAMBO
(East Africa)
14-WIDOWS' TEARS
(California, U. S. A.)
15-STAUBBACH FALLS*
(Switzerland)
16-TRUMMELBACH
(Switzerland)
17-FIUME LATTE†
(Italy)
18-REMBISSDAL-FOS
(Norway)
19-MULTNOMAH FALLS
(Oregon, U. S. A.)
20-VETTIS
(Norway)
21-GERSOPPA
(India)
22-KING EDWARD VIII
(British Guiana, S. A.)
23-KAIETEUR
(British Guiana, S. A.)
24-FAIRY FALLS
(Washington, U. S. A.)
25-SKYTJA-FOS
(Norway)
26-CASCADE DE LA PISSE
(France)
27-MALETSUNYANE
(South Africa)
28-BRIDALVEIL FALL
(California, U. S. A.)
29-NEVADA FALL
(California, U. S. A.)
30-BOWEN FALL
(New Zealand)
31-VORINGFOS†
(Norway)
32-AFDALSFOS
(Norway)

WATER PLANTS
FOR HOME CULTIVATION

Old and New Plants for Use in Home Aquaria and Garden Pools

By E. J. ALEXANDER

Associate Curator, The New York Botanical Garden

AMATEUR gardeners have shown great interest in aquatic plants that may be easily grown in home aquaria and pool gardens. The New York Botanical Garden has featured these among its exhibits, endeavoring to acquaint the public with some of the most attractive and interesting of the cultivated aquatic and swamp plants. In addition to ones already well-known, the writer will describe some that are less familiar, with which the reader may like to try his hand.

Besides these already fairly well-known species, others are described here because of their undoubted value for aquaria and pools, could they be introduced. It is hoped, in fact, thus to arouse interest in their collection and subsequent cultivation.

Aquatic plants, though many belong to the same families as terrestrials, are found to have definite peculiarities of structure. As a general rule they are simpler than land plants.

In true aquatics (submerged plants) there are but few types of leaves: broad-elliptic or oblong, long and straplike, or short and extremely narrow, or divided into a number of fine threads. These leaves, as well as the stems, have very little cuticle, or hard, protecting surface, so that water containing the dissolved salts and gases needed by the plant for food passes in easily. There are no air-pores, and but few wood-vessels, and such roots as are present are not for absorbing food, but merely to fasten the plant to the bottom; there are very few

if any root-hairs. These plants grow rapidly, often branch freely, and reproduce mostly by vegetative means instead of by seed; often they do not flower freely. In a few cases, flowers are fitted for pollination under water, the water acting as a pollen-carrying medium, and some are adapted for pollination at the surface. In most, however, the floral parts are borne above the water where pollination is effected as in land plants, either by wind or by insects.

On the vast majority of floating leaves the entire undersurface is transformed into a thick, spongy, but fleshy tissue. Leaf-stalks or stems which are inflated have the same structure, as an aid in keeping them afloat. These floating leaves otherwise have the same general structure as those of land plants, but they bear air-pores (stomata) on the upper surface, which is covered with cuticle or wax to prevent wetting.

While water plants represent only a small percentage of seed-bearing plants, they are widely scattered through the plant kingdom. The greater number, however, are found among the more simply organized plant groups.

At the bottom of the class of flowering plants is the large order of Naiads, containing nearly all of the truly aquatic members of the division of monocotyledons. In this group are the two similar appearing genera, *Zannichellia*, the horned-pondweeds, and *Ruppia*, the ditch-grasses, both consisting of tangled masses of threadlike stems and leaves.

Photograph by courtesy of
J. K. Small

WATER-HYACINTH

Eichornia crassipes is a native of tropical South America.   In Florida where this plant has become a pest, it is known as "lilac-devil"

WATER-POPPY

Hydrocleis nymphoides, native of tropical America, is a handsome subject for planting out in summer in ponds or pools, where its large, yellow flowers make a fine display

WATER-MOSS
A plant of cold waters is *Fontinalis antipyretica* of the north temperate zone. To do well in aquaria, this must have cool water, as heat kills it

The pondweeds, genus *Potamogeton*, are attractive plants in nature with elliptic or short, straplike leaves, beautifully veined, underwater, or in some species narrow, grasslike leaves. Some, as they approach the flowering stage, develop elliptic, floating leaves. Only a few of them, however, are satisfactory under cultivation.

The genus *Naias* contains a number of species, mostly slender-stemmed and much-branched, with short, slender, bright green leaves, usually toothed.

Still among the Naiads, the genus *Aponogeton*, the water-hawthorns, have underwater leaves which are long and ribbon-like, tongue-shaped, or elliptic, with elliptic floating leaves and forked spikes of fragrant flowers. The lace-plant of Madagascar, with large, broadly elliptic leaves consisting solely of a lace-like, open network, is one of the members of this genus, though it is sometimes separated out under the name of *Ouvirandra*.

The water-plantains, *Alisma*, and the arrowheads, *Sagittaria*, both familiar plants around New York, as well as a number of related genera, are also much used. They mostly have straplike underwater leaves, and elliptic or arrow-shaped ones above water. A few species have floating leaves and one has tubular-shaped ones. They all have white, pink, or yellowish flowers.

The so-called flowering rushes are most attractively represented by the water-poppy, *Hydrocleis nymphoides*, whose floating stems bear heart-shaped leaves. Its flowers look like large three-petaled yellow poppies afloat on the surface. The flowering rush itself is a large, handsome, hardy plant, well suited to outdoor use.

The frog-bits have a number of representatives among which are two of the most important aquarium plants, wild

AT THE EDGE OF A
POND

At the right is a plant-
ing of papyrus. In the
left rear are lotuses,
and in the foreground,
water-hyacinths, par-
rot's-feather, and
water lilies

WATER LILY

The best known and
most beautiful of aqua-
tics can, because of the
variation in size among
different species, be
grown in a large aqua-
rium, a tub, or small
pool, as well as in large
tanks and ponds

ONE OF THE FINEST OF THE MILFOILS

Myriophyllum pinnatum is bright green in color. Note the two types of leaf.   The less dissected ones are on shoots which were aërial, but, upon being submerged, the more divided underwater form developed

celery and water-weed.   The wild celery or eel-grass, *Vallisneria*, is recognized by its long ribbon-like leaves and spirally coiled stalks, which carry the female flowers to the surface and withdraw them again after pollination. *Anacharis,* the water-weed, has the short, narrow leaves borne in close whorls along the stem.

The true frog-bit is a floating plant with heart-shaped leaves and three-petaled white flowers. The related water soldier or water-aloe, a European plant, has aloe-like leaves with spiny margins, and white, three-petaled flowers. The plant sinks to the bottom in winter when the leaves become incrusted with lime from the water, and rises to the surface in the spring, because of the relative lightness of the young leaves.   The two genera *Boottia* and *Ottelia* are other foreign members of this family which are also very deserving of cultivation.   *Boottia* has long, beauti-

fully veined leaves underwater, and heart-shaped ones above, sometimes growing two or three feet high, while *Ottelia* has leaves varied in shape, which often reach a foot in length in running water.   So much for the greater majority of monocotyledonous aquatics.

THE WATER-NUT, *Trapa natans*, NATIVE OF EURASIA.   A LITTLE-USED CURIOSITY IS THIS FLOATING PLANT SUPPORTED BY ITS BLADDERY-INFLATED LEAFSTALKS. THE "NUTS" ARE EDIBLE

ADAPTED FROM REICHENBACH

Icones Flora Germanica

TWO GRACEFUL AQUATIC PLANTS
The plant at the left is the fanwort, *Cabomba caroliniana,* a close relative of the water lily, native of the southeastern United States. *Sphagnum macrophyllum,* a recently introduced moss, is on the right. The sphagnum has lost its green color and is transparent with a brownish cast

Among the higher Monocotyledons in the Order of Poales, the grasses and sedges, are some swamp plants already in cultivation as aquatics. The only truly aquatic grass is the Asiatic genus *Hygrorrhiza,* with broad, lance-shaped leaves floating on the surface, dangling feathery roots in the water. Species of *Scirpus* and *Eleocharis* of the sedges are both used under the name of hair-grass. When kept under water, they consist only of masses of threadlike, branched stems. *Websteria submersa,* a recently introduced sedge, bears its threadlike leaves in dense clusters. The papyrus-plant, *Cyperus papyrus,* though very large, is valuable for outdoor pools. The so-called umbrella palm, *Cyperus alternifolius,* with a number of grasslike leaves borne umbrella-like at the top of the long stem, is also rather popular.

In the family of the arums and calla lilies are some of the most decorative of aquatic plants. The best, because readily available and easily grown, is *Cryptocoryne,* two types of which are used, one with long, narrow, tongue-like leaves, and one with elliptic leaves sometimes heart-shaped at the base. How many species are involved is doubtful, as flowers, which are necessary for satisfactory identification, are rare. *Pistia,* the water-lettuce or shell-plant, with velvety, pale green leaves, is an attractive floating plant. The golden-club (genus *Orontium*), while too large for an aquarium, is fine for outdoor pools, where its large blue-green leaves and club-shaped spikes of yellow flowers are quite showy.

A number of members of the duckweed family are used as surface-floaters. These tiny plants are the smallest flowering plants known, consisting of scalelike plant bodies with solitary or few roots, or in some cases none at all. Some of them appear individually as mere green

THREE EXCELLENT AQUARIUM PLANTS
On the left is *Naias flexilis*, a fragile plant, not much in use at present; in the center, one of the bladderworts, *Utricularia;* on the right *Anacharis canadensis*, native of North America

dots on the water, some like a few green threads.

The genus *Mayaca* forms its own family. The plants look like overgrown mosses, but have small white, three-petaled flowers. These plants may be recognized by their two-pronged leaf-tip easily seen under a lens.

A few species of *Eriocaulon,* the pipeworts. with stiff, dagger-shaped leaves in a cluster, and long-stalked heads of flowers, looking like hatpins, are also used.

DISTINCTIVE TYPES AMONG AQUATICS
On the left is one of the *Potamogetons;* in the center, one of the figworts, *Herpestis rotundifolia;* on the right is the parrot's-feather, this submerged form being not as attractive as the surface-running one

Juncus repens, a rush with a flattened, two-edged stem, bearing at its joints tufts of a few flattened leaves, is cultivated under the name of underwater palm. Most rushes in fact, are swamp or wet-ground plants.

The showiest of monocotyledonous aquatics are the members of the pickerelweed family. Some of these have fleshy, round, or elliptic leaves, and grow in mud or shallow water; some float by means of inflated spongy leaf-stalks, and some have grasslike leaves. All, except one yellow species of the grassy-leaved ones, have blue or lilac flowers.

Passing into the dicotyledonous division of plants, the number of aquatics is proportionately much smaller.

In the buttercup genus are nearly a score of aquatic species with finely dissected leaves, long floating stems, and white or yellow flowers. Some have the surface leaves cut or lobed but not dissected.

The beauties among aquatics are the water lilies. The fanworts, genus *Cabomba*, scarcely betray their relationship to the true water lilies, for they have finely dissected, opposite leaves on a stem that trails through the water; only at flowering time do a few round or elliptic floating leaves develop.

The water shield, *Brasenia*, has elliptic, floating leaves with the stalk centrally attached, giving them the appearance responsible for the common name. The lotuses have very large shieldlike leaves borne well above the water, and large yellow, white, or pink flowers.

The true water lilies, whose round, floating leaves and beautiful sweet-scented flowers in shades of white, yellow, pink, rose, red, blue, and purple, and with variously purple-mottled leaves, are familiar water-garden subjects. The spatterdocks or yellow pond lilies have similar leaves, but their flowers are less showy, appearing like small, yellow balls afloat. In the young state they are frequently used in aquaria, as their earlier leaves are submerged. Most of the remaining members of this family, although equally attractive, are too large for home cultivation.

Ceratophyllum, the hornwort, which forms its own family and is also appro-

On the left is *Mayaca fluviatilis* of tropical America; on the right *Naias flexilis robusta*, more stiff-growing than the typical form

priately called mare's-tail, coontail, or foxtail, is a submerged plant with close whorls of forked, threadlike leaves, a beautiful thing in an aquarium.

In the mustard family, the aquatics are the well-known watercress, and the tiny, little-known awlwort, *Subularia*. The tiny plants such as *Subularia*, *Limo-*

BUCKBEAN, *Menyanthes trifoliata*, A HANDSOME PLANT OF COLD BOGS IN EURASIA AND NORTH AMERICA

sella, and *Littorella* should be particularly useful in underwater landscaping where subjects which will never reach a large size are desired.

In the sundew family, *Aldrovanda*, a relative of the Venus's flytrap, has the same habit of growth as the hornwort, with the addition of leaf-tips formed to catch insects by a quick spring motion.

The spurge family has but one true aquatic representative, *Phyllanthus fluitans*, of South America. It is a floating or shallow-water plant with a running stem bearing nearly round leaves, and looks much like a *Salvinia*.

The genus *Callitriche* has members which are similar in appearance to and often confused with *Anacharis*. In fact, they go by the name of dwarf-anacharis. These may, however, be distinguished by the three veins in the leaves, whereas in the true genus *Anacharis* there is only one

vein. So similar to *Callitriche* that flowers are sometimes required to determine which is which, is the waterwort, *Elatine*, member of a small aquatic family.

In the evening-primrose family, members of the genus *Isnardia*, called Ludwigias by reason of their original botanical name, are much used. They have obovate often reddish leaves on long running stems. The sister genus *Ludwigiantha*, with short, narrow leaves, is often confused with it.

The water-nuts, interesting natives of Europe and Asia, with peculiarly shaped floating leaves and horned, nutlike fruits, are excellent for outdoor pools or ponds.

The popular water-milfoils, *Myriophyllum*, are the most feathery of all aquatics, with their stems densely clothed with finely dissected leaves. The closely related genus *Proserpinaca* is a delicate plant when grown submerged, quite similar but less leafy. The true mare's-tail, *Hippuris*, with leaves like *Anacharis*,

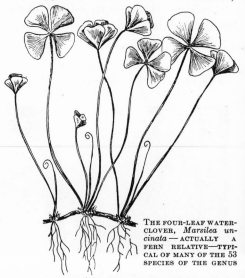

THE FOUR-LEAF WATER-CLOVER, *Marsilea uncinata* — ACTUALLY A FERN RELATIVE—TYPICAL OF MANY OF THE 53 SPECIES OF THE GENUS

but in whorls of 6–12 each, is also a member of the same family.

The pennywort, *Hydrocotyle*, often found bordering wet meadows, or in shallow water, is being grown as an aquarium plant. A member of the carrot family, it has running stems from which long-stalked, round leaves arise. *Lilaeopsis*, a related genus, has flattened, paddle-shaped leaves only about an inch long. Other members of this family will develop finely cut leaves when grown under water.

Among the primroses, two wet-ground plants are used—the water-pimpernel, with a lettuce-like cluster of small leaves. and the moneywort or creeping-Charlie, with long flexible stems and small round leaves in pairs.

Noteworthy as truly aquatic are the two featherfoils, *Hottonia inflata*, the curious American species, and *Hottonia palustris*, the European, which resembles a milfoil, except for the spike of purplish flowers which gives it the name of water violet.

In the buckbean tribe of the gentian family, we find a few interesting genera. Best known of these is the genus *Nymphoides*, called floating-heart, or water-snowflake, with heart-shaped floating leaves and clusters of short-stalked white or yellow flowers at the base of each leaf. The buckbean, *Menyanthes trifoliata*, with large fleshy, cloverlike leaves and a handsome spike of hairy pinkish-white flowers, is a good subject for shallow ponds.

Among the figworts, the family of the foxgloves and snapdragons, there are many creeping plants with small round or paddle-shaped leaves which grow in shallow water, among them the mudwort, *Limosella*, which alters its leaves to rushlike ones when submerged. One Oriental genus, *Limnophila*, which has delicate, finely cut leaves similar to those of *Myriophyllum* is worth attempting to obtain from Asia.

The family from which we obtain sesame or benne-seed has an aquatic member, *Trapella*, with leaves and seed pods somewhat like those of the waternut, but with tubular flowers. This rare Chinese plant is deserving of cultivation.

The largely aquatic family of the bladderworts has many members which grow floating just beneath the surface of the water. They have slender stems and leaves so finely dissected as to appear like clusters of green threads. These leaves bear tiny bladders with bristles at their mouths, in which minute aquatic animals are trapped.

Among the plantains, the shoreweed *Littorella* is the only aquatic—a small

THE MERMAID-WEED, *PROSERPINACA PECTINATA*
A native of cold swamps in North America. Related to the water-milfoils, this plant is coarser and more densely leafy when grown in shallow water

Aldrovanda vesiculosa

A CURIOUS PLANT OF THE OLD WORLD, WHOSE LEAVES ACT AS "FLY TRAPS." ADAPTED FROM ENGLER & PRANTL. *Pflanzenfamilien*

AQUATIC BUTTERCUPS. — THREE TYPES OP WATER-CROWFOOTS, *Ranunculus Lenormandi, R. heterophyllus, R. trichophyllus.* NATIVES OF EUROPE. ADAPTED FROM *Further Illustrations of the British Flora* BY BUTCHER & STRUDWICK

Trapella sinensis, A RARE FLOATING PLANT NATIVE OF CHINA, ADAPTED FROM *Annals of Botany*

plant with rushlike leaves one or two inches long.

In the Lobelia family, *Lobelia Dortmanna,* the water lobelia is aquatic. This has a cluster of short, blunt, rushlike leaves, with a flowering stalk that rises well above the water.

The family of the daisies and thistles has fine aquatic members which might well be cultivated. *Sclerolepis,* native of southern coastal swamps, is similar in appearance to the mare's-tail, *Hippuris,* but has a head of pink flowers. The water-marigold of northeastern North America, *Bidens Beckii,* has leaves much like *Cabomba,* but more finely cut, and a daisy-like head of yellow flowers. The genus *Cotula* has a member with *Ceratophyllum*-like leaves, growing only on the Cape of Good Hope. The two genera *Pectis* and *Erigeron* each have a desirable aquatic member in Mexico.

Besides the preceding flowering plants, a number of algae, hepatics, mosses, ferns, and fern-like allies are also aquatic and greatly ornamental.

Among the algae the two genera *Chara* and *Nitella* are used in aquaria. These plants consist of many much-branched green stems, the stems having whorls of branches, which are commonly again branched.

Among the hepatics, *Riccia fluitans* is used, forming carpets of green on or just under the surface of the water. The plant-bodies are long, slender, and forked. Another member of the same family, *Ricciocarpus natans,* broader and coarser and floating on the surface, is rarely found in aquaria but might well be more widely introduced.

Among the mosses the genus *Fontinalis* is best known, its long, much-branched plants growing attached to rocks, the branches floating in the water. In the genus *Sphagnum* are some species which can be made aquatic. These have brown stems and the dense branches are closely set with pale yellow-green leaves, which usually lose all color when submerged for a long time. These, with *Potamogeton* and *Ceratophyllum* require cool water for growth. Other mosses no doubt will also be found usable as aquaria are developed.

Among the ferns the genus *Ceratopteris*, known as floating ferns, are attractive underwater as well as floating plants. They have much-branched, coarse, fern-like leaves when mature, but in the young stage are not divided, but are frequently deep-lobed.

Among the fern-allies the number of aquatics is larger. The genus *Azolla* floats on the surface, its plant-body resembling a *Riccia*, but more frilly and lacelike. *Salvinia* also floats on the surface, its round, hairy fronds and feathery "roots"—which are strangely modified leaves—being distinctly attractive. Members of the genus *Marsilea* are very popular, but identification of species is impossible without the fruiting-bodies. All of them have four-parted, long-stalked leaves which somewhat resemble four-leaf clovers. The quillworts, *Isoëtes*, have long tufts of tubular leaves, in the bulblike bases of which are borne the reproductive spores. The plants look like clumps of seedling onions, and all of them may be grown completely submerged.

Some amphibious plants still retain the ability to become either terrestrial or aquatic, as will be found by planting seeds in soil both above and under water, in which case, although the first-formed leaves are similar, later ones will take on totally different forms. Many swamp plants or even those of damp ground may be adapted to aquatic conditions, in which case the process can be observed in the change of leaf-form. Plants with long, narrow, untoothed leaves become narrower and longer in proportion, while those with toothed or broad leaves become dissected, and some lose the leaf-blade entirely, the more or less modified petioles serving as leaves.

Water plants naturally are much more widespread than land plants, because their seeds are often carried by migrating water fowl, and because water conditions in different regions are so much more alike than those of land, that these plants have less difficulty in taking hold.

One should use extreme care, therefore, as to what aquatic plants are allowed to spread in the open, as a lesson has been learned by the introduction of the South American water-hyacinth into Florida and tropical Asia and the introduction of the water-weed into Europe. In both cases, the plants spread with such rapidity as to choke up navigable waters, thus presenting serious problems of eradication.

THE WATER-SNOWFLAKE, *Nymphoides indicum*, NATIVE OF ASIATIC TROPICS

Tigers of the Ditchwater

▲ HERE a large water-tiger has captured a smaller brother. When full-grown, they are a little more than two inches in length.

▲ APPROPRIATELY KNOWN AS WATER-TIGERS, these larvae of predacious diving-beetles are for the moment peaceful. They are taking in air through the tips of their abdomens.

Dramas as tense as any in jungle or ocean depth are enacted under our very eyes by the larvae of diving-beetles known as water-tigers, or water devils

By HAROLD V. GREEN

EVERY boy has dreams of adventure. Occasionally, o n e does grow up to become a Frank Buck searching the jungles for strange animals or a William Beebe descending into the ocean to study the dwellers of the deep—but most do not.

The average man, caught up in life's currents, pushes aside all thoughts of exploration as his 'responsibilities' grow. The adventurer's life is not for him. But how wrong he is; the jungles are no farther away than the weed-patches in his back yard; admirable oceans —in miniature—lie in near-by ditches. These tiny worlds, peopled by Lilliputians, are beneath his feet, often beneath his notice.

From the quills of the ancients came the expression, "*Natura maxime miranda in minimis*"—Nature is most wonderful in little things. An examination of the pictures shown here would seem to support this statement. These water-world killers were "discovered" in a roadside ditch, while I was on a "safari" in a near-by cemetery.

Anyone, anywhere, can have a m a z i n g adventures exploring among the multitude of fascinating creatures close at hand. Such journeys cost little, and the only hardship to be suffered is wet feet!

◄ TADPOLES are meat and drink to many denizens of the ditch-water deeps. Here is a dramatic tragedy in the making. The funny-faced tadpole has no way of recognizing the danger that lies ahead.

➤ ONE LESS FROG-TO-BE. With an unbelievably rapid whiplike motion, the water-tiger has disemboweled the tadpole. The water-tiger is accustomed to striking hard enough to pierce the horny armor of its brothers and sisters or other insects; hence it has struck the tadpole an unnecessarily violent blow. The placid surface of many a pool conceals battles of this sort, chapter after chapter in an endless conflict that has gone on since earlier geologic eras.

Weevil

A Weevil is defined as a beetle with a snoutlike head; most weevils are small, and their larvae eat out the interior of nuts, fruit, and grain, or bore into the pith of trees and other plants. But the term in its broadest sense does not fit into well-defined boundaries in the scientific classification of insects. The broad blunt beak of the example shown here distinguishes it from most of the other members of the weevil family. There are about fifteen species in its genus, *Eupagoderes*. All are found in southwestern United States, but not much is known about their habits.

Richard L. Cassell photo

WHEAT

AND CIVILIZATION

By Clark Wissler
Late Curator of Anthropology
The American Museum of Natural History

After several hundred thousand years of primitive life, how did man suddenly discover all the basic inventions that underlie our civilization?

Rendition of early illustrations by
PAUL RICHARD

After Carl Whiting Bishop, Annual Report of the Smithsonian Institution, *1940*

ARCHAEOLOGY tells us that civilization first emerged on the edges of three widely separated mud flats at the mouths of as many rivers, or around the deltas of the Nile, the Euphrates, and the Indus. Each of these rivers runs the main part of its course through an arid terrain, the world's greatest stretch of desert lands. Westward from the Nile lie 2,500 miles of the Sahara; eastward, between the Nile and the Red Sea is a long narrow desert; between the Red Sea and the Euphrates lies the great Arabian desert; between the Euphrates and the Indus lie the semiarid and desert lands of Iran and Baluchistan; immediately east of the Indus is the Indian desert. Though little rain ever falls on the lower courses of these three rivers, their upper branches traverse areas where heavy rains are periodical, causing annual floods in the deltas.

One would least expect to find the dawn of civilization in such a setting, yet on the edges of these deltas we find the ruins of pre-dynastic Egypt, of Sumer, and of ancient India. Here emerged the first planned cities the

◄ THE SPREAD OF WHEAT CULTIVATION is indicated by the following approximate dates: valley of the Nile 5000 B. C.; Euphrates and Indus, 4000 B. C.; China, 2500 B.C., and England 2000 B.C. Further, the use of the cart, plow, and bronze spread over about the same area between 3500 and 400 B. C. Since these are important traits in ancient civilization, we can say that the area for wheat is also the area of ancient civilization. Note again that China and England are marginal and that the elements of civilization reached them last, diffused from the ancient centers of Egypt, Sumer, and India

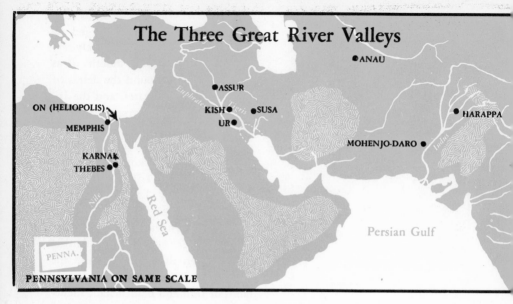

The Three Great River Valleys

ANAU

ASSUR

ON (HELIOPOLIS)
MEMPHIS

KISH   SUSA
UR

HARAPPA

MOHENJO-DARO

KARNAK
THEBES

Red Sea

Persian Gulf

Euphrates

PENNA.

PENNSYLVANIA ON SAME SCALE

▲ EARLIEST CENTERS OF CIVILIZATION as defined by the ruined cities of On, Ur, and Mohenjo-Daro, the best known early sites.

world ever knew, such as On (Heliopolis), Ur, and Mohenjo-Daro, all flourishing about 4000 B. C.

Until recently Egypt was believed the oldest and so the mother of civilization, but archaeological research in Sumer around the year 1926 revealed cities of a more advanced type than in the Egypt of 4000 B. C. Then a few years later cities on the Indus were uncovered which threaten to contest the lead of Sumer. Expert opinion, however, tends to concede a slight lead in priority to Sumer. Yet archaeology goes further in giving satisfactory proof that Sumer and her successors along the Euphrates passed on to Europe much of the "glory that was Greece" and so can justly claim to be the "mother of Euro-American civilization."

There is little reason to suspect that these three centers of civilization developed independently, since they are not only contemporaneous but when looked at closely their respective ways of living follow a common fundamental pattern. This pattern is characterized by cereals, domestic animals, the plow, the wheel, metals, writing, calendars, and cities. It is difficult to realize that these were then unique, novel traits of culture, appearing in the world for the first time. And what is more they are still the fundamentals of civilization.

Again archaeology tells us that man had existed for several hundred thousand years before civilization happened. In the meantime he had overrun the entire world, but his numbers were limited by the amounts of wild foods available and his ability to seize them.

In contrast civilization arose some ten thousand years ago and was scarcely under way before 4000 B. C. What amazing changes has mankind

BARLEY

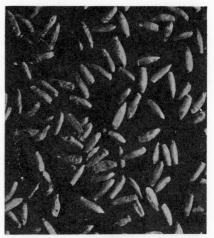

RYE

OATS

WHEAT

EARLIEST KNOWN BREAD

➤ AT THE ANCIENT EGYPTIAN site of Deir el Bahri the elements of civilization appear associated with wheat and barley. Strange as it may seem, some loaves of bread survived owing to the dry climate. A magnifying glass shows barley to have furnished at least part of the flour. Age estimated at 3500 to 4000 years

Courtesy of The Metropolitan Museum of Art

experienced during these last 6000 years! But even more astonishing is it that between 7000 and 4000 B. C. were made all the basic inventions underlying our civilization. Nothing so revolutionary happened before or since.

The change in the way of living which set off this burst of inventive genius was the discovery of agriculture and the domestication of animals. We speak of this as revolutionary because it was a radical step. Throughout the long stretch of Old Stone Age time man simply gathered his food when and where nature made it available. For ages man was blind to his opportunities. Instead of pursuing and killing game animals, thus making them scarce and wild, he could have lived in friendly co-operation with them, protecting and conserving them, and living in luxury on their increase by the simple device of saving females and sacrificing the males. His native intelligence would soon reveal to him the principle of improvement by selective breeding. Within a generation or two he could have come into control of his animal food supply, instead of being dependent upon what nature offered him. All this seems so obvious to us that we are moved to lament the stupidity of man during 400,000 years of the Old Stone Age.

Yet the less obvious was to discover what could be done with the seeds of wild grasses. We now know that the most concentrated form in which nature supplies food is in seeds, but again it took man about 400,000 years to realize the significance of seeds—to see that in the application of his particular brand of intelligence to the exploitation of seeds lay the key to his future. We may never know just when and where some primitive genius first achieved insight as to how seeds could be multiplied and improved, but we do know that with the raising of wheat in the region of the three great river deltas the first civilizations emerged.

The Cereals

We gave the cereals first place in the fundamental characteristics of civilization because that is the verdict of history. The data from archaeology reveal that wheat, barley, and millet are the cereals which appear first. Later emerge rye, oats, and rice, all originally wild grasses. From the earliest known graves in the delta of Egypt come seeds of wheat and barley. In the delta of the Euphrates millet seems slightly earlier than wheat and barley; in the Indus valley, wheat appears with barley.

Everywhere wheat was preferred as it is still. It is abundant in yield, can be readily stored, preserved for a long time, and easily transported. Wild wheat (emmer) and barley survive in a few localities, ranging from Mount Hermon in Palestine eastward into central Iran both found growing together as man probably noticed them before he began to cultivate them. Wheat is superior for bread because of its high gluten content, so we may say that wheat bread is the basis of civilization, proof of which lies in its use as a symbol of life.

Domestic Animals

Not only are the ancient cereals still of vital importance, but the leading food animals—cattle, sheep, goats, and swine—are still the best. Their bones appear in the remains of these ancient first civilizations, and there is abundant evidence of their

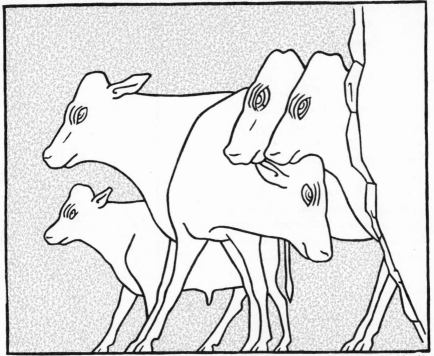

After James Henry Breasted, The Scientific Monthly

⋀ SKULLS exist proving Egyptians bred both hornless and long-horned cattle, suggesting a long period of skillful breeding. 29th century B. C.

After James Henry Breasted, The Conquest of Civilization

⋀ THE DONKEY was the primary beast of burden and everywhere preceded the horse. Women and children rode it, men walked. Egyptian drawing, Pyramid Age

➤EGYPTIANS milked from the right side. Cow's legs were tied to protect the milker. 28th century B. C.

early domestication in surviving sculptures and frescoes on the walls of temples and tombs. Aside from the ox, the first draft animal to appear is the donkey; the horse appears some 1,000 years later, and the camel still later.

We find early sculptures and wall paintings showing the milking of cows in stables. Many such pictures found in Egypt appear modern in that the hind legs of the cow are tied to prevent her kicking the milker, and the calf is kept in front of the cow to check any tendency to "hold up her milk," a trick still used by our farmers. There are lifelike scenes of cattle being driven and led from pasture to stable. In one instance a man walks in front of the cow with her new-born calf on his shoulders, a sure way to induce her to follow.

The wild ancestors of cattle, sheep, goats, swine, and the donkey seem to have lived in and immediately around the three great centers in which these ancient civilizations emerged. Hunting scenes in which wild bulls, boars, and donkeys are pursued furnish evidence that the wild species were not immediately exterminated by domestication. We suppose it was an accident of nature that the wild ancestors

After Leon Legrain, The Univ. of Penna. Museum Journal, 1924

➤ IN UR cows were milked from the rear, like goats, suggesting that the milking of goats may have preceded the milking of cows

After V. Gorden Childe, Man Makes Himself

of the best domesticated seed grains, food and draft animals evolved in the same part of the world.

The Wheel and the Cart

If you wish to evaluate the wheel as a trait of civilization, try to imagine what would be left if the prin-ciple of rotation were completely blotted out. Power-driven transportation would disappear. Away would go windmills, water wheels, steam and electric power. All goods must then be carried on the backs of men and animals, in rowboats or in small sailing vessels. Even hand- and foot-driven machinery would be elimi-

After Leon Legrain, The Univ. of Penna. Museum Journal, *1924*

⋏ AN ANCIENT CARTOON for a "bedtime story," showing foxes milking a goat, suggesting that people of the time milked goats from behind. We note further that the concept of the fox as a trickster is ancient, perhaps handed down from the Old Stone Age. The original drawing was found at Ur ·

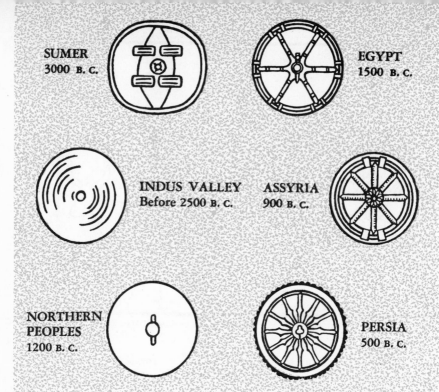

SUMER 3000 B. C.

EGYPT 1500 B. C.

INDUS VALLEY Before 2500 B. C.

ASSYRIA 900 B. C.

NORTHERN PEOPLES 1200 B. C.

PERSIA 500 B. C.

After James Henry Breasted, Ancient Times

▲ THE PLACE AND TIME for the origin of the wheel are obscure. Its distribution over the ancient world closely followed the ox and the donkey

nated. We cannot conceive of a worthwhile world entirely ignorant of the wheel. The earliest known wheeled vehicles appear in Sumer, four wheelers drawn by donkeys. A little later we meet with the chariot, or cart, first drawn by donkeys, then by horses. Ox-drawn carts, also, are shown in ancient drawings and sculpture.

▼ THE EARLIEST portrayed war chariot had four wheels and was drawn by donkeys. Sumer, about 3000 B. C.

Courtesy of The Library of Science and Culture

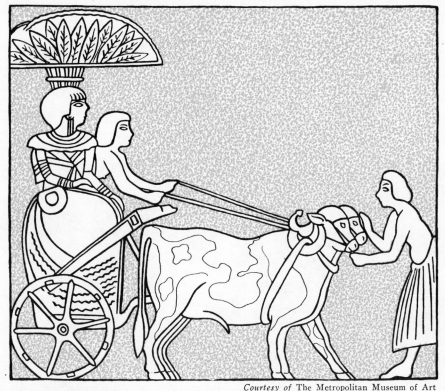

▲ THE OX was sometimes used with a chariot in Egypt, as shown by this wall picture. The passenger is appropriately a woman. The men drove horses

▼ CATTLE CROSSING A CANAL. Two breeds of cattle appear in this scene, horned and hornless. Note the calf carried before its mother to lead the herd. The Egyptians took pride in their cattle, often showing herds on the march and in stables. The animals were used for draft, milk, and beef. The domestication of cattle may have preceded agriculture. In our alphabet, "A" is of ancient origin, derived from the picture of an ox head, inverted. Date of drawing about 3000 B. C.   *After Breasted,* The History of Egypt

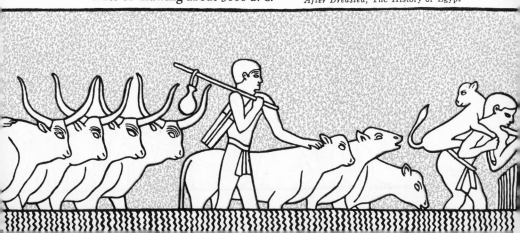

Courtesy of the Chicago Natural History Museum

PERUVIANS PLANTING POTATOES

▼ EGYPTIAN PLOW drawn by cows. Note the two handles. It has been proposed that the Egyptian hoe, as shown at right, was the original form of the plow. But the simple digging stick and its successor the foot-plow are now considered the probable parental forms

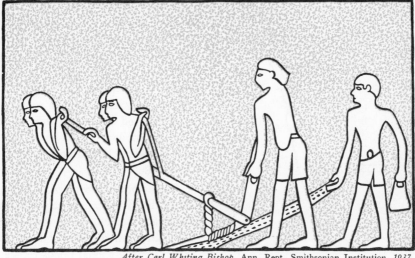

After Carl Whiting Bishop, Ann. Rept. Smithsonian Institution, 1937

▲ AN EGYPTIAN man-drawn plow. Grain is sown by casting into the furrow. 18th Dynasty, about 1400 B. C.

◄ THE ABORIGINAL FOOT-PLOW was an improved digging stick used to turn sod and hard ground. Simple forms of the foot or digging-stick plow were used in western Europe within the last century

After James Henry Breasted,
The History of Egypt

The Plow

The old theory was that the plow developed from the hoe, but now that we have more data on the early forms of the plow, it is clear that it evolved from the digging stick, a stick pushed into the ground to break up the soil. Possibly the first plow was drawn by men as shown in an Egyptian wall picture, but in other Egyptian drawings oxen and even donkeys are yoked to the plow. In one of the Egyptian drawings the grain seems to be thrown so that the plow will cover it, but a sketch on a seal from Babylon goes a step further in showing a seeding machine, the seed being dropped into a funnel which discharges it behind the point of the plow. This is a near parallel to a modern type of machine for sowing wheat.

These ancient plows seem crude and simple, yet the type survived until recent times. Around 1550 the Spanish introduced the plow and oxen into Mexico and thence to the Indians. As late as 1900 Pima and

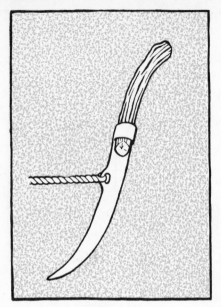

Papago Indians were using crude wooden plows in Arizona and northern Mexico, examples of which are in the collections of the American Museum of Natural History. Some of these were provided with stone points, indicating that the stone age still lingered here. The plow of today, the modern mould-board plow, was invented by Thomas Jefferson, about 1800.

No doubt the sowing of grain preceded the invention of the plow. The Egyptians sometimes sowed wheat and barley on the mud flats of the Nile after the annual floods receded, and drove flocks of sheep and cattle

⋏ JAPANESE ceremonial plow in the form of a digging stick with an iron blade, drawn by man-power. From a drawing by the author; specimen in the museum of Tokyo

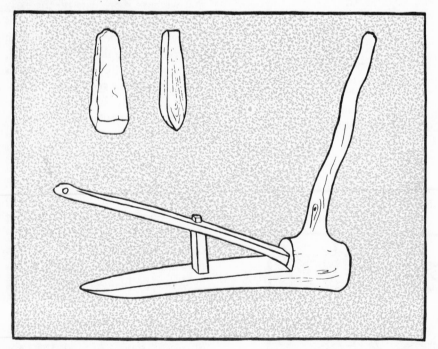

⋏ A SURVIVAL of the primitive plow is found among the Indians in Arizona and Mexico. As late as 1850, some of these plows were used with detachable wooden or even stone points

Courtesy of the Univ. of Penna. Museum Journal, *1910*

↟ Earliest known mechanical seeder. An ancient seal from the Euphrates country shows this plow equipped with a hopper to receive and sow the seed

over the soft ground to tread the seed into the soil, not merely to plant it but to protect it from birds. It is possible that sowing wheat began in the deltas by merely scattering the grain after the waters receded. Farming would thus be simple, since each year nature would spread a fresh layer of fine soil over the fields.

Inventions in the Long Pre-Civilization Period

We should not overlook the important fact that man was a speaking, thinking inventor for several hundred thousand years before the relatively recent civilization boom. Fire was probably his first great invention.

After Carl Whiting Bishop, Ann. Rept. Smithsonian Institution, *1937*

↟ Early Greek plow, from a vase painting. All these ancient plows used cattle, not horses. The horse appears relatively late in ancient civilization and was at first valued for its speed and use in war

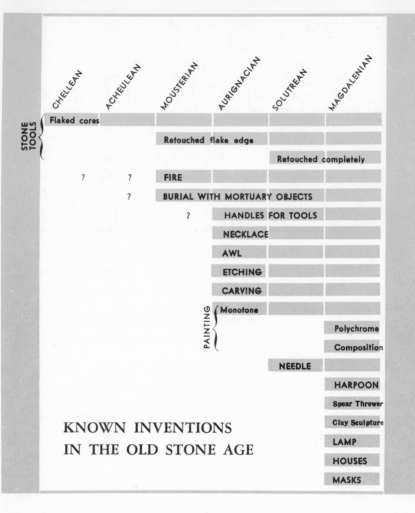

KNOWN INVENTIONS
IN THE OLD STONE AGE

Inventing a handle for the stone axe was another great step. Twisting string was another. Then the inventions of art—line drawing, sculpture, clay modeling, color painting, perspective, and composition—all appear before civilization. The invention of needles in Solutrean time tells of another great step. Again the burial of the dead with mortuary offerings proves that early man was by no means slow in constructing a religious philosophy. The chart we give for outstanding inventions during the Stone Age speaks for itself. It reveals part of the preparation man had made for the rapid, astonishing speed of achievement in civilization when the release came.

As a nomadic hunter man could never grow numerically strong. Even with the best possible social organization, camps of hunters must be small and scattered. Critical studies of living conditions among surviving savages gives no ground for believing that the population of the world under a purely hunting and gathering economy could have been large. The approximate land area of the world is 50,000,000 square miles; the estimated land needed per capita to support a hunting population is seven to ten square miles. Then in round numbers the expected primitive population of the world in 7000 B. C. would not exceed 7,000,000—about the population of New York City.

Yet we know that cities of moderate size accompanied the rise of civilization and that achievements of civilization would have been impossible without local concentration of thousands of adult human beings.

A Possible Explanation

The reader may still be perplexed as to why it was just here in these deltas and narrow river valleys in the midst of deserts that civilization happened. The answer may be that these were the most favorable places. As local environments they were very much alike. What we do know is that these rivers flooded regularly once a year, that the people found it easy to grow cereals there, that cattle, donkeys, swine, sheep, and goats were in the country. We expect these ani-

mals would crowd into the fine feeding grounds of the deltas at least at the times of the year when the pasture on the arid uplands was thinnest. When man was forced to seek refuge in the same place, he found the animals in possession. Wild animals, wild plants, wild men, all predatorily inclined, crowded into the same narrow river valleys, and, not unlike flood victims on a raft, were forced by necessity to adopt a more economical use of space. Man's type of behavior was best able to cope with this new situation. He may never have faced the like of it before, but if so, he had failed. As a hunter with several hundred thousand years of experience with animals, he knew how to fight off the lions and other carnivores to protect the peacefully

▼ EGYPTIAN WAR CHARIOT. Well trained horses were guided chiefly by words, but usually by a separate driver. The chariot spread to Europe and was used effectively by the ancient Britons in wars against the Romans

After James Henry Breasted,
Ancient Times

▲ THE EGYPTIAN King Ramses III, hunting wild oxen in the delta marshes of the Nile. In the Euphrates country, hunters speared lions from chariots and sometimes from horseback

After James Henry Breasted,
A History of Egypt

inclined ruminants. Nature herself gave yearly demonstrations of planting crops of grasses and of irrigating the marginal dry lands. So man could begin to co-operate with the herbivorous animals and to exploit plants. Because of increasing food supply, his own numbers increased geometrically, cities arose, herds multiplied, and cereals improved.

The many pictures of kings killing lions, wild cattle, etc., may not be just sport but symbolic of man's war against the wild animals from without that menaced the increase of his tame herds and threatened his growing crops. Also there were envious nomadic hunters on the outskirts, learning to be farmers and herders by imitation, ready to raid and dispossess the civilized of their rich lands, herds, and cities. New blood and abilities were ready to displace

the old to carry on to greater achievements.

Most of this is speculation, but whatever the causes, it did happen. Once man sensed that he could by self-discipline produce more and more food and comfort, a few centuries would suffice to rear mighty cities and great civilizations. Significant changes in the ways of living would follow within a single generation.

Yet at the outset the ages-old nomadic hunters might need something more than the shock of a strange environment to break old habits; at least nature was kind enough to offer yearly demonstrations in sowing and irrigating. We shall never know, but the facts we have hastily reviewed offer some hints as to how it may

have been that civilization arose around these river deltas as revolutions in living. The explanation may lie in the commonplace circumstance that for part of the year man could graze his herds upon the dry lands marginal to the rivers, while producing enough grain and hay along the borders of the river to stable-feed the animals when pastures failed seasonally. What we call civilization may be little more than wise integration of farming and animal husbandry.

▼ ONE OF THE FINEST sculptures in low relief depicts a wounded lion struck by arrows and paralyzed by a punctured spine. Ancient peoples hunted probably not just for sport but to protect their herds

After James Henry Breasted, The Conquest of Civilization

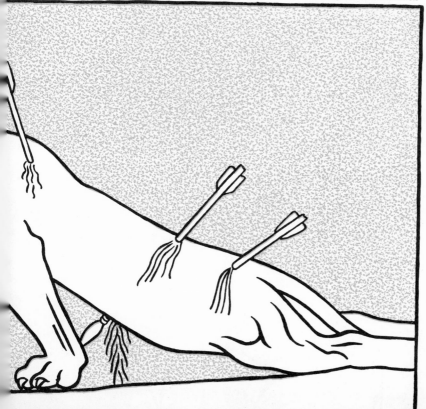

Whooping Crane

A bird that is perilously
near extinction

ONLY ABOUT TWO DOZEN WHOOPERS survive in the world. Vigorous measures are being made to preserve them.

Charles A. Keefer, U.S. Fish and Wildlife Service

BECAUSE of their immense size, the prenuptial dance of the whooping cranes is one of the great dramas of the bird world. The male bird walks off into shallow water and bows towards the female, who steps into the water beside him. They begin by leaping together, but it is the male who leaps most often. He leaps high over her posturing figure.

How to Tell a Whooping Crane from other Similar Birds

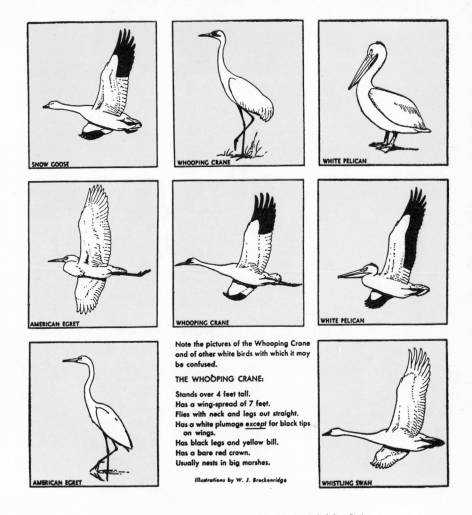

SNOW GOOSE

WHOOPING CRANE

WHITE PELICAN

AMERICAN EGRET

WHOOPING CRANE

WHITE PELICAN

AMERICAN EGRET

Note the pictures of the Whooping Crane and of other white birds with which it may be confused.

THE WHOOPING CRANE:

Stands over 4 feet tall.
Has a wing-spread of 7 feet.
Flies with neck and legs out straight.
Has a white plumage *except* for black tips on wings.
Has black legs and yellow bill.
Has a bare red crown.
Usually nests in big marshes.

Illustrations by W. J. Breckenridge

WHISTLING SWAN

After Robert Porter Allen, National Audubon Society

The JACKSNIPE'S *Wing-Song*

A bird that sings   without voice

By BEN EAST

THE Wilson Snipe has no power to sing. His vocal accomplishments are limited to a sharp *"scaip! scaip!"* of alarm and a few notes of curiosity or protest on his nesting grounds. But on his downward dive he beats out these strange pulsing notes known as winnowing.

Authorities did not first agree as to how he did it. And it might seem impossible to find out, for the snipe sounds his courtship serenade far aloft, in the lonely solitude of the "wide blue yonder," far from man's eyes. But ever since 1858 European scientists have been observing the common European snipe and experimenting to find the secret.

Manson-Bahr mounted the outer tail feathers on a cork attached to a string and rod, and by whirling this contrivance he made an almost perfect imitation of the music. Another experimenter showed that the tremolo effect was added by the vibration of the snipe's wings, which produced certain overtones modifying the music of the tail quills.

Drawing by Dot Barlow

⋏ FROM the "wide blue yonder" comes a soft, haunting cadence as the jacksnipe dives earthward toward his mate

The wing-song has, to humans on the ground far below, the quality of a far-off, soft whistle, broken into short syllables, pulsing with a haunting cadence. It floats earthward like the music of a spirit bird.

The male bird keeps it up for hours, doubtless to the delight and satisfaction of the shy hen waiting somewhere in the boglands below. Even to human ears, spring has no bird note more unusual and mystic.

WHERE DO INSECTS GO IN
WINTER?

Under snow and ice, they employ many strange
methods for defying the silent enemy of life

By EDWIN WAY TEALE
All photographs by the author

IN a winter world of frozen earth, scudding snow, and bare, complaining branches, where are the insects which filled the autumn fields with sound and action? What has become of the grasshopper and the dragonfly, the ant and the cricket? How does a housefly spend the months of cold? Where is the firefly's light when snow piles high? In what manner do katydids and yellow jackets, monarch butterflies and whirligig beetles bridge the icy gap from fall to spring?

In all their forms—as eggs, as larvae, as nymphs, as pupae, as adults—the insects pass through the season of cold. Examination of the table which accompanies this article will reveal the winter ways of the common insects.

Those which lie dormant in the egg stage, occupy infinitely varied resting places. In days before the steely brilliance of frost silvers the grass clumps or there comes the night of the first freeze, the females of many species are busy depositing their eggs according to the age-old dictates of instinct.

◄ THIS MANTIS, preying on a bee, will not survive the winter; but a remarkable ball of froth, manufactured by the female, will carry the eggs over to the next spring

With abdomens thrust into the soft soil, short-horned grasshoppers bury pods of eggs encased in protective layers of gummy secretion. Clinging head downward to weed stems and twigs, female praying mantises produce those remarkable, walnut-sized balls of froth which solidify to form the housing for between 125 and 350 eggs. Lilliputians among the insects—the aphides, leaf hoppers, and tree hoppers—cement their minute eggs to plant tissues and to diminutive ledges and ravines of tree bark. Also inserted in bark of twigs of trees and shrubs are the eggs of those ghostly melodists of the summer night, the snowy tree crickets.

The robber fly

One afternoon in mid-September, I noticed a movement in a tiny open space between small clumps of grass. At first it seemed that a hunting wasp was stinging its prey on the bare ground. Then I saw that the insect was a gray robber fly, one of those great-eyed, streamlined huntresses which dive like hawks upon flying prey and wrap long, hooked legs about their victims. The fly was stabbing the tip of its abdomen again and again into the loose soil. At each stab, its ovipositor was planting eggs as a mechanical corn-planter deposits the kernels of grain.

▼ A PREDATORY aquatic monster in miniature, the nymph of the damsel fly (above) survives the winter beneath the ice of ponds and streams

▼ CARPENTER ANTS winter in galleries of wood. One ant may wall itself up for the winter in a little sawdust room beneath the bark of a tree

Katydids follow a different procedure in laying their overwintering eggs. Along a twig or around the edge of a leaf, the angular-winged katydid cements its eggs in overlapping lines. In one instance, a katydid, kept as a pet, embroidered its eggs along the edge of a stiff white collar found in an open bureau drawer.

One of the strangest stories connected with the depositing of winter eggs is that of the bagworm moth. The female spends her entire life within her pine cone shaped bag. Wingless and grublike, she gives off a perfume which attracts the male to her hiding place. After mating has taken place, the female fills most of the pupal shell with eggs. Then she plucks down from her own body to make a protecting plug for the eggs. After this is completed, her work is done. The eggs remain safely protected within their tightly secured bag to hatch when winter has passed.

In other instances, eggs hatch before winter comes, and the larvae remain dormant during the period of cold. The caterpillars of the viceroy butterfly, for example, eat until they are partially grown; then they roll themselves within leaves and hibernate for the winter. In the case of the Regal Fritillary, the larvae — black and yellowish-red, with two rows of black-tipped yellow spines running down their backs — hibernate when they are extremely small and emerge to dine on violet leaves as soon as spring has come.

Probably the most familiar of all the hibernating larvae are the wooly bears, the caterpillars of the Isabella Tiger Moth, the "bearewormes" of the Middle Ages. You find them, like upholstered doughnuts, curled beneath

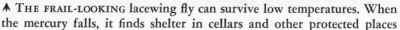

▲ THE FRAIL-LOOKING lacewing fly can survive low temperatures. When the mercury falls, it finds shelter in cellars and other protected places

old boards and logs. Sometimes, during thaws, they revive and crawl about even in midwinter.

Among the beetles, a large proportion winter as larvae. As soon as cold weather comes, wire worms, the children of the click beetles, work their way down through soil or rotting wood to a depth of six inches or more. The white grubs of the May beetles always descend until they are safely below the frost line. Fireflies hibernate as larvae, burying themselves in log mold or leaf mold on woodland floors. Snug within their branching tunnels, engraver beetle larvae lie dormant through the inhospitable months of cold.

▼ THE SNOWY TREE CRICKET has no liking for winter snows, despite its name. This ghostly melodist of the summer night hides its eggs in bark, and dies

Winter in the water

Other larvae spend the winter in a far different world—beneath the ice of ponds and streams. The black flies and midges of the next spring overwinter as aquatic larvae. Their habitat is also the home of those predatory underwater monsters in miniature, the nymphs of the damsel flies and dragonflies. Beneath submerged rocks in flowing streams, the larvae of the Dobson flies—the hellgramites of the angler—likewise endure a period of adversity.

Seventeen times in succession the nymph of one land dwelling insect passes through the season of ice and snow before it reaches its adult stage. This, of course, is the so-called seventeen-year locust, the celebrated periodical cicada of the New World. As a

◄ A GREAT-EYED, streamlined huntress, the robber fly deposits her eggs in the ground like a mechanical corn planter. Winter rids the air of her prey; but on summer days you will see her perched as shown below, resting between hawklike attacks

minute, molelike creature, it hatches during the summer from eggs deposited in the tissues of twigs. Dropping to the ground, it creeps into a crack or burrows down through the soil until it reaches a plant root. There, it begins sucking sap. Year after year it lives its damp, dark underworld existence; moving to larger and larger roots as it increases in size. During a succession of winters, it lies in comparative dormancy during the months when snow and ice-laden gales lash the bare branches of the trees overhead.

Almost entirely exposed to such gales are the chrysalids of several of the butterflies. The familiar white cabbage butterfly overwinters as a chrysalis near the site of its food supply. Swallow-tail butterflies bridge the gap until spring in the same form. And so, oftentimes, does the doughty Red Admiral. Among the moths, additional protection is provided for the pupa, either by the spinning of a silken cocoon or by having the transforma-

▼ THE ANGULAR-WINGED katydid cements its flat eggs in overlapping rows along a twig or the edge of a leaf. A pet one used the edge of a stiff collar

tion from larva to pupa occur underground or in a protected cranny. Thus, the larva of the Sphinx moth burrows its way beneath the surface of the soil before it changes into the distinctive jug-handled pupa, in which form it passes the winter.

Among the bleak grays of a January landscape, the cocoons of the great silk moths—the Cecropia, Polyphemus, Luna, and Promethea—provide heartening sights for those who know the gorgeous insects which will emerge from them. They are like bluebirds — harbingers of spring.

On one small wild cherry tree, I once found more than a dozen Promethea cocoons, each attached to its twig with a reenforcing sleeve of silk. There is, in a single Polyphemus cocoon, upwards of half a mile of silk thread. Unlike the Promethea cocoons, those of the Polyphemus and Luna are only insecurely attached to twigs, so they usually fall like nuts in the grip of the winter gales. Among the

HALF A MILE of silk thread is spun by the Polyphemus moth for its winter "blanket." The cocoon usually falls from its twig in winter gales

▼ WHEN BEES ball together to survive the cold, those at the center generate heat as they engage in a sort of dance. They change places at intervals with those exposed to the cold. The temperature within the ball may be as much as 65°F. above that of the air

▲ In flocks sometimes numbering millions, the
monarch butterfly migrates southward on its
lightly loaded wings, to winter along the Gulf

drifted leaves, the cocoons are perfectly camouflaged and are rarely seen.

Also rarely seen are the insects
which hibernate as adults. Each winter, in every shed and barn and attic,
around every haystack and grass
clump and mullein rosette, under
woodpiles and fallen logs and flat
stones, adult insects are lost in the
long sleep of hibernation. Unconscious
of the violence of the wind or the intensity of the cold or the sweep of the
blizzard about them, they lie dormant.
The Seven Sleepers of the mammal
world find their counterpart multi-

plied many-fold in the world of the
insects.

Hardy adults

The housefly, many mosquitoes, the
termite, the stink bug, the Colorado
potato beetle, the chinch bug, the
cockroach, and the elm leaf beetle—
some of the least-loved insects—usually live through the winter months
as adults. In one tussock of Sudan
grass, a scientist in eastern Kansas
once found more than 500 hibernating chinch bugs. Frequently, I have

▼ No DRAGONFLIES would liven next summer's landscape in northern climes if their young nymphs could not survive the winter beneath the ice of ponds and streams

LADYBIRD BEETLES gather by millions to winter among the rocks in the West. Tons have been scooped up and shipped to orchards to consume pests

▼ Aphids on a rosebud. These lay "winter eggs" cemented in plants. Sometimes they are kept in nests of ants. The young that hatch out are all females; males are produced later. The generations are rapid

Ladybirds by the million

discovered, in the rosette of a mullein plant, a score or more of wintering insects which had pushed their way down between the wooly leaves as though tucking themselves between warm blankets.

Ants often fall into their long stupor while clustered together in masses within the tunnels below-ground or in the galleries excavated in decaying tree trunks above-ground. Sometimes a single carpenter ant will build up a little wall of sawdust about itself beneath the loose bark of a dead tree. In this tiny room, it retires for its long winter sleep.

In contrast to its solitary slumber, the ladybird beetles cluster together, sometimes literally by the millions, and spend the winter in masses among the rocks of western mountains. Tons of these insects have been scooped up and carried down to the orchard regions of the Pacific Coast where they have been "planted" in springtime to consume pests infesting the fruit trees. In the region of my garden, nothing so spectacular happens. But I do see ladybirds tucking themselves away under loose boards, beneath the bark of long dead trees, and under piles of discarded rubbish. Not infrequently, these beneficial beetles hibernate indoors, coming out of their hiding places on the milder winter days.

Another insect that spends the winter as an adult is the nimble, nervous,

▼ FOR SEVENTEEN YEARS the nymph of the periodical cicada lives underground. Finally emerging, the "seventeen-year locust" leaves its nymphal skin *(far right)* and appears as shown adjacent

predatory tiger beetle, a creature so alert it darts into the protecting grass if the shadow of a cloud passes over the hot bare earth which forms its hunting ground. A protected place beneath some rotting log is its usual hibernaculum. Frail by comparison but surprisingly tough in its resistance to cold is the filmy winged parent of the aphis lion, the luna-green lacewing

fly. This golden-eyed insect can fly at a temperature below 40° F., and it is said that it can walk at 20°—twelve degrees below freezing. In cellars, cracks in bark, woodpiles, and beneath loose boards, the lacewings find protection when the mercury descends and winter settles down.

Each spring, for half a dozen years, I have watched bumblebee queens coursing low over my hillside, investigating every cranny, grass tussock, mouse nest, and mole tunnel, searching for the best site for the summer's colony. I have seen some of the insect cities thus established flourish and prosper. During the same summers, I have watched the nests of the paper-making wasps enlarge, ring by ring, starting with a single central cell which clung to its support like a tiny goblet placed upside down. From single queens, both of these types of insect cities expanded into communi-

ties with hundreds of busy inhabitants. Then, each year, as autumn cold gripped the hillside, every one of the insects in the teeming nests disappeared forever—every one except the young fertilized queens. They crawl into hollow logs or push their way beneath piles of rubbish and there, anchored by feet and jaws, fall into the deathlike sleep of hibernation. Through them, their species carries over to another season of sunny skies.

Similarly, the hornets and yellow jackets survive and reproduce their thriving commonwealths. Some of the parasitic ichneumon flies, allied to the wasps, also hibernate as fertilized females, while the small carpenter bees, both males and females, retire when winter comes to the protection of their tunnels in twigs and canes.

Unique among all the more than 600,000 kinds of insects listed by science is the method used by honeybees

▼ AMONG THE HARDIEST of the hibernating adults are the water striders. They may be seen skating across open water in streams in midwinter

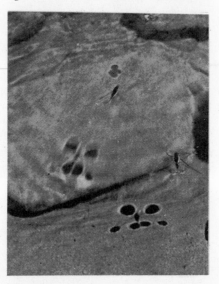

▲ THE SHORT-HORNED grasshoppers thrust their abdomens into the soft soil and bury pods of eggs encased in protective layers of gummy secretion

▲ THE GRASSHOPPERS that skim over the summer fields perish with winter, but their descendants survive through carefully laid eggs or as nymphs

to maintain the life of the colony from fall until spring. They employ an efficient "muscular furnace" to heat the hive or the hollow tree in which they have stored their honey.

Gathering in a great ball, they cling together in a closely packed cluster. The bees at the center of the mass then engage in a sort of insect dance, stepping back and forth, flipping their wings, moving their antennae. From time to time, the insects at the outside of the cluster change places with the dancers at the center. Heat is radiated from the bodies of the bees, and the close-packed cluster acts as an insulating shell which keeps the warmth from being dissipated into the outer cold. Tests have revealed that the temperature within such a ball of insects is as much as 65° F. above that of the air outside the hive.

The migrating monarch

Honeybees use up so much energy in flying that it would be impossible for them to migrate to the South when shortening days and increasing chill warn that winter is at hand. But the black-and-orange milkweed butterfly, the monarch, can follow the birds on its lightly loaded wings to find a warmer climate. In streaming flocks, sometimes numbering millions, these familiar insects drift down the North American continent to winter along the Gulf.

Left behind by the departing monarchs, small aquatic insects prepare for winter in varied ways along the northern watercourses. The back swimmers and water boatmen gather together in glittering black clouds among the aquatic vegetation. Many cling throughout the winter to tangles of plants which give off oxygen by photosynthesis. Dr. Ann Haven Morgan, of Mount Holyoke College, reports one instance in which masses of from ten to fifty dormant water boatmen were found clustering about small air pockets beneath the ice. Whirligig beetles begin to disappear as soon as the temperature descends to the 50° mark. They drop downward to the mud of the pond or the stream bottom, there to lie dormant throughout the months of cold.

Among the hardiest of the hibernating adults are the spider-legged water striders. I have seen them emerging from debris along the banks of small streams to skate across the chill water of an open space during a mild day in mid-January. They belong to that extremely small group of insects which are seen between the first heavy freeze of autumn and the coming of spring. The most spectacular members of this group are the so-called "snow fleas," or springtails. Some winters they appear on the surface of the snow in such vast numbers that they resemble clouds of drifting dust.

Heralds of Spring

As winter nears its end, one of the earliest of the hibernating adults to appear on the wing is the mourning cloak or "thaw butterfly." During the period of greatest cold, it remains hidden within some cranny or hollow tree. Sometimes as early as in February I have encountered one fluttering about among the trees of a sheltered glade. In March, when the first green grass is pushing up — braving the chill—mourning cloaks are sure to be abroad, their fluttering, cream-bordered wings adding a touch of life to the gray of the landscape.

They, like a host of other insects, have passed safely through the ordeal of ice and snow. They have achieved, in their way,—as other insects have in theirs—a victory over the silent antagonist of all insect life—the winter Cold.

▼ MOST CRICKETS pass the winter as eggs, but some as almost mature nymphs. It would be difficult to think of any method that insects have not developed through the long ages to triumph over winter

A WHERE do all the flies go in the wintertime? Those that live, survive the cold in a sluggish condition in attics and other protected places

> THE FEMALE BAGWORM MOTH spends her entire life within this pine-cone-shaped bag. After luring the male and mating, she fills most of the pupal shell with eggs and makes a protecting plug from down plucked from her body

HOW THEY SURVIVE THE WINTER

INSECT	WHERE	IN WHAT FORM
Ant	Hibernating in wood or soil	Adult
Ant Lion	In the ground	Larva or Pupa
Aphid	Cemented in plants, sometimes kept in the nests of ants	Egg
Bagworm Moth	Within the protection of a silken bag	Egg
Black Fly	In the water	Larva
Bumblebee	Hibernating in hollow logs or protected crannies	Young Fertilized Queen
Cabbage Butterfly	Near the site of its food	Chrysalis
Caddis Fly	Usually under water as a larva. A few winter as pupae. A few gradually transform into adults during winter	Larva, Pupa, or Adult
Carolina Locust	Buried in the soil	Egg
Carpenter Ant	Hibernating in galleries in wood	Adult
Carpenter Bee (small)	Hibernating in tunnels in twigs	Adult
Chinch	Hibernating, usually, in	Adult
Katydid	As an egg cemented to leaves or twigs or placed in plant tissues	Egg
Lacewing Fly	Often hibernates with adult mosquitoes in dark cellars and similar protected places	Adult
Ladybird Beetle	Hibernates in masses, often at the base of haystacks, under loose boards, etc.	Adult
Luna Moth	Within a silken cocoon	Pupa
May Beetle	Below frost line for two or three years	Larva
May Fly	Semi-active, in the water	Nymph
Midge	Dormant	Larva
Monarch Butterfly	Migrates to the South	Adult
Mosquito	As a hibernating adult; sometimes as a dormant larva	Adult or Larva
Mourning Cloak Butterfly	Hibernates in hollow trees and protected crannies	Adult
Paper-making Wasp	As a hibernating fertilized queen	Adult
Polyphemus Moth	Within a silken cocoon	Pupa
Promethea Moth	Within a silken cocoon	Pupa
Red Admiral Butterfly	As a pupa and a hibernating adult	Pupa or Adult
Red-legged	In the ground	Egg

Insect	Where / how found in winter	Overwintering stage
Cicada	Beneath the ground	
Click Beetle	Usually as a larva. During the last winter underground, as an imprisoned adult	Nymph
Cockroach	Hibernating in rotten wood and forest litter. In heated houses, as an active adult	Larva or Adult
Colorado Potato Beetle	Hibernating in groups	Adult
Crane Fly	In the ground	Larva
Cricket	Usually as an egg, sometimes as a nymph	Egg or Nymph
Damsel Fly	In the water	Nymph
Dobson Fly	In the water	Larva
Dragonfly	In the water	Nymph
Elm Leaf Beetle	Often in attics	Adult
Engraver Beetle	Within tunnels in wood	Larva
Firefly	In log mold or leaf mold	Larva
Grasshopper	As an egg usually; a few as nymphs	Egg or Nymph
Gypsy Moth	Cemented to bark and covered with moth scales	Egg
Honeybee	In a cluster, warmed by muscular activity	Adult
Hornet	Hibernating as a fertilized queen	Adult
Housefly	In attics and protected spots	Adult
Ichneumon Fly	In rotting wood, as an adult. In parasitized cocoon, as a pupa	Adult or Pupa
Isabella Tiger Moth	Under boards, stones, logs, and refuse, as a "wooly bear"	Larva
Regal Fritillary Butterfly	As an overwintering larva	Larva
Robber Fly	In soil or rotting wood	Egg or Larva
Snowy Tree Cricket	In bark	Egg
Sphinx Moth	Buried in the ground	Pupa
Springtail	Often active in midwinter	Adult
Squash Bug	Hibernating in grass and under litter	Adult
Stink Bug	As a hibernating adult	Adult
Swallowtail Butterfly	As an exposed chrysalis	Chrysalis
Termite	In wood	Adult
Tent Caterpillar Moth	As an egg cemented to a twig	Egg
Tiger Beetle	Hibernating under logs or litter	Larva or Adult
Viceroy Butterfly	Within a rolled leaf	Partly Grown Larva
Walking Stick	As an egg dropped on the leafcover of the forest	Egg
Water Boatman	Usually as a hibernating adult; in one case, at least, as an egg	Adult or Egg
Water Strider	Semi-active	Adult
Whirligig Beetle	On mud of pond or stream bottom	Adult
White-faced Hornet	As a hibernating fertilized queen	Adult
Yellow Jacket	As a hibernating fertilized queen	Adult

Can We Save the Gray Wolf?

Photo by T. C.
Stanwell-Fletcher

By Edwin D. Neff

On the very borderland of extinction, the gray wolf stirs man with mixed emotions. Will hate or admiration for this symbol of the unconquerable wilderness win out?

IT seems only yesterday that the late Ernest Thompson Seton wrote his story of that magnificent outlaw, Lobo, king of the wolves. He told how Lobo evaded every device of man—traps, poison, guns —for five incredible years. How he was finally brought down, heartbroken and the fight gone out of him, through the capture of his beloved mate, Blanca. It was Seton himself who finally trapped Lobo. But he must have realized that even helpless in the traps, the wolf was the true victor. For Seton, reflecting perhaps the compassion of all gallant men for the vanquished, could not kill him. And Lobo, re-fusing compassion, died, his eyes not on his captor but on the dusty reaches of the New Mexico valley that had been his hunting ground.

Today, Lobo is a symbol for all his kind, for the gray wolf is nearly gone from this country.

Stanley P. Young of the U. S. Fish and Wildlife Service, a top authority, estimates there are fewer than 1000 gray wolves in the United States, a dangerously low figure. And these 1000 are virtually restricted to the northern extremes of three States, Wisconsin, Michigan, and Minnesota, though there are larger numbers in Mexico, Canada, and Alaska.

Yet even on the borderland of extinction, the gray wolf breeds controversy. Cattlemen and hunters want no part of any scheme to protect him. Wildlife conservationists, fearing that an authentic figure of the American wilderness is disappearing, urge that controls stop short of extinction. But, as we shall see, the number of practical sanctuaries within this country are frighteningly few. Most people prefer to admire old Lobo in somebody else's preserves.

His principal enemy, not only today but throughout history, is, of course, the keeper of livestock. Yet bounties are hard to defend in states where livestock is of little economic importance. Sportsmen decry the gray wolf's attacks on game, yet there still are areas within this country where protected game has become so plentiful it is destroying its own food supplies. More consideration should be given to the value of the wolf as a control factor in the normal wildlife picture. In some regions, the wolf's damage to domestic stock might be greatly outweighed by his reduction of game out of balance with its environment.

The problem is clear, though by no means simple. Can a just plea be made for this animal, despite his past depredations, and is there any practical possibility of preventing his extinction?

Even if we had made no mention up to this point of the animal in question, the reader would have had good reason to wonder about him. What nature of beast is this that can stir up such controversy? Why do men hate him and at the same time betray flashes of reluctant admiration? Why could Seton devote every ruse to his capture, then find himself unable to destroy his prisoner?

The key to these questions is the nature of the animal itself. He is the very symbol of unconquerable forces. He gives no quarter, asks no quarter. Few men have tamed him. Though he is the ancestor of man's most devoted servant, the dog, he himself refuses servitude. Given any kind of odds, he can outsmart, outfight man. And throughout this country's history, man has been his worst enemy. Man killed off the wolf's natural food source—game. Then nothing remained but for the wolf to attack man's livestock. And when this happened, man trapped him, poisoned him, shot him. Warfare against the wolf reached the point where his extermination was debated in the halls of Congress. Federal funds were voted to hire professional hunters and to pay learned scientists to plot against him.

Still, hunted and hated, the favorite object of man's wrath, the gray wolf fought on. He trotted deftly around the traps; he sniffed contemptuously at poisoned carcasses; he stayed beyond the range of guns. And in the predawn stillness of the shrinking wilderness his stirring howl indicated to the apprehensive settlers the wolf's indifference to man. Yet man finally won. Or rather his money, his weapons, and his science won, driving the wolf into a comparatively few acres in the northern extremes of the states we mentioned. Once, he had roamed nearly the whole continent,

 **AMNH Photo**

A **Midnight** in midwinter on Gunflint Lake in Minnesota: Eastern Timber Wolves in an American Museum habitat group. The northern lights cast their eerie glow over a scene that has gripped thousands of visitors

even to within less than 500 miles of the North Pole itself. In the North, the wolf has yet to experience the systematic campaigns of extermination practiced in parts to the south. But from Arctic America come complaints of wolf concentrations, wolf predation, and the initiation of systematic poisoning. And one suspects it may be only a matter of time before even these northern wolves may be on the list of animals

threatened with extinction.

The story of this battle to survive is as romantic as the gray wolf himself. But before we begin, let's take a closer look at old Lobo. In general he physically resembles a German Shepherd dog and has a thick coat of hair. Despite the term "gray," individual gray wolves may be almost any color between white and black. Scientists believe these color variations may be due to variations in light, temperature, and humidity in different parts of the continent. Size too, varies. Weights range between 60 and 175 pounds, though the latter size is found only in Alaska and the Mackenzie River country in Canada. His shoulder height may be between 26 and 38 inches.

His efficiency as a hunter stems from a combination of strength, endurance, and exceptional cunning. There is a story of an Arizona female wolf who dragged a seven-pound trap through more than six miles of dense thicket, keeping well ahead of the unencumbered dogs pursuing her and finally doing grim battle with two of the dogs before their master shot her. A Canadian archbishop told a far more amazing story of a black wolf who dragged a steel trap and the wooden block to which it was attached for 90 miles through snow and in bitter cold for 30 days, apparently without food. The wolf was a walking skeleton when finally killed.

Stories of the gray wolf's speed are probably exaggerated. He has been clocked at 28 miles an hour, and while he doubtless can do better for short distances, his famous distance-eating lope is about half that speed. However, he can keep up a steady pace all night.

Wolf hunters say it is not speed but this great endurance that helps to make the gray wolf such a formidable predator. Many of the larger four-footed animals can outspeed the wolf for short distances, but he can run longer. He is not a sprinter but a distance runner, and his patience is infinite.

Even more impressive than these stories of endurance are the examples of his cunning. Newfoundland hunters tell how wolves actually seemed to conspire against their prey. Coming upon a herd of deer, the wolves would divide, a few hiding along the deer trail, while others slipped around to the windward of their prey and chased them into the trail, where they were pounced upon by the hidden wolves.

Stories like these seem to show that the wolf can think himself out of specific situations and is not dependent entirely upon instinct.

The wolf, like all other powerful carnivores, is a capable and ruthless killer. He employs his powers in the most efficient manner, and when

U. S. Forest Service Photos

there are several wolves in a group they may attack a large animal from every side. If hunting has been poor and the wolves are ravenous, some of them may actually begin devouring an overwhelmed animal before it has died or while it is yet being killed by other members of the pack. Stories told of the ruthless technique of the wolf probably illustrate the extremes to which this predator may go upon occasion, but in the majority of instances the wolf presses for an immediate kill, with few, if any, unusual practices.

Much has been written of the wolf's single-minded devotion to his mate and his family. Unlike most animals, the wolf mates for life, and the young remain with the parents until two or even three years of age. The whelps are born during early

TYPICAL WOLF COUNTRY in Minnesota, one of the three states to which the wolf is now practically restricted. *Above*: a scene in Chippewa National Forest. *At left:* aerial view looking northward across Sucker and Birch lakes into Canadian territory

spring in dens. By late summer or early fall, when their teeth are coming along, they are taken out to the hunting runway to learn their trade. At first, the parents bring food to the youngsters at resting points along the runway. Later, the youngsters join in the hunt and are taught the technique of the kill. This technique and the hunting methods require co-operation; hence, the family sticks together and may even take on a few stragglers.

There are many stories of this devotion. Lobo's love for his little white mate Blanca is perhaps the best known. His determination to find her after she had been trapped and killed led him straight into an ambush he most certainly would have avoided otherwise and, indeed, had avoided many times. But with Blanca gone he lost his cunning.

Young tells of a reverse situation in which a female, seeking her trapped mate, never missed a night searching the area where he had been caught. After two weeks, she herself was trapped not 20 yards from the spot. In another instance, a wolf family tried to free a trapped member by overturning large stones on the snare. The captive wolf couldn't have done it, for both his forelegs were held by the trap.

It is this trait of sticking together that probably has created the myth of the wolf pack, popularly supposed to number in the hundreds. There are early American woodcuts showing a pack of at least a hundred wolves surrounding a log cabin in a forest clearing. The fact is that while several wolf families will band together for a short time, the number is never very large. The usual wolf "pack" consists of a family group and perhaps a few strays.

Another legend is that of the "lone wolf." Young believes "lone" wolves are simply animals grown too old to run with the younger ones, animals whose teeth are too far gone to enable them to fight

effectively. These lone animals will follow the others at a distance, eating game they have left. When the old wolf's teeth are gone, he dies, for they are one of his principal weapons.

In his prime, the wolf has perhaps the most powerful bite of any creature near his size. A wolf can take off the tail of a yearling calf at one snap, and there is a case on record where a wolf killed a calf with a single crunch of his muscular jaws, dividing its spine. A male wolf, trapped by a hunter in southern Arizona, severed a two-inch juniper limb with one terrible slash. The hunter was using the stick to push a can of water toward the wolf. Suddenly, the animal struck out like a snake.

"Another inch or two," the hunter recalled the other day, "and he would have taken the calf out of my leg, or maybe snapped off the leg itself."

No wonder then that men have always feared and hated—and admired—the wolf, have fought him with every means at hand in nearly every corner of the globe. In America, it was often a battle for survival. For in a new country, both man and wolf depend first upon wild game, then upon livestock. The battle between men and wolves in this country began almost with the first settler. Indeed, the first reference in our literature seems to have been made by Captain John Smith, that colorful adventurer of England and Virginia, in 1609, the very year that livestock was first brought to Jamestown from the mother country. From that time on, the warfare with the "master predator" was one of the grimmest battles the colonists had to fight. As early as 1630, the wolf had become an outlaw in Plymouth Colony, and two years later the Grand Assembly at James City placed the first bounty on wolf pelts. And bounties still remain in many states.

The Proceedings of the Worcester (Mass.) Society of Antiquity tell how wolves attacked "greatly to the annoyance of the settlers, and many a time did they start in the middle of the night to defend their pigpens and sheepfold, the brave housewife joining in the combat."

George Washington, confronting the same problem that had troubled John Smith more than a century before, speculated that sheep raising might have been one of the most profitable colonial investments except for wolves and wrote to England for advice. Alas, the English experts, unable to visualize America's vast distances, could not understand why the colonists could not fence in their flocks as was the

(Below) ON THE TRAIL. *Big wolves such as these once frequented our West and Northwest. Attacking sheep, calves, and colts, they were a constant source of worry to ranchmen, and it was inevitable that such meat-eaters should be hunted down. But even ranchmen will give credit to their unusual intelligence among animals*

(A group of timber wolves in The American Museum of Natural History; *AMNH photo*)

custom in England's tiny pastures!

The war with the wolves continued on through the seventeenth, eighteenth, and nineteenth centuries as the settlers pressed on across the Alleghenies and the vast Mississippi basin and into the Far West. And there a curious thing happened, perfectly illustrating the two sides to this story. In the West, the principal prey of the wolves had been the buffalo hordes. But when pioneers discovered that the grasses of the western plains were ideal livestock feed at no cost, they killed off the buffaloes and substituted their sheep and cattle. That brought them in direct competition with the wolves, for these predators now had no food left except that belonging to man. In the eyes of nature, livestock now became the legitimate prey of wolves.

It was a war to the bitter end. In early Oregon, the famous "wolf meetings" were held. Settlers who could agree on nothing else banded together to plot against the wolf, and from these meetings grew Oregon's Territorial Government. Hence this mighty animal shaped Oregon's history.

Guards, guns, traps, bounties, and poison were arrayed against the wolves. At one time, the use of strychnine reached the point where no rangeman would pass a carcass of any kind without loading it with poison. Cattlemen bought deerhounds and greyhounds to hunt wolves, burned thickets where wolves hid, and formed associations to raise big bounties.

Still, the wolf fought on. The cattlemen had destroyed his buffalo prey, but livestock was easier game, and the wolf prospered. After the turn of the century, frantic livestock men turned to the Federal Government for help, and in 1915, on the eve of war with Germany, Congress took time out to appropriate $125,-000 to fight predators. The Federal battle began mainly within the National Forests, but later appropriations covered the grazing lands.

The appropriation of 1915 brought the U. S. Biological Survey, then under the Department of Agriculture, into the picture and thus began the first scientific approach to wolf extermination. The scientists soon turned up new wrinkles. One of the most effective was to kill wolf whelps in their breeding dens. The whelps were literally dug out of the dens and destroyed. The Federal men also discovered that the scent of strange wolves seemed to cause the animal to lose its head. Traps bearing the scent of wolves captured far from the scene were found to have a deadly allure, so that normally cautious animals could be easily taken.

These techniques turned the tide. By the late '20's, the big gray wolf no longer was an economic problem, and the Federal co-operative warfare against him began to peter out. For a time, little attention was paid to the animal, but today there are signs of concern. Perhaps, some say, the campaigns to destroy him were a bit too vigorous. Perhaps the bill against the wolf contains some unfair particulars. At any rate, quieter, more rational voices are being heard in the Grand Jury room.

One of these belongs to Dr. Olaus

**A wolf reveals its close relationship to a dog in
the way it cracks and gnaws a bone.**

J. Murie, retired Federal biologist, and now president of the Wilderness Society. Dr. Murie believes the estimate of 1000 remaining gray wolves indicates danger of extinction. He believes steps should be taken to save this "picturesque element of the wilderness."

Dr. Clarence Cottam, Assistant Director of the U. S. Fish and Wildlife Service, states that wolf control is no longer necessary and adds, "We would hate to see this magnificent animal disappear."

It is almost too late. The wolf is outlawed nearly everywhere except in the National Parks, and the problem is to find him a sanctuary without stirring up cattlemen and sportsmen.

The apparent solution—use of the big National Parks—is virtually ruled out owing to the wolf's vast hunting range. Big as many of the parks are, they are too small to contain wolf migrations. Yellowstone, for example, is surrounded by cattle country. In winter, the Park game migrates down from the mountains and into the surrounding grazing land. Wolves would follow the game, and cattle depredations would probably result. A soon-to-be published study by the Fish and Wildlife Service shows that about one-half of the Yellowstone coyote population moved out of the Park in winter, and only one-half that number returned. One coyote, tagged in the park, was picked up 115 miles away two years later. Wolves migrate farther than coyotes.

Olympic National Park in Washington State would be a more likely wolf sanctuary, except for the protests of sportsmen. There is little cattle raising in the area, but there is game, and hunters argue that wolves would follow the game out of the Park and into their preserves.

The most practical suggestion seems to be that of Dr. A. M. Stebler, of the University of Michigan's laboratory of vertebrate biology. At a recent session of the North American Wildlife Conference in Milwaukee, he suggested Isle Royale National Park in Michigan as a "good possibility."

Isle Royale is a 210-mile stretch of heavily forested wilderness surrounded by the waters of Lake Superior and containing a surplus of game, particularly moose, all protected by law. There may be wolves there today but not in any number. Dr. Stebler suggested that the island offers "an interesting and excellent opportunity to follow through with a study of predator relationships, wherein both relations [prey and predator] are reasonably restricted geographically." He thought Isle Royale offered a natural refuge for the remnants of the Great Lakes' wolf population and the chance to determine what controls on the island's game the presence of a wolf population would offer.

Conrad L. Wirth, Assistant Director of the National Park Service, is inclined to agree with Dr. Stebler. However, Wirth cautions that the introduction of wolves on Isle Royale would have to be on an experimental basis at first. Too many might threaten even an overabundant moose population. But a limited number of wolves would be actually beneficial, since the moose now are so numerous they are eating themselves out of house and home.

In spite of these arguments, there remains some opposition to the introduction of wolves in Isle Royale. Aside from the possibility that they might leave on the ice some severe winter, this island, without wolves, offers a good opportunity to study a game population with no natural controls. There are arguments for and against.

Seemingly, only one more possibility for a wolf sanctuary exists in this country—the Superior Roadless Areas in which both the United States and Canada have an interest.

(The Canadian area is called the International Peace Memorial Forest.)

The portion in the United States consists of 1,038,000 acres of wilderness in the northeast corner of Minnesota along the Canadian boundary. It is under the jurisdiction of the U. S. Forest Service. It is natural wolf country, and again there is plenty of game. But under Forest Service policy, the game belongs to the State, not the Federal Government, and Minnesota permits hunting in season. That raises the ancient objection that hunters have against the wolf. There are a few wolves in the area now. Forest Service officials suggest that more wolves be introduced and that they be made game animals, in season, to placate the hunters. The wolves would also serve as a natural balance for a surplus deer population in the remote areas of the wilderness, where hunters seldom go.

In summary, it seems fair to conclude that the gray wolf has an honest claim to existence. No one seriously argues that he is any longer a real threat to livestock or game in this country. He is a traditional and romantic figure in our history; he is one of the few remaining memorials to America's once unspoiled wilderness. Those who love the wilderness should still be allowed to see wildlife, both prey and predator, in natural distribution. The sight of a gray wolf loping through the forest on his ancient quest, or the eerie, thrilling sound of his lonesome howl before daybreak, ought to persuade men that their hearts can still respond gallantly to the call of the wild.

Wolf Spider

This Wolf Spider, exhibiting two large eyes and four smaller ones, represents a group which for the most part do not spin snares but chase and capture their prey. Some of them dig tunnels in the earth as hiding places. The name of the family to which the Wolf Spiders belong, Lycosidae, is derived from the Greek word for "wolf", *Lykos*.

Henry B. Kane photo

Wombat

The Wombats are burrowing marsupials, or pouched animals, resembling small bears. They are found in Australia and Tasmania and are classed under the genus *Phascolomys*. Larger ones weigh more than a hundred pounds, but extinct forms approached the grizzly bear in size. Wombats live on grass and leaves, and they dig deep burrows, in which they bring forth one young at a time.

Courtesy of the N. Y. Zool. Soc.

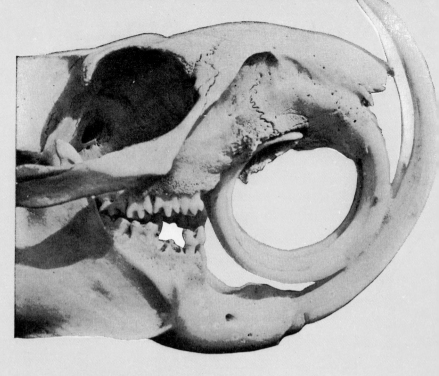

RODENTS keep a chisel edge on their cutting teeth by sharpening the uppers and lowers against each other. This woodchuck skull shows how the teeth keep growing if something prevents the sharpening

NORMALLY, THIS IS HOW A WOODCHUCK SHARPENS ITS TEETH

↑ THE WOODCHUCK, like other rodents, can swing its lower jaw far forward to sharpen its cutting teeth. The lower teeth put a sharp edge on the uppers and vice versa

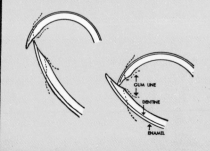

◄ THE HARDER ENAMEL on the outer surface of the teeth wears away the softer dentine in each case, as at left

A Woodchuck Who Needed Tooth-Straightening

If a groundhog doesn't grind down his teeth, they grow longer and longer

➤ A LIVING WOODCHUCK with properly formed teeth and face

By FRANK GEHR

HOW the animal that bore these teeth managed to survive and grow fat remains something of a mystery. It lived near Harpursville, New York; and although its eating habits must have been seriously altered by such an extreme condition of malocclusion, the animal appeared to be in good health. The cutting teeth failed to meet and to be ground down as they grew. The upper teeth curved back around and pierced the bone above the mouth on both sides. The lowers had cut grooves through the flesh of the nose and continued upward to where the animal could keep watch on his own teeth. In some cases, the upper incisors of rodents with this type of misfit come back up, pierce the brain, and kill the animal.

Desert Dwellers —

Inside and Out

By CHARLES FRANKLIN PARKER

Camera and X-ray photographs by CHARLES A. LEAKE

FOR many years medical science has used X-ray for diagnosing human ills. Now, with the emphasis on visual aids in teaching, the time may not be far when the fruits of such techniques as these will be in more general use, both in classrooms and museums.

This procedure involves something more than the usual photographing of animals in their natural habitat. For X rays, the specimens must not only be captured but specially prepared. According to Mr. Leake,

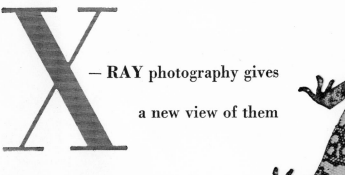

— RAY photography gives

a new view of them

◄ AS THIS X-RAY VIEW SHOWS, the Arizona Gila Monster (*Heloderma suspectum*) possesses, in addition to the usual internal skeleton (endoskeleton), an easily recognized "skin armor," or exoskeleton. This latter is clearly evident here in the form of innumerable little dots representing "skin bones," or osteoderms, in the beaded covering that anyone remembers if he has seen this animal. Of special interest is the ovoid outline in the position of the stomach on the right side, which may well represent an undigested egg, probably of some quail or dove. There are a few independent reports of Gila Monsters swallowing the eggs of Gambel's quail without breaking them, and this X ray may provide confirmatory evidence. The Gila Monster was photographed 48 hours after it was captured near Congress Junction, Arizona. The more opaque object on the left side, presumably in the intestine, is apparently the calcareous shell of an egg. It has partly collapsed, probably from the effect of digestive juices, but the harder fragments are still sticking to the tougher membranes

his procedure with these cold-blooded animals is to cool
them by refrigeration to the point of reducing but not
stopping their activity, so that they will remain relatively immobile for the seconds required in taking the
X-ray picture. After the picture has been taken, the

➤ THIS X-RAY VIEW of a Bull Snake, photographed while
the animal was still alive, shows clearly the snake's skeleton. In the loop farthest to the left can be seen the remains
of a small rodent that the snake has eaten. The rodent's
head is in the region where the semicircular white area
is visible. The bones of the rodent's spinal column extend
to the right, parallel to those of the snake. The snake was
about six feet long

animal can be kept until the plate has been developed. If necessary, the specimen can then be re-refrigerated for another try.

This process requires access to X-ray equipment and a knowledge of X-ray techniques. Most communities

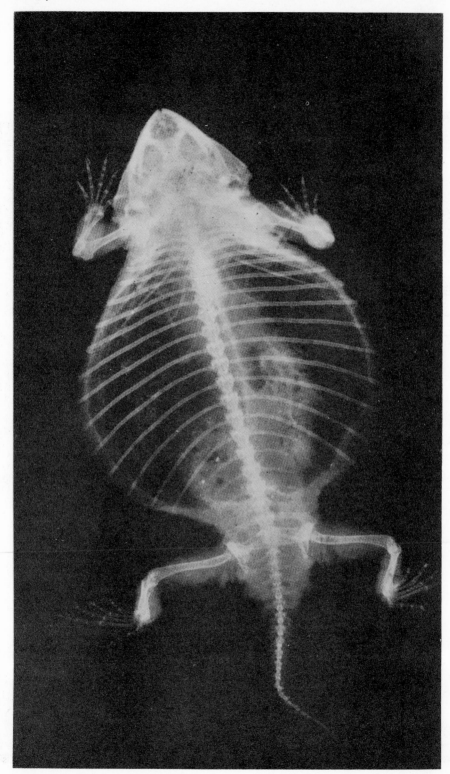

have the equipment, and it should not be difficult to interest a trained technician. The accompanying X rays had special handling by the Eastman laboratories.

One cannot but believe that the use of this technique would be valuable for instructional purposes. A library of slides might be developed from which schools could rent or borrow examples for classroom use. Museums may also find ways in which X-ray views can add to the clarity of their exhibits. Or somebody may be encouraged toward a new hobby—that of collecting X-ray views showing the bony architecture of widely differing animals.

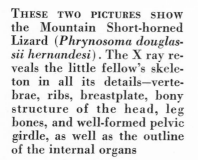

THESE TWO PICTURES SHOW the Mountain Short-horned Lizard (*Phrynosoma douglassii hernandesi*). The X ray reveals the little fellow's skeleton in all its details—vertebrae, ribs, breastplate, bony structure of the head, leg bones, and well-formed pelvic girdle, as well as the outline of the internal organs

Penetrating the Petal

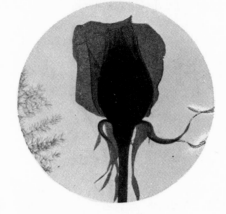

X-ray shadowgraphs show that with flowers,

beauty is more than skin deep

By LEWIS WAYNE WALKER

X-ray Shadowgraphs by C. J. WITKOWSKI

AN inquiring mind, medical training, first-class laboratory equipment, and an eye for beauty has enabled Dr. C. J. Witkowski to give his X-ray machine a pleasant recess from eying the innards of humans. At the same time, this combination has enabled humans to view flowers as they have rarely been viewed before. In reality, these pictures are shadowgraphs resulting from the passage of light through plant tissues and thence onto sensitized film. Texture, consistency, and depth, so different from flesh and bone, made considerable research necessary before successful results were obtained.

Dr. Witkowski's machine originally had a range of between 50,000 and 85,000 volts, a power that was far too strong for botanical subjects. So he constructed a special transformer to reduce the setup to about 15,000 volts. These weakened rays successfully penetrated the delicate

Rose

Hibiscus

petals and leaves but were stopped by the thicker twigs and branches, which registered as dark shadows.

Although the results are masterpieces of beauty, they have little scientific significance. But in the future—who knows? Perhaps mineral content, such as the iron in the spinach that is supposed to have made a man of Popeye, will be discernable to an X-raying botanist of tomorrow and thus open up new fields. At present, these shadowgraphs may give some debutante the inspiration for an evening gown.

Carnation

Calla Lily

Moonflower

Zebra

▼ THE MARKINGS on zebras are always different, like fingerprints. These are Grant zebras, which are closely related to the extinct quagga, an animal whose stripes were restricted to the region of the head and shoulders. The quagga vanished from the African scene a little over 70 years ago. To the left is an eland, and in front of it a Roberts gazelle.

AMNH photo

Index

How To Use This Index

The reader will gain in both value and pleasure from reading and using this work if he makes full use of the Index on the succeeding pages. The Index has been arranged so as to locate for the reader the maximum amount of important data to be found within the pages of the work.

In part, the contents of the work have already been indexed. That is, individual articles have been arranged under a keyword heading and in turn placed in alphabetical order according to these headings. Thus, you may find what you are seeking by looking under the proper key word in the main body of the work.

In addition, many hundreds of subjects are referred to within the body of articles. These have been separately indexed when the references contain sufficient information about the subjects to warrant special citation. When you find no index reference to a specific subject, such as a species of plant or animal, you may find general data on the subject under the broader heading to which the subject belongs. Illustrations are indicated in the index by the term *"illus."* Authors of articles are also cited in the Index.

Index

PUBLICATIONS
OF
THE AMERICAN MUSEUM OF NATURAL HISTORY

If you have enjoyed this work, you should also enjoy the many popular publications currently available from the American Museum of Natural History. They may be ordered by name and number or letter. When ordering, print your name and address and enclose indicated postage.

Address all orders and inquiries to:

MAN AND NATURE Publications
The American Museum of Natural History
79th St. and Central Park West
New York 24, N. Y.

NUMBER

INDIANS OF THE PLAINS
By Robert H. Lowie   *Price $4.75, postage 12¢*   1
This clearly written handbook acquaints the student and general reader with many of the basic points in the study of this North American Indian culture.

INDIANS OF THE NORTHWEST COAST
By Phillip Drucker   *Price $5.75, postage 12¢*   10
This plainly written account discusses the topography and climate of the territory along the coast from the Columbia River in Washington to southern Alaska, as well as customs, religion, art and social organization of its inhabitants.

THE STORY OF THE MINERALS
By Herbert P. Whitlock   *141 pages, 53 illustrations. Cloth bound.*
                                        Price 85¢ postage 8¢   12
This authoritative book explains the "How" and "Why" of mineralogy in connection with the exhibit of minerals in Morgan Memorial Hall of the Museum.

THE DINOSAUR BOOK
By Edwin H. Colbert   *Price $5.00, postage 12¢*   14
In this popular book, Dr. Colbert creates a vivid picture of the lost world of the geologic past when strange and fantastic creatures dominated the earth. Hundreds of photographs, line drawings and charts.

ANDEAN CULTURE HISTORY
By William C. Bennett and Junius B. Bird   *Being revised*   15
The emphasis in this volume is on Peruvian prehistory.

THE HABITAT GROUPS
OF NORTH AMERICAN BIRDS
By Frank M. Chapman   *64 pages, 36 illustrations. Paper bound*
                                        Price 50¢, postage 10¢   28
This booklet describes the localities, habits of the birds and other interesting facts pertaining to 28 of the habitat groups.

HOW ABOUT THE TENT CATERPILLAR
By Frank E. Lutz   *10 pages, 18 illustrations. Paper bound.*
Reprint from Natural History   *Price 15¢, postage 5¢*   35
Common questions about an insect that attacks wild cherries, orchard trees, and ornamentals are answered in this publication.

NUMBER

INTRODUCTION TO HUMAN ANATOMY
By William K. Gregory and Marcelle Roigneau   *77 pages, 41 illustrations.*
Paper bound.   *Price 75¢, postage 10¢*   86
This booklet describes the origin and functions of the skeleton, muscular, digestive, and nervous systems of the human body from ancient fishes of Devonian times to modern civilized man.

ARTISTS AND CRAFTSMEN
IN ANCIENT CENTRAL AMERICA
By George C. Vaillant   *102 pages, 152 illustrations. Paper bound*
                             Price $1.45, postage 10¢   88
A reconstruction of the life and customs of ancient Mexico and Central America, this booklet will fascinate the layman as well as student of archaeology.

STAR LEGENDS
AMONG THE AMERICAN INDIANS
By Clark Wissler   *29 pages, 1 illustration. Paper bound*
                        Price 50¢, postage 5¢   91
How the sun, moon, earth and many of our other heavenly bodies were created according to Blackfoot Indian lore was told to Dr. Wissler by Wolf-head and translated orally by an English-speaking Indian.

MASKS
By Clark Wissler   *32 pages, 64 illustrations. Paper bound*
                        Price 45¢, postage 5¢   96
Masks, still used in many countries of Asia, go back to the Stone Age. This pamphlet describes and illustrates the use of masks among American Indians as well as around the world.

PEARL DIVERS
By Roy Waldo Miner   *15 pages, 39 illustrations. Paper bound*
                          Price 55¢, postage 5¢   104
A scientist who accompanied the expedition to the South Pacific that collected materials for the American Museum's Pearl Divers Group describes his experiences and the unusual kinds of life encountered on the coral atoll of Tongareva.

CANYONS UNDER THE SEA
By Harold E. Vokes   *5 pages, 3 illustrations. Paper bound.*
Reprint from Natural History.   *Price 10¢, postage 5¢*   105
About 130 miles from Manhattan Island is a canyon under the sea about 50 miles long that begins 500 feet under the surface. In this guide scientists consider the possible explanation of this and other submarine canyons.

THE FILM OF LIFE
By G. Miles Conrad   *8 pages of drawings with captions. Paper bound.*
Reprint from Natural History.   *Price 20¢, postage 5¢*   109
Since only the thinnest surface film on the earth contains life, Dr. Conrad explains (with illustrations) the five primary conditions that govern the presence of life.

INSECTS, TICKS AND HUMAN DISEASES
By Frank E. Lutz and C. H. Curran   *38 pages, 8 illustrations. Paper bound.*
                                        Price 50¢, postage 5¢   113
This booklet describes insects, ticks, and related forms, and explains the role they play in the transmission of the various diseases. It also gives directions for the control of the insects.

INSECT CONTROL IN THE
VEGETABLE GARDEN
By C. H. Curran   *32 pages, 28 illustrations. Paper bound*
                       Price 30¢, postage 5¢   117

Written during the war for victory gardens, this book contains information applicable at any time and shows the way to save time, worry and expense that result from insect ravages. Useful table of insecticides.

GENERAL GUIDE TO THE AMERICAN MUSEUM OF NATURAL HISTORY

Paper bound.   *Price $1.50, postage 1 lb. parcel post rate*   118

Both visitor and non-visitor will enjoy this book, generously illustrated, and offering descriptions of the exhibits that cover every section of the globe.

MURALS IN THE ROOSEVELT MEMORIAL

By William Andrew Mackay and A. A. Canfield   12 illustrations. Paper bound
Price 35¢, postage 5¢   119

Decorating the large central hall of Roosevelt Memorial Building in the Museum are symbolic murals, here described, of scenes from the life of the 26th president of the United States.

A WORLD FULL OF PEOPLE

By Harry L. Shapiro   *9 pages, 10 illustrations.*
Reprint from Natural History. Paper bound.   *Price 15¢, postage 5¢*   125

The facts of population are here discussed, giving the reasons why some peoples have increased more rapidly than others and current trends in population growth.

BIRDS OF PARADISE

By Ernest Mayr   *14 pages, 22 illustrations, three of them in full color.*
Paper bound. Reprint from Natural History.   *Price 55¢, postage 5¢*   127

Little-known facts about the daily life of birds of paradise and their historical background are included in this interesting account.

LIFE OF THE WATER FILM

By Lorus J. Milne and Margery J. Milne   *7 pages, 6 illustrations.*
Paper bound. Reprint from Natural History.   *Price 25¢, postage 5¢*   130

The lives of water striders, mosquito wrigglers, larvae, snails, Hydra, and other aquatic life in a fresh-water pond are here described with the part played by the surface film in their lives.

FROM THE NECK UP

By Harry L. Shapiro   *12 pages, 31 illustrations. Paper bound.*
Reprint from Natural History.   *Price 50¢, postage 5¢*   131

Hair styles, facial decorations, ear rings, nose and lip ornaments, necklaces, goggles and a great variety of hats and head-dresses devised by primitive and civilized man are covered in this pamphlet.

THE LIFE HISTORY OF THE MONARCH BUTTERFLY

By Lucy W. Clausen   *14 pages, 13 illustrations. Paper bound.*
Price 35¢, postage 5¢   132

This fascinating booklet outlines the complete metamorphosis of the higher insects as exemplified by the monarch butterfly.

AUGUST ON FIRE ISLAND BEACH

By Robert Cushman Murphy   *16 pages, 9 illustrations, Paper bound*
Price 40¢, postage 5¢   134

In this charming essay, the author describes the vegetation, animal life and topography of one of the few remaining nature spots near New York City.

INDIANS OF THE MONTANA

By Harry Tschopik, Jr.   *23 pages, 30 illustrations. Paper bound.*
Price 75¢, postage 5¢   135

A concise picture of the life and customs of the world's most primitive peoples, this book includes a detailed discussion of the process of head shrinking.

PICTORIAL MAPS AND CHARTS

The following charts have proved popular for framing and are well adapted for use as wall decorations in camps, lodges, schools, and in the home. Order by letter designation (A, D, etc.) Minimum order 25¢ plus 10¢ postage.

A. ***S.O.S. for a Continent.*** Conservation problems in North America graphically portrayed (19 x 26 inches) .... 10¢

C. ***The Cycle of Life.*** Vital facts concerning the size, reproduction, and life span of 49 mammals. (12 x 18 inches) .... 5¢

D. ***Family Tree of the Dinosaurs.*** 21 major types of dinosaurs and how they evolved. (11 3/4 x 17 inches) .... 5¢

E. ***Environment and Locomotion in Mammals.*** Swimming, running, climbing, flying, and other methods of travel illustrated by 41 selected animals. (12 x 18 inches) 5¢

F. ***Major Movements of European Population.*** Vital changes' in the population map of the world (1492-1942). (12½ x 19 inches) .... 5¢

G. ***Indian Tribes of North America.*** (15½ x 17½ inches) .... 5¢

K. ***Urner-Edwards Field Chart.*** Bird check list. (7 x 8 inches) ....2 for 5¢
postage 2¢

L. ***Principal Orders of Insects.*** Complete descriptions of metamorphosis, immature, and adult forms (19 x 27 inches) .... 10¢

M. ***Grandfather Fish and His Descendants.*** Family tree of the vertebrates.......... 10¢

N. ***African Tribal Map & Booklet*** $2.00
postage 35¢

NATURAL HISTORY MAGAZINE

The popular magazine of The American Museum of Natural History contains abundantly illustrated articles for the general public. Among the fields it covers are exploration, primitive man, amateur science, nature photography, gems, minerals, pets, and the wonders of nature. It contains stories of Museum expeditions and describes interesting discoveries and exhibits. Teachers find it extremely helpful. No intelligent home should be without it. NATURAL HISTORY magazine is published monthly except in July and August. A subscription is $5.00 the year and includes associate membership in the Museum. Add 50¢ for Canadian and foreign postage.

Order from:
JOSEPH R. SAULINA, Circulation Manager
American Museum of Natural History
Central Park West at 79th Street
New York 24, N. Y.

THE JUNIOR NATURAL HISTORY MAGAZINE

A unique publication for children of eight to fifteen is *Junior Natural History Magazine,* which is published monthly throughout the year by the American Museum. Its contents touch on all phases of natural history, and while it is written in easy-to-understand language, it does not "talk down" to its readers. It is profusely illustrated and attractively designed. As one of its subscribers wrote: "I find *Junior Natural History Magazine* very useful in school for my science class, as it serves to illustrate more clearly the lessons which are not offered in a very exciting manner in text books." A subscription is $1.50 the year. Add 25¢ for Canadian and foreign postage.

Order from:
>JOSEPH R. SAULINA, Circulation Manager
>American Museum of Natural History
>Central Park West at 79th Street
>New York 24, N. Y.